GARRIE L. TUFFORD

SEP 2 6 1958

GARRIÉ L. TUFFORD

GENERAL CHEMISTRY

The transition from primitive society to our modern way of
living has been made possible by the modification of natural
materials, the synthesis of new substances, and the harnessing
of chemical changes to provide an abundance of energy.

A. W. Laubengayer

PROFESSOR OF CHEMISTRY
CORNELL UNIVERSITY

▶ General Chemistry

Revised Edition

RINEHART & COMPANY, INC., NEW YORK

► Preface

The extended use of the first edition of this text demonstrated its effectiveness for all serious college students, including those who intend to take more chemistry, or who wish a thorough and sound chemical background for work in related fields, such as physics, engineering, geology, the biological sciences, and medicine. At the same time, experience with the book and recognition of the gradual increase in precollege training in general science suggested certain major changes which would make the volume more useful and attractive to student and teacher. Accordingly, it has been thoroughly revised, with care being taken to restrict it to such a length as to make it most useful for reasonable study assignments.

The order has been changed by introducing the atomic concept as soon as possible in the first chapter and by moving to an early position details of atomic structure, the periodic table, and elementary theories of chemical bonding. Succeeding chapters have been rewritten to take full advantage of this background and to eliminate ambiguous and involved passages. The chapter on colloidal systems has been placed immediately after the discussion of solutions.

Most of the figures have been redrawn and many new ones have been added to emphasize the particle character of matter and the three-dimensional aspects of atoms, molecules, and ions. These figures are designed to brighten and clarify the presentation without increasing the amount of straight textual material. More use is made of problems to illustrate the quantitative laws and principles, and the lists of review exercises at the ends of the chapters have been expanded. A table of logarithms and a section giving answers to the numerical exercises have been added to the appendix.

Two pictorial sections with concise, descriptive legends have been introduced to supplement the main treatment and to stimulate interest. The first section outlines with pictures the contributions of outstanding scientists to the historical development of chemistry. The second presents, with the aid of photographs and simple diagrams, a sampling of important applications of chemistry in industry to provide materials which are important in our modern pattern of living. Care has been taken to include only such pictures as have definite educational value.

In general, the text is planned to carry the student from the familiar to the unfamiliar, from the macro behavior of matter to the micro and the submicro considerations with which he is unfamiliar. Descriptive and experimental chemistry dealing with the more common forms of matter is introduced from the start to provide a sampling of observations which can be used in the development of fundamental chemical principles. The simplest and most easily demonstrated aspects are presented first, with the gradual unfolding of the more complicated ideas. This is in line with certain principles which, in the opinion of this author, cannot be emphasized too much in the teaching of science; not to ask the student to take authority when he can have facts; not to guess when he can know. Although the progression of topics chosen in this book has been arranged carefully, there is considerable latitude for varying the assignments without loss of the basic logic.

A good deal of emphasis has been placed on modern concepts of chemical bonding as related to the electronic structures of the elements. Structural discussions, based upon the wealth of data now available for inorganic as well as organic substances, have been introduced in some detail. A vigorous effort is made to induce the student to consider the three-dimensional nature of chemical systems, to get him to realize that atomic, ionic, and molecular dimensions and the spatial configurations of these systems are fully as important in determining their properties as are the number of valence electrons.

In the discussion of solution phenomena, an attempt is made to indicate how complicated such solution phases are and how little is known about the actual units that are involved. Because of this dubious state of knowledge concerning the exact compositions of the complex solvated ions, the formulation of such complexes has been handled with considerable restraint. The use of net reactions and equations has been favored.

Terminology has been kept as simple as possible. A strong effort has been made to establish the exact way in which each scientific term is to be used at the point in the book where this term is first employed. Where a choice of terms is possible, self-descriptive terms and those in common use have been given preference.

I wish to acknowledge with gratitude the kind assistance given by many friends in the preparation of this book.

Drs. M. J. Sienko, Mary Jo Treat, and E. C. Broge helped with the collection and checking of much of the material for the first edition. Professor E. R. Van Artsdalen and Dr. R. A. Reinhardt at Cornell University, and Professor G. R. Hill at the University of Utah, contributed many valuable suggestions based upon the use of a preliminary edition. Professor O. J. Sweeting of the University of Colorado, Professor Howard Hunter of Clemson College, Professor Henry Taube at the University of Chicago, and Professor W. J. Frierson of Agnes Scott College provided critical reviews of the preliminary edition.

The revision of the book has benefited from comments made by many teachers who have used the first edition. Professors W. Bernard King of Iowa State College, J. D. Porter of Union College, and Eugene C. Winslow of the University of Rhode Island kindly provided comprehensive evaluations of the first edition, with detailed suggestions for the revision, and Professors George H. Cady of the University of Washington, Eric Hutchinson of Stanford University, and Edward L. King of the University of Wisconsin have appraised the revised manuscript and have indicated numerous possibilities for improvement.

I am particularly grateful to colleagues at Cornell University for help with the revision. Dr. R. F. Porter has read much of the revised manuscript and Steven J. Fitch has checked the numerical exercises. Professor C. W. Mason has made available the photographs for Figures 45 and 112b, and he and Professor H. F. Wiegandt have been very helpful in suggesting sources of material for the pictorial section on applications of chemistry.

I am indebted to the authors and publishers of the following books from which material has been reproduced in modified form: Figures 15, 16, and 21 from *The Nature of the Chemical Bond*, by Linus Pauling (Cornell University Press); Appendix IV from *Oxidation Potentials*, by W. M. Latimer (Prentice-Hall, Inc.). Figure 54 has been used with the kind permission of Professor W. H. Zachariasen of the University of Chicago.

The pictorial sections have been made possible by the generous cooperation of many different sources of illustrative material; by-lines under the illustrations indicate these sources.

The editorial staff of Rinehart and Company have been most patient and helpful with the enterprise from start to finish, and Mr. Felix Cooper has shown imagination and understanding in executing the drawings for the figures.

I especially wish to thank Grace Ware Laubengayer for her splendid help and encouragement in the preparation of this book.

A. W. L.

Ithaca, New York
April, 1957

▶ Contents

APPENDIX

INDEX   569

▶ Pictures

APPLICATIONS OF CHEMISTRY IN INDUSTRY

GENERAL CHEMISTRY

Chapter 1

▶ **Chemistry**

▶ **Some Basic Concepts**

1. CHEMISTRY. ITS ROLE IN OUR LIVES

Chemistry is the field of knowledge dealing with the composition, properties, and changes of matter, the laws governing its behavior, and the theories which have been developed to explain this observed behavior.

The importance to everyone of this basic study is readily appreciated. Our bodies and our environment are composed of matter and must obey the fundamental laws summarizing its behavior. Our existence, health, and comfort depend, in large part, on our ability to adapt matter to our needs. The energy associated with matter and with the changes which it undergoes makes possible the work we do and is essential to the life process. Progress in chemistry not only has made it possible to use natural materials more advantageously but also has led to the creation of a vast number of new materials which serve us well. The introduction of such materials rapidly changes the pattern of our daily lives. Since nonchemists as well as chemists have a very real stake in chemistry, some understanding and appreciation of this science not only satisfies our curiosity but helps us to use matter more wisely. Because chemistry is nothing more than organized common sense based firmly on quantitative experiments, it provides excellent training in careful observation and logical thinking.

2. THE PLACE OF CHEMISTRY IN SCIENCE

Science, in the broad sense, may be considered to be organized knowledge. Because of the enormous range thus defined and the limitations of human mental capacity, it is convenient to divide the general field into separate sciences. Then scientists may concentrate on particular areas and so gain a more thorough and fundamental understanding in these limited provinces. *Mathematics* deals with numbers, space, and time; pure mathematics is not concerned with what is numbered or what occupies space. It is possible for the mathematician to handle his problems with great precision. *Physics and chemistry* are concerned with nonliving materials. The physicist studies the properties common to

1

various forms of matter and the ways in which matter is associated with energy.   He makes as exact measurements as possible on selected portions of matter and attempts, by the application of mathematics, to state his results with the greatest possible certainty.   He endeavors to understand and account for his observations by developing satisfactory theories about the nature of matter and energy.   The chemist considers the properties and changes of specific forms of matter as related to their chemical composition, and tries to bring to bear on his studies the basic concepts of mathematics and physics.   The *biological sciences* are concerned with living organisms which are built up of elaborate combinations of chemical substances; a fundamental understanding of the properties and behavior of the organisms can be obtained only if the basic tools of mathematics, physics, and chemistry are employed.   *Geology and astronomy* apply mathematics, physics, and chemistry to particular regions in space.

As shown in Figure 1, we see that, in going from mathematics to biology, the problems considered become progressively more complex as

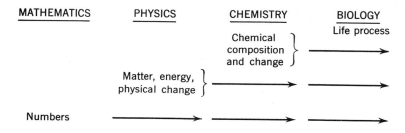

Fig. 1.   Interrelations of the sciences.

the science of numbers has superimposed upon it, first, the physical aspects of matter, then, its chemical behavior, and finally, the life process. It becomes increasingly difficult to work with high precision as the systems become more complicated.   Accordingly, while physics has advanced to a highly quantitative position, chemistry is less exact in its treatment, and the biological sciences are in a still more descriptive and qualitative stage of development.

The dependence of one field of science on others is apparent, and the border lines between separate sciences are indistinct.   In fact, the areas of overlapping among the various fields are of particular interest if we wish to gain a comprehensive and general understanding of nature.   One hears much these days of physical chemistry, chemical physics, biophysics, biochemistry, geophysics, geochemistry, astrophysics, and other borderline fields.

The introduction of a considerable amount of elementary mathematics and physics in the earlier chapters of this book should not surprise the student. It is essential for an understanding of the more complicated phenomena of chemistry.

3. THE SCIENTIFIC METHOD

In chemistry the method of study common to all the experimental sciences is employed. Matter and its changes are observed carefully, and as much *factual information* as possible is accumulated. If conditions are rigidly controlled, a given experiment always leads to the same results, and any skilled experimenter can reproduce these results. There is great satisfaction in each personal verification of a scientific truth. You will experience this in your own work in the laboratory.

The extensive array of facts thus established may be summarized and correlated in the form of general *scientific laws*. Such laws are only as good as the facts on which they are based. Should new facts be discovered which do not agree with the laws, then the laws must be revised accordingly.

Scientific theories are developed to explain chemical facts and laws by setting up models of matter and suggesting mechanisms which will give a better understanding of chemical phenomena. Since theories must be consistent with facts and laws, theories may be tested by suitable experiments. The discovery of new facts or laws may necessitate revision of a theory, so that chemical theories are constantly undergoing modification and growth. Theories are especially valuable in that they allow us to predict how matter should behave, and experiments set up to test such predictions lead to further expansion of our factual knowledge. In later chapters you will see in detail how this method works.

Frequently, the guesses made in developing a theory are proved to be pictures of reality and thus change into facts. "The dreams of today often become the truths of tomorrow." For example, the guess that all gases consist of a collection of particles which we call molecules was made to account for the behavior of gases long before it was possible to isolate and prove the existence of individual molecules. Ways have since been found to isolate many kinds of such molecules and to establish their individualities. The existence of molecules has been proved and is now accepted as a fact.

By combining exact experimentation with the development of laws and theories, our knowledge in the science progresses at a rapid pace. Curiosity, imagination, and the desire to establish order are the driving forces in this progress. It is stimulating to realize that much is still unknown and that the solution of one problem usually suggests interesting new questions about nature. Everyone has the opportunity to contribute to the advance of science.

4.   THE CRITICAL ATTITUDE IN SCIENCE

A critical state of mind is imperative for the student of science. Robert Boyle helped our modern era in science off to a good start in 1661, when he published "The Skeptical Chemyst," in which he urged the necessity of carefully testing theories by experimentation.   Each of us has the right to doubt and to demand experimental proof.   Perhaps the most important benefits to be derived from the study of chemistry are an appreciation of the scientific method and the development of a critical inquiring attitude.   It is not sufficient merely to ask *what, where,* and *when;* become interested also in *how* and *why.*

5.   CHEMICAL TERMINOLOGY

The description of exact experimental conditions and results and the clear statement of laws and theories necessitate careful and precise expression.   Specific scientific terms must be developed and employed with care.   In chemistry a vast specialized terminology has arisen which is likely to appall and confuse the beginner.   In this book we will need a good deal of this terminology but we will restrict it as much as possible, introduce it gradually, and endeavor to establish clearly the meaning of each term the first time it occurs.   The first time each new term is used it will be printed in italics for emphasis.   As far as possible we shall avoid formal definitions, because these frequently are ambiguous.   Instead, we shall stress the correct use of the term by giving examples.   The student will find in the precise use of such scientific words a new power of expression and understanding.

6.   MATTER

Chemistry, we have said, deals with matter.   What is matter, and how is it recognized?   This is best answered by citing examples and describing its characteristics.   Familiar examples of matter are wood, iron, water, aluminum, sulfur, air, salt, and sugar.   The whole universe is composed of matter having certain characteristics which allow us to recognize it.

Matter occupies space, and its presence may be demonstrated by taking advantage of this quality.   Portions of wood, iron, or water are easily perceived by sight and by feeling.   The presence of air is not so readily detected, but when we try to put other matter, such as water, into a bottle full of air, we get clear evidence that the space is already occupied.   As shown in Figure 2, water will not fill a bottle thrust into water unless the air is allowed to bubble out.

Matter possesses mass.   The *mass* of any portion of matter refers to the amount of matter present.   The relative masses of ordinary samples of matter are usually determined by weighing and expressing the masses in terms of weight. Any object at the surface of the earth is attracted toward the center of the earth by the force of gravity. The magnitude of this pull depends upon the mass of the object, the mass of the earth, and the distance between their centers. This pull is the *weight* of the object. When we weigh the object we balance its attraction to the earth against the attraction of the standard weights to the earth. The mass of the object is then taken to be equal to the mass of the standard weights that balance it. Because the mass of the earth is constant and the distance of the objects and the weights from the center of the earth is the

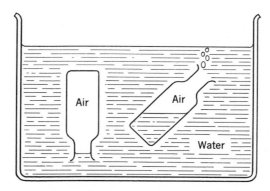

Fig. 2.   Displacement of air from bottle by water.

same, the mass of the object is equal to the mass of the weights. Mass is proportional to weight and is taken to be numerically equal to weight when the weighing is performed at the surface of the earth. A boulder is found to weigh 20.5 lb; its mass therefore is taken to be 20.5 lb.

It is important to recognize the distinction between mass and weight. The mass of a body is a fixed property of the body by itself and is independent of other objects, whereas the weight of a body involves the attractive force between it and the earth and is directional in nature. The mass of a piece of iron is the same regardless of whether it is at the surface of the earth or 1,000 miles out in space, but its weight varies with the distance from the center of the earth. The pull of gravity decreases as the distance from the center of the earth increases.

We can take advantage of the fact that matter has weight and mass to detect and compare the amounts of matter with which we work. A bottle full of air weighs more than does the bottle after the air is pumped out. The difference in weight is a measure of the amount of air that is present. A certain block of iron is found to weigh 10 g while another weighs 20 g. The latter has twice the mass of the former.

Weighing is not the only method for measuring mass. We can observe the effect on an object of forces other than gravitation. *Matter exhibits inertia;* because of its mass, it tends to remain at rest or in a state of uniform motion. Forces must act on matter and work must be done to set matter in motion or to change the motion of matter. The amount of work required to achieve a given effect is proportional to the mass of the matter, and if we measure the amount of work we can calculate the mass. Work must be done to set a bicycle in motion; therefore a bicycle is composed of matter. The existence of air may be detected when the air in motion (wind) strikes a surface, such as your cheek, or when it moves a sailboat.

It is conventional in chemistry to use the metric system of weights and measures. This is summarized in Appendix I, together with equivalents in the foot-pound system which is commonly used in industry.

7. ATOMIC NATURE OF MATTER

The most fundamental question we can ask about matter concerns its constitution. What is the secret of its structure? Samples of matter of a size we can easily observe, such as a silver coin, a drop of water, a sheet of iron, a granule of sugar, or a pane of window glass may appear to the eye to be continuous and uniform in structure. But we all know that a silver coin can be divided into smaller pieces and these in turn into still smaller fragments. How far can this subdivision be carried? Can we, by very special methods, divide the coin indefinitely and still have silver, or is there an ultimate limit to this subdivision? Experiments prove that when subdivision is carried far enough we arrive at the smallest particle that can exist and still be silver. This is the *atom* of silver.

All matter is made up of atoms. Any sizable portion of matter can be shown to be a collection of an enormous number of atoms. For example, a drop of water of ordinary size contains about 5,000,000,000,000,000,-000,000, that is, 5×10^{21} atoms (see Appendix for use of exponential numbers). From this almost incredible number of atoms in a drop of water, it follows that the individual atoms must be extremely small and weigh very, very little. They are so minute that we cannot hope to see single atoms even with the aid of the most powerful microscope; we can only see massive objects built up of a very large number of atoms. Nevertheless, special methods can be used to detect and to measure individual atoms. They are found, on the average, to have diameters of the order of only 10^{-8} cm.

There is abundant proof that in the universe there are many different kinds of atoms having different characteristics. Each minute atom has definite weight which may be taken as a measure of its definite *atomic mass*, and a characteristic *atomic size* under given conditions. Each particular atom is also identified with a certain tendency either to combine chemically with other atoms or to lack the ability for chemical combination; this is known as the *chemical behavior* of an atom.

The nature of an object built up of atoms must depend upon the kinds and numbers of atoms that are present and on the way in which these atoms are associated. For example, a silver coin is composed of a tremendous number of silver atoms, all of the same size and chemical behavior and packed together in a certain way. This gives the silver coin certain characteristics which differentiate it from other forms of matter. The atoms present in a drop of water are of two different kinds, each quite different from silver atoms. These two kinds of atoms in water are associated in a particular way. The drop of water has characteristics quite different from those of the silver coin. It becomes quite clear that, if we are to gain an understanding of the behavior of matter, we must find out all we can about its constituent atoms.

It has taken mankind a long time to establish clearly the atomic nature of matter. As early as 500 B.C. the Greek philosophers, such as Democritus and Leucippus, debated the problem but could only guess that matter might be atomistic. They had no good way to test their theory by experiment, and the problem remained unanswered for the next 23 centuries. Finally, about A.D. 1800, development of the chemical balance made it possible for chemists such as Lavoisier, Proust, Dalton, and Berzelius to make accurate measurements of the weights of matter involved in chemical change. As we shall see in the next chapter, the facts then discovered led Dalton and others to the belief that matter must be made up of atoms. But Dalton and his contemporaries had no way of isolating and identifying individual atoms. It was not until about 1900 that new experimental physical methods were developed for proving the existence of atoms and studying them in detail. And very soon it became clear not only that all matter is built up of atoms, but that atoms themselves are complex in structure and are built up of subatomic units. The term *atom* has become the catchword of the twentieth century, familiar to all who read the newspaper or listen to the radio.

Much of our discussion in this book will be devoted to the study of the nature of atoms in general, the kinds of atoms that are known, and how these atoms are involved in the materials found in nature and those we create in the laboratory. *The notion of the particle nature of matter is basic in chemistry.*

8. ATOMS AND THE CHEMICAL ELEMENTS

In terms of *chemical behavior*, about 100 different kinds of atoms are now recognized. The atoms of a specific *chemical element* all have the same chemical behavior. Since there are about 100 chemically different kinds of atoms, there must be the same number of elements. Iron, silver, copper, sulfur, oxygen, and hydrogen are familiar elements. A bar of pure iron consists of a collection of iron atoms, each possessing the same chemical characteristics, each of the same size.   A piece of sulfur is made up of atoms of sulfur, all of the same size and chemical behavior. But sulfur atoms differ markedly from iron atoms.   One of our major objectives will be to try to learn how this difference arises.

The chemical elements are listed alphabetically in Table 1, which appears for convenient reference on the inside of the front cover of this book.   The names of the elements have originated in a variety of ways. Some are derived from the name of an abundant source, such as *boron* from *borax*.   Others are named from the region or locality where they were discovered; *germanium* from *Germany*.   Still other names are derived from properties or behavior; thus *gold* from *gelb* (yellow), and *hydrogen* because it *generates water*.   By international agreement, the names of the chemical elements have been standardized for use throughout the world.

9. KINDS OF ELEMENTS. METALS AND NONMETALS

No two chemical elements are exactly alike; each has its own characteristics.   The chemist endeavors to discover the characteristics of each element and compares its behavior with that of the other elements. With about 100 elements to consider, this study includes an enormous volume of knowledge which must be carefully organized if any one person is to be able to master it.   Such organization is accomplished by assigning the elements to classes depending upon certain similarities.   Knowing the general characteristics of each class, when told that a given element belongs to a given class, we immediately have an indication of what behavior to expect.

A simple but very effective and useful classification of the elements that we will start to use immediately labels them as *metals* or *nonmetals*. The *metals* are those elements, such as iron, copper, silver, tin, aluminum, calcium, and sodium, which have a bright and shiny luster (reflecting light strongly), which are good conductors of heat and electricity, and which are malleable and ductile (can be rolled or hammered into sheets or drawn into fine wire).   Their chemical behavior is also quite similar. Under ordinary conditions all of the metals, excepting mercury, are solids; mercury is a liquid.   The *nonmetallic* elements, such as sulfur, phosphorus, and iodine, when in the solid state under ordinary conditions, are brittle and are poor conductors of heat and electricity.   A number of the nonmetals, for example nitrogen, oxygen, hydrogen, and chlorine, are gases under ordinary conditions.   The rest of the nonmetals are solids, excepting bromine which is a liquid.

In Table 1 heavy type indicates the nonmetals, the rest of the elements being metals.   Titanium is listed as a metal; accordingly we can expect that it will be a bright, shiny solid and that objects made of it will conduct heat and electricity well.   Arsenic is in heavy type; it should be brittle and a poor conductor of electricity. Further details concerning the respective characteristics of metals and nonmetals will be introduced as we proceed.

10. CHEMICAL SYMBOLS AND ATOMIC NUMBERS

Chemical symbols are used to signify the atoms of the various chemical elements. Modern symbols consist of the capitalized initial letter of the name of the element, with the addition in some cases of a second letter when this is necessary to distinguish between two elements with the same initial letter. Thus, the symbol for carbon is C, that for calcium is Ca, and that for cesium is Cs. In some cases the symbol is taken from the Latin or German name for the element: Fe for iron (ferrum), W for tungsten (wolfram). The symbols used internationally for all the elements are given in Table 1. *Note that the second letter of the symbol is never capitalized and that no period is used after the symbol.*

In Table 1 each element is assigned an *atomic number*. Atomic numbers, sometimes symbolized by Z, are the serial numbers of the elements when they are arranged in order of increasing complexity of their atoms. The complete significance of atomic numbers will become clear when we discuss atomic structure in Chapter 4. It will suffice for the present to remember that atomic numbers vary from 1 to over 100, each integral value being used for one particular element. By giving the atomic number of an atom we identify it as an atom of a specific element. The atomic number of silver is 47; every silver atom has this number. Atoms of sulfur have a different atomic number, 16. Chemists can specify a particular element by giving its name, its chemical symbol, or its atomic number; of these the atomic number is, as we shall see, the most definitive.

11. ATOMIC MASSES, ISOTOPES, AND ATOMIC WEIGHTS

We find experimentally that each individual atom has definite mass, but this mass is not necessarily the same for all atoms of a given element. That is, the atoms of an element all have the same atomic number but may be of several varieties which differ in atomic mass. Each of these varieties is called an *isotope* of the element. For example, two isotopes are found in nature for the element chlorine. All atoms of chlorine have the atomic number 17 and are of the same size, but two different values for their atomic masses are known. Only one isotope of sodium is found in nature; all of its atoms have the same mass as well as the same atomic number. A piece of iron has four isotopic kinds of iron atoms present.

In any large sample of an element as ordinarily found in nature, the relative abundance of its isotopes is constant. About 75 per cent of the chlorine atoms in any natural chlorine-containing material have one characteristic mass; the other 25 per cent of the chlorine atoms have another

Table 1.   The Chemical Elements, Their Symbols, Atomic Numbers, and Atomic Weights

Element	Symbol	Atomic Number	Atomic Weight	Element	Symbol	Atomic Number	Atomic Weight
*Actinium	Ac	89	227	Mercury	Hg	80	200.61
Aluminum	Al	13	26.97	Molybdenum	Mo	42	95.95
*Americium	Am	95	241	Neodymium	Nd	60	144.27
Antimony	Sb	51	121.76	**Neon**	Ne	10	20.183
Argon	A	18	39.944	*Neptunium	Np	93	237
Arsenic	As	33	74.91	Nickel	Ni	28	58.69
*Astatine	At	85	216	Niobium	Nb	41	92.91
Barium	Ba	56	137.36	**Nitrogen**	N	7	14.008
*Berkelium	Bk	97	249	Osmium	Os	76	190.2
Beryllium	Be	4	9.02	**Oxygen**	O	8	16.0000
Bismuth	Bi	83	209.00	Palladium	Pd	46	106.7
Boron	B	5	10.82	**Phosphorus**	P	15	30.98
Bromine	Br	35	79.916	Platinum	Pt	78	195.23
Cadmium	Cd	48	112.41	*Plutonium	Pu	94	239
*Calcium	Ca	20	40.08	*Polonium	Po	84	210
Californium	Cf	98	249	Potassium	K	19	39.096
Carbon	C	6	12.010	Praseodymium	Pr	59	140.92
Cerium	Ce	58	140.13	*Promethium	Pm	61	147
Cesium	Cs	55	132.91	*Protactinium	Pa	91	231
Chlorine	Cl	17	35.457	*Radium	Ra	88	226.05
Chromium	Cr	24	52.01	**Radon**	Rn	86	222
Cobalt	Co	27	58.94	Rhenium	Re	75	186.31
Copper	Cu	29	63.54	Rhodium	Rh	45	102.91
*Curium	Cm	96	242	Rubidium	Rb	37	85.49
Dysprosium	Dy	66	162.46	Ruthenium	Ru	44	101.7
*Einsteinium	E	99	251	Samarium	Sm	62	150.43
Erbium	Er	68	167.2	Scandium	Sc	21	45.10
Europium	Eu	63	152.0	**Selenium**	Se	34	78.96
*Fermium	Fm	100	253	**Silicon**	Si	14	28.06
Fluorine	F	9	19.00	Silver	Ag	47	107.880
*Francium	Fr	87	223	Sodium	Na	11	22.997
Gadolinium	Gd	64	156.9	Strontium	Sr	38	87.63
Gallium	Ga	31	69.72	**Sulfur**	S	16	32.066
Germanium	Ge	32	72.60	Tantalum	Ta	73	180.88
Gold	Au	79	197.2	*Technetium	Tc	43	99
Hafnium	Hf	72	178.6	Tellurium	Te	52	127.61
Helium	He	2	4.003	Terbium	Tb	65	159.2
Holmium	Ho	67	164.94	Thallium	Tl	81	204.39
Hydrogen	H	1	1.0080	Thorium	Th	90	232.12
Indium	In	49	114.76	Thulium	Tm	69	169.4
Iodine	I	53	126.92	Tin	Sn	50	118.70
Iridium	Ir	77	193.1	Titanium	Ti	22	47.90
Iron	Fe	26	55.85	Tungsten	W	74	183.92
Krypton	Kr	36	83.7	Uranium	U	92	238.07
Lanthanum	La	57	138.92	Vanadium	V	23	50.95
Lead	Pb	82	207.21	**Zenon**	Xe	54	131.3
Lithium	Li	3	6.940	Ytterbium	Yb	70	173.04
Lutetium	Lu	71	174.99	Yttrium	Y	39	88.92
Magnesium	Mg	12	24.32	Zinc	Zn	30	65.38
Manganese	Mn	25	54.93	Zirconium	Zr	40	91.22
*Mendelevium	Mv	101	256				

Nonmetals are in boldface type.
* Single isotopes, resulting from nuclear change.

mass.   Because all atoms of chlorine have the same chemical behavior, no change in the relative abundance of its isotopes occurs when matter undergoes ordinary changes.   For any collection of chlorine atoms in ordinary samples of matter, the isotopic ratio is fixed and characteristic. There will therefore be an *average atomic mass* characteristic of chlorine which will depend upon the atomic masses of the different isotopes and the percentage of each.   In chemistry we usually work with such large numbers of atoms that the average atomic mass of an element can be counted on to be constant.   The determination of these average atomic masses is important.

It is possible to measure the masses of individual atoms with a high degree of accuracy.   The atom of the most common isotope of hydrogen is found to have a mass of 1.674×10^{-24} g; the common atom of oxygen has a mass of 2.656×10^{-23} g.   From these masses of the various isotopes of an element and the relative abundance of the different isotopes, the *average atomic mass* of each element may be determined.   However, these atomic masses, expressed in ordinary weight units, such as grams, are very small and inconvenient to use.

The chemist usually prefers to express the masses of the atoms by comparing them to the average mass of oxygen atoms, using *atomic-mass units*.   These units have been arbitrarily so selected that the average mass of oxygen atoms will be 16.0000 of the units.   The average mass of the atoms of any element expressed in this way is called its *chemical atomic weight*.   The atomic-mass unit was chosen to be one-sixteenth of the average mass of oxygen atoms because, in terms of this unit, many of the elements have atomic weights close to whole numbers and none have atomic weights less than one atomic-mass unit.   On this scale hydrogen has an atomic weight of 1.008, the average mass of the hydrogen atoms in a large sample being only about one-sixteenth of that of the oxygen atom.   Sodium has an atomic weight of 23.00, calcium 40.08, and chlorine 35.46.

As we shall see later, it is possible to determine chemical atomic weights by studying quantitatively the way elements combine.   The accepted atomic weight of each element is given in Table 1.   Remember that these atomic weights are *merely numbers* relating the average atomic mass of the atoms of each element to that of oxygen taken arbitrarily as 16.00.   In order to simplify the calculations we will make in this book, we will round off the atomic weights at two digits after the decimal point, except for hydrogen, keeping in mind that this limits accordingly the number of significant digits in the answer.   (See Appendix III for a discussion of significant figures.)

The role of the isotopic varieties of atoms of an element in fixing the atomic weight may now be seen.   The two natural isotopes of chlorine have masses on the atomic weight scale of 35.0 and 37.0.   Any ordinary sample of the element always contains 75.4 per cent of isotope 35.0 and

24.6 per cent of isotope 37.0.   The average atomic weight of chlorine, therefore, is about 35.5.   This constitutes an independent check of the value 35.46 obtained by chemical studies of chlorine.

The characteristic mass of an atom of an isotope is indicated by its *mass number*.   By giving the atomic number and mass number of an atom, we identify it as belonging to a certain isotope of a given element. It is conventional to do this by giving the symbol for the element, preceded by the atomic number as a subscript and followed by the mass number as a superscript.   Thus the two isotopes of chlorine are symbolized as $_{17}Cl^{35}$ and $_{17}Cl^{37}$.

The experimental fact that isotopes exist demands an explanation. How is it possible that atoms of the same element can behave alike chemically but differ in mass?   In Chapter 4, examination of the structure of atoms will give us a reasonable answer.

12.   GRAM ATOMS AND THE AVOGADRO NUMBER

A *gram atom* of an element is the number of grams of that element equal to its atomic weight.   Thus, one gram atom of hydrogen is 1.008 g of hydrogen, one gram atom of oxygen is 16.00 g of oxygen.   For each element, one gram atom will be a specific weight of that element.   If we select any weight of an element we can readily calculate how many gram atoms we have.

$$\frac{\text{Number of gram atoms in a}}{\text{given weight of an element}} = \frac{\text{weight in grams of the element}}{\text{grams per gram atom}}$$

EXAMPLE: How many gram atoms are there in 64.00 g of oxygen?

$$\frac{\text{Number of gram atoms}}{\text{in 64.00 g of oxygen}} = \frac{64.00 \text{ g}}{16.00 \text{ g per gram atom}} = 4.000 \text{ gram atoms}$$

Notice that this calculation is made in the same way that you figure the number of dozens of apples in a total number of apples.

The term *gram atom* as applied to atoms is much like the term *dozen* as applied to ordinary objects.   It specifies a fixed number of individual units.   It can be shown experimentally that there is a fixed number of atoms, about 6.02×10^{23}, in one gram atom of any element.   This value is called the *Avogadro Number*.   Be sure to remember this number because we will use it frequently.   (The more exact value of the Avogadro Number is 6.0228×10^{23}, but for convenience we usually will use the simpler figure.)   Thus, 16.00 g of oxygen, 40.08 g of calcium, 32.07 g of sulfur, and 1.008 g of hydrogen each contain 6.02×10^{23} atoms of the element.   Gram atoms are quantities of about the same magnitude as those we work with in the laboratory and are very convenient to employ to specify the number of atoms we use.   If we say that a system contains three gram atoms of oxygen and six gram atoms of hydrogen, we know that there are present twice as many atoms of hydrogen as there are atoms of oxygen.

When the number of gram atoms of an element is known, it is easy to calculate approximately the actual number of atoms present.

Number of atoms = number of gram atoms $\times$ the Avogadro Number

EXAMPLE: How many atoms are there in 64.00 g of oxygen?

$$\text{Number of atoms in 64.00 g of oxygen} = \frac{64.00 \text{ g}}{16.00 \text{ g}} \times 6.02 \times 10^{23}$$
$$= 24.1 \times 10^{23} = 2.41 \times 10^{24}$$

It is evident that atoms must have very tiny actual weights in terms of grams. The average weight of a single atom of any element can be calculated approximately from its atomic weight by making use of the Avogadro Number.

$$\text{Average weight of one atom in grams} = \frac{\text{grams per gram atom}}{\text{the Avogadro Number}}$$

EXAMPLE: The atomic weight of oxygen is 16.00. What is the average weight of an oxygen atom?

$$\text{Average weight of one atom of oxygen} = \frac{16.00 \text{ g}}{6.02 \times 10^{23}} = 2.66 \times 10^{-23} \text{ g}$$

13. THE DISCOVERY, ABUNDANCE, AND DISTRIBUTION OF THE ELEMENTS

The time chart of the discovery of the elements given in Fig. 3 shows how the list of known elements grew from the earliest history of mankind up to the present. The ancients became familiar with a few which were readily available in nature as free elements or which were obtained by chance by very simple treatment of their minerals. The alchemists accidentally uncovered a few more when they carried out crude chemical experiments in their attempts to change common materials to gold. In the 1700's, chemical experimentation and thinking became more scientific, and, spurred on in 1661 by Robert Boyle's definition of chemical elements, a considerable addition was made to the list. The development of quantitative methods for analyzing materials and the use of electric current for decomposing them led to a great surge of discovery of new elements in the early 1800's. The invention of the spectroscope in 1860 provided a new means of identifying elements. The development of the Periodic Table in 1870 made possible the prediction of undiscovered elements with clues concerning their properties, and this greatly stimulated the search for new elements. The discovery of X-rays and radioactivity in 1895 and 1896 gave still more effective means for identifying elements, and the recent synthesis of new elements by powerful atom-smashing methods has further extended the list.

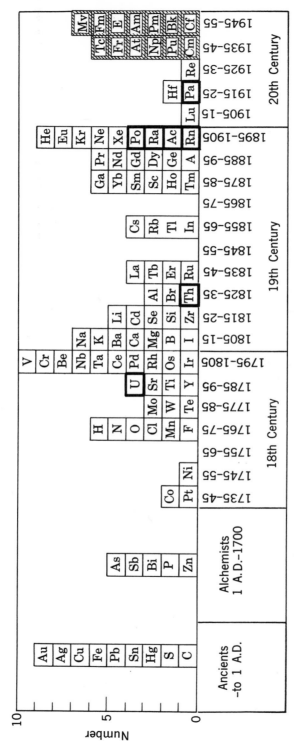

Fig. 3. Time chart of the discovery of the elements.

Heavy frames indicate radioactive elements occurring naturally. Shaded frames indicate elements that were discovered by synthesis in the laboratory.

Table 2. Weight Percentages of Common Elements

Element	*Earth	Atmosphere	Sea Water	Dry Soil	Vegetation, Dry	Human Body
Oxygen	49.52	23.2	85.79	47.3	42.9	65.0
Silicon	25.75			27.7	3.0	
Aluminum	7.51			7.8		
Iron	4.70		2×10^{-6}	4.9	0.04	0.004
Calcium	3.39		.05	3.47	0.62	1.6
Sodium	2.64		1.14	3.0	0.43	0.3
Potassium	2.40		0.04	2.46	1.68	0.4
Magnesium	1.94		0.14	2.24	0.38	0.05
Hydrogen	0.88	0.007	10.67	0.22	6.1	10.2
Titanium	0.58			0.50		
Chlorine	0.188		2.07	0.06	0.22	0.3
Phosphorus	0.12			0.12	0.56	0.9
Carbon	0.087	0.01	0.002	0.19	44.3	17.5
Manganese	0.08			0.08		
Sulfur	0.048		0.09	0.12	0.37	0.2
Barium	0.047					
Chromium	0.033					
Nitrogen	0.030	75.5			1.62	2.4
Fluorine	0.027		1×10^{-4}	0.10		
Zirconium	0.026					
Nickel	0.018					
Strontium	0.017		0.001			
Vanadium	0.016					
Copper	0.010		1×10^{-6}			
Uranium	0.008		1×10^{-7}			
Tungsten	0.005					
Zinc	0.008		5×10^{-7}			
Lead	0.002		5×10^{-7}			
Cobalt	0.001					
Boron	0.001		4×10^{-4}			
Tin	1×10^{-4}					
Bromine	1×10^{-4}		0.008			
Mercury	1×10^{-5}					
Iodine	1×10^{-5}		4×10^{-6}			
Silver	1×10^{-6}		3×10^{-8}			
Platinum	1×10^{-7}					
Gold	1×10^{-7}		6×10^{-10}			
Radium	1×10^{-10}		5×10^{-16}			
Argon		1.3				
Neon		0.0013				
Helium		7×10^{-5}				
Krypton		3×10^{-4}				
Xenon		4×10^{-5}				

* Average composition 10-mile crust, hydrosphere, and atmosphere.

This summary shows the important role played by the development of new experimental tools and techniques in the expansion of chemistry. Each time a new experimental method becomes available, a new wave of discovery follows.

It is possible to make rough estimates of the relative abundance of the various elements in the portion of the earth which is accessible to us, as shown in Table 2. For comparison the percentages by weight of the elemenst most abundant in dry soil, dried vegetation, and the human body are given.

Notice that the mass of one element, oxygen, almost equals that of all the other elements comprising the earth. The atmosphere consists largely of oxygen and nitrogen. Oxygen and hydrogen predominate in sea water, which also contains considerable amounts of sodium and chlorine and traces of most of the other elements. Traces of many elements have been shown to be important for plant and animal life.

Because the atomic weights are different for the various elements, the order of abundance by weight percentage is not necessarily the same as the order of abundance in terms of atoms. The relative abundance of the atoms may be calculated by dividing the weight percentage of each element by its atomic weight. Thus we find that although, by weight, oxygen is more than 56 times as abundant on the earth as hydrogen, the ratio of oxygen atoms to hydrogen atoms is only about 4:1. In the body there are only two atoms of oxygen for every five atoms of hydrogen.

14. SUBSTANCES—ELEMENTS AND COMPOUNDS

All matter is made up of atoms, but these we cannot see directly. However, when we study sizable portions of matter we can detect the presence of distinct *substances* or forms of matter, each having particular identifying characteristics. Iron, water, salt, and sugar are such substances. Each pure substance has a fixed composition and certain characteristics, and all portions of it are exactly alike. We may distinguish between two kinds of substances—elements and compounds. These are best defined in terms of the atoms of which they are composed.

As we have already seen, an *element* is a substance composed of atoms of identical chemical behavior (identical atomic number). In terms of the kinds of atoms present, elements are the simplest forms of matter that exist. They cannot be separated into two or more other substances by ordinary chemical means.

Compounds are substances formed by the chemical union or combination of the atoms of two or more elements in fixed proportions. A compound may be decomposed to yield the separate elements that compose it. The chemist establishes the compound nature of a substance either by *analyzing* (taking it apart) into the elements or by showing that it can be *synthesized* (built up) from two or more elements.

Take the case of the substance water. When an electric current is passed through water, under proper conditions, the water is decomposed (*electrolyzed*), and two gaseous substances having the properties of hydrogen and oxygen are formed. These two gases, under certain conditions, combine violently to produce water. We conclude that water is a compound of hydrogen atoms and oxygen atoms. Chemists have not been able to break down hydrogen or oxygen into other elements by any ordinary chemical change, nor has anyone produced them by the chemical combination of other substances. Hydrogen consists of atoms all having the atomic number 1; oxygen has only atoms of the atomic number 8. Water has present in it both of these kinds of atoms.

Other powerful experimental methods make it possible to determine unquestionably whether a substance is an element or a compound. Table salt is found to be a compound made up of sodium and chlorine atoms. Sugar is a combination of atoms of carbon, hydrogen, and oxygen.

Since all but six of the elements are known to take part in the formation of compounds, the number of combinations of two or more elements is enormous. Hundreds of thousands of compounds have been studied in detail, and new ones are rapidly being discovered and added to the list of known substances which we have at our disposal.

15. MIXTURES

Many materials with which we deal are *mixtures* of substances. Air is a mixture of a number of elements and compounds, a sugar sirup is a mixture of water and sugar, soil contains many different compounds, and wood is built up of a great variety of substances. These substances present in a mixture may be separated by nonchemical methods. The relative amounts of the various substances present in a mixture can vary continuously, usually over a wide range, and the composition of a mixture is not constant but is variable. We can mix sand with sugar in any weight ratio we please to produce mixtures of these two substances. Varying amounts of sugar may be added to a given amount of water to produce an infinite series of sugar sirups.

16. PROPERTIES OF MATTER

Each pure substance has, under given conditions, specific characteristics or *properties* that serve to identify it and to distinguish it from other substances. *Physical properties*, such as color, density, melting point, hardness, crystal form, and mechanical strength, may be described without reference to other substances. *Chemical properties* refer to the tendency of the substance to change to, or react with, other substances. Properties may be discussed *qualitatively*, that is, in a general sense. For example, water is said to be tasteless and odorless; it flows readily;

it shows no appreciable tendency to decompose at ordinary temperatures, but at very high temperatures it tends to break up into hydrogen and oxygen.   Properties may be described *quantitatively* by measuring them accurately under certain fixed conditions and assigning definite numerical values: at normal atmospheric pressure water freezes at 0° C and boils at 100° C; it has a density of 0.997 g per ml at 25° C.

It is important to remember that the properties of a substance are fixed for given conditions but may change if the conditions are altered. Water is always colorless, but the rate at which it reacts with iron increases as the temperature is raised.   When the properties of a substance are given, the conditions under which they were observed should be specified.

The *properties of a mixture* are determined by the nature and amounts of the substances which are present.   Because it is possible to vary the relative amounts of the substances in a mixture, its properties are found to vary continuously as the composition changes.   Thus, the sweetness of a sugar sirup increases with increase of the relative amount of sugar that is present; the density of a mixture of alcohol and water decreases as the percentage of water decreases.

17.   STATES OF MATTER

Matter can exist in the solid, liquid, and gaseous states, which may be distinguished by certain qualities, as shown in Figure 4.   A *solid*, such as a piece of ice, is rigid and maintains its particular shape; its volume

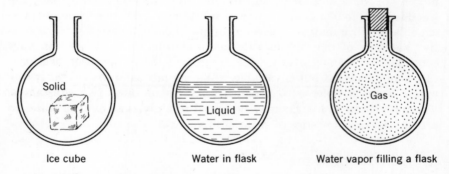

Ice cube   Water in flask   Water vapor filling a flask

Fig. 4.   Solid, liquid, and gaseous states of the substance water.

changes only slightly with change in conditions.   A *liquid*, such as water, flows readily to take the shape of the container, but a liquid maintains a horizontal upper surface, and its volume changes only slightly with change of conditions.   Matter in the *gaseous* (or vapor) *state*, such as water vapor, flows readily and spreads out into all the available space, maintaining neither shape nor volume.

Note that the same substance, water, can exist in three different states, depending upon the temperature and the pressure. When these conditions change, conversion from one state to another may occur. When warmed, solid ice tends to melt to liquid water, which, when heated sufficiently, may change into water vapor.

18. CHEMICAL SYSTEMS. PHASES

A *chemical system* is a specific portion of matter in a given region of space which has been selected for study. Such a system may be a flask of air, a block of pure iron, or a definite amount of a mixture of water and sugar. By restricting attention to such a definite system, it is possible to study it in great detail and to describe it with great precision. In a *homogeneous* system all portions are exactly alike or vary continuously in composition, structure, and behavior; no boundaries at which the prop-

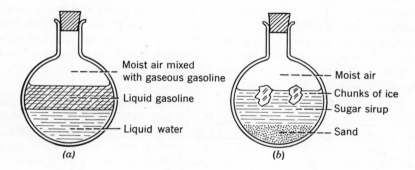

Fig. 5. **Phases in chemical systems.**

erties change abruptly are observed between various portions. A crystal of salt has the same composition and structure throughout and is a homogeneous system. The mixture of gases which we call the air becomes less dense as we go higher, but there are no boundaries between various portions. It is homogeneous. Any pure substance in a given state is homogeneous, and mixtures may be homogeneous. Homogeneous mixtures, such as a sugar sirup, are usually called *solutions*. In a *heterogeneous system* all portions are not uniform in composition, structure, or characteristics; boundaries at which the properties change abruptly may be perceived between various regions. In a flask containing both air and water a definite boundary is observed between the liquid and the gases that are present. The separate particles of the two substances may readily be detected in a mixture of fragments of sand and sugar. A system involving chunks of ice floating in water is heterogeneous.

The term *phase* refers to identical homogeneous portions of matter.

Therefore a system, such as a sample of air, or solid sugar, or sugar sirup, has only one phase present. A heterogeneous system consists of two or more phases with distinct boundaries between them. In a mixture of sand and sugar the fragments of sand constitute one phase, those of sugar constitute a second phase. If the system selected is the contents of a flask having air, water, and gasoline present, the three phases indicated in Figure 5a are observed. A flask containing sand, chunks of ice floating on sugar sirup, and moist air above the sirup has four phases present, as shown in Figure 5b.

19. CHANGES OF MATTER

Matter ordinarily undergoes two kinds of change. A *physical change* is one that involves no change in composition of matter. The original substances persist, and no new substances are formed. Grinding large crystals of sugar to a fine powder, making up a sirup by adding the sugar to water, heating the sirup to drive off the water as steam so that crystals of sugar appear, and packaging the crystalline sugar for sale to the housewife—all these are physical changes that do not alter the chemical composition of the sugar and the water. The atomic combinations characteristic of these substances persist.

A *chemical change* involves the formation of new substances at the expense of the original material, the composition changing because of changes in the mode of combination of the atoms present in the system. When pure sugar is heated sufficiently, it froths, steam bubbles off (which may be cooled to give liquid water), and charring occurs to produce an inert, black, solid residue that does not dissolve in water and has no sweet taste. If we cool the system to the original temperature and observe the over-all changes in properties that have taken place, we conclude that those properties characteristic of the substance sugar have disappeared while those characteristic of water and the element carbon have appeared. Hydrogen and oxygen atoms, originally present in the sugar, escape, combined in the new substance, water, leaving atoms of carbon behind. A chemical change has occurred, the colorless crystals of sugar being destroyed and the new substances, water and carbon, being formed. Obviously, in the course of this chemical change, physical changes also have taken place. The chemist uses the term *reaction* to refer to a chemical change. In ordinary chemical reactions, atoms are not destroyed; the ways in which they are combined are altered.

Less commonly, matter undergoes *radioactive change*, in which the original atoms are transformed into other atoms having different atomic numbers or atomic masses. Such extraordinary changes will be discussed in some detail later, after we have arrived at an understanding of the structure of matter.

20. STUDY METHODS

Many students beginning the study of chemistry get into difficulty because they have not yet learned to study properly.   Chemistry is such a complicated subject that the student must organize his efforts properly if he wishes to make satisfactory progress.   In studying the assignments in this book, make a practice of writing an outline as you read, abstracting the principal idea of each paragraph.   This writing forces you to concentrate on the material in the book and to think about it carefully.   Writing will also fix each point in your mind, and the outline will emphasize the connections between the various topics.

Let us illustrate.   You have just finished reading Section 19, Changes of Matter.   Your study outline might read:

"Matter undergoes two common kinds of change
    Physical change—no new substance formed, the original ones persist.
        Examples: grinding sugar to a powder; evaporating water from a sirup.
    Chemical change—new substances are produced, atoms change their
        mode of combination.
    Example: charring of sugar to produce carbon and steam.
    Radioactive change is less common—atoms are transformed to other
        atoms."

After you have finished the reading assignment, close your book and go over your written outline to see if you have grasped the essentials of each topic you have listed.   If not, study that section in your book again. After reviewing your outline, work through the exercises at the end of each chapter which pertain to the material you have studied.   These exercises provide a test of your mastery of the subject.

Answers to many of the exercises involving mathematical calculations are given in the Appendix.   It is best to check with these *after* you have worked the problem.   In working the problems indicate clearly the steps in the reasoning you have used and label all quantities with the proper units.

The accumulated outlines of your daily assignments will be of help when you are reviewing for comprehensive examinations.

EXERCISES

1. In what respects do the establishment and continued existence of scientific laws differ from the establishment and existence of the laws of a country?

2. Why has the practice of medicine not advanced to the degree of precision achieved in building bridges?

3. What evidence can you cite to prove that an inflated automobile tire contains matter?

4. Making use of Appendices I, II, and III
a) Convert 5 km to centimeters, millimeters, angstroms.

b) Convert 125 ml to liters, cubic centimeters, quarts.

c) Convert 400 g to kilograms, milligrams, pounds.

5. The atomic diameter of iron atoms is about 2 angstrom units. (See Appendix I.)   How many of these atoms laid side by side would be needed to produce a row as long as the diameter of a human hair, which is about 0.04 mm?

6. What characteristics of different kinds of atoms have been stressed in this chapter?

7. Looking over the names of the elements in Table 1, suggest possible derivations of five names not discussed in Section 8.

8. a) Which are more numerous, metallic or nonmetallic elements?

b) What two elements account for about 75 per cent of the mass of the earth that is accessible to us?

9. In view of the general properties of metals and nonmetals, from which class, and why, would you select an element suitable for: a) a mirror? b) insulating an electrical circuit? c) cooking utensils? d) cable for transmission of electrical power?

10. Explain why the atomic weights given in Table 1 actually are "average" values for most of the elements.

11. a) What weight of the element sodium constitutes one gram atom of that metal?

b) Calculate the average weight in grams of a single atom of this element.

12. Calculate the number of atoms present in 60.05 g of the element carbon, making clear the reasoning you use.

13. The average atomic mass of the atoms of gold is 3.28×10^{-22} g.   Show how this number can be used to compute the atomic weight of gold.

14. A system contains 5 gram atoms of silver and 10 gram atoms of sulfur. How many atoms of sulfur are there per atom of silver?

15. a) If 30.0 per cent of the atoms of an element have the mass number 65.0 and the remainder have the mass number 63.0, what is the chemical atomic weight of the element?

b) What is the element?

16. Making use of the chart of the discovery of the elements, calculate the percentage of our present list of elements that were: a) known to the ancients; b) discovered since 1800.

17. What elements are present in higher percentages in the body than in dry soil?

18. The early chemists could find no way to decompose lime into two or more other substances, but when the metal calcium was discovered, it was found to unite vigorously with oxygen to form lime.   What is your conclusion as to whether lime is an element or a compound?

19. A granite tombstone is observed to be made up of coarse shiny flakes of mica, colorless crystals of quartz, and gray granules of feldspar.

a) How many phases are present in the tombstone?

b) Is it a homogeneous or a heterogeneous system?

20. In which state, solid, liquid, or gaseous, would you classify each of the following under ordinary conditions: a) kerosene? b) a diamond? c) soda pop? d) your breath? e) a penny? f) molasses?

21. A ring containing a diamond mounted in platinum is dropped into a bottle that is half full of water and is open to the air. The bottle is then stoppered. List the phases that are present in the bottle, specifying whether each is solid, liquid, or gaseous.

22. Which of the following involve chemical change: a) the melting of ice? b) the burning of coal? c) pumping water through a pipe? d) breaking a bottle? e) making wine from grape juice?

Chapter 2

▶ **Some Facts about Chemical Change**

▶ **Dalton's Atomic Theory**

21. QUANTITATIVE EXPERIMENTS ON CHEMICAL CHANGE

We have already discussed the qualitative aspects of chemical change. By observing a system in which chemical change is taking place, it is possible to establish what substances are being used up and what new substances are being formed. But the chemist also tries to answer the question, how much? The development of the chemical balance in the latter part of the eighteenth century made it possible to weigh matter exactly, and its effective use by Lavoisier and others was the starting point of modern chemistry. Weight gives a precise measure of the mass or amount of matter that is present. By use of the chemical balance, the *quantitative aspects* of chemical change may be studied. Weighing experiments have provided facts dealing with the weight relations in chemical change. These facts have been summarized in quantitative laws believed to govern all chemical changes. It has been possible to account for these laws by considering how the atoms which constitute all matter behave in chemical change. The whole procedure is an excellent example of the operation of the scientific method.

22. THE CONSERVATION OF MATTER IN CHEMICAL CHANGE

One of the most fundamental questions we can ask about a system undergoing chemical change concerns the total quantity of matter in the system. Does it remain constant, or does it change? This has been answered decisively by countless weighing experiments. One of the simplest ways to do such an experiment makes use of the piece of apparatus devised by Landolt and shown in Figure 6.

Substances *A* and *B* are placed in opposite ends of the bent glass tube which then is sealed and weighed. The tube is subsequently inverted so that the substances mix and react. The tube and its contents are then weighed again. Once the tube has been sealed, no matter can enter or leave it. Repetition of this experiment for a great many chemical changes has always given the same answer. Within the limits of accuracy of the weighing operation, the total weight of the system remains constant. Many other experimental methods have provided similar data. These facts may be summarized to give the *Law of Conservation of Matter: There is no change, detectable by ordinary weighing, in the total quantity of matter in a system when ordinary chemical change occurs.*

If we select a given amount of matter to experiment with, and if chemical change occurs, we should always be able to account for the total quantity, regardless of what actual substances are involved. If 100 g of sugar is completely charred by heating, the total weight of carbon and

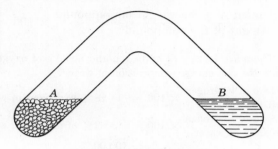

Fig. 6. Landolt's apparatus.

water formed must be 100 g. When 10 g of water is partially electrolyzed, the total weight of the hydrogen and oxygen formed, plus the weight of the undecomposed water that remains, must be just 10 g. Such chemical accounting for all of the matter in a chemical system is called making a *weight balance.* This is like accounting for what has happened to the total sum of money you started out with on a shopping expedition.

23. DEFINITE COMPOSITION OF PURE COMPOUNDS. PERCENTAGE COMPOSITION

A second important quantitative question concerns the weights of elements which combine chemically to form pure compounds. Can elements combine in all proportions by weight, or do they react only in certain definite weight ratios?

Careful experiments can be made in which the chemical balance is employed to determine accurately the weights of the elements used to form a given weight of a compound. Or we may determine the weights of the elements obtained when a given weight of a compound is decomposed. Consider the elements hydrogen and oxygen which combine to form the compound, water. When 11.18 g of hydrogen reacts with oxygen to form water, 88.82 g of oxygen is used up and 100.0 g of water is formed. When the experiment is repeated using 1.118 g of hydrogen, 8.882 g of oxygen combines with it and 10.00 g of water is formed. Even if more than 8.882 g of oxygen is made available, only 8.882 g combines with the 1.118 g of hydrogen. Regardless of the actual weights used, oxygen and hydrogen are found always to react in the same fixed proportions by weight when they combine to form water.   And when 100.0 g of water is decomposed completely, 11.18 g of hydrogen and 88.82 g. of oxygen form. The conclusion is that the compound, water, is always composed of hydrogen and oxygen in the same proportion by weight.

The *percentage composition* of a compound specifies the per cent by weight of each element (parts by weight in 100 parts by weight of the compound).

$$\frac{\text{Weight of element in given weight of compound}}{\text{Weight of the compound}} \times 100 = \begin{matrix}\text{per cent of}\\\text{element in}\\\text{compound}\end{matrix}$$

EXAMPLE: There are 1.118 g of hydrogen and 8.882 g of oxygen in 10.00 g of water.   What is the percentage composition of water?

$$\frac{1.118 \text{ g of hydrogen}}{10.00 \text{ g of water}} \times 100 = \ \ 11.18\% \text{ hydrogen in water}$$

$$\frac{8.882 \text{ g of hydrogen}}{10.00 \text{ g of water}} \times 100 = \ \ 88.82\% \text{ of oxygen in water}$$

$$\overline{100.00\%}$$

The percentage composition of pure water by weight is always 11.18 per cent hydrogen and 88.82 per cent oxygen.   Of course the percentages of the elements in a compound should add up to 100 per cent.

The analysis and synthesis of a great number of pure compounds have led to the *Law of Definite Composition: A substance always has the same elements present in the same proportions by weight.*   The percentage composition of each substance is fixed, and, once having established this composition, we may be sure that every sample of the pure substance will always show this specific composition.   Another way of stating this conclusion is that, when elements combine to form a compound under given conditions, they do so in a fixed combining weight ratio.

Knowing the percentage composition of a substance, we can calculate the weight of any, element present in a given weight of the compound, confident that the Law of Definite Composition holds.   The total weight of the compound is multiplied by the decimal equivalent of the per cent of the element.

EXAMPLE: How much hydrogen is there in 500 g of water if water is 11.18 per cent hydrogen?

The weight of hydrogen in 500 g of water = 500 g $\times$ 0.1118 = 55.9 g

24. DALTON'S THEORY OF ATOMS IN CHEMICAL CHANGE

We have accumulated some laws that apply generally to chemical change.   How can these be explained?

John Dalton did this quite successfully in 1805 when he proposed *Dalton's Atomic Theory*.   This assumed that elements must consist of particles and, in modified form, may be summarized in the following statements:

a) All elements consist of minute discrete particles called *atoms*.

b) Atoms of a given element are alike and have the same mass.

c) Atoms of different elements differ, each element having unique atoms.

d) Chemical changes involve the union or separation of atoms in fixed numerical ratio. Atoms are neither created nor destroyed when chemical change occurs.

This theory accounted so satisfactorily for the laws of chemical change that it was generally accepted. We need only to substitute "average mass" for "mass" in statement (b) to bring this theory in line with what we now know about the elements. It then satisfactorily accounts for the conservation of matter and the definite composition of compounds.

If atoms of an element have definite average mass which does not change appreciably during chemical change, and if the total number of atoms in a system remains constant, the total mass of the system will be constant. If elements come only in definite atomic bundles of fixed average mass and these atoms combine in a fixed ratio in forming a compound, the ratio of the masses of elements present in the compound must be fixed.

Atoms of hydrogen, in the free element or in its compounds, each have a given average mass of 1.008 on the atomic weight scale. The atoms of oxygen have an average mass of 16.000. If, in the formation of water, two atoms of hydrogen always are used for every atom of oxygen, there will be 2.016 parts by weight of hydrogen for every 16.000 parts by weight of oxygen in 18.016 parts by weight of water. Calculation of the percentage composition by weight of water from these values gives 11.18 per cent hydrogen and 88.82 per cent oxygen. This is the same as the percentage composition found experimentally for water, so the atomic ratio of 2:1 must be correct.

25. CHEMICAL FORMULAS

The chemist uses a *chemical formula* to designate a particular substance, thus summarizing what elements are present and the atomic ratio of their atoms. This is done by writing the symbols of the elements and following each symbol with a numerical subscript so that the atomic ratio is indicated. We have seen that the analysis and synthesis of water show it to be composed of atoms of hydrogen and oxygen in the ratio of 2:1. The formula for water therefore is written as H_2O. (The subscript is omitted when it is 1.) Of course, the formula H_4O_2 would involve the same atomic ratio and the same percentage composition, and thus might be a possibility. But the *simplest formula* for a substance makes use of the smallest whole numbers for subscripts, and, for the time being, we will concern ourselves only with simplest formulas.

The formula NaCl for table salt tells us that it is composed of sodium and chlorine atoms in equal numbers. The formula $CaCO_3$ for limestone indicates that calcium, carbon, and oxygen atoms are combined in the numerical ratio $1:1:3$. The simplest formula for sulfur is S, because it is an element.

Whenever we write a formula we show our confidence in the Law of Definite Composition and in the idea that matter is atomic in structure.

26. EXPERIMENTAL DETERMINATION OF SIMPLEST FORMULAS

Experimentally, simplest formulas are derived by determining what elements are present in the compound and the weight of each in a given weight of the compound. Dividing the weight of each element by its gram-atomic weight gives the number of gram atoms of each element in the given weight of the compound. The ratio of the gram atoms of the elements present is equal to the ratio of atoms present, because gram atoms of all elements contain equal numbers of atoms, 6.02×10^{23}. The ratio may be reduced to simplest terms by dividing by the smallest number of gram atoms.

EXAMPLE: A sample of 10.00 g of a compound is found to contain 2.729 g of carbon and 7.271 g of oxygen. What is the simplest formula for this compound?

Note that the sum of the weights of carbon and oxygen is equal to the weight of the sample; this is convincing proof that it contains only these elements.

$$\frac{2.729 \text{ g of carbon}}{12.01 \text{ g of carbon per gram atom}} = 0.227 \text{ gram atoms of carbon}$$

$$\frac{7.271 \text{ g of oxygen}}{16.00 \text{ g of oxygen per gram atom}} = 0.454 \text{ gram atoms of oxygen}$$

$$\text{Ratio of gram atoms of carbon to gram atoms of oxygen} = 0.227 : 0.454$$

$$= \frac{0.227}{0.227} : \frac{0.454}{0.227} = 1:2$$

Since the ratio of gram atoms of carbon to gram atoms of oxygen is $1:2$, the ratio between their atoms also must be $1:2$, and the simplest formula for the compound must be CO_2.

EXAMPLE: A compound is found to be 69.94 per cent iron and 30.06 per cent oxygen by weight. What is its simplest formula?

The percentages by weight tell us that in 100.0 g of the compound there are 69.94 g of iron and 30.06 g of oxygen.

$$\frac{69.94 \text{ g of iron}}{55.85 \text{ g per gram atom of iron}} = 1.25 \text{ gram atoms of iron}$$

$$\frac{30.06 \text{ g of oxygen}}{16.00 \text{ g per gram atom of oxygen}} = 1.88 \text{ gram atoms of oxygen}$$

$$\begin{aligned} \text{Ratio of gram atoms of iron to} & = 1.25 : 1.88 \\ \text{gram atoms of oxygen} & \\ & = \frac{1.25}{1.25} : \frac{1.88}{1.25} = 1:1.5 \end{aligned}$$

Because only whole atoms take part in forming compounds, we must multiply by a number, in this case 2, which will clear the ratio of fractions. The atoms of iron and oxygen therefore are in the ratio of 2:3, and the simplest formula for ferric oxide is Fe_2O_3.

Because of small experimental errors in the determination of composition by weight, the atomic ratios calculated will usually not involve exact small whole numbers. However, they commonly will be so close to some ratio of small whole numbers that these are quite clearly the subscripts to be used in the simplest formula. As we shall see later, there are other ways of checking these atomic ratios to make sure they are correct.

27. FORMULA WEIGHTS

The *formula weight* of a substance is equal to the sum of the atomic weights of the atoms indicated by the formula.

Formula weight = sum of atomic weights of all atoms
in formula

EXAMPLE: What is the formula weight of NaCl?

Formula weight of NaCl = atomic weight of sodium + atomic
weight of chlorine
= 23.00 + 35.46
= 58.46

EXAMPLE: What is the formula weight of H_2O?

Formula weight of H_2O = 2 (atomic weight of hydrogen) +
atomic weight of oxygen
= 2(1.008) + 16.000
= 18.016

Such formula weights are in terms of atomic-mass units, relative to the atomic weight of oxygen as 16.000.

28. GRAM-FORMULA WEIGHTS AND NUMBERS OF ATOMS

Gram-formula weights are the formula weights taken in grams. Thus, one gram-formula weight of NaCl is 58.46 g and is a definite quantity of that compound.   18.016 g of water constitutes one gram-formula weight of H_2O.

Any given weight in grams of a substance may also be expressed in terms of the number of gram-formula weights.

$$\frac{\text{Number of grams of substance}}{\text{Grams per gram-formula weight}} = \text{number of gram-formula weights}$$

EXAMPLE: How many gram-formula weights of sodium chloride are there in a bottle containing 2,631 g of that substance?

$$\frac{\text{Total grams of NaCl}}{\text{Grams per gram-formula weight of NaCl}} = \frac{2631 \text{ g}}{58.46 \text{ g}} = \begin{array}{l}45.00 \text{ gram-} \\ \text{formula weights} \\ \text{of NaCl}\end{array}$$

The chemist likes to talk in terms of gram-formula weights because it enables him to compute readily the actual numbers of atoms in a given sample and compare the numbers of atoms in different samples. Remember that one gram atom of any element is a collection of the Avogadro Number, 6.02×10^{23}, of atoms of that element.

One gram-formula weight of NaCl is made up of two contributions, one gram atom of sodium and one gram atom of chlorine. Therefore one gram-formula weight, 58.46 g, of NaCl consists of 6.02×10^{23} atoms of sodium and the same number of atoms of chlorine. In the 2,631 g of NaCl in the bottle just mentioned, there are 45.00 gram-formula weights of NaCl and therefore there are present 45.00 gram atoms of sodium and 45.00 gram atoms of chlorine.

$$\begin{array}{l}45.00 \text{ gram atoms} \\ \text{of sodium}\end{array} \times \begin{array}{l}6.02 \times 10^{23} \text{ atoms} \\ \text{per gram atom}\end{array}$$

$$= 271 \times 10^{23} = 2.71 \times 10^{25} \text{ atoms of sodium}$$

There will be the same number of atoms of chlorine present.

The chemist also usually chooses to express quantities of substances in terms of gram-formula weights because these are amounts of materials convenient for use in laboratory experimentation. However, in large-scale work other weight units may be preferred. Kilogram-formula weights, pound-formula weights, or ton-formula weights also refer to definite quantities of a substance. It must be remembered, if these are used, that the Avogadro Number holds only for gram atoms and that kilograms, pounds, or tons must be converted to grams if you wish to use the Avogadro Number for calculating the actual number of atoms present.

29. PERCENTAGE COMPOSITION FROM FORMULAS

If the correct formula for a compound is known, the per cent by weight of each element in the compound may easily be calculated.   This will be

equal to the fraction of the total weight which is due to the element, multiplied by 100.

EXAMPLE: Calculate the percentage composition of limestone, which has the formula $CaCO_3$. (See Table 1 for atomic weights.)

$$\text{Per cent of calcium} = \frac{1 \times \text{atomic weight of calcium}}{\text{formula weight of } CaCO_3} \times 100$$

$$= \frac{40.08}{40.08 + 12.01 + 3(16.00)} \times 100 = \frac{40.08}{100.09} \times 100 = \quad 40.04\%$$

$$\text{Per cent of carbon} = \frac{12.01}{100.09} \times 100 = \qquad\qquad\qquad\qquad 12.00\%$$

$$\text{Per cent of oxygen} = \frac{3(16.00)}{100.09} \times 100 = \qquad\qquad\qquad\qquad 47.96\%$$

$$\text{Total } \overline{100.00\%}$$

Expressing the composition of compounds by weight percentages is very useful when we wish to compare the richness of various compounds as sources of an element. Water is 11.18 per cent hydrogen by weight, whereas HCl is only 2.76 per cent hydrogen. Weight for weight, water is more than four times richer in hydrogen than is HCl.

30. CHEMICAL COMBINING CAPACITY, VALENCE, AND EQUIVALENT WEIGHTS

Weighing experiments can be done to determine the definite weight ratios in which two elements combine, and these weight ratios are a result of the atoms of the elements combining in a definite atomic ratio. The atoms of one element have a certain capacity to combine with the atoms of the other element when a compound is formed. This is referred to as *chemical combining capacity*.

Table 3. Equivalent Weights

Weights of Elements Combining		Compound Formed	Simplest Formula
1.008 g hydrogen	8.000 g oxygen	water	H_2O
1.008 g hydrogen	35.46 g chlorine	hydrogen chloride	HCl
1.008 g hydrogen	20.04 g calcium	calcium hydride	CaH_2
1.008 g hydrogen	23.00 g sodium	sodium hydride	NaH
8.000 g oxygen	35.46 g chlorine	chlorine monoxide	Cl_2O
8.000 g oxygen	20.04 g calcium	calcium oxide	CaO
8.000 g oxygen	23.00 g sodium	sodium oxide	Na_2O
35.46 g chlorine	20.04 g calcium	calcium chloride	$CaCl_2$
35.46 g chlorine	23.00 g sodium	sodium chloride	NaCl

Typical data obtained by weighing experiments, such as those given in Table 3, will allow us to study the chemical combining capacity of one gram atom of hydrogen in forming compounds with several elements, and to see how this is related to the combining capacities these other elements show in combining with each other. It is evident from the facts in Table 3 that 8.000 g of oxygen, 35.46 g of chlorine, 20.04 g of calcium, and 23.00 g of sodium all have the same chemical combining capacity in forming the compounds listed, since these amounts combine with 1.008 g of hydrogen. And these amounts are also involved in the weight ratios observed when oxygen, chlorine, calcium, and sodium combine with each other. These amounts of elements, which will combine with or take the place of 1.008 g of hydrogen, are known as the *gram-equivalent weights* of the elements because they indicate the weights of the various elements which are chemically equivalent in combining capacity under given conditions.

These facts can be interpreted in terms of the atomic theory of Dalton. To do this we convert the weights of the elements to gram atoms and these will indicate the atomic ratios. For example, 1.008 g of hydrogen is one gram atom and consists of 6.02×10^{23} atoms of hydrogen. The numbers of atoms of each of the other elements taking part in the reactions in Table 3 can be calculated likewise. They turn out to be the Avogadro Number of atoms of chlorine and of sodium and half this number of atoms of oxygen and calcium. The combining ratios in terms of atoms, therefore, are those indicated by the subscripts in the formulas. Chlorine and sodium combine in a 1:1 atom ratio with hydrogen and with each other. Oxygen and calcium combine in a 2:1 atom ratio with hydrogen, chlorine, or sodium and in a 1:1 atom ratio with each other. Hydrogen, chlorine, and sodium atoms therefore have the same chemical combining capacity per atom, while oxygen and calcium have twice this capacity. The atoms of each element have a combining capacity in a given compound equal to, or some whole multiple of, the combining capacity of hydrogen atoms. Because the combining capacity of the hydrogen atom is the same in all ordinary reactions and is the lowest encountered whenever chemical change takes place, it is taken as the standard and considered to be 1.

The term *valence* was introduced in about 1850 to describe the tendency of elements to combine. Because the use of this term has varied down through the years, some confusion exists about its meaning. We must, therefore, be careful to define just how it will be used in this book. We will consider valence to be synonomous with combining capacity. *The numerical valence of an element will be taken as the number of units of chemical combining capacity per atom of the element.* Accordingly, the valence of hydrogen is taken as 1 and, in the compounds listed in Table 3, oxygen and calcium have a valence of 2 while sodium and chlorine have a valence of 1. (Later, in Chapter 5, we shall define valence more precisely when we consider the theories of chemical bonding between atoms.)

Because one gram atom of hydrogen consists of the Avogadro Number of hydrogen atoms and each atom has a combining capacity of 1, the total combining capacity of 1.008 g of hydrogen is the Avogadro Number of units.   *One gram-equivalent weight of any element in forming a compound makes use toward other elements of 6.02 × 10²³ units of combining capacity.* The 8.000 g of oxygen that combines with 1.008 g of hydrogen to form water is one-half a gram atom of oxygen and consists of one-half the Avogadro Number of atoms.   Each atom of oxygen uses two units of combining capacity in the reaction.   Therefore, 8.000 g of oxygen employs the Avogadro Number of units of combining capacity toward hydrogen and is the gram-equivalent weight of oxygen in this reaction.

31.   MULTIPLE COMBINING PROPORTIONS AND VARIABLE COMBINING CAPACITY

We have seen that when a reaction takes place under given conditions, elements combine in a certain atomic ratio to form a specific compound of constant composition.   It has also been discovered that, by varying the experimental conditions, more than one compound may be formed by the same elements.   An outstanding example is the series of five compounds formed by oxygen and nitrogen that are listed in Table 4.   These are pure substances formed under different conditions.   Each is characterized by specific properties, and each always has the definite percentage composition given in the table.   The simplest formulas calculated from the percentage compositions are in the last column.

Table 4.   Compounds of Nitrogen and Oxygen

Name	% Nitrogen	% Oxygen	Simplest Formula
Nitrous oxide	63.65	36.35	N_2O
Nitric oxide	46.68	53.32	NO
Nitrogen trioxide	36.86	63.14	N_2O_3
Nitrogen dioxide	30.45	69.55	NO_2
Nitrogen pentoxide	25.94	74.06	N_2O_5

It is clear from the formulas that nitrogen can be combined in more than one atomic ratio, but in each case this is a ratio of small whole numbers.   The Law of Conservation of Matter and the Law of Definite Composition are obeyed in the formation of each compound.   This must mean that the atoms of one of the elements can show more than one combining capacity, depending upon the conditions.   In the series of compounds given in Table 4, the combining capacity of oxygen is believed to be constant at 2.   The combining capacity of nitrogen atoms apparently can be 1, 2, 3, 4, or 5.   Many of the elements have more than one combining capacity toward other elements.

32.   GRAM-EQUIVALENT WEIGHTS AND GRAM-ATOMIC WEIGHTS

It should be apparent from the foregoing discussion that there is a simple relationship between the gram-equivalent weight of an element in forming a compound and its gram-atomic weight; the gram-atomic weight is either equal to, or some whole multiple of, the gram-equivalent weight. If the combining capacity used by the atoms of an element toward other elements in forming a compound is one unit per atom, then the gram-equivalent weight of the element in this reaction is equal to its atomic weight. If the combining capacity toward other elements is two units per atom, only one-half the Avogadro Number of atoms are needed to provide that number of units of combining capacity, and the gram-atomic weight is twice the gram-equivalent weight.

The gram-atomic weight of an element
$$= \begin{array}{c} \text{the gram-equivalent} \\ \text{weight of the element} \\ \text{in a reaction} \end{array} \times \begin{array}{c} \text{the number of units of} \\ \text{combining capacity used} \\ \text{per atom toward other elements} \end{array}$$

This relationship has provided an excellent method for the determination of atomic weights by studying the weights of elements used to form compounds. For instance, 1.008 g of hydrogen is found to combine with 16.033 g of sulfur to form hydrogen sulfide. Therefore in this reaction the gram-equivalent weight of sulfur is 16.003 g. The gram-atomic weight of sulfur, accordingly, must be 16.033 g or some whole multiple of this value, depending upon the number of units of combining capacity each atom of sulfur is using to combine with hydrogen. It is not possible by simple weighing experiments to settle this question. The answer must be obtained by other studies of the reaction and of the compound. In the case of hydrogen sulfide, its behavior as a gas makes it quite certain that each sulfur atom shows two units of combining capacity toward hydrogen. Accordingly

$$\begin{array}{c} \text{The gram-atomic} \\ \text{weight of sulfur} \end{array} = 16.033 \text{ g} \times 2 = 32.066 \text{ g}$$

The correctness of this value can be checked by a number of other methods.

It is not necessary to determine the gram-equivalent weight of an element by getting it to combine with hydrogen. Any method which will tell what weight of an element is providing the Avogadro Number of units of combining capacity will suffice. For example, many metals react with acids to replace hydrogen. The weight of a metal which replaces 1.008 g of hydrogen must be using the same combining capacity as that amount of hydrogen and is the gram-equivalent weight of the metal in the reaction.

EXAMPLE: 3.500 g of element Z replaces 0.504 g of hydrogen in a reaction.
a) What is the gram-equivalent weight of Z in this reaction?
b) If the combining capacity of each atom of Z in this reaction is 4, what is the gram-atomic weight of Z?

a) Dividing the weight of Z by the weight of hydrogen it replaces gives the weight of Z equivalent to one gram of hydrogen. Multiplying this by 1.008 g will give the weight of Z equivalent to 1.008 g of hydrogen; this is the gram-equivalent weight of Z in the reaction.

$$\text{The gram-equivalent weight of } Z = \frac{3.500 \text{ g of } Z}{0.504 \text{ g of hydrogen}} \times \frac{1.008 \text{ g of}}{\text{hydrogen}} = 7.00 \text{ g of } Z$$

b) $$\text{The gram-atomic weight of } Z = \frac{\text{the gram-equivalent}}{\text{weight of } Z} \times \frac{\text{the combining capacity}}{\text{per atom of } Z}$$

$$= 7.00 \text{ g} \times 4 = 28.0 \text{ g}$$

33. NEED FOR FURTHER DETAILS ABOUT ATOMS

The modified Dalton Atomic Theory we have so far considered accounts for the weight relations observed for chemical change of sizable portions of matter, but it leaves unanswered some further very important questions. What is there about atoms which is responsible for their ability to combine with other atoms to form compounds? Why do atoms of different elements combine in certain definite whole-number ratios? How is it possible for atoms of the same elements to combine in more than one ratio? Why have we been so careful to speak of the "average" atomic mass for the atoms of an element?

Dalton simply considered each atom to be an indivisible lump of fixed mass which persisted through all changes. He had no explanation of why atoms combine. It has gradually become clear that *atoms really are complex in structure*, and it has been possible to find out much about the way atoms are constituted. By considering, in Chapters 4 and 5, the complex structure and behavior of individual atoms, we can hope to get a better understanding of their behavior in chemical change.

EXERCISES

1. What limiting qualification is made in the Law of Conservation of Matter as given in this chapter?

2. a) What is the percentage composition of a compound if 10.0 g of it are formed when 4.0 g of sulfur combines with oxygen?

b) What quantitative chemical law are you relying upon in your calculation?

3. What is the percentage composition of the compound formed when 23.0 g of sodium combines with 8.00 g of oxygen?

4. In the formation of a compound it is found that for every 3.00×10^{23} atoms of carbon, 6.00×10^{23} atoms of hydrogen are required. What is the simplest formula for the compound?

5. A chemist synthesizes a new compound from two elements.

a) What weight measurements should be made if he wants to determine the simplest formula for this compound?

b) What chemical laws does he assume to be true when he works out this formula?

6. What is the simplest formula for a substance composed of 50.05 per cent sulfur and 49.95 per cent oxygen?

7. What is the simplest formula for a substance containing 61.73 per cent tungsten and 38.27 per cent fluorine?

8. a) Calculate the percentage composition of calcium chloride, which has the formula $CaCl_2$.

b) How many tons of calcium will there be in 1,000 tons of calcium chloride?

9. How was Dalton's Atomic Theory consistent with the existence of a series of compounds of oxygen and nitrogen?

10. Strontium forms two compounds with oxygen; one contains 84.36 per cent strontium, the other 73.25 per cent strontium.

a) Calculate the simplest formula for these two compounds.

b) Compare the number of gram atoms of strontium per gram atom of oxygen in the two compounds.

11. The formula for sodium hydride is NaH. How many grams of sodium are there in 48.02 g of this compound?

12. Compare quantitatively the compounds AgCl and Ag_2S as sources of silver.

13. 10.0 g of the hypothetical element X reacts completely when it is heated with 60.5 g of element Y, and 50.0 g of a compound is formed as the only product.

a) How many grams of Y remain unchanged? What chemical law are you assuming?

b) What is the percentage composition of the compound?

c) If the atomic weight of X is 40.0 and the atomic weight of Y is 80.0, what is the simplest formula of the compound?

d) How many gram-formula weights of the compound were formed?

e) How many gram atoms of Y reacted with X?

f) How many atoms of X were present in the 50.0 g of the compound?

g) If Y has a valence of 2, what is the valence of X?

14. Calculate the gram-equivalent weight of arsenic in the compound AsH_3.

15. 0.504 g of hydrogen combines with 9.04 g of another element in forming a compound. What is the gram-equivalent weight of this element in the reaction?

16. Calculate the gram-equivalent weight of nitrogen in each of the compounds N_2O and NO_2. (See Section 31.)

Chapter 3

▶ Energy and Matter

34. ASSOCIATION OF MATTER WITH ENERGY

The basic concept of matter is one of the foundation stones of physical science. Another basic concept, that of energy, is of equal importance. Matter is always associated with energy, and energy changes always accompany chemical changes. It is necessary that these two basic concepts and their interrelation be understood thoroughly if a grasp of the fundamentals of chemistry is to be achieved.

Energy is the capacity to do work. The amount of energy possessed by a given chemical system may be measured by determining the amount of work which that system can do. The muscles of a golfer do work on a golf club by causing it to move rapidly. The rapidly moving golf club is able to do work on a golf ball, causing it to move from its position. The rapidly moving golf ball crushes the blades of grass it strikes and displaces the soil on which it falls. The muscles of the golfer, the moving golf club, the golf ball in motion in the air all possess energy, which is made evident by their ability to accomplish work on other material systems. *Work* is a process by which energy is transferred from one portion of matter to another.

35. FORMS OF ENERGY

Two general classifications of energy are recognized.

a. Kinetic energy is energy of motion. Masses of matter in motion possess such energy. A rapidly moving golf club and a golf ball in flight both possess kinetic energy. A revolving top, a speeding automobile, and a falling stone have kinetic energy by virtue of their motion. If the body is a large portion of matter moving as a whole, the motion is visible, and the energy is usually called *mechanical energy* because it is the sort of energy we are concerned with in the moving parts of machines. When the moving body is an atom or group of atoms, the invisible motion is associated with another kind of kinetic energy called *heat*. Electric current involves the flow of a stream of electrons (see Chapter 4), and therefore the expenditure of *electrical energy* also involves motion. *Light* and *sound* and *radio waves* are kinds of energy involving wave motion.

For a body possessing the mass m and the velocity v, it can be shown that the

$$\text{Kinetic energy (K.E.)} = \tfrac{1}{2}mv^2$$

b. Potential energy is that energy which matter has stored in it by virtue of its relative position, configuration, or chemical composition. A chunk of iron at a given distance from the center of the earth is, because of its mass and the mass of the earth, attracted to the center of the earth. The system iron-earth possesses potential energy due to the relative positions of the two bodies. A bow held in a fixed bent form has no motion and therefore does not possess kinetic energy, but when the string is released, the shape of the bow changes and it can do work moving an arrow. It is apparent that the bent bow possesses *potential energy of configuration* because of the relative position of its parts in the distorted shape and because of the tendency of these parts to move back to restore the normal shape. A mixture of hydrogen and oxygen will explode under the proper conditions, and sound, heat, light, and mechanical motion result. In the original mixture of the elements, the atoms of hydrogen are combined with other atoms of hydrogen and the atoms of oxygen are each attached to other atoms of oxygen. When the chemical change occurs, the atoms of hydrogen and oxygen change their state of combination, that is, their positions with respect to each other and their interactions. A mixture of hydrogen and oxygen has potential *energy of chemical composition*, some of which is transformed to sound, heat, light, and mechanical energy when water is formed. The potential energy of a system may be measured by determining the amount of work it will do.

36. TRANSFORMATION OF ENERGY

One form of energy may undergo transformation to other forms, several examples already having been cited. Heat and light energy from the sun are absorbed by plants, causing rearrangement of atoms to form new compounds, such as sugar, with an equivalent amount of chemical energy stored in them. The golfer eats some of this material, and it reacts in the body with oxygen to form new substances, energy being released in the form of heat and muscular motion. The kinetic energy of the muscles is transferred to the golf club, causing it to move, and, in turn, some of this kinetic energy is transferred to the golf ball. During the ball's rise in the air, some of its kinetic energy is converted to potential energy of position, since its distance from the center of the earth increases. When it falls, its rate of motion toward the center of the earth increases at the expense of its potential energy. Some of the kinetic energy due to the motion of the ball as a whole may be converted to heat because of friction with the air. When the ball hits the turf, some of the kinetic energy is changed to heat, and work is also done displacing the grass and soil and in distorting the shape of the ball.

In the electrical generator, mechanical energy of the moving parts is transformed to electrical energy. This, in turn, is transformed into heat when the electric current passes through the heating coil of an electric toaster, or into light in the fluorescent tube, or into chemical energy when the current is used to alter chemical composition in the electrolysis of water.

37. CONSERVATION OF ENERGY AND MATTER

We have seen that energy can be transformed from one form to another. When such energy changes occur, does the total amount of energy remain constant or is some lost or gained? In experiments with ordinary physical and chemical changes, no appreciable change of the total amount of energy can be detected, using ordinary methods. When a certain quantity of one form of energy is lost, an equivalent amount of other forms of energy appears. Energy apparently is conserved, as summarized in the *Law of Conservation of Energy: Energy is neither gained nor destroyed in ordinary physical and chemical changes.* We will make much use of this law in our efforts to account for the energy changes in chemical systems.

However, in certain extraordinary changes, such as that exploited in the atomic bomb, it has been shown that matter may be converted to energy and that the system loses appreciable matter and gains in energy. The reverse conversion of energy to matter can also be demonstrated. Einstein suggested that this conversion conforms to the relationship

$$E = mc^2$$

where E is the energy, m is the mass of matter converted, and c is the velocity of light. When m is expressed in grams and c is taken as 3×10^{10} cm per sec, E will be the energy in ergs. Ergs of energy can be converted to kilowatts per hour of electrical energy. According to this, conversion of 3,000 g of matter will produce 75 billion kw-hr of electricity, about the same amount of energy as was generated by the total hydroelectric power industry in the United States in the year 1945. The most plausible explanation that has been advanced to account for the source of the enormous amount of energy constantly being radiated by the sun suggests such conversion of matter to energy.

If we wish to be very precise and take into account the possible interchange of matter and energy, we can combine the separate laws of the conservation of energy and of matter. *The total amount of matter and energy available in the universe is fixed.* However, in the ordinary changes of everyday life, the amount of interchange between matter and energy is inappreciable, and the separate conservation laws may be counted on to govern all such ordinary changes.

38. ATOMISTIC NATURE OF ENERGY

When matter is divided in chemical change, the ultimate particles of the elements taking part in such change are found to be the atoms.   In a similar fashion, experiment has shown that energy also is atomistic in nature.   For example, light of a given color has been found to consist of tiny units of energy called *photons* or light *quanta*.   With change in the color of light, the magnitude of the quanta change.   Light is an electromagnetic wave form of energy, and light of a given color corresponds to a certain wave frequency.   The amount of energy, E, per quantum can be calculated by use of the equation

$$E = h\nu$$

where ν is the frequency of the light and h is a constant.

The amount of energy of a quantum is proportional to its frequency. A quantum of violet light has about twice as much energy as a quantum of red light, since violet light has about twice the frequency of red.   Shining violet light on matter provides energy in larger bundles than are available if red light is used.   Such quanta of energy occupy somewhat the same position in energy considerations as do the atoms in matter. When light energy is taken up by matter and chemical changes take place, the light quanta are converted into quanta of chemical energy in the new substances formed.

39. HEAT AND TEMPERATURE

We have seen that heat is considered to be kinetic energy involving the motion or oscillation of individual atoms or groups of atoms.   When matter becomes hotter, its particles move faster.   Heat energy is particularly important in chemistry because in most chemical changes chemical energy is transformed into heat, or vice versa.   In discussing heat, two aspects are important, namely, its intensity and its quantity.

The *intensity of the heat energy* of a system is measured by its temperature, usually expressed in chemistry in terms of degrees centigrade (° C). The centigrade scale for measuring temperature is set up with the freezing point of water at atmospheric pressure as 0°, and the boiling point of water at atmospheric pressure as 100°.   Each degree centigrade is one one-hundredth of the temperature interval between these points.   Unless otherwise specified, temperature values given in this book will be on the centigrade scale, and the C will be omitted.   A given sample of water may be at a temperature of 20°, or it may be at some other temperature, such as 100°.   The *quantity of heat energy* is usually measured in terms of

calories.   One *calorie* is the amount of heat necessary to raise the temperature of one gram of water one degree centigrade, or more specifically,
from 14.5 to 15.5°.

To lower the temperature of a system, heat must be withdrawn, the
quantity of heat energy of the system being lowered.   To raise the temperature of a system the quantity of heat must be increased.   The quantity of heat required to change the temperature of one gram of any
substance one degree centigrade is called its *specific heat*.   This is a
characteristic property of each substance.   The specific heat of water at
15° is 1.000 cal per g per ° C, that of iron at 20° is 0.107.   The quantity
of heat associated with a given change in temperature of a given quantity of a substance is fixed.

EXAMPLE: How much heat must be added to 100 g of iron to raise its temperature from 10.0° to 30.0°?

$$\text{Heat required} = \text{quantity of substance} \times \begin{array}{c}\text{change in}\\\text{temperature}\end{array} \times \begin{array}{c}\text{specific heat}\\\text{of the substance}\end{array}$$

$$= 100 \text{ g of iron} \times 20.0° \times 0.107 \text{ cal per g}$$
$$\text{of iron per °C}$$

$$= 214 \text{ cal}$$

Such a calculation is accurate providing the specific heat of the substance
is constant over the temperature range involved and no conversion of
heat to other forms of energy occurs.

The specific heats of the metals in the solid state have been used to
calculate their approximate atomic weights.   According to the law of
Dulong and Petit, the product of the specific heat of a solid metal at
room temperature and its atomic weight should equal approximately 6.3.
Therefore,

$$\frac{\text{The atomic weight}}{\text{of a metal}} = \frac{6.3}{\text{specific heat}}$$

$$\frac{\text{The atomic weight}}{\text{of iron}} = \frac{6.3}{0.107} = 59$$

While this value is only approximate, it is near enough to the accurate
atomic weight of iron to indicate, if the combining capacity of iron is
unknown, what multiple of the equivalent weight of iron should be taken
as its atomic weight.   Equivalent weights can be determined with great
accuracy and, when multiplied by the proper factor, can be used to give
very good values for the atomic weights.

EXAMPLE: 5.585 g of iron reacts with hydrochloric acid and 0.2016 g of hydrogen is replaced.   Calculate an accurate value for the atomic weight of iron.

$$\begin{array}{c}\text{The gram-equivalent}\\\text{weight of iron}\\\text{in this reaction}\end{array} = \frac{5.585 \text{ g of iron}}{0.2016 \text{ g of hydrogen}} \times \begin{array}{c}1.008 \text{ g of}\\\text{hydrogen}\end{array} = 27.92 \text{ g of iron}$$

The gram-atomic weight of iron must be some whole multiple of its gram-equivalent weight.   As shown above, knowledge of the specific heat of iron and of the laws of Dulong and Petit enables us to conclude that the gram-atomic weight of iron must be approximately 59.

27.92 g of iron per gram-equivalent weight $\times$ 2 = 55.84 g

This is the nearest to 59 of any whole multiple of the gram-equivalent weight we can take.   Therefore 55.84 is an accurate value for the atomic weight of iron.   Now, as we have seen in Chapter 2,

$$\text{Gram-equivalent weight} \times \frac{\text{combining capacity}}{\text{per atom}} = \text{gram-atomic weight}$$

Therefore, in the above reaction the iron atoms must be using a combining capacity of 2.

40. EXOTHERMIC AND ENDOTHERMIC CHANGES

When a physical or chemical change involves the evolution of heat, the change is said to be *exothermic*.   A change in which heat is absorbed is called *endothermic*.   When water is cooled, heat is taken away from the water and it undergoes an exothermic change: to raise the temperature of water, heat must be added to it and the change for water is endothermic. Wood burning in air liberates heat, and the process is said to be exothermic.   When steam is heated to extremely high temperatures, it decomposes to give the elements hydrogen and oxygen with the absorption of heat; this change is endothermic.

In many changes, energy in the form of light or electricity may be emitted or absorbed.   In such cases the more general terms *exoenergic* and *endoenergic* are appropriate.   Water may be decomposed into hydrogen and oxygen by means of the electric current.   Electrical energy is absorbed in the change, and it therefore is endoenergic.   When the lightning bug emits light it is undergoing an exoenergic change.

Even though the actual change may involve energy emitted or absorbed in forms other than heat, it is common practice in chemistry to calculate the equivalent in heat energy and then specify the total energy change in terms of calories of heat.   Because of this, changes are commonly called endo- or exothermic even though other forms of energy actually are involved.

41. ENERGY AND STABILITY OF A SYSTEM

It is important to know how energy is associated with matter and what exothermic and endothermic changes are possible.   The addition of energy to a system promotes the kinds of changes which involve the absorption of energy, and the energy content of the system is thereby increased. A system rich in energy tends to change in some exothermic fashion to go to a lower energy content. Energy-rich systems therefore are less *stable* and are more likely to undergo change than systems possessing less energy. We say the latter are thermally more stable.

EXERCISES

1. What transformations of energy are involved in: a) the use of gasoline to run an automobile? b) the production of electric power from water stored in a reservoir high in the mountains and the subsequent use of this electric power to electrolyze water?

2. Compare the ways the mass and the velocity of a moving particle contribute to the kinetic energy of the particle.

3. Which will possess the greater kinetic energy, a bullet weighing 2 g and traveling at a speed of 1,000 m per second or a bullet weighing 4 g and traveling at a speed of 500 m per second?

4. If they are to have the same kinetic energy, which would have to be moving faster, an atom of $_{17}Cl^{35}$ or an atom of $_{17}Cl^{37}$?

5. What violation of the Law of Conservation of matter makes possible the atomic bomb?

6. How are energy and matter related in the Einstein equation?

7. If 0.0001 g of matter (the smallest weight detectable by the chemical balance) is completely converted to energy, how many ergs will be produced?

8. One calorie equals about 4×10^7 ergs. How many grams of water could be heated from 14.5 to 15.5° by the energy produced in (7)?

9. a) If the specific heat of a metal is 0.056, what is its approximate atomic weight?
    b) The gram-equivalent weight of this metal is found to be 38.25 g. What is an accurate value for its atomic weight?
    c) What is the combining capacity of its atoms?

10. In photosynthesis, the process whereby plants convert water and carbon dioxide to other substances, sunlight is absorbed.
    a) Is photosynthesis an endoenergic or an exoenergic process?
    b) Are the products of this change more or less stable than the mixture of water and carbon dioxide?

Chapter 4

▶ **Atomic Structure**

▶ **The Classification of**

the Elements

42. THE COMPLEX STRUCTURE OF ATOMS

Throughout the greater part of the nineteenth century the idea that the atom was indivisible prevailed. Gradually, however, research in electrochemistry, investigation of the nature of the electrical discharge through gases, and experiments in the field of radioactivity led to the conclusion that atoms are divisible. They behave as if they are *complex systems* built up of *smaller units* that seem to be separated by relatively great distances. Moreover, electrical charges are intimately associated with the structure of atoms.

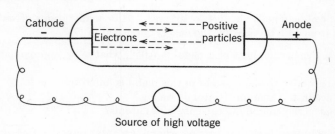

Source of high voltage

Fig. 7. The gas discharge tube.

The electrical discharge through a gas such as hydrogen gives clear evidence of the complex electrical nature of atoms. When the discharge tube shown in Figure 7 is filled with hydrogen at a low pressure and a high voltage is established between the anode and the cathode, negatively charged particles stream away from the cathode and travel at high speeds in straight lines through the tube. These negative particles are called *electrons*. When fast-moving electrons strike certain solids, such as zinc sulfide, some of their energy is converted to light which can be seen. Screens coated with zinc sulfide can be used to detect electrons and to observe the path followed by a beam of electrons. Experiment shows that, under proper conditions, atoms of all the elements will emit elec-

44

trons, and therefore these particles are assumed to be present in all atomic systems.

The nature of the electron was demonstrated in 1897 by J. J. Thomson and others by taking advantage of the fact that it is electrically charged and has mass. As shown in Figure 8, when a beam of fast-moving electrons is generated in a gas-discharge tube, the beam normally travels in a straight line. However, when such a beam traverses a magnetic field, the electrons are deflected from their straight-line path. They are forced aside owing to electrical interaction of their charges with the magnetic field. When a magnetic field of known strength is used, the amount of deflection suffered is a function of the velocity, the charge, and the mass of the electron. The experiment can be modified by the addition of an electrical field so that it is possible to determine the ratio of charge to mass.

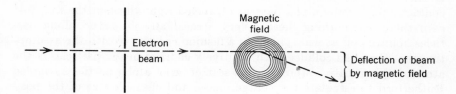

Fig. 8.   Deflection of a beam of electrons by a magnetic field.

The charge of the electron can be found by another independent experiment. Millikan charged tiny oil droplets by adding or removing one or more electrons. These charged oil droplets were introduced into an electrical field between two charged plates. The effect of their interaction with the electrical field on the rate at which they would settle owing to gravitational forces was observed. The data obtained were used by Millikan to calculate an accurate value for the charge of the electron. Knowing the charge of the electron and the ratio of charge to mass, the mass could then be computed.

All electrons have been found to be identical, having the same charge and the same mass. The mass of the electron at rest is only 9.107×10^{-28} g. This is about 0.000548 atomic-mass units or only about 1/1,836 of the total mass of the common hydrogen atom. The electron has a negative charge of 1.602×10^{-19} coulombs, which is the smallest quantity of negative electricity ever isolated. For convenience, this quantity of charge is assigned the value of unity, $1-$, for evaluating charges in atoms.

In the gas-discharge tube containing hydrogen there also are observed positively charged and more massive particles, called *protons*, that move toward the cathode. It is possible to determine the charges and masses of protons using the method already described for electrons. The proton has a mass of 1.674×10^{-24} g or 1.00756 atomic-mass units, which is almost the weight of the common hydrogen atom.   The electrical charge of the proton is 1+, just equal in magnitude but opposite in sign to the charge of the electron.   This positive charge of the proton is the smallest quantity of positive electricity observed.

In the operation of discharge tubes containing gases other than hydrogen, electrons are always observed, together with positively charged heavier units which vary in charge and mass, depending upon the elements present in the tube.   This indicates clearly that all atoms are composed of electrons plus some kind of positive particles.   What is the nature of the positive particles and how are they associated with electrons in atoms?

In 1911 Rutherford performed an experiment which threw considerable light on this problem.   He shot a beam of alpha particles (obtained by radioactive change) at a thin piece of metal foil.   Alpha particles are very small, compared to atoms, and have a mass of 4 and a charge of 2+.   Rutherford found that, although the atoms in the foil apparently were in contact, most of the alpha particles traveled right through the foil, just as if there was nothing there.   Very occasionally, however, alpha particles bounced off at wide angles in a fashion consistent with the assumption that they had collided with positively charged heavy particles in the atoms.   Quantitative study of this scattering of alpha particles enabled Rutherford to calculate the charge, mass, and effective size of the positive particle in the atom.   He suggested that it was at the center of the atom and called it the *nucleus* of the atom.   He found the nucleus always had a mass almost equal to the mass of the atom, and that its charge was always some whole multiple of the charge of the proton.

43.   THE NUCLEAR ATOMIC MODEL

On the basis of the experimental data described above, Rutherford proposed the *nuclear theory of atomic structure*.   This is summarized in Figure 9.   Each atom is believed to have a central, positively charged nucleus which is responsible for practically all of the mass of the atom, that is, for its *mass number*.   The positive charge is the same for the nuclei of all the atoms of an element and is always some whole multiple of the charge of the proton.   The nuclei of hydrogen atoms always have a charge of 1+, those of oxygen 8+, and those of chlorine 17+.   In fact, it is the positive charge of the nucleus that determines the *atomic number* of an atom.   In the neutral atom of each element, the nucleus is surrounded by as many electrons as there are unit plus nuclear charges.   Thus, neutral hydrogen atoms always have one electron each, those of oxygen have eight electrons each, and those of chlorine 17.   Electrostatic forces of attraction account for the negative electrons being held to the positive nucleus.

The fact that most alpha particles pass through atoms without being deflected indicates that atoms are very diffuse structures, with apparently much free space between the nucleus and the electrons. The electrons behave as if they are moving very rapidly in the extranuclear region with a certain probability of being at any given position within the sphere surrounding the nucleus.

Atomic nuclei have diameters of the order of only 1×10^{-13} cm, whereas the diameter of the average atom is about 2×10^{-8} cm. The atomic diameter of the average atom is about 200,000 times the nuclear diameter. Electrons behave in some respects as if they are only slightly

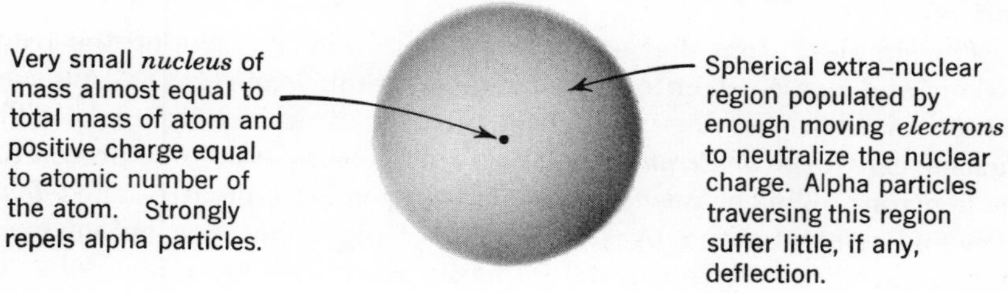

Very small *nucleus* of mass almost equal to total mass of atom and positive charge equal to atomic number of the atom. Strongly repels alpha particles.

Spherical extra–nuclear region populated by enough moving *electrons* to neutralize the nuclear charge. Alpha particles traversing this region suffer little, if any, deflection.

Fig. 9. The nuclear model of the atom.

larger than nuclei. How, then, can we account for the relatively large volume of atoms? This is believed to be due to the very rapid movement of the electrons, by virtue of which the electrons "occupy" the extranuclear region and are thus responsible for practically all of the volume of the atom. They repel other atoms from the extranuclear region.

44. NUCLEAR STRUCTURE AND ISOTOPES

It is now known from a study of radioactive change (to be discussed in a later chapter) that atomic nuclei, exclusive of the nucleus of the simplest isotope of hydrogen, are complex in structure. They are built up of certain units and disintegrate to give such units. What are these units and how do they constitute nuclei?

The theory of nuclear structure, which at present seems to fit the facts best and still is rather simple, postulates that *nuclei are composed of protons and neutrons*. We have already seen that the proton has a charge of $1+$ and a mass very close to one atomic-mass unit. The *neutron*, discovered by Chadwick in 1932, is an electrically neutral particle which has a mass of 1.00893, a value also very close to one atomic-mass unit. A nucleus composed of protons and neutrons will therefore have a total charge equal to the number of protons and a mass approximately equal to the sum of the protons and neutrons. (The actual mass is slightly smaller than this because of the conversion of a very small amount of mass to energy, which is emitted when the nucleus is formed.) A nucleus containing 11 protons and 12 neutrons will have an atomic number of 11 and a mass number of 23. It will be the nucleus of an atom of sodium.   This nucleus will be associated with 11 electrons to give the neutral sodium atom, but the electrons contribute so little to the mass that the atomic weight of sodium will be very close to 23.

The proton-neutron theory of nuclear structure provides an excellent explanation for the existence of isotopes of an element.   All of the nuclei of an element are assumed to have the same number of protons and electrons, but the number of neutrons may vary; $_{17}Cl^{35}$ will have 17 protons and 18 neutrons in its nucleus, whereas $_{17}Cl^{37}$ has 17 protons and 20 neutrons.

The simplest atom that can form is $_1H^1$.   This has one proton for its nucleus and one electron occupying the extranuclear region.   A second isotope of hydrogen has a nucleus of mass 2 and charge 1+.   This nucleus, called the *deuteron*, is believed to be composed of one proton and one neutron.   This heavier isotope of hydrogen is frequently called *deuterium* and is symbolized by $_1H^2$ or $_1D^2$.   Only about one out of every 5,000 atoms of the hydrogen we ordinarily work with has a mass of 2; the rest have a mass very close to 1.   Accordingly, the atomic weight of hydrogen is very close to 1.   A third isotope of hydrogen, $_1H^3$, can be synthesized by the addition of a neutron to the deuterium nucleus, but this isotope is not stable and is not found in nature to any appreciable extent.

By increasing the number of protons in nuclei by jumps of one, a series of nuclei which increase in atomic number by unit jumps will result. These usually have somewhere near the same number of neutrons as protons, and the mass numbers and atomic numbers go up accordingly. Thus we can account for all the isotopes of all the elements.   Some combinations of protons and neutrons are so strongly bonded together that they persist in nature and are called *stable nuclei*.   Other nuclear combinations are less stable and undergo spontaneous radioactive change to more stable nuclei.

It should be remembered that the theory of nuclei being composed of protons and neutrons is still just a reasonable guess.   However, it has the advantage of being simple, it seems to be consistent with the experimental facts, and it serves to integrate these facts.   As more facts about nuclear behavior are discovered, it is likely that this theory will undergo revision.

45.   STRUCTURAL CHARACTERISTICS OF SOME OF THE LIGHTER ATOMS

The charge and mass of the nucleus and the number of electrons of all neutral atoms can be determined exactly by various experimental methods.   Table 5 lists these characteristics for the stable isotopes of some of the lighter elements arranged in order of increasing complexity. It shows how protons and neutrons are assumed to take part in determining atomic and mass numbers of isotopes.   The relative abundance listed for the stable isotopes of each element are for the isotopic mixtures as they occur in nature and in the materials with which we usually work. These abundance data and the mass numbers of the isotopes can be used, as we have already seen, to calculate the average atomic weights employed in chemistry. Note that the order obtained by arranging the elements in order of increasing atomic number is also the order of increasing atomic weights. There are a few exceptions to this among the elements of higher number (see cobalt and nickel).

Table 5. **Atomic Structures of the Stable Isotopes of Lighter Elements**

| Element | Iso-topes | Nucleus | | | | Elec-trons | Atomic Num-ber Z | Mass Num-ber | Rela-tive Abun-dance (%) |
		Charge	Mass	Pro-tons	Neu-trons				
Hydrogen	$_1H^1$	1+	1	1	0	1	1	1	99.88
	$_1H^2$	1+	2	1	1	1	1	2	0.02
Helium	$_2He^4$	2+	4	2	2	2	2	4	100.0
Lithium	$_3Li^6$	3+	6	3	3	3	3	6	7.5
	$_3Li^7$	3+	7	3	4	3	3	7	92.5
Beryllium	$_4Be^9$	4+	9	4	5	4	4	9	100.0
Boron	$_5B^{10}$	5+	10	5	5	5	5	10	18.4
	$_5B^{11}$	5+	11	5	6	5	5	11	81.6
Carbon	$_6C^{12}$	6+	12	6	6	6	6	12	98.9
	$_6C^{13}$	6+	13	6	7	6	6	13	1.1
Nitrogen	$_7N^{14}$	7+	14	7	7	7	7	14	99.62
	$_7N^{15}$	7+	15	7	8	7	7	15	0.38
Oxygen	$_8O^{16}$	8+	16	8	8	8	8	16	99.76
	$_8O^{17}$	8+	17	8	9	8	8	17	0.04
	$_8O^{18}$	8+	18	8	10	8	8	18	0.20
Fluorine	$_9F^{19}$	9+	19	9	10	9	9	19	100.0
Neon	$_{10}Ne^{20}$	10+	20	10	10	10	10	20	90.0
	$_{10}Ne^{21}$	10+	21	10	11	10	10	21	0.27
	$_{10}Ne^{22}$	10+	22	10	12	10	10	22	9.73

46. THE BEHAVIOR OF ELECTRONS IN ATOMS

In chemical change the nucleus of an atom is believed to persist unaltered, but the electrons undergo rearrangement. They seem to be directly involved in determining the chemical characteristics of atoms. Therefore, it is particularly important in chemistry to know as much about the electrons as can be discovered.   First we will consider how the electrons are believed to be behaving in single neutral atoms.   Then we will be in position to discuss how the electron may take part in chemical change.

It has turned out to be extremely difficult to conceive of a model for the structure of atoms that describes adequately the way the particles in the atoms are behaving.   The models first suggested were mechanical ones which treated the nucleus and the electrons as discrete particles of fixed size that were undergoing mechanical motion just like large pieces of matter.   For instance, Rutherford suggested that some of the prop-

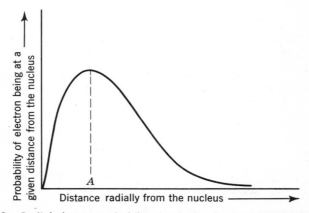

Fig. 10.   Radial electron probability distribution for the hydrogen atom.

erties of atoms could be accounted for by considering atoms to be miniature solar systems, with spherical electrons revolving in orbits about a spherical central nucleus.   The electrons were called planetary electrons and the laws governing the solar planetary system were supposed to be obeyed by the atom.   Such "pictures" of atoms are still widely used, and the terminology has carried over to other more recent theories.

However, closer study of atoms has demonstrated that such mechanical models are not satisfactory.   Electrons do not behave entirely like discrete particles; some of their behavior indicates wave characteristics. Accordingly, a mathematical *wave mechanical theory* of atomic structure has been developed.   This endeavors to describe atomic systems more accurately.   It has succeeded in accounting for the properties of very simple atoms reasonably well, but still has difficulty in dealing with the more complicated atoms.   Much effort is being made to modify it so that it will be more satisfactory.   This theory is far too complicated to consider in detail in an elementary course.   We must simplify the model and employ a less accurate, but nevertheless a very useful, qualitative description.

The atomic number specifies the number of electrons in a neutral atom. These electrons seem to be in a constant state of motion about the nucleus. Thus, the one electron in an atom of hydrogen "occupies" the extranuclear region because of its very rapid motion toward and away from the nucleus. The ability of the electron to occupy space is like that of a couple of dancers who are jitterbugging; their intense activity effectively keeps other couples out of a considerable area. On the average, the electron behaves as if it is spread out over the whole extranuclear region as a sort of electron cloud. The probability of the electron being at a given distance radially from the nucleus in the hydrogen atom can be represented by the graph shown in Figure 10.

This means that the electron behaves as if it is spending most of its time in a shell of about radius *A* concentric with the nucleus. The concept of a series of successive *shells of electrons* concentric with the nucleus is similarly useful for accounting for polyelectronic elements.

47. ELECTRONIC ENERGY LEVELS

In the hydrogen atom there will be electrostatic attraction between the positively charged nucleus and the negative electron. According to Coulomb's Law, on the average, this force holding the electron to the nucleus will be proportional to the product of their charges and inversely proportional to the square of the average distance between them. There will be a definite amount of energy for the atom in this state, and the electron is said to be at a certain *energy level*. In order to move the electron so that, on the average, it is farther away from the nucleus, work must be done against the force of attraction. The atom will gain in energy in this process, and the electron is said to go to a *higher energy level*.

One of the pecularities of atoms is that they cannot absorb energy in just any amount; the energy must be added as one of a limited number of different sized quanta. (See Section 38.) This led Bohr to suggest that there are only a certain number of energy levels in the hydrogen atom in which the electrons can be located. These are represented by the horizontal lines in Figure 11. When the electron is in the lowest energy level (the one where, on the average, it is nearest the nucleus), it will be held most firmly, and the energy for the atom will be the minimum possible value. This constitutes the most stable state for the atom, and it is said to be in the *ground state*.

Bohr suggested that the electron might jump from one energy level to another, as indicated by the verticle double arrows in Figure 11. When the electron jumps from the ground-state level to any level of higher energy, the atom is said to go to an *excited state*. Such a jump from a lower energy level to a higher energy level requires the absorption of a quantity of energy just equal to the difference in energy of the two levels; a certain bundle of energy, such as a quantum of light of a particular frequency is required. By finding out by spectroscopic studies what frequencies of light the hydrogen atom can absorb, it is possible to identify the energy levels and determine their differences in energy.

When the atom is in an excited state the electron may jump back to any lower energy level. In the process a quantum of energy of appropriate frequency will be emitted, such as light of a given color. Study of the energy emitted by excited atoms will provide information about the energy levels of the electrons. Each different jump corresponds to the change in energy for the system by a quantum of light of a certain frequency.

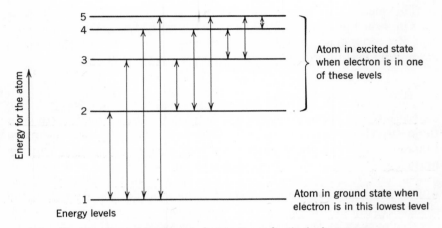

Fig. 11. Energy levels and electron jumps for the hydrogen atom.

The electronic energy levels available for the electrons in atoms having more than one electron can also be identified by studying the way in which quanta of energy may be added or lost by the atomic systems. The quanta of energy need not be light quanta; they may be in other forms of energy, such as heat or electricity.

48. CLASSIFICATION OF ENERGY LEVELS

We can summarize much precise information about the electrons in atomic systems by cataloguing the electronic energy levels that are possible and then specifying the energy levels in which there are electrons. Conventionally, this is done by classifying energy levels according to *shells* and *subshells*. Each subshell includes a certain fixed number of *orbitals*. Each orbital can accomodate two electrons. The classification system for the first four shells is summarized in Table 6.

The shells are thought of as being concentric with the nucleus and at increasing average distances. Accordingly, they are numbered 1, 2, 3, 4, 5 . . . and are called by the letters K, L, M, N, O, . . . , starting from the nucleus. The subshells are known as s, p, d, f . . . subshells. The number of subshells in a shell is equal to the number of the shell. For instance, shell 1 consists of only an s subshell which we specify by labeling it the 1s subshell. Shell 3 is divided into 3s, 3p, and 3d subshells.

Table 6.   Classification of Energy Levels for Atoms

Shell	1	2		3			4			
	K	L		M			N			
Subshell	1s	2s	2p	3s	3p	3d	4s	4p	4d	4f
Number of orbitals	1	1	3	1	3	5	1	3	5	7
Maximum number of electrons per subshell	2	2	6	2	6	10	2	6	10	14
Maximum number of electrons per shell	2	8		18			32			

The number of orbitals is fixed for each kind of subshell. One orbital is found in every s subshell, three orbitals in p subshells, five in d subshells, and seven in f subshells. Electrons in the orbitals of a given subshell of an atom are at the same energy level in that atom, but they differ from orbital to orbital in certain other respects.

Each orbital can accomodate two electrons, but these differ from each other with respect to their magnetic behavior. This is specified by saying that the two electrons in an orbital must have opposite *spin*. By assuming the negatively charged electron to be spinning on its axis in a given direction, it is possible to account for the fact that atoms which have one electron in an orbital show *paramagnetism;* they are attracted by an external magnetic field. Two electrons with opposite spins in an orbital counteract each other magnetically, accounting for the fact that when electrons are paired in an orbital there is no resultant paramagnetism.

49.   RELATIVE ENERGIES OF ELECTRONS IN SUBSHELLS AND ORDER OF FILLING OF ORBITALS

The energy-level classification is used as a basis for describing the energy levels of all of the electrons for an atom when it is in the ground state. The ground state of minimum energy for the atom is believed to be attained by assigning the electrons stepwise to the available orbitals of lowest energy. To do this we must first know how the orbitals rank in energy. This is summarized in Figure 12. Each orbital is indicated by a short heavy horizontal line whose vertical position on the chart indicates its relative energy. All of the orbitals in a given subshell are of the same

energy.   In any shell the energy increases from s, to p, to d, to f subshells.
Notice that in the higher shells the subshells overlap in energy, for
instance, the $4f$ orbitals are of higher energy than the $5p$ orbitals.

Now we can see how the electrons will add to the energy levels in suc-
cession as the elements increase in atomic number.   <u>The electrons always</u>

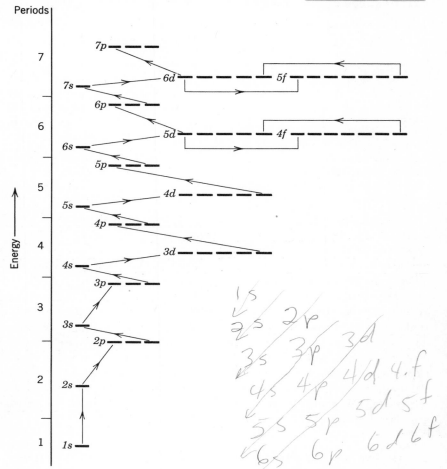

Fig. 12.   Relative energy of electrons in subshells and order of filling of orbitals as
periods develop.

<u>go into the orbital of lowest energy which is not already occupied.</u>   When
there are available a number of orbitals of equal energy, the electrons add
one to each of these orbitals until all are in use, and then additional electrons double up until each orbital in the subshell has two electrons.

The one electron of the hydrogen atom in the ground state is in the $1s$
orbital.   The additional electron available in the helium atom also enters

the 1s level to fill it.   The lithium atom has two of its three electrons in the 1s level and one in a 2s orbital.   The light lines with arrows in Figure 12 indicate how the electrons are believed to add stepwise, going from hydrogen through the elements in order of increasing atomic number. There are some slight departures from this scheme with some of the elements of high atomic number.

50.   ELECTRON CONFIGURATIONS OF ATOMS IN THE GROUND STATE

As described in the foregoing section, it has been possible to work out a reasonable assignment of electrons to orbitals for the single neutral atom of each element when it is in the ground state.   This electron distribution is termed the *electron configuration* of the atom.   Table 7 gives the electron configuration generally accepted for each of the elements.   The numbers in heavy type are for the electrons in subshells that are expanding.   When you check the expansion taking place in the electronic content of the subshells with increasing atomic number, you will observe that it agrees in most cases with the order of filling of orbitals suggested in Figure 12.

The electron configuration of the atoms of any element in the ground state can be given in detail by listing the subshells that are being used and indicating the number of electrons in each subshell by means of a subscript.   No superscript is used when the number of electrons is 1. Thus the electron configuration for hydrogen is $1s$, that for oxygen is $1s^2\, 2s^2\, 2p^4$, and that for copper is $1s^2\, 2s^2\, 2p^6\, 3s^2\, 3p^6\, 3d^{10}\, 4s^1$.   Often the electron configuration is given more simply by listing only the total number of electrons in each shell, for instance, 2, 6 for oxygen, and 2, 8, 18, 1 for copper.

Many of the properties of atoms, besides the way in which they absorb or emit energy, turn out to be closely related to their electron configurations.   Atoms which have certain features of configuration in common can be expected to show some similarity in behavior.   In particular, this is true of the chemical behavior of the elements.   Knowledge of the accepted electron configurations will help us to organize and understand the chemical and physical properties of matter.

51.   PERIODICITY OF PROPERTIES AND THE PERIODIC LAW

Suppose we first examine some of the facts about the way certain properties of the elements vary with change in atomic number.   Then we can see if this parallels any significant change in the electron configurations that have been assigned to the elements.

As soon as chemists had succeeded in determining the atomic weights of a considerable number of the elements, it became apparent that there was some correlation between the magnitude of these atomic weights and

Table 7. Electronic Configurations for Atoms in the Ground State

Element	Atomic No.	1s	2s	2p	3s	3p	3d	4s	4p	4d	5s
H	1	1									
He	2	2									
Li	3	2	1								
Be	4	2	2								
B	5	2	2	1							
C	6	2	2	2							
N	7	2	2	3							
O	8	2	2	4							
F	9	2	2	5							
Ne	10	2	2	6							
Na	11	2	2	6	1						
Mg	12	2	2	6	2						
Al	13	2	2	6	2	1					
Si	14	2	2	6	2	2					
P	15	2	2	6	2	3					
S	16	2	2	6	2	4					
Cl	17	2	2	6	2	5					
A	18	2	2	6	2	6					
K	19	2	2	6	2	6		1			
Ca	20	2	2	6	2	6		2			
Sc	21	2	2	6	2	6	1	2			
Ti	22	2	2	6	2	6	2	2			
V	23	2	2	6	2	6	3	2			
Cr	24	2	2	6	2	6	5	1			
Mn	25	2	2	6	2	6	5	2			
Fe	26	2	2	6	2	6	6	2			
Co	27	2	2	6	2	6	7	2			
Ni	28	2	2	6	2	6	8	2			
Cu	29	2	2	6	2	6	10	1			
Zn	30	2	2	6	2	6	10	2			
Ga	31	2	2	6	2	6	10	2	1		
Ge	32	2	2	6	2	6	10	2	2		
As	33	2	2	6	2	6	10	2	3		
Se	34	2	2	6	2	6	10	2	4		
Br	35	2	2	6	2	6	10	2	5		
Kr	36	2	2	6	2	6	10	2	6		
Rb	37	2	2	6	2	6	10	2	6		1
Sr	38	2	2	6	2	6	10	2	6		1
Y	39	2	2	6	2	6	10	2	6	1	2
Zr	40	2	2	6	2	6	10	2	6	2	2
Nb	41	2	2	6	2	6	10	2	6	4	1
Mo	42	2	2	6	2	6	10	2	6	5	1
Tc	43	2	2	6	2	6	10	2	6	6	1
Ru	44	2	2	6	2	6	10	2	6	7	1
Rh	45	2	2	6	2	6	10	2	6	8	1
Pd	46	2	2	6	2	6	10	2	6	10	
Ag	47	2	2	6	2	6	10	2	6	10	1
Cd	48	2	2	6	2	6	10	2	6	10	2

Table 7. Electronic Configurations (Cont.)

Element	Atomic No.	1s	2s	2p	3s	3p	3d	4s	4p	4d	4f	5s	5p	5d	5f	6s	6p	6d	7s
In	49	2	2	6	2	6	10	2	6	10		2	1						
Sn	50	2	2	6	2	6	10	2	6	10		2	2						
Sb	51	2	2	6	2	6	10	2	6	10		2	3						
Te	52	2	2	6	2	6	10	2	6	10		2	4						
I	53	2	2	6	2	6	10	2	6	10		2	5						
Xe	54	2	2	6	2	6	10	2	6	10		2	6						
Cs	55	2	2	6	2	6	10	2	6	10		2	6			1			
Ba	56	2	2	6	2	6	10	2	6	10		2	6			2			
La	57	2	2	6	2	6	10	2	6	10		2	6	1		2			
Ce	58	2	2	6	2	6	10	2	6	10	1	2	6	1		2			
Pr	59	2	2	6	2	6	10	2	6	10	2	2	6	1		2			
Nd	60	2	2	6	2	6	10	2	6	10	3	2	6	1		2			
Pm	61	2	2	6	2	6	10	2	6	10	4	2	6	1		2			
Sm	62	2	2	6	2	6	10	2	6	10	5	2	6	1		2			
Eu	63	2	2	6	2	6	10	2	6	10	6	2	6	1		2			
Gd	64	2	2	6	2	6	10	2	6	10	7	2	6	1		2			
Tb	65	2	2	6	2	6	10	2	6	10	8	2	6	1		2			
Dy	66	2	2	6	2	6	10	2	6	10	9	2	6	1		2			
Ho	67	2	2	6	2	6	10	2	6	10	10	2	6	1		2			
Er	68	2	2	6	2	6	10	2	6	10	11	2	6	1		2			
Tm	69	2	2	6	2	6	10	2	6	10	12	2	6	1		2			
Yb	70	2	2	6	2	6	10	2	6	10	13	2	6	1		2			
Lu	71	2	2	6	2	6	10	2	6	10	14	2	6	1		2			
Hf	72	2	2	6	2	6	10	2	6	10	14	2	6	2		2			
Ta	73	2	2	6	2	6	10	2	6	10	14	2	6	3		2			
W	74	2	2	6	2	5	10	2	6	10	14	2	6	4		2			
Re	75	2	2	6	2	6	10	2	6	10	14	2	6	5		2			
Os	76	2	2	6	2	6	10	2	6	10	14	2	6	6		2			
Ir	77	2	2	6	2	6	10	2	6	10	14	2	6	7		2			
Pt	78	2	2	6	2	6	10	2	6	10	14	2	6	9		1			
Au	79	2	2	6	2	6	10	2	6	10	14	2	6	10		1			
Hg	80	2	2	6	2	6	10	2	6	10	14	2	6	10		2			
Tl	81	2	2	6	2	6	10	2	6	10	14	2	6	10		2	1		
Pb	82	2	2	6	2	6	10	2	6	10	14	2	6	10		2	2		
Bi	83	2	2	6	2	6	10	2	6	10	14	2	6	10		2	3		
Po	84	2	2	6	2	6	10	2	6	10	14	2	6	10		2	4		
At	85	2	2	6	2	6	10	2	6	10	14	2	6	10		2	5		
Rn	86	2	2	6	2	6	10	2	6	10	14	2	6	10		2	6		
Fr	87	2	2	6	2	6	10	2	6	10	14	2	6	10		2	6		1
Ra	88	2	2	6	2	6	10	2	6	10	14	2	6	10		2	6		2
Ac	89	2	2	6	2	6	10	2	6	10	14	2	6	10		2	6	1	2
*Th	90	2	2	6	2	6	10	2	6	10	14	2	6	10	1	2	6	1	2
*Pa	91	2	2	6	2	6	10	2	6	11	14	2	6	10	2	2	6	1	2
*U	92	2	2	6	2	6	10	2	6	10	14	2	6	10	3	2	6	1	2
*Np	93	2	2	6	2	6	10	2	6	10	14	2	6	10	4	2	6	1	2
*Pu	94	2	2	6	2	6	10	2	6	10	14	2	6	10	5	2	6	1	2
*Am	95	2	2	6	2	6	10	2	6	10	14	2	6	10	6	2	6	1	2
*Cm	96	2	2	6	2	6	10	2	6	10	14	2	6	10	7	2	6	1	2
*Bk	97	2	2	6	2	6	10	2	6	10	14	2	6	10	8	2	6	1	2
*Cf	98	2	2	6	2	6	10	2	6	10	14	2	6	10	9	2	6	1	2
*E	99	2	2	6	2	6	10	2	6	10	14	2	6	10	10	2	6	1	2
*Fm	100	2	2	6	2	6	10	2	6	10	14	2	6	10	11	2	6	1	2
*Mv	101	2	2	6	2	6	10	2	6	10	14	2	6	10	12	2	6	1	2

* Probable configurations.

the properties of the atoms.   By 1868 to 1870, enough accurate data had become available so that, working independently, Mendeléeff in Russia and Lothar Meyer in Germany were able to outline the nature of this relationship in considerable detail.   They summarized their conclusions in the Periodic Law, which stated that the properties of the elements are periodic functions of their atomic weights.

When our modern theory of the structure of atoms was developed, it was shown that the Periodic Law holds better if atomic numbers are used rather than atomic weights.   The generalization has therefore been modified to a more accurate and useful modern *Periodic Law: The properties of the elements vary in a periodic fashion with increase in their atomic numbers.   If the elements are listed in the order of their atomic numbers, we find that their properties change in a gradual way as the numbers increase, but that this variation is not continuous.   Every so often the properties start a new cycle of variation, and periodically certain characteristics reappear.*

For example, consider the maximum chemical combining capacity which atoms of different elements achieve toward hydrogen atoms.   Table 8 lists the first 20 elements in order of ascending atomic number in successive horizontal sequences.   For each element there is given the formula for the substance in which that element shows its maximum combining capacity toward hydrogen.

Table 8.   Periodicity of Combining Capacity of Elements toward Hydrogen

Element	H							He
Atomic number	1							2
Formula of substance	HH							none formed
Electrons in shells	1							2

Element	Li	Be	B	C	N	O	F	Ne
Atomic number	3	4	5	6	7	8	9	10
Formula of substance	LiH	BeH_2	BH_3	CH_4	NH_3	H_2O	HF	none formed
Electrons in shells	2, 1	2, 2	2, 3	2, 4	2, 5	2, 6	2, 7	2, 8

Element	Na	Mg	Al	Si	P	S	Cl	A
Atomic number	11	12	13	14	15	16	17	18
Formula of substance	NaH	MgH_2	AlH_3	SiH_4	PH_3	H_2S	HCl	none formed
Electrons in shells	2, 8, 1	2, 8, 2	2, 8, 3	2, 8, 4	2, 8, 5	2, 8, 6	2, 8, 7	2, 8, 8

A hydrogen atom tends to combine with one other hydrogen atom. With each unit increase in atomic number there is a change of one in the number of hydrogen atoms combined per atom of the element in the substance, and this proceeds in cycles.   Every so often inert elements such as helium, neon, and argon, which have zero combining capacity, appear. Helium and neon are followed, respectively, by lithium and sodium, elements having a combining capacity of one, and these in turn are followed by elements berylium and magnesium which have a combining capacity of two.   The increase in combining capacity toward hydrogen in each horizontal sequence rises to a peak of four and then decreases by unit decrements to zero at the next inert element.   The pattern of change in the sequence lithium through neon is repeated in the sequence sodium

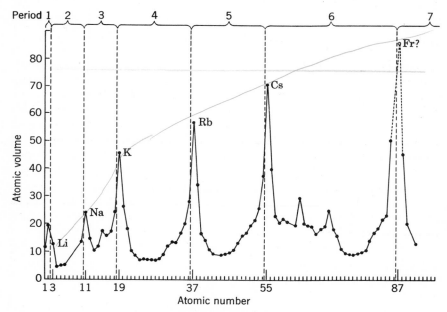

Fig. 13.   Periodicity of atomic volume.

through argon.   Such periodic fluctuation of combining capacity continues through the rest of the elements, but it becomes more complicated with elements of higher atomic numbers.

The pattern of change of combining capacity toward oxygen also is periodic but differs in some respects from that toward hydrogen.   For instance, for the elements in the third horizontal sequence in Table 8, the maximum combining capacity toward oxygen starts at one for sodium and increases by jumps of one to seven for chlorine, dropping back to zero for argon.

Figure 13 shows how the *atomic volumes* of the elements vary with increasing atomic number.   The atomic volume of an element is the volume of one gram atom of that element in the solid state.   Because one gram atom of any element has 6.02×10^{23} atoms present, by comparing atomic volumes we can get a rough comparison of the relative volumes (sizes) of the atoms when they are packed together in the crystals of the element.   We recognize in this curve the strong evidence for the periodic variation of the atomic volumes of the elements with increasing atomic number.

Many other properties of the elements show periodic variation with increasing atomic number, as we shall see later.   It was the observation of such periodic variations of many of the properties of the elements which clearly established the Periodic Law.   What is the cause of these periodic reappearances of certain characteristics?

52. PERIODICITY OF ELECTRON CONFIGURATION AND THE PERIODIC LAW

The Periodic Law is now recognized to be the result of the periodic building up of the shells of electrons as the atomic number increases. As successive shells of electrons develop, there is a repetition in structure of the outer shells, and this gives rise to a repetition of properties.   This repetition of the number of electrons in the outermost shells is shown in Table 8.   The number of electrons in each successive shell of the atom is given under the symbol for that atom.   The periodic expansion of each successive shell of electrons is emphasized in the table by breaking the serial list of the elements up into successive horizontal sequences.   Atoms listed under each other are seen to have the same number of electrons in their outermost shells.   Since the number of electrons in the outermost shell of an atom is very important in determining its properties, we can see why H, Li, and Na should show strong resemblance, such as all having a combining capacity of one.   Be and Mg, each with two electrons in its outermost shell, should be similar; both have a combining capacity of two toward hydrogen.

As the number of electrons in the outer shell continues to increase, the combining capacity toward hydrogen increases to a maximum of four and then decreases to zero when the outer-shell electrons have increased to eight; the combining capacity toward oxygen increases to a higher maximum before dropping to zero.   As the electron configurations expand from that of one inert gas to the next, a given property varies through a complete cycle.

Table 9 summarizes the electronic structures of the inert gases. These elements, the first five of which occur in small amounts in the atmosphere, have atoms that show no chemical activity.

As we go through the list of the elements from each inert gas to the next, and as the atomic numbers increase stepwise, there develops a sequence, or *period*, of elements in which the structure of the outermost shells of electrons is changing in regular fashion, with corresponding regular change in properties (see Table 7).   The expansion in electron configuration in each period is seen to involve the filling of certain sub-shells with electrons.

Table 9.   Electronic Structures of the Inert Gases

Inert Gas	Shells						Elements in Periods	
	1	2	3	4	5	6		
He	2						H—He	2
Ne	2	8					Li—Ne	8
A	2	8	8				Na—A	8
Kr	2	8	18	8			K—Kr	18
Xe	2	8	18	18	8		Rb—Xe	18
Rn	2	8	18	32	18	8	Cs—Rn	32

53. PERIODIC TABLES OF THE ELEMENTS

Periodic Tables are charts that classify the elements in horizontal *periods* in order of their increasing atomic number.   Furthermore, these charts are so devised that elements having similar electronic structures in the outermost shells are placed in the same vertical *groups*.   Elements in the same groups, therefore, will have similar properties.   A large number of variations of the arrangement of the elements in such Periodic Tables have been suggested in efforts to produce charts that show most effectively the various relationships between the elements.   It will be useful for us to have several of these tables available.   Table 10 is the Bohr long table.   Each horizontal sequence is a period.   Lines connect the elements having similar numbers of electrons in their outermost shells; these belong to the same groups.   The first period is unique; it consists of only two elements.   The second and third periods are more typical of the rest of the Periodic System.   Each contains eight elements, which are representative of the vertical *groups*.   Periods IV and V have 18 elements each.   Period VI has 32 elements and Period VII probably is a duplicate of VI, as far as the elements have been discovered.

Table 11 is a somewhat different version of the long Periodic Table. The periods are spread out more than in the Bohr chart, and the various divisions of elements are labeled.   The vertical groups are represented in Periods II and III by the so-called *typical elements*.   For example, Li and Na are the typical elements of Group I; Be and Mg are the typical elements of Group II.   In the longer periods, each vertical group is divided into A and B subgroups.   The A subgroup elements come early, and the B subgroup elements come later in their respective periods. Three elements in the middle of each long period bridge the interval between the A and B subgroup elements, and all three are placed in Group VIII.   The elements with atomic numbers 58 to 71 all resemble

Table 10. Bohr Periodic Table

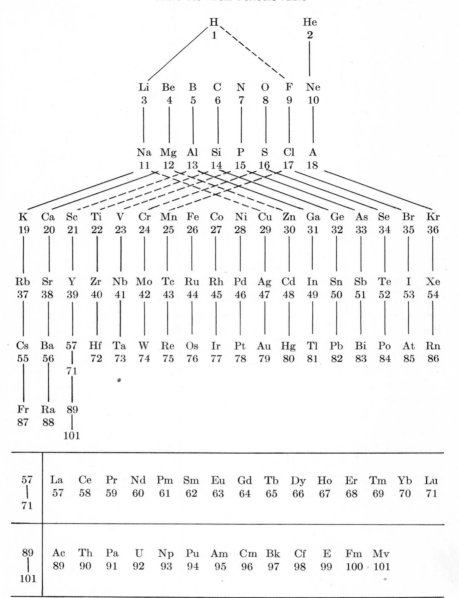

element 57, lanthanum, very closely and are assigned to the same IIIA subgroup position as lanthanum. In Period VII the elements following actinium, 89, are very much like it and are, accordingly, all placed in the IIIA subgroup. This chart is advantageous because it shows clearly the respective locations of the metals and the nonmetals. The significance of the term *transition metals* will be considered later.

Table 11. The Long Periodic Table

Metals ——— Nonmetals

Group	I	II	IIIA	IVA	VA	VIA	VIIA	VIII	VIII	VIII	IB	IIB	III / IIIB	IV / IVB	V / VB	VI / VIB	VII / VIIB	O
Subgroups	IA	IIA	IIIA	IVA	VA	VIA	VIIA		VIII		IB	IIB	IIIB	IVB	VB	VIB	VIIB	O
Period I	H 1																	He 2
Period II	Li 3	Be 4											B 5	C 6	N 7	O 8	F 9	Ne 10
Period III	Na 11	Mg 12											Al 13	Si 14	P 15	S 16	Cl 17	A 18
Period IV	K 19	Ca 20	Sc 21	Ti 22	V 23	Cr 24	Mn 25	Fe 26	Co 27	Ni 28	Cu 29	Zn 30	Ga 31	Ge 32	As 33	Se 34	Br 35	Kr 36
Period V	Rb 37	Sr 38	Y 39	Zr 40	Nb 41	Mo 42	Tc 43	Ru 44	Rh 45	Pd 46	Ag 47	Cd 48	In 49	Sn 50	Sb 51	Te 52	I 53	Xe 54
Period VI	Cs 55	Ba 56	57 — 71	Hf 72	Ta 73	W 74	Re 75	Os 76	Ir 77	Pt 78	Au 79	Hg 80	Tl 81	Pb 82	Bi 83	Po 84	At 85	Rn 86
Period VII	Fr 87	Ra 88	89 — 101															

— Transition Metals —

Elements 57 — 71	La 57	Ce 58	Pr 59	Nd 60	Pm 61	Sm 62	Eu 63	Gd 64	Tb 65	Dy 66	Ho 67	Er 68	Tm 69	Yb 70	Lu 71
Elements 89 — 101	Ac 89	Th 90	Pa 91	U 92	Np 93	Pu 94	Am 95	Cm 96	Bk 97	Cf 98	E 99	Fm 100	Mv 101		

Short Periodic Tables, such as that shown in Table 12, are common. In these short tables the zero group elements, the inert gases, are placed at the beginning of each period, and the long periods are doubled up into two *series*, which are placed under the short periods. The A subgroup

Table 12.   Short Periodic Table of the Elements

Group	0	I	II	III	IV	V	VI	VII	VIII		
Period I		H 1									
Period II	He 2	Li 3	Be 4	B 5	C 6	N 7	O 8	F 9			
Period III	Ne 10	Na 11	Mg 12	Al 13	Si 14	P 15	S 16	Cl 17			
Period IV	A 18	K 19	Ca 20	Sc 21	Ti 22	V 23	Cr 24	Mn 25	Fe 26	Co 27	Ni 28
		Cu 29	Zn 30	Ga 31	Ge 32	As 33	Se 34	Br 35			
Period V	Kr 36	Rb 37	Sr 38	Y 39	Zr 40	Nb 41	Mo 42	Tc 43	Ru 44	Rh 45	Pd 46
		Ag 47	Cd 48	In 49	Sn 50	Sb 51	Te 52	I 53			
Period VI	Xe 54	Cs 55	Ba 56	57 | 71	Hf 72	Ta 73	W 74	Re 75	Os 76	Ir 77	Pt 78
		Au 79	Hg 80	Tl 81	Pb 82	Bi 83	Po 84	At 85			
Period VII	Rn 86	Fr 87	Ra 88	89 | 101							

elements form the first series, and the B subgroup elements form the second series of each long period. Such a short period chart emphasizes the relationships between the typical elements and the subgroups.

54. VARIATION OF PROPERTIES WITH POSITION OF ELEMENT IN PERIODIC TABLE

We have seen how the atomic structures of the elements vary across the periods and down the groups in the Periodic Table. As a given period develops, the numbers of electrons in the outermost shells increase in a stepwise fashion. This electronic expansion for each period is correlated with a gradual change of properties of the elements. As we read down a given group, the number of shells of electrons increases, and this also may be expected to be accompanied by gradual changes in properties for the elements of each group, although there are very strong group similarities.   It is rather dangerous to make sweeping generalizations about the way the elements vary in properties with their positions in the Periodic System because of the complicated way in which the long periods develop.   To be accurate, the variations in each period and group need detailed discussion, and we shall do this later on.   For the present, however, it will be useful to make some general but less precise observations.

The properties usually vary in regular fashion across the second and third periods.   In the long periods, starting with IV, properties change regularly up through the IB elements; then, there may be quite a reversal, and following this, the properties again change in a regular fashion.

As shown in Table 11, the metals occur in the first part of the periods, the nonmetals toward the end.   Metallic character decreases, and nonmetallic character increases, as the atomic number increases in a given period.   Metallic character increases, and nonmetallic nature decreases down each group.   The change from metallic to nonmetallic character is gradual, and intermediate elements, such as germanium and arsenic, are neither distinctly metallic nor nonmetallic.   Such elements are sometimes referred to as *metalloids*.

The *sizes* of atoms vary with position of the elements in the periods and groups.   In general, as can be seen in Figure 13, the atoms at the beginning of a period have relatively large atomic volumes.   As atomic numbers increase in a period, the atomic volumes decrease until a minimum is reached at the middle of the period, and then they increase again. As one might suspect, the atoms increase in size down the groups as the number of shells of electrons increases.

Other properties of the atoms show similar periodicity, and we shall pay particular attention to this in the rest of this book.   If we know how properties change with position of the element in the Periodic Table, we can better appreciate the relationships among the elements.

55.   PREDICTION OF UNDISCOVERED ELEMENTS AND THEIR PROPERTIES

Because of the regularity with which properties of elements change across the periods and down the groups, it is possible to *predict* very accurately the characteristics of a given element.   Its properties should be intermediate between those of its neighbors on either side in the period and above and below it in the group.   If the properties of the neighboring elements are known, then one can estimate what the properties of a given element should be.   When Mendeléeff worked out his version of the Periodic Table in 1868, he had to leave numerous spaces unfilled because the elements belonging in these spaces had not been discovered.   But he was able to predict their existence and to give a detailed description of what their properties should be.   These predictions stimulated other scientists to search for these elements, and the work was made easier because of the descriptions of their characteristics that Mendeléeff had made. When the elements were finally isolated, it was found that Mendeléeff had done a remarkably good job in predicting their properties. This success led to universal acceptance of the Periodic Table, and it has become one of our most important aids in systematizing chemical facts and theories.

EXERCISES

1. a) Compare electrons, protons, and neutrons with respect to mass and charge.

b) In what regions in atoms are these different units believed to reside?

2. How does the nuclear theory of the structure of atoms account for the fact that most of the fast-moving alpha particles that are shot at an atom pass through without being deflected from their path?

3. a) How does the contribution made to the mass of the common hydrogen atom by its electron compare to the contribution made by its nucleus?

b) Compare the contribution of the electron with that of the nucleus to the volume of the hydrogen atom.

4. a) If the atoms in one gram-atomic weight of an average element were lined up in contact in single file, approximately what would be the length in centimeters of the line of atoms?

b) How many miles is this?

5. What per cent of the total volume of an average atom is the volume of its nucleus?

6. An atom has an atomic number of 83 and a mass of 210.

a) Predict the composition of its nucleus and account for the nuclear charge and mass.

b) How many electrons will this neutral atom have?

c) Give similar details for an atom that would be isotopic with the foregoing atom.

7. How are electrons in atoms believed to be affected when light of a given frequency is absorbed by the atom?

8. a) Is the change exoenergic or endoenergic when an atom goes from its ground state to an excited state?

b) In which state will the atom have the greater stability?

9. Which will be at the higher energy level: a) a $2s$ or a $4s$ electron? b) a $3s$ or a $3d$ electron?

10. a) List the detailed electron configurations of magnesium and calcium atoms and point out what they have in common and how they differ.

b) Write the simplest formula for the compound calcium might be expected to form with hydrogen.

11. a) In terms of the specific energy levels which fill with electrons, trace the expansion in electron configuration that occurs across the third and fourth periods of the periodic table.

b) How does this account for the fact that there are only eight elements in the third period, whereas there are 18 elements in the fourth period?

12. How is the variation of the atomic volume with increasing atomic number in agreement with the Periodic Law?

13. How can the Periodic Law be accounted for by the use of the theory of atomic structure?

14. a) What correlation can you suggest between the relative values for the atomic volumes of lithium, sodium, potassium, rubidium, and cesium as given in Figure 12 and the variation in their atomic structures?

b) How can this be used to justify the value suggested on the chart as probable for francium?

15. a) What are the bases for the arrangement of the elements in the long Periodic Table?

b) How are the terms *period, group,* and *subgroup* used in connection with this table?

16. a) From their position in the Periodic Table, predict which will be more metallic, lithium or boron?

b) Which will have the larger atom, helium or argon?

Chapter 5

▶ Chemical Bonding
▶ Ions and Molecules

56. ELECTRONIC REARRANGEMENT IN CHEMICAL CHANGE

When elements combine, we say that *chemical bonding* is set up between the atoms of these elements. When the atoms separate the chemical bonding is destroyed. It is now generally believed that chemical bonding comes about because of the tendency for some of the electrons in the neutral atomic systems to undergo rearrangement, the number of electrons closely associated with each atom changing. The atomic nuclei persist unchanged but become associated with more or fewer electrons.

In the preceding chapter, the close connection between the periodicity of the electronic structures of atoms and the periodicity of their properties has been emphasized. The correlation of the number of electrons in the outermost shells of the atoms with the combining capacities which they show is particularly striking. Since we are interested in understanding the factors that govern the chemical behavior of atoms, we will consider in detail the electronic theories that have been developed to account for the way atoms are observed to combine.

Chemical activity is believed to involve interaction between the outermost shells of electrons of the atoms, since the combining capacity of atoms varies with the number of electrons in these shells. This idea seems reasonable because when atoms collide, the outermost and more loosely bound electrons will be subjected to strong interaction. *The formation of compounds is best explained if we assume that the electrons tend to undergo rearrangement to a more stable configuration. This tendency is believed to be responsible for chemical activity.*

The most stable atoms we know of are those of the inert gases helium, neon, argon, krypton, xenon, and radon. Their atoms show no tendency to combine with other kinds of atoms. They have zero combining capacity. The electronic structures of these inert elements have been summarized in Table 9. We find that certain numbers of electrons, 2, 8, 18, and 32, seem to be particularly favored in their shell structures, and shells having such numbers of electrons presumably have high stability. All

68

of these shells of electrons consist of completed subshells in which each orbital is occupied with a pair of electrons.   Except for helium, all the inert gas atoms have eight electrons in their outermost shells.   Apparently, when electrons are grouped together in such combinations, they are all bound firmly to the nucleus, and the atom is particularly inert; it seems to be effectively saturated with electrons and has no tendency to interact with other atomic systems.

We now believe that atoms of elements that do not have the very stable inert-gas structures tend to attain them in chemical change by losing electrons or by becoming associated with more electrons.   We assume that it is this tendency for electronic rearrangement toward the inert-gas configurations that is responsible for chemical activity.   This is true especially of the elements in the first three periods and of those elements immediately preceding and following the inert gases in the long periods.   Elements in the middle of the long periods tend to change to certain other electron configurations of relatively high stability.

57. VALENCE ELECTRONS

The chemical combining capacity, or valence, of an atom is thought to be determined by the number of electrons that take part in the rearrangement when chemical change occurs.   The electrons which can undergo rearrangement most readily will be those in the higher energy levels, those electrons that are least firmly bound in the atoms.   Valence, therefore, must be correlated with the number of s and p electrons in the outermost shell of the neutral atom.   The valence is usually equal to the number of electrons that must become associated with, or that must be lost by, the atom in order that it attain a more stable configuration (usually that of the nearest inert gas).   For the transition metals, d electrons in the second outermost shell, and in some cases f electrons in the third outermost shell, also may contribute to the combining capacity.   Because the electrons in the outermost shell (and sometimes those in the d and f subshells of the second and third outermost shells) control the valence, these electrons are called *valence electrons*.

58. ELECTRONIC SYMBOLS

It is convenient to have some concise way of describing the manner in which electrons take part in chemical change.   Electronic symbols can be used effectively for this purpose.   The chemical symbol is used to stand for the *core*, or *kernel*, of the atom, that is, its nucleus and all of the electrons except the valence electrons.   A dot is added for each valence electron.   Thus, the following electronic symbols stand for the neutral atoms of the elements hydrogen through argon.

H ·   He :

Li ·   · Be ·   · B ·   · C ·   · N :   · O :   · F :   ·: Ne :

Na ·   · Mg ·   · Al ·   · Si ·   · P :   · S :   · Cl :   : A :

These electronic symbols focus attention on the electrons that are important in chemical activity and show the relations of the various atoms to the nearest inert gases.

59.   VARIETY IN KINDS OF CHEMICAL BONDING

According to our present theories, chemical bonding may be set up in a number of different ways, depending upon the manner in which the redistribution of valence electrons takes place.   The type of chemical bonding established should be a function of the electronic configurations of the atoms involved.   We may hope to be able to correlate the properties of substances with the kinds of bonding.   We should find it possible to establish a classification of substances in terms of the way in which their atoms are combined, and each class should have certain general characteristics which are consequences of their type of bonding.   Let us see how successful such efforts have been.

60.   IONIZATION AND IONS

One kind of electronic rearrangement which is common involves the complete transfer of electrons from or to the neutral atom.   When one or more electrons are lost by a neutral atom, the atomic system as a whole becomes positively charged because the positive charge on the nucleus exceeds the total number of negative electronic charges.   The system is then called a *positive ion*.   When one or more electrons are gained by a neutral atom, a *negative ion* is formed.   The process of *ionization* involves the complete loss or gain of one or more electrons by neutral atoms.   The number of units of charge on the ion depends upon the number of electrons transferred.

An ion of an element is designated by using the symbol for that element and indicating the number of units of net positive or negative charge per ion.   The hydrogen atom may lose one electron to form the positive hydrogen ion, H^+, or it may gain one electron to form the hydride ion, H^-; the sodium atom loses one electron to form the sodium ion, Na^+.   A calcium atom loses two electrons to form a calcium ion, Ca^{2+}, and an aluminum atom loses three electrons to form an aluminum ion, Al^{3+}. The chlorine atom gains one electron to produce the chloride ion, Cl^-, whereas the oxygen atom gains two electrons to give the oxide ion, O^{2-}.

The iron atom can ionize in two different ways. Under certain conditions two electrons are lost and the ferrous ion, Fe^{2+}, is formed; under other conditions three electrons are lost, and the ferric ion, Fe^{3+}, results. The particular way in which an atom tends to ionize depends upon its atomic structure and the conditions that prevail.

Atoms following the inert gases and having only a few electrons in their outermost shells, tend to lose these electrons and attain the inert-gas structures. The loss of electrons leaves the atoms positively charged, and they then are positive ions. For instance, the lithium atom, with one more electron than the helium structure, loses this electron readily to form the lithium ion. Magnesium loses two electrons to form the magnesium ion. We can write expressions using electronic symbols to describe these changes, enclosing the ion in brackets and employing the symbol e^- for the electron.

$$\text{Li} \cdot = [\text{Li}^+] + e^-$$
$$\cdot \text{Mg} \cdot = [\text{Mg}^{2+}] + 2e^-$$

The electronic symbols for the positive ions indicate that all the electrons in the outermost shells have been lost. The metals all tend to go to a more positive condition, forming positive ions by losing one or more electrons. Elements toward the beginning of each period show the greatest tendencies to form positive ions because they can attain the structure of the preceding inert gas by losing only a few electrons. The greater the number of electrons that must be lost, the less will be the tendency for the element to form positive ions.

Atoms that closely precede an inert gas and that lack very few electrons of having an outermost shell of eight electrons tend to gain enough electrons from other atoms to attain the inert structure, to build up the outermost shell to eight electrons. These atoms thus become negatively charged to form *negative ions.*

$$\cdot \ddot{\text{F}} : + \ e^- = \left[\ : \ddot{\text{F}} : \ \right]^-$$

$$\cdot \ddot{\text{Cl}} : + \ e^- = \left[\ : \ddot{\text{Cl}} : \ \right]^-$$

$$\cdot \ddot{\text{O}} : + 2e^- = \left[\ : \ddot{\text{O}} : \ \right]^{2-}$$

$$\cdot \ddot{\text{S}} : + 2e^- = \left[\ : \ddot{\text{S}} : \ \right]^{2-}$$

The electronic symbols for negative ions indicate the attainment of eight electrons in the outermost shells. Elements form negative ions more readily the closer they are to the ends of their periods, that is, the more nonmetallic they are.

Electron configurations can be given for ions just as is done for neutral atoms.   Thus the electron configuration for Li^+ is $1s^2$, the same as that for a neutral helium atom.   The electron configuration of O^{2-} is $1s^2\ 2s^2\ 2p^6$, which is also that of F^- and the neutral atom of neon.   Systems that have the same total number of electrons are said to be *isoelectronic;* O^{2-}, F^-, Ne, Na^+, and Mg^{2+} are all isoelectronic.

61.   IONIZATION POTENTIALS, ELECTRON AFFINITIES, AND ELECTRONEGATIVITY

There are a number of ways to discuss more quantitatively the tendency for atoms to ionize.   Looking at these will give us a better appreciation of the factors which determine the ease of ionization.

The ionization of an atom to give a singly charged positive ion involves removal of one of its least firmly held electrons against the force of attraction binding it to the atom.   This electron will be in a given energy level for the ground state of the atom, and a certain minimum amount of energy must be added to separate the electron completely to give the ion.   This minimum amount of energy required for ionization is called the *ionization energy.*   It is found by determing the minimum energy in volts that is required to remove completely the electron from the atom; this minimum voltage is called the *first ionization potential* of the atom.   The electrons that remain on the singly charged ion will be held more firmly, but if the voltage is increased sufficiently, a second electron is stripped off to leave a doubly charged positive ion.   The voltage required to remove the second electron is the *second ionization potential* of the atom.   As many ionization potentials may be measured as there are electrons in the atom.

Table 13 lists ionization potentials for helium and neon and the three elements that follow each in the order of atomic number.   We can see what the general pattern is for such sequences which are associated with the formation of positive ions.   The values for the potentials above the dotted lines are for the valence electrons in the s and p energy levels of the outermost shell.   These values are seen to be small compared to the values given below the dotted line for the electrons which are in much lower energy levels.   The electrons in these lower energy levels are bound so firmly that they are not available to take part in chemical bonding.

As we go across the periods there is an increase in the number of electrons that must be lost in order to give positive ions which have the electron configuration of the preceding inert gas.   When more than one electron must be lost to give a stable ion, not only is the first ionization potential involved, but one or more of the higher ionization potentials also applies.   The first ionization potential for Be is 9.3, its second is 18 volts.   The energy necessary to strip the first electron from beryllium is less than that for lithium, but the Be^+ ion does not have the stable inert-gas configuration.   To attain this structure in Be^{2+}, an additional and very much larger amount of ionization energy is required to remove the second electron.   The formation of Be^{2+} is much more difficult than the formation of Li^+.   In general, ionization to form positive ions of inert-gas configuration becomes increasingly difficult across a period as the number of electrons to be lost becomes greater.

Table 13.   Ionization Potentials, Volts

Elements	He	Li	Be	B	Ne	Na	Mg	Al
Electron Configuration	2	2, 1	2, 2	2, 3	2, 8	2, 8, 1	2, 8, 2	2, 8, 3
Ionization Potentials								
First	25	5.4	9.3	8.3	22	5.1	7.6	6.0
Second	54	76	18	25	41	47	15	19
Third		122	154	38	64	72	80	28
Fourth			218	259	97	99	109	120
Fifth				340	126	139	141	154

Figure 14 shows the variation of the first ionization potentials with increase in the atomic number, the dotted lines indicating the successive periods.   The periodicity of such potentials and its correlation with the

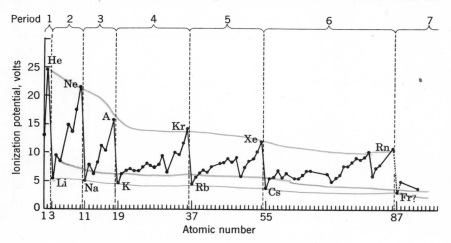

Fig. 14.   Periodicity of ionization potential.

periodic variation of electron configuration are clear.   The first element in each period has the lowest ionization potential, while the inert gas at the end of the period has the highest potential.   Notice also how the ionization potentials decrease down the groups in the Periodic Table.   For instance, the first ionization potentials for Li, Na, K, Rb, and Cs, respec-

tively, are 5.4, 5.1, 4.4, 4.2, and 3.9 volts.   This reflects the decrease in
binding of the *s* electrons in the outermost shell, as the atoms increase in
effective size and these electrons on the average are farther from the
nuclei.

The tendency of an atom to gain electrons to form a negative ion is
called its *electron affinity*.   This can be measured by studying the ease
with which the extra electrons can be removed from the ion to give the
neutral atom.   Electron affinities are found to be negligible early in the

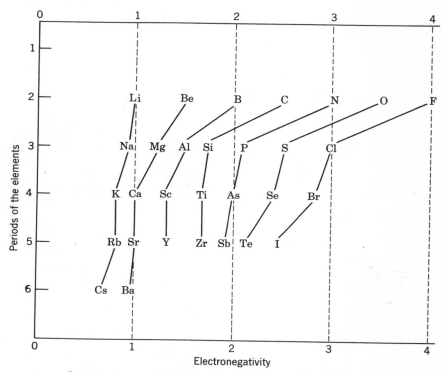

Fig. 15.   Electronegativity of common elements (after Pauling).

periods but to increase rapidly toward the end of the periods and down the
groups.   Accordingly, the tendency to form negative ions is only appreciable for the last few elements in each period preceding the inert gas,
increasing to a maximum for the element just before the inert gas.   Thus,
in the second period the electron affinity is very small for carbon and
varies in the order of C < N < O < F.   Electron affinities decrease
down a group, the order F > Cl > Br > I being observed.

Another very useful concept used to describe the tendency of an atom
to attract electrons is that of *electronegativity*.   This refers to the ability
of an atom in a compound to pull electrons to it.   Figure 15 shows how

the values for the relative electronegativities, as estimated by Pauling for some of the more common elements, vary with the positions of these elements in the Periodic Table.   High electronegativity means that an atom has a strong tendency to form negative ions.   Low electronegativity means that an atom has a strong tendency to form positive ions.   Atoms of intermediate electronegativity do not form ions readily.

We can summarize how ionization varies with the position of an element in the long Periodic Table as follows.   The tendency for ionization to form positive ions is very high for cesium in the lower left-hand corner of the table, and decreases upward and to the right through the table. The tendency for the formation of negative ions is greatest for fluorine in the upper right-hand corner, and decreases as we go to the left and down the table.

62. SIMPLE AND COMPLEX IONS

So far we have spoken only of ions consisting of a single atom that has become charged by losing or gaining completely one or more electrons. Such monatomic ions are usually called *simple ions*.

Table 14.   Some of the More Common Ions

Positive		Negative	
Aluminum	Al^{3+}	Acetate	$C_2H_3O_2^-$
Ammonium	NH_4^+	Bromide	Br^-
Barium	Ba^{2+}	Carbonate	CO_3^{2-}
Calcium	Ca^{2+}	Chlorate	ClO_3^-
Chromic, or chromium (III)	Cr^{3+}	Chloride	Cl^-
Cobaltous, or cobalt (II)	Co^{2+}	Chromate	CrO_4^{2-}
Cupric, or copper (II)	Cu^{2+}	Fluoride	F^-
Cuprous, or copper (I)	Cu^+	Hydride	H^-
Ferric, or iron (III)	Fe^{3+}	Hydroxide	OH^-
Ferrous, or iron (II)	Fe^{2+}	Iodide	I^-
Hydrogen	H^+	Nitrate	NO_3^-
Magnesium	Mg^{2+}	Oxide	O^{2-}
Manganous, or manganese (II)	Mn^{2+}	Permanganate	MnO_4^-
Mercuric, or mercury (II)	Hg^{2+}	Peroxide	O_2^{2-}
Nickel	Ni^{2+}	Phosphate	PO_4^{3-}
Potassium	K^+	Sulfide	S^{2-}
Silver	Ag^+	Sulfate	SO_4^{2-}
Sodium	Na^+		
Zinc	Zn^{2+}		

Complex ions are built up of two or more atoms, the group as a whole having lost or gained one or more electrons and being either positively or negatively charged.   Such complex ions tend to act as units in chemical changes in much the same fashion as do simple ions.   Complex ions are indicated by using the symbols for the constituent elements, together with subscripts to define the number of each kind of atom per ion and signs indicating the charge.   Thus, the carbonate ion, $CO_3{}^{2-}$, consists of one atom of carbon united with three atoms of oxygen, two electrons having been gained in its formation as the double negative charge indicates.   The bonding between the atoms in a complex ion will be discussed later in Chapter 14.

Table 14 lists in alphabetical order some of the more common simple and complex ions.

The name of a simple positive ion is that of the element, except where the existence of two or more ions for the same element makes it necessary to distinguish between them.   This has often been done by using the endings *-ous* and *-ic*, the former being employed for the ion of lower charge.   An alternate and more specific method rapidly coming into practice uses Roman numerals in parentheses following the name of the element to indicate the charge on the ion, as indicated in Table 14. The name of a simple negative ion is derived from the name of the element and has the ending *-ide*.   The names of complex ions will be considered later.

63. THE SHAPES AND SIZES OF SIMPLE IONS

Monatomic ions are assumed to be spherical and of fixed size under given conditions.   The effective *sizes of ions* can be calculated from data obtained by the study of crystals by X-ray methods.   The distances between the centers of adjacent ions can usually be measured accurately, and then it is possible to assign to each ion its effective contributing radius.   Figure 16 shows how these *crystal ionic radii* vary with increasing atomic number.   The ions are shown tremendously magnified in size, the scale in angstrom units being indicated in the lower left corner.   (The radii for the highly charged positive ions are hypothetical because these ions are not known.)   Each horizontal row includes the negative and positive ions that have the same number of electrons, together with the inert-gas atom with which they are isoelectronic.   All the ions in the second row have the electronic configuration $1s^2\,2s^2\,2p^6$, which is that of the neutral neon atom.   Across each of these rows the crystal ionic radius decreases markedly with increase of the charge of the nucleus, which tends to pull the fixed number of electrons in closer.   For each vertical group of ions having the same charge, the ionic radius increases with increase in the number of shells of electrons.   Notice that the ions of the B subgroup elements are smaller than the ions of the A subgroup elements in their respective periods.   The radii of ions vary periodically with increasing atomic number.

Complex ions have more complicated shapes because they are aggregates of two or more atoms.   The spatial configurations of complex ions will be discussed in a later chapter.

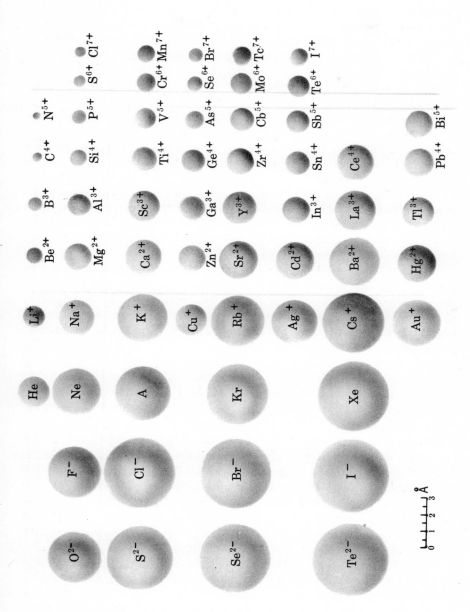

Fig. 16. The crystal radii of ions (after Pauling).

64.   IONIC BONDING AND IONIC SUBSTANCES

When positive ions approach negative ions closely, strong electrical forces of attraction are set up because of the difference in kind of electrical charge.   Each ion tends to surround itself with ions of opposite charge, and a compound is formed which is electrically neutral as a whole. It therefore contains positive and negative ions in such numbers as to provide equal numbers of positive and negative charges.   This constitutes *ionic bonding* (the term *electrovalent bonding* is also used but the self-descriptive term *ionic bonding* is preferable).

Such bonding is set up between sodium and chlorine atoms when these two elements are brought together under proper conditions.   The sodium atoms each lose one electron to form positive sodium ions, and the chlorine atoms each gain one of the electrons thus made available to form negative chloride ions.   These positive and negative ions associate strongly to give the solid compound, sodium chloride.   Since for every sodium ion formed one chloride ion must be produced, sodium and chlorine combine in equal numbers of atoms to form sodium chloride, which has a fixed composition and is electrically neutral as a whole.   This accounts for the simplest formula, NaCl, for this compound.

Figure 17a shows the pattern in which the sodium and chloride ions are packed in the crystals, the symbols for the ions being used to indicate the centers of the ions.   Large crystals are built up by the continuation of this pattern in three dimensions.   In 17b the outlines of the entire ions are sketched in to show their respective sizes and the fact that they are in close contact in the crystal.   Each sodium ion in the interior of the crystal has six chloride ions as near neighbors, and each chloride ion has six sodium ions about it.   The number of nearest neighbors is referred to as the *coordination number* of each ion.

The electrostatic bonding forces that hold the sodium and chloride ions together are strong when the ions are packed closely together.   These forces are exerted equally in all directions.   Therefore *the valence of each ion, which it possesses because of its charge, is shared by all of its neighboring ions of opposite charge*.   In the sodium chloride crystal, each sodium ion is bonded to six neighboring chloride ions, although each sodium ion has a charge and a valence of only one.   However, each sodium ion shares the valence of six neighboring chlorine ions so that, in the crystal as a whole, the total number of units of positive valence is balanced by the total number of units of negative valence.

Ionic bonding is favored when elements having only a few electrons in their outermost shells combine with elements only a few electrons short of the stable number of eight.   Ionic bonds usually are formed when the more active metals combine with the more active nonmetals.   The more to the left and the lower the metal is in the long Periodic Table, and the more to the right and the higher the nonmetal is in the table, the greater

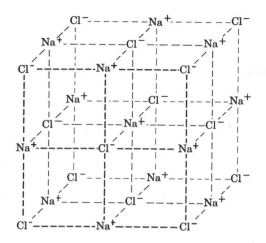

(*a*) Position of centers of ions in space

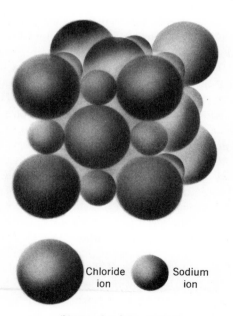

Chloride ion   Sodium ion

(*b*) Ions in close contact

Fig. 17.   The ionic structure of sodium chloride.

will be the tendency for ionic bonding.   When the difference in electronegativity of two elements is large, the bonding between them is likely to be ionic.

65.   FORMULAS FOR IONIC COMPOUNDS

When calcium unites with chlorine, each calcium atom loses two electrons, and each chlorine atom gains one electron.   Twice as many chloride ions as calcium ions are formed, and the two ionic species associate to produce the compound, calcium chloride, which has the formula $CaCl_2$. Since calcium ions and oxide ions have charges of $2+$ and $2-$, respectively, they associate in equal numbers to form calcium oxide.   Therefore the formula for calcium is CaO.

The ratio in which any kind of positive ion will associate with any kind of negative ion to form a compound is determined by the charges of the ions. Simplest formulas are the only kind we can write for an ionic compound because the ionic ratio is the thing which is characteristic.   The actual number of ions varies with the size of the sample.   Keeping this in mind, it is easy to predict the formula for any ionic compound if you know the charges of the ions which form it.   Table 14 has listed 19 common positive ions and 17 common negative ions.   Since any positive ion will combine with any negative ion to give an ionic compound, you should now be able to predict the formation of, and the correct formulas for, a very large number of ionic compounds.   As an example, consider the possibility of compound formation by barium and phosphate ions, Ba^{2+} and PO_4^{3-}.   Combining these ions in the simplest ratio that will give equal numbers of positive charges, we derive the formula $Ba_3(PO_4)_2$ for the compound.   The name barium phosphate for this compound is obtained by combining the names of the ions.   In writing ionic formulas and in naming ionic compounds, the positive ion is always given first.   If complex ions, such as the PO_4^{3-} ion, are taken more than once in a formula, the formula for the ion is placed in parentheses and a subscript placed after the parentheses is used to indicate the number of these ions in the ionic ratio.

The formula for an ionic compound tells nothing about the coordination numbers of the ions.   These numbers are characteristic for each compound but vary from compound to compound, depending upon the simple ionic ratios, the relative sizes of the ions, and other factors.   They always must be such that the substance as a whole is electrically neutral. In CsCl the coordination number of both cesium and chloride ions is eight, rather than six as in NaCl. Cs^+ is larger than Na^+, and more Cl^- can pack about Cs^+ than about Na^+.   In MgF_2 crystals the coordination number for F^- is six while that for Mg^{2+} is three.

Electronic formulas may be written for ionic compounds to indicate the electron configurations of the component ions by combining the electronic symbols for the elements.

$$\text{Li}^+ \left[\; : \overset{..}{\underset{..}{F}} : \; \right]^- \qquad \text{Mg}^{2+} \left[\; : \overset{..}{\underset{..}{F}} : \; \right]^-_2 \qquad \text{Na}^+ \left[\; : \overset{..}{\underset{..}{Cl}} : \; \right]^- \qquad \text{Cs}^+ \left[\; : \overset{..}{\underset{..}{Cl}} : \; \right]^-$$

66. MOLECULES AND COVALENT BONDING

Ionic bonding accounts very satisfactorily for the combination of atoms that are quite different in electronegativity. However, it is not at all adequate for describing the bonding between identical atoms or for bonding between atoms not much different in electrical character. This is the problem encountered when we consider *molecular substances.*

A molecular substance is composed of *molecules*, electrically neutral structural units consisting of one or more atoms. The inert gases are the simplest examples of molecular substances. Their molecules are single atoms because these atoms are completely inert and form no bonds to each other. All other molecular substances are composed of *polyatomic molecules*, having two or more atoms combined chemically. Each molecular substance has its own distinctive molecule of given composition and properties. Collections of these molecules constitute the large samples of molecular substances that we ordinarily work with.

Hydrogen gas is composed of discrete and relatively independent diatomic hydrogen molecules, each consisting of two hydrogen atoms strongly bonded to each other. We accordingly write the molecular formula H_2 for this molecule. Fluorine, oxygen, and nitrogen also exist as the diatomic molecules, F_2, O_2, and N_2. The common molecule of phosphorus is P_4, and all of the other nonmetallic elements likewise are molecular. The compound, hydrogen fluoride, has one atom of hydrogen bonded to one atom of fluorine in the HF molecule. The molecules of water, ammonia, and methane are, respectively, H_2O, NH_3, and CH_4. All these molecules consist of atoms which are either identical or very little different with respect to electronegativity. How are they bonded together?

To explain the bonding effect in such chemical systems, G. N. Lewis in 1916 suggested that atoms may gain the stable valence shell structures of the inert gases by *sharing pairs of electrons.* Hydrogen atoms, having but one electron each, need a total of two to approximate the structure of helium. Each of two hydrogen atoms can furnish one electron to constitute a pair of electrons that may be shared by the two nuclei, giving each hydrogen atom something close to the electronic structure of helium. For the combination of the two neutral hydrogen atoms we write the equation

$$H \cdot + \cdot H = H : H$$

and arrive at an electronic formula for the hydrogen molecule. Two fluorine atoms, by setting up a shared pair of electrons, may gain the neon structure

$$: \overset{..}{\underset{..}{F}} \cdot \; + \; \cdot \overset{..}{\underset{..}{F}} : \; = \; : \overset{..}{\underset{..}{F}} : \overset{..}{\underset{..}{F}} :$$

Unlike atoms also may be bonded in this fashion

$$\overset{\displaystyle H}{\underset{\displaystyle H}{H : \overset{..}{\underset{..}{C}} : H}} \qquad \overset{..}{\underset{\displaystyle H}{H : \overset{..}{N} : H}} \qquad \overset{..}{\underset{\displaystyle H}{H : \overset{..}{O} :}} \qquad H : \overset{..}{\underset{..}{F}} : \qquad : \overset{..}{O} :: C :: \overset{..}{O} :$$

| methane | ammonia | water | hydrogen fluoride | carbon dioxide |

As seen for carbon dioxide, some atoms may share two or even three pairs of electrons and have *multiple bonding*. The nitrogen atoms in the N_2 molecule are united by triple electron-pair bonding.

$$: N :: N :$$

Each shared electron pair is composed of one electron contributed by each atom joined by the bond, and each shared pair accounts for *one unit of valence for each of the two atoms.* Each of the two atoms involved in the bond becomes associated with one more electron for every *normal covalent bond* formed in this fashion, and the structure of the atom approaches the structure of the inert gas following it. Obviously, the number of covalent bonds that a given atom will form depends upon the number of electrons that it needs in its outermost shell to complete this to eight electrons (except in the case of hydrogen). Carbon forms four normal covalent bonds, nitrogen forms three, oxygen forms two, and fluorine forms one.

Covalent bonding and molecular character are to be expected for compounds formed by the union of elements whose atoms are short four or fewer electrons of having inert-gas structure, and where the atoms bonded together are either identical or not too greatly different in electronegativity. The normal covalent bond is especially suitable for linking *electronegative, nonmetallic* elements together.

Elements in the same group of the Periodic Table tend to form the same number of covalent bonds per atom because they all lack the same number of electrons of having inert-gas structures. Compare the electronic formulas for the molecules below with those for methane, ammonia, water, hydrogen fluoride, and carbon dioxide.

$$\overset{\displaystyle H}{\underset{\displaystyle H}{H : \overset{..}{\underset{..}{Si}} : H}} \qquad \overset{..}{\underset{\displaystyle H}{H : \overset{..}{P} : H}} \qquad \overset{..}{\underset{\displaystyle H}{H : \overset{..}{S} :}} \qquad H : \overset{..}{\underset{..}{Cl}} : \qquad : \overset{..}{S} :: C :: \overset{..}{S} :$$

| monosilane | phosphine | hydrogen sulfide | hydrogen chloride | carbon disulfide |

The capacity of atoms of elements to form covalent bonds varies periodically with position in the Periodic Table and can be predicted from knowledge of electronic configuration.

67. THE SHAPES AND SIZES OF MOLECULES

Because the molecules of helium and the other inert gases consist of single atoms, they are spherical in shape and increase regularly in size, as shown in Figure 16.   Polyatomic molecules can be expected to have much more complicated shapes, depending upon the number of atoms and their relative positions in space.

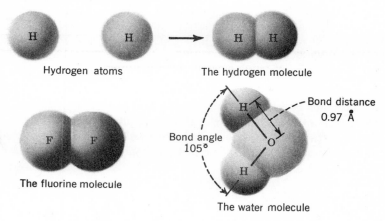

Fig. 18.   Structures of the H_2, F_2, and H_2O molecules.

We can consider the formation of the hydrogen molecule to involve the union of two spherical hydrogen atoms so that their electronic regions overlap to produce the dumbbell shaped molecule shown in Figure 18. This overlap is identified with the high electron density established between the two nuclei by the sharing of the pair of electrons which constitutes the covalent bond.   All other diatomic molecules, such as F_2, have dumbbell shapes but different sizes.   The water molecule has two hydrogen atoms which overlap the oxygen atom to which they are bound. Molecules in which there are more than two atoms will have two or more covalent bonds in certain directions with respect to each other to produce a molecule of definite shape.   This is shown for the water molecule in Figure 18 where heavy dashes are used between the nuclei to indicate the covalent bonds.   The term *bond angle* refers to the angle between two bonds, and the term *bond distance* refers to the distance between the centers of atoms which are linked together.

A number of experimental methods can be used to find out how the atoms are arranged in molecules.   The positions in space of the centers of the constituent atoms relative to each other can be determined, and the angles between the bonds formed by a given atom can be calculated. Figure 19 shows the three-dimensional structures of the NH_3, CH_4, and CO_2 molecules.

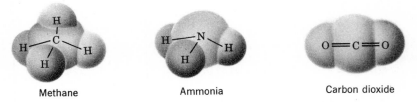

Methane   Ammonia   Carbon dioxide

Fig. 19.   Structures of the CH_4, NH_3, and CO_2 molecules.

68.   COVALENT BOND RADII

The *bond distance* between the centers of two atoms that are covalently bonded can be measured.   In Figure 20 the bond distance in the chlorine molecule is shown to be 1.98 Å.   Since the two atoms are identical, each is thought to contribute equally to the bond distance.   Therefore one-half of this distance, 0.99 Å, is called the *single covalent bond radius* of chlorine in the molecule, there being just one bond between the two atoms.

Single covalent bond radius, 0.99 Å

Single covalent bond distance, 1.98 Å

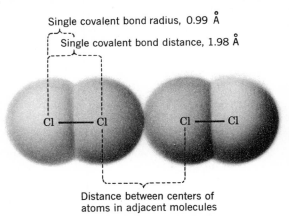

Cl —— Cl   Cl —— Cl

Distance between centers of
atoms in adjacent molecules

Fig. 20.   Dimensions of molecules of chlorine.

The distance between chlorine atoms in adjacent molecules, when these are packed together as closely as possible, is found to be greater than the bond distance between the atoms in the same molecule.   This reflects the fact that when atoms are covalently bonded they interpenetrate, whereas when there is no bond they do not approach so closely.   The discrete nature and definite boundaries of each molecule are apparent.

Figure 21 shows the variation with atomic number of the single covalent bond radii of the elements most likely to form covalent bonds, the four elements preceding the inert gas in each period.

In each period the single covalent bond radius decreases with increasing nuclear charge, the interpenetration of the atomic systems becoming greater. The covalent radius increases down each group as the number of shells of electrons increases. When the number of covalent bonds between two atoms becomes greater, the interpenetration of the two atoms increases, and the bond radius becomes smaller. The single covalent bond radius of carbon is 0.771 Å, its double bond radius is 0.665 Å, and its triple bond radius is 0.602 Å.

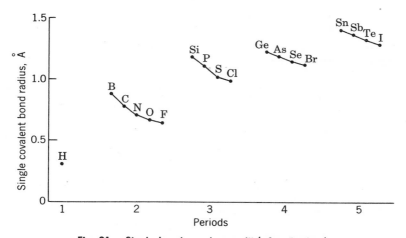

Fig. 21.   Single bond covalent radii (after Pauling).

The covalent bond radii are found to be suprisingly constant in different molecules. If the number of covalent bonds between two atoms and the corresponding covalent radii are known, the distance between the centers of the two atoms can be estimated, taking the sum of the radii.

69. WRITING FORMULAS FOR MOLECULAR SUBSTANCES

The formulas for molecular substances are written in various ways, depending upon how much information we wish to give. The *empirical molecular formula*

$$H_2O$$

indicates that each molecule of water is composed of two atoms of hydrogen and one of oxygen. The molecular formula of a substance is not always the same as the *simplest formula* we have discussed in Chapter 2. Hydrogen peroxide has an atomic ratio of hydrogen to oxygen of 1:1, so its simplest formula is HO. However, study of its molecule shows that this actually consists of two atoms of hydrogen and two atoms of oxygen.

Its molecular formula is H_2O_2. This can be verified by determining the weight of the molecule by various methods which will be discussed later.

A *structural formula* gives more information by using dashes to indicate which atoms are bonded together, as when we write the formula

$$H—O—H$$

This may be further refined by indicating the relative positions in space of the atoms by the directions in which the bonds are directed. Thus we indicate a bent-chain molecule for H_2O.

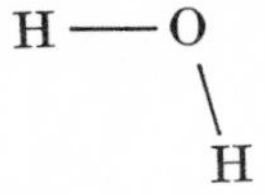

$$H \longrightarrow O$$
$$\diagdown$$
$$H$$

This may be further amplified by indicating the bond angle and the bond distances, using the symbols to designate the positions of the centers of the atoms.

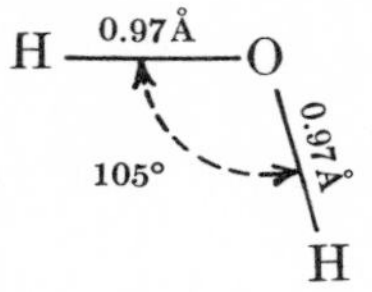

$$H \xrightarrow{\text{0.97Å}} O$$
$$105° \quad 0.97\text{Å}$$
$$H$$

If we wish to show how the electrons are involved in bonding together the atoms, we write an *electronic formula,* in which we indicate all the electrons in the outermost shell of each atom, whether these electrons are shared or unshared. The electronic formula for water is, therefore

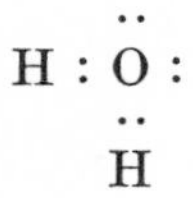

$$\overset{..}{H : O :}$$
$$\overset{..}{H}$$

The dash used in structural formulas to indicate a covalent bond becomes a pair of shared electrons in electronic formulas. The formula

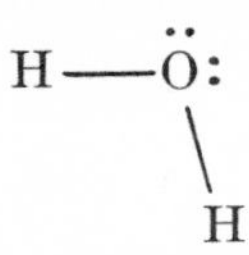

$$H \longrightarrow \overset{..}{O}:$$
$$\diagdown$$
$$H$$

is very effective for indicating the electron configuration as well as the spatial configuration of the molecule.

By combining this with a three-dimensional sketch we can describe, in addition, the interpenetration of the bonded atoms, as shown in Figure 22. This summarizes a very large amount of information.

It is very misleading to use dashes to indicate bonding in ionic systems, thus giving an incorrect idea of the atomic setup. The formula Na—Cl would indicate that one sodium atom is bonded to one specific chlorine atom. We know that this is not so in salt crystals or in molten salt. The structural formula sometimes written for calcium fluoride, F—Ca—F, is also quite erroneous. Crystals of calcium fluoride actually have eight fluoride ions close to each calcium ion and four calcium ions close to each fluoride ion. The substance is ionic, not covalent, and the use of the structural molecular formula is incorrect.

Fig. 22. **The water molecule.**

70. POLARITY OF SUBSTANCES

A system is electrically *polar* if its center of positive electricity is not at the same point as its center of negative electricity. If the two centers coincide, then the system is *nonpolar*. A molecule may be either non-polar or somewhat polar, depending upon the kinds of atoms that are present and the directions of the bonds in the molecule. Let us see why this is true.

A covalent bond for a given atom is *directed toward a specific neighboring atom* because the pair of electrons is shared strongly by the nuclei of the two atoms involved. If the atoms so bonded together are identical, as in H—H, the pair of bonding electrons will be shared equally, and the center of negative electricity due to the electrons will be identical with the center of positive electricity due to the nuclei. The covalent bond in this case is *nonpolar* and the hydrogen molecule is nonpolar.

If a covalent bond is formed between atoms of different electronegativity, such as hydrogen and chlorine in H—Cl, there will be a shift of electrons toward the more electronegative atom, and the bond is somewhat polar. The H—Cl molecule as a whole is electrically neutral, but its center of negative charge is toward the chlorine atom and its center of positive charge toward the hydrogen atom. As shown in Figure 23*a*, the polarity of the H—Cl bond and of the molecule can be considered a *vector* represented by the arrow with its head toward the more electronegative atom. If we so desire, the length of the arrow can be used to indicate diagrammatically the magnitude of the polarity.

The polarity of the H—Cl molecule can be demonstrated by placing it in the strong electrical field between positively and negatively charged plates, as shown in Figure 23*b*. The molecule tends to line up with the electrical field, like a bar magnet lines up with a magnetic field, and the magnitude of this tendency is a measure of the amount of polarity of the molecule. The nonpolar H—H molecules will have no tendency to line up with the electrical field.

The situation is more complicated with polyatomic molecules, such as H_2O, where there are two or more bonds per molecule.   As shown in Figure 23*c*, each of the H—O bonds in the water molecule is polar because oxygen is more electronegative than hydrogen.   The two H—O bond polarities add up as vectors to give a net polarity to the molecule as a whole.   Water molecules have a strong tendency to line up with an electrical field.   Notice that the amount of polarity of the molecule depends not only on the difference in electronegativity of the atoms but also upon the angle between the bonds.   The bond angle for water is 105 deg.   If it were larger, the vector sum of the bond polarities would be smaller and the polarity of water would be smaller.

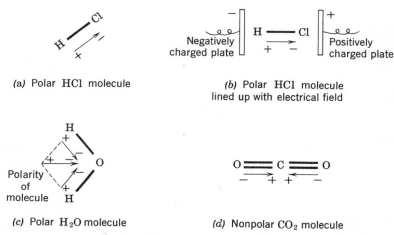

(a) Polar HCl molecule

(b) Polar HCl molecule
lined up with electrical field

(c) Polar H_2O molecule

(d) Nonpolar CO_2 molecule

Fig. 23.   Polarity of bonds and molecules.

It is possible to have a molecule in which the individual bonds are quite polar but where the molecule as a whole has no polarity.   The polarity of the various bonds may be in such directions that they oppose and cancel each other.   In the CO_2 molecule, as shown in Figure 23*d*, each oxygen atom has two covalent bonds to the carbon atom, and all three atoms lie in a straight line so that the bond angle is 180 deg.   Each oxygen atom is more electronegative than the carbon atom, and the two C=O bonds have considerable polarity, as indicated by the arrows.   However, the bond polarities are in opposite directions and just counterbalance each other.   Therefore, the CO_2 molecule as a whole is nonpolar and has no tendency to line up with an electrical field.

The degree of polarity of molecules is important in determining much of their behavior.   Upon close approach to each other, polar molecules will tend to line up with the negative end of one attracted to the positive end of another.   There will be no such tendency for lining up between nonpolar molecules.   Accordingly, we can expect that nonpolar molecules will have much less tendency to stick together than do polar molecules. The high polarity of water molecules is very important in determining the physical and chemical behavior of water and its effectiveness as a solvent, as we shall see later.

71. COMPARISON OF IONIC AND MOLECULAR SUBSTANCES

The foregoing discussion of chemical bonding and of the substances which are believed to involve ionic and covalent bonding has emphasized the importance of learning as much as possible about the particle nature of matter. It is possible to correlate electron configuration and position in the Periodic Table with the tendency for atoms to form ions or molecules, and these two kinds of building blocks give rise to two broad classes of substances.

Ionic substances, because they are combinations of positive and negative ions, are always compounds. The forces of attraction between ions of opposite charge are strong, and, at ordinary temperatures, ions are held in close contact in regular crystal patterns. Ionic substances are always solids at room temperature and usually have high melting points. LiF melts at 870°, MgF_2 at 1396°, and NaCl at 804°. Ionic solids melt to give ionic liquids in which there are still very strong attractive forces between the ions, so that the liquids have little tendency to vaporize. Ordinarily, we do not deal with ionic compounds in the gaseous state.

Molecular substances may be either elements or compounds. Their molecules contain atoms covalently bonded together, each bond being directed exclusively toward one neighboring atom. Covalent bonds vary in strength, depending upon the atoms that are bonded together. Hydrogen-hydrogen bonds are strong, and hydrogen molecules can be heated to very high temperatures before the covalent bond is broken. The hydrogen molecule is said to have high *thermal stability*. Hydrogen-iodine covalent bonds are weak, and HI molecules are not very stable; they break up readily when heated. Cane sugar chars readily when it is heated. That is because some of the covalent bonds in its molecules undergo rupture and rearrangement. *The attractive forces between molecules are always weak.* Substances having small nonpolar molecules are likely to be gases or low-boiling liquids under ordinary conditions. As molecules increase in size, mass, and polarity, they usually become less volatile and their melting and boiling points increase; they are apt to be present as liquids or solids at room temperature. Substances with huge molecules, such as graphite, have high melting points.

72. PREDICTION OF BOND TYPE AND PROPERTIES

The theory of the nature of chemical bonding just described has proved to be very useful in allowing us to predict the possibility of chemical reaction and the nature of the products formed.   If we know what kinds of atoms are being brought together, and if we are familiar with the conditions that favor the various bonding mechanisms, we can predict from the known electronic structures of the atoms what kind of bonding is likely to be set up.   From the nature of the bonding predicted for the system, we can make reasonable guesses as to what the properties of the system are likely to be.   The theory also provides a very satisfactory framework in which we can fit the vast array of observations gained by experimental work, and in this fashion the theory helps to unify our knowledge of chemical systems.

73. BONDING IN METALS

We have considered the chemical-bonding theories that have been developed to account for ionic and molecular substances.   Metals and their alloys constitutes a third class of materials.   Neither the ionic-bonding theory nor the covalent-bonding theory accounts for the bonding in metallic systems.   We shall postpone discussion of the structure and bonding in metallic systems until a later chapter where the general properties of the metals and a theory of bonding consistent with these properties will be summarized.

EXERCISES

1. a) Why is it important to know the electron configurations of the inert gas atoms if we wish to account for the chemical bonding of the other elements?
  b) What features are characteristic of the electron configurations of the inert gases?

2. a) Which electrons in an atom are known as its valence electrons?
  b) Why is it reasonable to expect these electrons to take part in chemical bonding?

3. Write the electronic symbols for each of the neutral atoms of the elements of the third period.

4. Write the electronic symbol for the atom in: a) the first place in the periodic table following each inert gas; b) the second place preceding each inert gas.

5. Write an expression, using electronic symbols, for the ionization you would predict for: a) potassium; b) bromine; c) barium; d) selenium.

6. a) Give the electron configuration in detail for argon.
  b) Write electronic symbols for four ions which are isoelectronic with argon.
  c) How do these ions vary in size with increasing atomic number?

7. a) How does the first ionization potential of an atom compare with its second ionization potential?
  b) What reasons can you suggest to account for this?

8. Making use of Table 13, predict which ion should form more readily: a) B^{3+} or Al^{3+}; b) Mg^{2+} or Al^{3+}; c) Na^+ or Mg^{2+}.

9. How does electronegativity vary: a) across the periods? b) down a group?
c) How does it correlate with the tendency to form positive and negative ions?
d) How does it correlate with the tendency to form covalent bonds?

10. Distinguish between simple and complex ions. Select three examples of each from Table 14.

11. Making use of Table 14, derive the formulas and names for 10 ionic compounds not already mentioned in this chapter.

12. Why is it necessary to supplement the formula for an ionic substance by giving the coordination numbers of its ions if you wish to describe the relationship of the positive and negative ions in a crystal?

13. a) On the basis of the geometry of the crystals of sodium chloride, account for the fact that it has the formula NaCl.
b) Are there discrete molecules in the crystal corresponding to the formula NaCl?

14. What are the essential differences between the way electrons undergo rearrangement in ionic and covalent bonding?

15. a) How can the electronegativities of the elements be used to predict what kind of bonding will be set up when two elements combine?
b) Predict whether ionic or covalent bonding is to be expected between: 1) potassium and fluorine; 2) carbon and nitrogen; 3) calcium and nitrogen; 4) nitrogen and chlorine; 5) cesium and bromine.

16. Write the electronic formulas for: a) the ionic substances NaF, $CaCl_2$, and MgO; b) the molecules Cl_2, CCl_4, HBr, H_2S, and CS_2.

17. Recalling the discussion in Section 66, write electronic formulas for the molecules you would expect to be formed when hydrogen combines with: a) germanium; b) arsenic; c) selenium; d) bromine.

18. Making use of Figure 21, compute the approximate distance between the centers of the following pairs of atoms when they share a pair of electrons: a) H—H; b) C—C; c) H—C; d) H—S.

19. Making use of Figure 15, predict which of the following bonds will be more polar: a) O—F, N—Cl, or P—F; b) Si—C, C—H, or C—S.

20. Account for the fact that H_2O molecules are polar but CO_2 molecules are not.

21. On the basis of Figure 15 and the discussion in Sections 67 and 70, would you expect molecules to be polar or nonpolar in: a) F_2; b) NH_3?

22. Indicate the significance of the terms *bond distance* and *bond radius*, illustrating by means of a molecular sketch.

23. a) Would you expect to get an ionic or a molecular compound when calcium combines with fluorine?
b) Would the compound be a gas or a solid at room temperature?

Chapter 6

▶ **Formulas and Moles**

▶ **Reactions and Equations**

74. CORRECT USE OF CHEMICAL FORMULAS

Chemical formulas are very useful for summarizing a great deal of information about substances. It is important to recognize their significance so that they can be used to maximum advantage. By writing a correct formula you can tell others much about a specific substance, and when you are given such a formula you should be able to derive the maximum amount of information from it.

We have seen how experiments can provide the facts necessary to establish the *simplest formula* for a substance. *If the substance is ionic, the simplest formula is the only one we can write.* It identifies the ions that make up the compound and specifies their ratio in the substance as a whole. If complex ions are present, this is apparent from the ionic formula. The simplest formula for a molecular substance provides knowledge of what atoms are present and gives their simplest numerical ratio, but it tells nothing about how the atoms are related to each other. *Molecular formulas* are more informative in that they represent the molecule which is characteristic of the substance. They should be used if possible when representing molecular materials.

It is conventional in writing formulas to put first the symbol for the element of lowest electronegativity. We write NaH, but we reverse the position of hydrogen in writing HCl because hydrogen is more electronegative than sodium but less electronegative than chlorine. (The formula NH_3 violates the rule, but people started to write it this way before the concept of electronegativity was developed, and the familiar usage has persisted.)

75. RADICALS

Certain groups of atoms tend to maintain their association through many chemical changes. Such groups are referred to as *radicals*, examples being CH_3, OH, and SO_4. The combining capacities of the atoms present in such a group are not completely satisfied, and the radical as a whole has some residual tendency for combination, a characteristic

92

CH₃COOH
C₂H₄O₂

valence. Because the carbon atom in CH_3 has formed only three covalent bonds and needs to form one more bond to approximate the neon configuration, the CH_3 radical has a valence of 1 and forms the compounds CH_3Cl and $NaCH_3$. The OH radical has a valence of 1 and is found in such compounds as CH_3OH. SO_4 forms H_2SO_4, having a valence of 2. Radicals may sometimes either gain or lose electrons completely to form complex ions, such as $(OH)^-$ or $(SO_4)^{2-}$, which take part in building ionic substances. In writing formulas in which a given radical or complex ion is taken several times, these are enclosed in parentheses, and a subscript is employed, which refers to all atoms inside the parentheses. In $Zn(CH_3)_2$ there are two CH_3 radicals to give two carbon and six hydrogen atoms for every zinc atom. $Al_2(SO_4)_3$ is composed of aluminum ions, Al^{3+}, and sulfate ions, $(SO_4)^{2-}$, in the ratio of 2:3.

If radicals or complex ions are treated rigorously enough, they may be broken down by chemical change into the constituent atoms.

76. NAMING COMPOUNDS

In order to avoid confusion and to convey the maximum amount of information, it is conventional in naming compounds containing only two elements to give the name of the less electronegative element first and then the root of the name of the more negative element combined with the ending -ide. In addition, prefixes may be used to indicate the numbers of atoms present.

NaCl	sodium chloride
CaS	calcium sulfide
SO_2	sulfur dioxide
SO_3	sulfur trioxide
N_2O_3	dinitrogen trioxide

For compounds containing more than two elements, the names of the radicals or complex ions that are present are used.

$Ca(OH)_2$	calcium hydroxide
Na_2SO_4	sodium sulfate
CH_3Cl	methyl chloride
$Zn(CH_3)_2$	zinc dimethyl

Unfortunately, these simple rules are not sufficient to cover all cases. Many common compounds, which became familiar before the above rules were agreed upon, were given *trivial names* which tell nothing about their composition; e.g., water, ammonia, methane. As we proceed, more extended usages will gradually be introduced.

77. DEDUCING FORMULAS FROM VALENCE

In any compound the total combining capacities or valences of the atoms must balance, as has been emphasized in the discussion of bonding. This requirement leads to the fact that atoms tend to combine in certain fixed ratios. A correctly written formula must meet this specification. If the characteristic valences of the atoms combining are known, it is often possible to deduce the simplest formula for the compound. Oxygen usually has a valence of 2 when it combines with a metal, and aluminum always has a valence of 3 when it combines with a nonmetal. When aluminum combines with oxygen, the ratio of the two kinds of atoms involved must be such that the total combining capacity of the aluminum atoms is just equal to the total combining capacity of the oxygen atoms. Hence, the simplest formula for the compound must be Al_2O_3. Conversely, if the correct formula for a compound is known, the valence of one of the elements may be calculated if the valences of the other atoms present are known. If we assume that oxygen has a valence of 2, then in ZnO, zinc has a valence of 2 and in TiO_2, titanium has a valence of 4.

It should be remembered, however, that the deduction of a formula from formal valence considerations does not guarantee that such a compound actually is formed. The existence of a compound of given composition *must be established by experiment.*

78. GRAM-FORMULA WEIGHTS AND MOLES

In Section 12 the term *gram-atomic weight* was introduced. The fact that one gram-atomic weight of any element consists of the Avogadro Number, 6.02×10^{23} atoms, was emphasized. In Section 28 gram-formula weights for compounds were considered, and again the Avogadro Number was used to calculate the numbers of atoms in given weights of material. Suppose we review and extend this in the light of what we now know about ions and molecules.

We represent ions by ionic formulas, such as Ca^{2+}, Cl^-, and NO_3^-. Since an electron has a relative mass of only 0.00054 mass unit, *ionic weights* may be taken to be essentially equal to the sum of the atomic weights of the atoms comprising the ion. Thus, the ionic weight of Ca^{2+} is 40.08, that of Cl^- is 35.46, and that of NO_3^- is $14.01 + 3(16.00)$ or 62.01. A gram-formula weight of an ion, *a gram ion*, is the number of grams of the ion equal numerically to the ionic weight: 40.08 g of Ca^{2+}, 35.46 g of Cl^-, and 62.01 g of NO_3^-. It can readily be seen that one gram ion of Ca^{2+} consists of the Avogadro Number, 6.02×10^{23}, of calcium ions, and that one gram ion of NO_3^- will have 6.02×10^{23} nitrate ions present.

We represent substances by formulas, and the *formula weight* of a substance is equal to the sum of the weights of the atoms in the formula.

The formula weight of NaCl is 58.46, while that for water is 18.016. If the substance is molecular and the formula used is a molecular formula, then the formula weight is the *molecular weight* of the substance. The molecular weight of water is 18.016 because H_2O is the correct molecular formula for water. *Gram-formula weights* and *gram-molecular weights* are the formula weights and molecular weights taken in grams. The gram-formula weight of NaCl is 58.46 g; the gram-molecular weight of water is 18.016 g.

The term *mole* is very convenient to use to refer to one gram-formula weight of an ion or of an ionic substance and to one gram-molecular weight of a molecular substance.

$$1 \text{ mole of } Ca^{2+} = 40.48 \text{ g of } Ca^{2+}$$
$$1 \text{ mole of } NO_3^- = 62.46 \text{ g of } NO_3^-$$
$$1 \text{ mole of } NaCl = 58.46 \text{ g of } NaCl$$
$$1 \text{ mole of } H_2 \quad = 2.016 \text{ g of } H_2$$
$$1 \text{ mole of } H_2O \quad = 18.016 \text{ g of } H_2O$$

The number of moles of an ion or substance in a given sample is calculated by dividing the weight in grams by the weight per mole in grams.

EXAMPLE: 80.16 g of Ca^{2+} is used in a reaction; how many moles of Ca^{2+} is this?

$$\frac{\text{Weight of } Ca^{2+} \text{ in grams}}{\text{Grams per mole of } Ca^{2+}} = \frac{80.16 \text{ g}}{40.08 \text{ g per mole}} = 2.0 \text{ moles of } Ca^{2+}$$

EXAMPLE: How many moles of sodium chloride is 146.15 g of this substance?

$$\frac{\text{Weight of NaCl in grams}}{\text{Grams per mole of NaCl}} = \frac{146.15 \text{ g}}{58.46 \text{ g per mole}} = 2.5 \text{ moles of NaCl}$$

EXAMPLE: How many moles of hydrogen are there in 20.16 g of this gas?

$$\frac{\text{Weight of } H_2 \text{ in grams}}{\text{Grams per mole of } H_2} = \frac{20.16 \text{ g}}{2.016 \text{ g per mole}} = 10.0 \text{ moles of } H_2$$

The chemist likes to use the term *mole* because it is a convenient way to specify quantities of ions or substances of the general magnitude in which they are commonly employed in the laboratory. Stating quantities of substances in terms of moles is particularly effective because, if the number of moles of a given ion or substance is known, we can then easily calculate the number of particles, whether they are ions, atoms, or molecules that are present.

One mole of H_2O consists of 6.02×10^{23} water molecules, and there are present two gram-atomic weights or $2 \times 6.02 \times 10^{23}$ atoms of hydrogen and one gram-atomic weight or 6.02×10^{23} atoms of oxygen. One mole of a molecular substance always consists of 6.02×10^{23} molecules.

$$5 \text{ moles of water} = 5 \times \text{gram-molecular weight of water}$$
$$= 5 \times 18.016 \text{ g of water}$$
$$= 5 \times 6.02 \times 10^{23} \text{ molecules of water}$$

5 moles of water
have present: 10 gram atoms of hydrogen
$10 \times 6.02 \times 10^{23}$ atoms of hydrogen
5 gram atoms of oxygen
$5 \times 6.02 \times 10^{23}$ atoms of oxygen

Recall that MgF_2 is an ionic substance:

$$5 \text{ moles of } MgF_2 = 5 \times \text{gram-formula weight of } MgF_2$$
$$= 5 \times 62.32 \text{ g of } MgF_2$$

5 moles of MgF_2
have present: 5 moles of Mg^{2+}
$5 \times 6.02 \times 10^{23}$ magnesium ions
2×5 moles of F^-
$2 \times 5 \times 6.02 \times 10^{23}$ fluoride ions

It is important to realize that *the term mole as applied to ions or molecules always specifies 6.02×10^{23} particles,* just as the term *dozen* is used to refer to 12 units of familiar objects. The chemist prefers to use moles rather than dozens because he usually works with such very large numbers of ions and molecules. The same number of moles of ions or molecules of different kinds have present the same number of ions or molecules, whereas the same weights of different kinds of ions or molecules have present different numbers of these units. Therefore, when we wish to think in terms of numbers of particles, specifying a quantity of material in terms of moles is better than specifying it by weight.

79. CHEMICAL EQUATIONS

The atoms of the elements are the fundamental units of the elements that are involved in chemical change. Substances that enter chemical reactions contain these atoms combined in molecules or present as ions. In chemical change the modes of combination of the atoms change, the atoms regrouping themselves to form new substances. In these ordinary chemical changes, the laws of definite composition and conservation of mass are always obeyed, the substances reacting and forming in definite fixed proportions by weight.

The *chemical equation* is used to summarize a chemical reaction. It tells by the use of formulas and signs what substances react and form in the change, and it is so written that the laws of chemical change are obeyed. Certain experimental information must be obtained before the correct equation can be formulated for a given reaction. *The writer must know what substances react and what products are formed, and he must be able to write the correct formulas for these substances.*

An equation, then, is written by:

a) Putting down on the left the correct formulas for the reacting units (reactants), then writing the equal sign, and on the right giving the correct formulas for the products. When water is decomposed by the electric current, hydrogen and oxygen are observed to be formed. We write

$$\text{Water} = \text{hydrogen} + \text{oxygen}$$
$$H_2O = \quad H_2 \quad + \quad O_2$$

b) Balancing the reacting substances against the products by applying the laws of conservation of mass and definite composition. Since atoms are neither destroyed nor created in ordinary chemical change, the same number of atoms of each element must appear in the products as entered the reaction. The numbers of atoms of each element on both sides of the equation must be equal. The equation is *balanced* by introducing a proper number before each formula.

$$2H_2O = 2H_2 + O_2$$

It is important to remember that the subscripts in the formulas may not be altered in the effort to balance the equation. This would violate the law of definite composition.

The equations for some other chemical changes thus far considered are:

$$\underset{\text{hydrogen}}{2H_2} \; + \; \underset{\text{oxygen}}{O_2} \; = \underset{\text{water}}{2H_2O}$$

$$\underset{\text{aluminum}}{4Al} \; + \; \underset{\text{oxygen}}{3O_2} \; = \; \underset{\text{aluminum oxide}}{2Al_2O_3}$$

$$\underset{\text{hydrogen}}{H_2} \; + \; \underset{\text{chlorine}}{Cl_2} \; = \; \underset{\text{hydrogen chloride}}{2HCl}$$

$$\underset{\text{sodium}}{2Na} \; + \; \underset{\text{chlorine}}{Cl_2} \; = \; \underset{\text{sodium chloride}}{2NaCl}$$

$$\underset{\text{calcium}}{Ca} \; + \; \underset{\text{chlorine}}{Cl_2} \; = \; \underset{\text{calcium chloride}}{CaCl_2}$$

$$\underset{\text{cane sugar}}{C_{12}H_{22}O_{11}} = \underset{\text{water}}{11H_2O} + \underset{\text{carbon}}{12C}$$

Such equations, in which the simplest formulas are used for ionic substances and molecular formulas are used for substances composed of discrete molecules, we will call *stoichiometric equations*. They can be used effectively for calculating the weights of substances involved in chemical changes, but often they do not describe accurately chemical changes that take place in solution. Chemists sometimes use *arrows instead of the equal sign* in writing equations, in order to emphasize the direction of the chemical change. For example

$$2H_2O \rightarrow 2H_2 + O_2$$

It is frequently very difficult to balance equations for complicated reactions by the simple inspection method outlined above.   Later, we will consider procedures that will help in these cases and also we will discuss other types of equations.

80. QUANTITATIVE SIGNIFICANCE OF EQUATIONS

A *correctly balanced equation*, established by precise experimentation, affords a very convenient and concise summary of much information about a given chemical change.   It specifies the substances involved, the elements present in the substances, and the relative numbers of moles, atoms, and molecules taking part.   It defines the relative masses or weights of the elements and substances reacting.   Thus, from the correct equation for the decomposition by electrolysis of water into hydrogen and oxygen, the following quantitative information may be deduced if the atomic weights of the elements are known.

	$2H_2O$	=	$2H_2$	+	O_2
Relative number of moles involved (number of times each formula is taken)	2		2		1
Relative reacting weights (number of moles × formula weight)	2×18.016		2×2.016		32.00
Relative number of molecules (if substances are molecular)	2		2		1

The relative volumes of the substances as gases under the same conditions are also indicated by the equation, as we shall see when the gaseous state of matter is discussed.

Although a given chemical equation does summarize many facts about a given chemical change, it does not tell anything about the conditions under which the reaction will take place.   The chemical equation must be supplemented by further descriptive details to accomplish this.

81. CALCULATIONS FROM EQUATIONS

The quantitative relations that are inherent in a chemical equation may be used for calculating the actual quantities of materials taking part in a reaction in a given system, as shown by working out the answers to the following problems:

EXAMPLE: How many moles of hydrogen and of oxygen are formed when 10 moles of water are electrolyzed?

The balanced equation is first written

$$2H_2O = 2H_2 + O_2$$

This tells us that two moles of hydrogen are formed for every two moles of water used up; therefore, 10 moles of water will yield $\frac{2}{2} \times 10$ moles of hydrogen.

$$\text{Moles of hydrogen formed} \atop \text{from 10 moles of water} = \frac{2}{2} \times 10 \text{ moles} = 10 \text{ moles}$$

Similarly,

$$\text{Moles of oxygen formed} \atop \text{from 10 moles of water} = \frac{1}{2} \times 10 \text{ moles} = 5 \text{ moles}$$

EXAMPLE: How many grams of water must be electrolyzed to give 96.00 g of oxygen, and how many grams of hydrogen will accumulate in this reaction?

The balanced equation

$$2H_2O = 2H_2 + O_2$$

shows that two moles of water must be used to give one mole of oxygen.

$$\frac{96.00 \text{ g of oxygen}}{32.00 \text{ g per mole of oxygen}} = 3.000 \text{ moles of oxygen}$$

$$\text{Moles of water that must be electrolyzed} \atop \text{to produce 3 moles of oxygen} = 2 \times 3 \text{ moles} = 6 \text{ moles}$$

$$1 \text{ mole of water} = 18.016 \text{ g}$$

Therefore,

$$\text{Grams of water that must be electrolyzed} \atop \text{to produce 96.00 g of oxygen} = 6 \times 18.016 \text{ g} = 108.1 \text{ g}$$

The equation also indicates that, for every mole of oxygen formed, two moles of hydrogen is produced.

$$\text{Moles of hydrogen formed when} \atop \text{3 moles of oxygen is formed} = 2 \times 3 \text{ moles} = 6 \text{ moles}$$

$$1 \text{ mole of hydrogen} = 2.016 \text{ g}$$

Therefore,

$$\text{Grams of hydrogen formed when} \atop \text{96.00 g of oxygen is formed} = 6 \times 2.016 \text{ g} = 12.096 \text{ g}$$

This problem can also be solved by first noting that the equation indicates that 2×18.016 parts by weight of water must be used to give 32.00 parts by weight of oxygen and 4.016 parts by weight of hydrogen. Then these weight ratios can be used to calculate the number of grams of water and the number of grams of hydrogen that are involved when 96.00 g of oxygen are formed. In this book, however, emphasis will be placed on the calculation of the number of moles involved in order to induce the student to think in these terms when dealing with quantities of chemicals.

It is important to realize that *the relative reacting weights* indicated by equations *are merely numerical ratios*. Not only can these ratios be used to arrive at the reacting weights in terms of grams as indicated above, but they also can be used with any other system of weight units. Thus, the equation

$$2H_2O = 2H_2 + O_2$$

tells us that when 36.032 lb of water are electrolyzed, 4.032 lb of hydrogen and 32.00 lb of oxygen are formed; 36.032 tons of water will yield 4.032 tons of hydrogen and 32.00 tons of oxygen.   It is possible also to use the idea of pound-moles or ton-moles.

When you work problems involving chemical change, first write down and balance the equation for the reaction.   Then set down each step you use to solve the problem, indicating clearly your reasoning and being careful to specify the units in which the quantities are expressed.   You will be assigned many problems, not to check your skill in mathematics but to give you experience in applying chemical principles.

82.   EQUIVALENT WEIGHTS IN CHEMICAL CHANGE

We are now in a better position to understand the full significance of the term *equivalent weight of an element*, first considered in Section 30. 1.008 g of hydrogen (one gram-atomic weight) contains 6.02×10^{23} atoms of hydrogen, each atom having a combining capacity of 1 because it either loses or gains one electron in forming ionic bonds, or furnishes one electron for a covalent bond.   Eight grams of oxygen is one-half the gram-atomic weight of oxygen and contains $\dfrac{6.02 \times 10^{23}}{2}$ atoms of oxygen.   But because each atom of oxygen furnishes two electrons for bonding to hydrogen in the formation of water, this number of oxygen atoms has the same total combining capacity as 6.02×10^{23} atoms of hydrogen.   *The gram-equivalent weight of an element, when it forms a compound, is that weight which provides the Avogadro Number, 6.02×10^{23}, of units of combining capacity toward other elements; this is the weight that gains or loses 6.02×10^{23} electrons to form ions or that furnishes 6.02×10^{23} electrons for the formation of covalent bonds to other elements.*   Since 6.02×10^{23} particles constitute one mole, we can restate the definition: *The gram-equivalent weight of an element, when it forms a compound, is the weight that gains or loses one mole of electrons to form ions or that furnishes one mole of electrons for the formation of covalent bonds to other elements.*

When magnesium metal combines with fluorine to form the ionic compound, MgF_2, each magnesium atom loses two electrons to form the Mg^{2+} ion, which shows a combining capacity of two toward fluorine.   A gram-atomic weight of magnesium will therefore use two moles of its electrons in this reaction.   The gram-equivalent weight of magnesium in forming MgF_2 is equal to its gram-atomic weight divided by two.   The fluorine atom gains only one electron in forming the F^- ion, so the gram-equivalent weight of fluorine in this reaction is equal to its gram-atomic weight.

We have seen that each oxygen atom in the molecule CO_2 uses two electrons to form two covalent bonds to the carbon atom.   Accordingly, the gram-equivalent weight of oxygen in forming CO_2 is equal to one-half its gram-atomic weight.   The carbon atom uses four of its electrons to bond to the two oxygen atoms, and its gram-equivalent weight is one-fourth of its gram-atomic weight.

If an element, such as iron, shows more than one combining capacity in reactions under different conditions, it will have a different equivalent weight for each combining capacity.   The ferrous ion, Fe^{2+}, has a combining capacity of two because two electrons are lost per atom of iron. Therefore when FeO is formed from iron and oxygen

$$\begin{array}{l}\text{The gram-equivalent}\\\text{weight of iron in}\\\text{forming FeO}\end{array} = \dfrac{\begin{array}{c}\text{the gram-atomic}\\\text{weight of iron}\end{array}}{\begin{array}{c}\text{electrons used}\\\text{per atom of}\\\text{iron in combining}\\\text{with oxygen}\end{array}} = \dfrac{55.85\text{ g}}{2} = 27.93\text{ g}$$

The Fe^{3+} ion has a combining capacity of three because three electrons are lost per atom of iron.   When Fe_2O_3 is formed from iron and oxygen

$$\begin{array}{l}\text{The gram-equivalent}\\\text{weight of iron in}\\\text{forming Fe}_2\text{O}_3\end{array} = \dfrac{\begin{array}{c}\text{the gram-atomic}\\\text{weight of iron}\end{array}}{\begin{array}{c}\text{electrons used per atom of}\\\text{iron in combining}\\\text{with oxygen}\end{array}} = \dfrac{55.85\text{ g}}{3} = 18.62\text{ g}$$

Iron atoms have 50 per cent greater combining capacity when they form Fe_2O_3 than when they form FeO because they use three electrons per atom in Fe_2O_3 and only two in FeO.

83. ENERGY CHANGES IN CHEMICAL REACTIONS

Whenever a chemical change occurs, there is a corresponding energy transformation involving the chemical energy of the system and some other form, usually heat.   It is important to determine whether a given chemical change is exothermic or endothermic and to measure the quantity of energy change that occurs when a given quantity of matter reacts. This energy change is a function of the particular chemical change, the quantities of substances reacting, and the conditions under which the reaction takes place.   When hydrogen combines with oxygen, water is formed, and we write the equation

$$2H_2 + O_2 = 2H_2O$$

to describe quantitatively the matter involved.   The evolution of heat during the reaction is easily apparent, the increase in quantity of heat for the system causing a very marked increase in its temperature.   The formation of water from oxygen and hydrogen is therefore an exothermic change.   We can measure the quantity of heat formed when two moles of hydrogen gas combine with one mole of oxygen gas to form two moles of steam at the same temperature and pressure.   It is 115,600 cal, and we can describe this by writing the equation

$$2H_{2(g)} + O_{2(g)} = 2H_2O_{(g)} + 115,600 \text{ cal}$$

This quantity of heat is a measure of the decrease in the chemical energy of the system when the elements combine to form water. Four atoms of hydrogen and two atoms of oxygen in the form of molecules of the separate elements have greater potential energy of composition than they have when combined with each other in molecules of water. The subscripts (g), (l), and (s) can be used to define the state of each substance as gaseous, liquid, or solid. This must be clearly understood because changes in the states of matter are either endo- or exothermic and contribute to the net quantity of heat measured. Likewise, the subscript (aq) is often used to indicate that a substance is in solution in water (aqueous solution), for example, $NaCl_{(aq)}$.

In the decomposition of water to hydrogen and oxygen by electrolysis, the electrical energy used is transformed into chemical energy which is stored in the new substances formed. The amount of electrical energy needed to decompose two moles of water, treated as steam, to oxygen and hydrogen at the same temperature and pressure is found by experiment to be just equivalent to 115,600 cal, the same quantity of energy produced by the formation of two moles of steam.

$$2H_2O_{(g)} + 115,600 \text{ cal} = 2H_{2(g)} + O_{2(g)}$$

The energy change involved in the formation of a compound from its elements is the same in absolute quantity as that associated with the reverse chemical change, the decomposition of the compound into the elements.

It is possible, therefore, by adding to the simple chemical equation a term indicating the direction and quantity of the energy change, to describe more completely what has happened. Thus, for other reactions already considered we may write

$$4Al_{(s)} + 3O_{2(g)} = 2Al_2O_{3(s)} + 760,000 \text{ cal}$$
$$2Ca_{(s)} + O_{2(g)} = 2CaO_{(s)} + 303,400 \text{ cal}$$
$$2NaCl_{(s)} + 196,660 \text{ cal} = 2Na_{(s)} + Cl_{2(g)}$$
$$2Na_{(s)} + 2H_2O_{(l)} = H_{2(g)} + 2NaOH_{(s)} + 67,180 \text{ cal}$$

Since the use of subscripts to indicate the state of a substance is bothersome, it is common practice to omit them when the substance is in its *standard state;* this is its characteristic state at atmospheric pressure and room temperature.

84.   ENERGY OF ACTIVATION FOR CHEMICAL CHANGE

Because the reaction of hydrogen with oxygen to form water is highly exothermic, we might expect that when these two elements are brought together at room temperature they will react vigorously. However, such is not the case, there being no appreciable reaction under these conditions. Some energy must be added to the molecules in the system before the reaction will go at an appreciable rate; this is usually done by heating the mixture to several hundred degrees centigrade. We say that the reacting molecules must be activated and we term the energy needed by the system to activate the molecules the *energy of activation.* All reacting systems require energy of activation; they will not react at absolute zero. The energy of activation can be estimated for a given reaction and is specific for that reaction. Reactions go more readily for systems that have low activation energies than for those where the energy of activation is high.

85. ENERGY CONSIDERATIONS AND THE CONTROL OF CHEMICAL CHANGE

Once having an estimate of the energy of activation for a given chemical change, we are able to specify the energy which a given system must possess in order that a given reaction will be initiated.

Having determined experimentally whether a given chemical change is endothermic or exothermic, we are able to say whether we must supply energy in the form of heat, light, or electricity in order to have the reaction continue or whether we can expect the reaction to occur with the liberation of energy in various forms. To obtain heat for our houses, we exploit some chemical reaction that is highly exothermic, such as the burning in air of natural gas, fuel oil, wood, or coal. To procure electrical energy, we build a battery or dry cell in which a suitable exothermic chemical change occurs. We can definitely eliminate all endothermic chemical changes as possibilities for heating our houses or for the operation of a battery.

To produce chemical substances formed by endothermic reactions, we must always provide suitable quantities of energy, so that the reaction can proceed. Thus, to make chlorine from sodium chloride, electrical energy must be added. And, from the equation with the energy term which describes the formation of aluminum oxide by burning aluminum in oxygen, we can predict that, in order to have any chance of producing aluminum metal from the aluminum oxide available in the earth, we must induce the aluminum oxide to absorb the proper amount of energy, and we must be prepared to foot the bill for this energy.

Knowing the exact amount of energy change involved in a given reaction for the number of moles of reacting substances or products as indicated by the equation, it is possible to predict quantitatively just how much energy will be made available or must be provided when any given amounts of materials react. If 10 moles of steam are formed by the combustion of hydrogen and oxygen, $5 \times 115,600$ cal of heat will be produced. In order to make 2 gram atoms of aluminum from aluminum oxide, $760,000/2$ cal of energy are needed.

An accurate knowledge of the energy changes involved in a given chemical reaction also allows us to control the extent to which that change will proceed.   We will consider this effect in detail later.

EXERCISES

1. Each oxygen atom in the following compounds gains two electrons by complete transfer.   What is the valence toward oxygen of the other element in each compound: a) BeO; b) TiO_2; c) Cr_2O_3; d) K_2O; e) La_2O_3?

2. Each sulfur atom in the following compounds uses two of its electrons to form covalent bonds with atoms of the other element.   What is the valence toward oxygen of the other element in each compound: a) SCl_2; b) SiS_2; c) P_4S_6?

3. Name the three compounds given in (2).

4. How is the Avogadro Number connected with: a) a gram atom of an element? b) a gram-equivalent weight of an element in a reaction? c) a mole of a molecular substance?

5. The correct molecular formula for acetylene is C_2H_2.
a) What is the weight in grams of 10 moles of this substance?
b) How many molecules of acetylene will be present in this amount?
c) How many atoms of carbon will be present?
d) What is the percentage composition of acetylene?

6. Deduce the correct formula for the ionic substance, magnesium phosphate, making use of information given in Table 14.   Calculate the number of moles of this compound, the number of gram ions of magnesium, and the number of phosphate ions which will be present in 131.46 g of the compound.

7. How many gram equivalents of calcium will be present in two moles of $Ca(NO_3)_2$?

8. a) How many calcium and chloride ions are there in six moles of $CaCl_2$?
b) How many calcium and chloride ions are there in 222.0 g of $CaCl_2$?

9. a) What is the weight in grams of two moles of CO_3^{2-}?
b) Calculate for this amount of CO_3^{2-}: 1) the total number of ions; 2) the total number of atoms of carbon; 3) the total number of atoms of oxygen; 4) the total number of negative charges; 5) the total number of units of combining capacity of the ions; 6) the number of gram-equivalent weights of the ions.

10. A storage vessel contains 51.09 g of ammonia which has the molecular formula NH_3.   Calculate for this quantity of ammonia: a) the number of moles; b) the number of molecules; c) the number of atoms of nitrogen; d) the number of atoms of hydrogen; e) the total number of covalent bonds in the molecules; f) the total number of units of combining capacity used by the nitrogen atoms in forming the ammonia; g) the number of gram-equivalent weights of nitrogen.

11. Balance the following equations:
a) $CH_4 + O_2 = CO_2 + H_2O$
b) $K + H_2O = H_2 + KOH$

c) $As + O_2 = As_2O_3$
d) $N_2 + O_2 = NO$
e) $SO_2 + O_2 = SO_3$
f) $Al + S = Al_2S_3$
g) $H_2SO_4 + Al = H_2 + Al_2(SO_4)_3$
h) $Mo + O_2 = MoO_3$

12. a) Balance the equation $H_2 + I_2 = HI$.
b) What are the relative number of moles of the reactants and the product in this reaction?
c) How do the number of molecules of HI formed compare with the number of molecules of iodine that are used up?
d) What is the gram-equivalent weight of iodine in this reaction?

13. In five steps, calculate the grams of oxygen needed to combine with **40 g** of aluminum.
a) Write the equation.
b) Calculate the moles of oxygen needed for each mole of aluminum.
c) Calculate the number of moles of aluminum given in the problem.
d) Calculate the moles of oxygen needed.
e) Convert the moles of oxygen needed to grams of oxygen.

14. a) What are the relative number of moles, the relative reacting weights, and the relative number of molecules that are involved in the decomposition of sugar, according to the equation given in Section 79?
b) How many grams of carbon will be formed when 10 moles of sugar decomposes?
c) How many pounds of water will be formed when 10 lb of sugar decomposes?

15. a) How many grams of calcium chloride can be prepared from 100 g of calcium?
b) How many chloride ions will be present in the sample of calcium chloride which is formed?

16. How many tons of sodium can be obtained from 50 tons of sodium chloride?

17. If 10 moles of oxygen is mixed with 10 moles of hydrogen and the mixture is exploded to form water, which element is present in the mixture in excess of that required for the reaction? How many moles of this element will remain after the reaction is completed?

18. What does the equation

$$N_{2(g)} + O_{2(g)} = 2NO_{(g)} - 43,000 \text{ cal}$$

tell about:
a) The state of each substance?
b) The relative number of moles of the substances involved in the change?
c) The relative number of molecules of the substances involved in the change?
d) The relative weights of the substances involved in the change?
e) The endothermic or exothermic nature of the formation of NO?
f) The number of calories of heat energy involved per molecule of nitrogen reacting?

19. What weight of sodium chloride is needed to produce 10 tons of chlorine, and how much energy will be required for this operation?

20. Using the data in Section 83, calculate the amount of energy:
a) Required to decompose 10 g of steam into hydrogen and oxygen gases.
b) Liberated when four moles of CaO is formed from calcium and oxygen.
c) Liberated when 0.5 gram atom of sodium reacts with water.

Chapter 7

▶ **Oxygen and Oxidation**

▶ **Ozone**

We have already mentioned oxygen as an example of a chemical element and have cited its behavior and some of its compounds to illustrate the fundamental principles of chemical change. We shall now consider this very important element in greater detail, becoming familiar with the more important facts concerning its physical and chemical nature.

86. THE ATOMIC STRUCTURE OF OXYGEN

Ordinary oxygen is a mixture of the three isotopes $_8O^{16}$, $_8O^{17}$, and $_8O^{18}$, with the first constituting 99.76 per cent of the atoms. All of these isotopes have very much the same chemical properties because they have the same electronic configuration, $1s^2\ 2s^2\ 2p^2$. The electronic symbol for oxygen is

$$\cdot \overset{\cdot\cdot}{\underset{\cdot}{O}} : \qquad 1s^2\ 2s^2\ 2p^4$$

It is in the second period and in Group VI of the Periodic Table, in the second place preceding the inert gas, neon. Accordingly, it is a nonmetal, and it has the second highest electronegativity of any of the elements.

87. OCCURRENCE OF OXYGEN

As has been shown in Table 2, page 15, oxygen is by far the most abundant element. It comprises a large proportion of minerals, water, air, and all living matter. By considering the manner in which the oxygen atoms are present in these materials, we can select the most suitable sources of this element.

Oxygen is present in the form of *molecules of the element* in the atmosphere of the earth, comprising about one-fifth of the air by volume. In the *combined form* it occurs in vast numbers of compounds. Water contains 88.9 per cent by weight of oxygen. Most mineral matter is built up of compounds of oxygen, those containing oxygen and the very abundant element silicon being particularly common. SiO_2 (quartz), $CaCO_3$ (limestone), and Fe_2O_3 (iron ore) are examples of such oxygen-bearing minerals, the oxygen in these compounds usually being very firmly bound and hence not easily available for use.   All plant and animal material contains a high percentage of oxygen.

88.   PREPARATION

Air and water are the cheapest sources of oxygen and are exploited for the production of the element on a large industrial scale.   For small-scale laboratory preparation, where convenience and purity are important, other compounds of oxygen that are easily decomposed are useful.

a. Extraction from the air.   The extraction of oxygen from air can be accomplished easily by physical methods, since air is a mixture of oxygen with other gases.   The air is liquefied and then fractionally evaporated to give reasonably pure oxygen in large amounts at very low cost.   Such oxygen is stored at high pressures and marketed in steel tanks.

b. Electrolysis of water.   As already indicated, water can be decomposed to oxygen and hydrogen by passage of an electric current.

$$2H_2O_{(l)} + \text{electrical energy} = 2H_{2(g)} + O_{2(g)}$$

Special electrolytic cells using water containing a small amount of sulfuric acid are commonly used, these cells being so designed that there is no danger of the hydrogen and oxygen mixing.   The operation of such a cell and the essential chemistry of this electrolysis will be considered in Chapter 19.   This method is convenient for large-scale production of very pure oxygen, when cheap electric power is available.

c. Heating certain compounds of oxygen.   There are many compounds from which to choose.   The less stable oxygen compounds break up more readily at lower temperatures and usually are preferred.   The following equations indicate some of the reactions which have been used:

$$\underset{\text{mercuric oxide}}{2HgO} = O_2 + \underset{\text{mercury}}{2Hg}$$

$$\underset{\text{manganese dioxide}}{3MnO_2} = O_2 + \underset{\text{trimanganese tetroxide}}{Mn_3O_4}$$

$$\underset{\text{barium peroxide}}{2BaO_2} = O_2 + \underset{\text{barium oxide}}{2BaO}$$

$$\underset{\text{potassium nitrate}}{2KNO_3} = O_2 + \underset{\text{potassium nitrite}}{2KNO_2}$$

$$\underset{\text{potassium chlorate}}{2KClO_3} = 3O_2 + \underset{\text{potassium chloride}}{2KCl}$$

The first and second reactions are of historical interest because Priestley, by heating HgO, and Scheele, by heating MnO_2, independently discovered oxygen around the year 1774.

MnO_2 must be heated to about 700° before it decomposes at a reasonable rate, and the decomposition of pure $KClO_3$ proceeds readily at

350 to 400°.   However, when $KClO_3$ is mixed with a small amount of MnO_2, the $KClO_3$ decomposes rapidly at only 200°, the MnO_2 remaining unchanged.   The presence of the manganese dioxide in contact with the potassium chlorate increases the speed of the decomposition of the latter. The temperature, at which this decomposition proceeds fast enough to be of practical use, is lowered considerably.   This effect is an example of *catalysis*, and the manganese dioxide is called a *catalyst*, or *catalytic agent*. A catalyst is a substance that influences the speed of a chemical change without itself undergoing any permanent change.   We speak of *positive* or *negative catalysts*, depending upon whether the reaction is speeded up or whether it is slowed down.   In the latter case, the term *inhibitor* is sometimes employed, especially when the negative catalyst is used to prevent the corrosion of metals.   By the proper choice and use of catalysts, the rates of chemical reactions can be controlled so as to make them much more adaptable for practical use.   We shall hear much more about catalysis.

Substances that liberate oxygen easily should be *handled with considerable caution*.   Mixtures of such compounds with combustible materials, such as charcoal, sugar, or wood shavings, may explode violently. Black gunpowder is a mixture of charcoal, sulfur, and potassium nitrate.

d. Action of sodium peroxide with water.   When sodium peroxide is dropped into water, oxygen is liberated and bubbles off, sodium hydroxide accumulating in solution.   Thus,

$$2Na_2O_2 + 2H_2O = 4NaOH + O_2$$

89. PROPERTIES OF OXYGEN

Oxygen, under ordinary conditions, is a colorless, odorless, tasteless gas which is a collection of molecules in which two atoms of oxygen are bonded together.   It would seem that, because each oxygen atom is two electrons short of neon, two atoms would combine by forming a double covalent bond to give the molecule

$$: \overset{..}{O} :: \overset{..}{O} :$$

in which each atom would be associated with eight electrons in the valence shell.   However, oxygen molecules are observed to be *paramagnetic;* they are attracted by a magnetic field.   This can only be accounted for by assuming that not all of the electrons in the molecule are paired.   Accordingly the oxygen molecule is believed to have the electron configuration

$$: \overset{..}{\underset{.}{O}} : \overset{..}{\underset{.}{O}} :$$

each atom having one unpaired electron and only seven electrons in its valence shell. The unusual paramagnetic behavior of oxygen can be used to detect its presence in gas mixtures because almost all other gas molecules have their electrons paired and are not paramagnetic.

Table 15. Properties of Oxygen

Atomic number	8
Atomic weight	16.00
Molecular formula	O_2
Molecular weight	32.00
Common valence	2
Boiling point, ° C	-182.97
Freezing point, ° C	-218.77
Weight, g/liter, 0°, atmospheric pressure	1.4290
Relative density (air = 1)	1.105
Solubility in water, ml/liter, 18°, atmospheric pressure	32.2
Color	none
Odor	none

The solubility of oxygen in water, though not large, is very important for marine life; this dissolved oxygen also helps to purify our drinking water by killing certain injurious bacteria.

90. COMPOUNDS OF OXYGEN

Oxygen forms compounds with nearly all the other elements, the only exceptions being helium and the other inert gases of the atmosphere. Recalling its high electronegativity and its need to associate with two more electrons, we can predict how oxygen will tend to bond to other elements. Oxygen will tend to gain electrons by complete transfer from the metals. The positive ions of the metals will pack together with the negative oxide ions to form ionic compounds, such as MgO and Al_2O_3, which will be high-melting solids. Oxygen atoms will form covalent bonds to the nonmetals to give molecular compounds. At room temperature these usually will be gases, such as CO_2 or NO, or volatile solids, such as P_4O_{10}.

91. OXIDES

The simplest or *binary* compounds of oxygen are those composed of oxygen and one other element. They are called *oxides*, the ending *-ide* being that used to specify binary compounds. In oxides oxygen has a valence of 2 toward the other element. In ionic oxides the oxygen atoms are present as *oxide ions*, O^{2-}, shown in Figure 24a, and we write ionic formulas such as

$$\left[Na^+ \right]_2 \left[\; \overset{..}{\underset{..}{:O:}} \; \right]^{2-}$$

Each oxygen atom in a molecular oxide has two covalent bonds toward the atoms of the other element, as shown in Figure 24b and 24c for H_2O and CO_2.

Many oxides can be produced by the direct reaction of oxygen gas with the other element; others must be prepared by indirect methods. Table 16 gives the equations for the formation of oxides of some of the

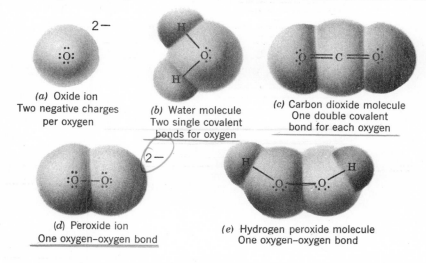

(a) Oxide ion
Two negative charges
per oxygen

(b) Water molecule
Two single covalent
bonds for oxygen

(c) Carbon dioxide molecule
One double covalent
bond for each oxygen

(d) Peroxide ion
One oxygen–oxygen bond

(e) Hydrogen peroxide molecule
One oxygen–oxygen bond

Fig. 24.   Bonding of oxygen in ionic and molecular compounds.

common metals and nonmetals, the energy change being indicated in each case. The reacting elements and the oxides produced are taken in their standard states.

In most cases the formation of the oxide is exothermic, and some of these reactions are highly useful as sources of energy for industrial and domestic use. Such reactions usually will proceed spontaneously once the proper conditions are established. A few of the equations indicate that the formation of the oxide is an endothermic reaction. In the majority of such cases the reaction will not proceed spontaneously, and in fact, such oxides cannot easily be prepared by direct combination. To allow comparison, the calories of heat involved per gram-equivalent weight of oxygen (8.000 g) reacting are given for each reaction. In a general way, it is true that the greater the exothermic character of the reaction, the greater will be the activity of the element toward oxygen, the more rapid the reaction under comparable conditions, and the more stable the oxide against thermal decomposition. CaO, MgO, Fe_2O_3, Al_2O_3, H_2O, P_4O_{10}, and CO_2 are very stable thermally, CuO is moderately stable, HgO is easily broken down by heating, and Au_2O_3 and Cl_2O are unstable at room temperature.

Since many elements have variable valence toward oxygen, there may be several oxides for a given element. Sulfur forms SO_2 and SO_3, and copper forms Cu_2O and CuO.

Table 16. Heats of Formation of Common Oxides

Equation for Formation	Calories per Gram-Equivalent Weight of Oxygen Reacting
$4Na_{(s)} + O_{2(g)} = 2Na_2O_{(s)} + 198,900$ cal	49,730
$2Ca_{(s)} + O_{2(g)} = 2CaO_{(s)} + 303,400$ cal	75,850
$2Mg_{(s)} + O_{2(g)} = 2MgO_{(s)} + 292,200$ cal	73,050
$4Al_{(s)} + 3O_{2(g)} = 2Al_2O_{3(s)} + 760,000$ cal	63,300
$4Fe_{(s)} + 3O_{2(g)} = 2Fe_2O_{3(s)} + 397,000$ cal	33,080
$2Cu_{(s)} + O_{2(g)} = 2CuO_{(s)} + 77,000$ cal	19,300
$2Hg_{(l)} + O_{2(g)} = 2HgO_{(s)} + 43,200$ cal	10,800
$4Au_{(s)} + 3O_{2(g)} = 2Au_2O_{3(s)} - 22,000$ cal	$-1,800$
$2H_{2(g)} + O_{2(g)} = 2H_2O_{(l)} + 136,740$ cal	34,185
$C_{(s)} + O_{2(g)} = CO_{2(g)} + 94,450$ cal	23,610
$P_{4(s)} + 5O_{2(g)} = P_4O_{10(s)} + 720,000$ cal	36,000
$S_{(s)} + O_{2(g)} = SO_{2(g)} + 70,920$ cal	17,730
$2Cl_{2(g)} + O_{2(g)} = 2Cl_2O_{(g)} - 36,500$ cal	$-9,130$
$N_{2(g)} + O_{2(g)} = 2NO_{(g)} - 43,000$ cal	$-10,750$

92. PEROXIDES

Some elements combine under certain conditions with more oxygen than would, at first thought, be predicted by the usual valence rules, and *peroxides* are formed. Thus, sodium forms not only the normal oxide Na_2O, but Na_2O_2 also can be prepared. Barium, whose valence is 2 toward oxygen, forms the normal oxide BaO and the peroxide BaO_2. The apparent exceptions to the valence rules, which such peroxides seem to present, are found to be no exceptions when the actual way in which the atoms are associated is determined experimentally. In the peroxides, half of the combining capacity of each oxygen atom is satisfied by the formation of a covalent bond to a second oxygen atom. Only one unit of combining capacity of each oxygen atom is used for bonding to the other element in the oxide. The peroxides of the metals are ionic and have present the *peroxide ion* O_2^{2-}, shown in Figure 24d. In this ion each oxygen has formed a covalent bond to the other oxygen atom and each has gained one electron by complete transfer. The molecular peroxide H_2O_2 has each oxygen covalently linked to the other, and each oxygen also is covalently bonded to a hydrogen atom, as shown in Figure 24e.

Peroxides are, in general, less stable than the normal oxides, and tend to liberate oxygen and revert to the normal oxides. When barium peroxide is heated sufficiently, oxygen gas and barium oxide are formed.

$$2BaO_2 = 2BaO + O_2$$

93. HYDROXIDES. ACIDS AND BASES

Many of the normal oxides react directly with water to form *hydroxides*. These contain the *hydroxyl group* in which half the valence of oxygen is exerted toward hydrogen, the radical having a valence of 1.

$$CaO \quad + H_2O = \quad Ca(OH)_2$$
Calcium oxide   water   calcium hydroxide

$$SO_3 \quad + H_2O = (HO)_2SO_2$$
Sulfur trioxide   water   sulfuric acid

The oxides are called *anhydrides*, since they may be thought of as being the hydroxides minus water.

The oxides of the more active metals form hydroxides that have a bitter taste, turn red litmus blue, and have other characteristic properties. This common behavior can be shown to be due to the fact that such hydroxides readily furnish hydroxide ions, OH^-. These hydroxides of the active metals are ionic compounds containing the positive ions of the metals, and hydroxide ions are indicated by the ionic formula for calcium hydroxide

$$Ca^{2+} \left[\; : \overset{\cdot\cdot}{\underset{\cdot\cdot}{O}}{-}H \; \right]_2^{-}$$

Hydroxides of this kind are called *bases*, and oxides that combine with water to form bases are termed *basic anhydrides*. In general, the strength of the hydroxides of the metals as bases, that is, their ability to furnish OH^-, decreases as the activity of the metal toward oxygen decreases.

Hydroxides of the nonmetals have a sour taste, turn blue litmus red, and have other properties which can be shown to be due to their ability readily to furnish hydrogen ions, H^+. Such hydroxides belong to the class of substances known as *acids*. These are molecular substances with the hydroxyl radical covalently bonded to the rest of the molecule, as in sulfuric acid

$$\begin{array}{c} H{-}O \\ \diagdown \\ \qquad SO_2 \\ \diagup \\ H{-}O \end{array}$$

Oxides that combine with water to form acids are called *acid anhydrides*. When acidic hydroxides react to furnish H^+, the hydrogen separates from the rest of the acid, behaving as the positive part of the substance. For example

$$\begin{array}{c} H{-}O \\ \diagdown \\ \qquad SO_2 = 2H^+ + SO_4{}^{2-} \\ \diagup \\ H{-}O \end{array}$$

Therefore, it is common practice, in writing the formulas for acidic hydroxides, to put the easily replaceable hydrogen at the beginning of the formula and the oxygen at the end.   The formula for the hydroxide formed by the addition of water to SO_3 is commonly written as H_2SO_4; it is called *sulfuric acid,* and the equation for its formation is usually written as

$$SO_3 + H_2O = H_2SO_4$$

Hydroxides of intermediate character which can furnish either OH^- or H^+, depending upon the conditions, are called *amphoteric hydroxides.* The hydroxides of many of the less active metals, such as $Zn(OH)_2$, are amphoteric.

The properties of the hydroxides vary regularly with the position in the periodic table.   Hydroxides of elements early in the periods are strongly basic.   As the atomic number increases across the periods, the hydroxides become less basic and more acidic.   Thus $NaOH$ is a very strong base, $Al(OH)_3$ is amphoteric, and $HClO_4$ is a strong acid.

Many hydroxides decompose, when heated sufficiently, to yield water and the oxide (anhydride).

$$Ca(OH)_2 = H_2O + CaO$$
$$H_2SO_4 = H_2O + SO_3$$

94. OXIDATION IN THE NARROW SENSE

When a substance combines with oxygen, *oxidation* is said to occur. (This term will be used in a much broader sense later on.)   The substance furnishing the oxygen is called the *oxidizing agent,* and the substance combining with oxygen is said to be *oxidized.*   In all the reactions we have considered in which various elements combine with oxygen, oxidation takes place.   When magnesium burns in air to form magnesium oxide, the magnesium is oxidized and the oxygen in the atmosphere is the oxidizing agent.   When iron rusts, oxidation of the iron occurs, the oxygen of the air again being the oxidizing agent and Fe_2O_3 being formed as the product.

Oxides that are low in thermal stability, such as HgO, furnish oxygen readily and are good oxidizing agents. Al_2O_3 and H_2O have the oxygen so firmly bound in the compound that they are very poor oxidizing agents. Obviously, the peroxides are excellent oxidizing agents since they are low in stability and have oxygen available.

95. COMBUSTION

The term *combustion* includes chemical changes that are exothermic and that proceed so rapidly that they are accompanied by flame.   The burning of wood, gas, coal, or magnesium in the air are familiar examples. The large amounts of energy liberated are made evident by the production, not only of heat, but also of light. The highly exothermic combustion of fuels furnishes us with much of the energy we need for various purposes.

To initiate combustion, the chemical system must be heated to its *kindling temperature*, the lowest temperature at which self-maintaining combustion can be started. This is the lowest temperature at which the reaction proceeds fast enough so that sufficient heat is produced per unit of time to warm the adjacent parts of the substance to the kindling temperature.

Spontaneous combustion occurs when the combustion begins without addition of heat from the outside. Suppose a material, such as linseed oil, undergoes slow oxidation by the air under conditions where the heat of the exothermic reaction is not dissipated but accumulates. The material will gradually warm up until the kindling temperature is reached and it bursts into flame. Active combustion then proceeds. Accumulations of compact bundles of oily rags or large amounts of wet hay are systems notorious for their tendency to undergo spontaneous combustion.

Explosions result when highly exothermic reactions take place so rapidly that large amounts of energy are released in a short period of time. Explosives, such as gunpowder, usually contain powerful oxidizing agents together with material that is readily oxidized. *Such combinations are very dangerous to handle and care should be taken to avoid them.*

96. RESPIRATION

Animal respiration involves oxidation. The air inhaled into the lungs provides oxygen to the hemoglobin in the red corpuscles of the blood, which carries it throughout the body where it oxidizes substances to produce heat and muscular energy. The body, in some unknown way, is able to regulate the rate of this oxidation so that the body temperature is kept very constant. The carbon dioxide formed in the oxidation is carried back to the lungs by the blood and is exhaled. Oxygen also plays an important part in plant respiration.

97. USES OF OXYGEN

Large amounts of oxygen gas are produced from air or water and are shipped at high pressures in steel cylinders, which are orange-colored so it will not be mistaken for some other gas. This gas makes possible the convenient production of high temperatures by means of oxyhydrogen and oxyacetylene torches. It is used to support respiration at high altitudes and in cases of pneumonia where the lungs cannot supply enough air. Since the cost of manufacturing oxygen is now low, owing to recent improvements in production methods, the relatively pure gas is being used industrially more and more, instead of air, when oxygen is needed.

98.   OZONE

When energy is provided in a proper fashion to diatomic molecules of oxygen, a decrease in volume of the gas occurs, and a new colorless gaseous substance having a pungent odor is formed.   This new substance is called *ozone*, and the reaction may be summarized as

$$3O_2 + 69,000 \text{ cal} = 2O_3$$

As indicated, the molecule of ozone is triatomic, three atoms of oxygen being combined to give each molecule.

The *formation* of ozone is an endothermic change and the energy can be supplied in a number of ways, including electrical discharge, heat, and

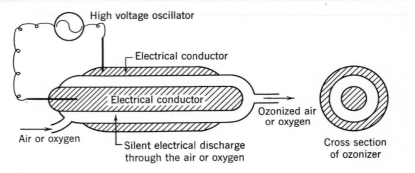

Fig. 25.   Ozonizer.

ultraviolet light.   Ozone is most conveniently made by use of the electrical discharge through oxygen or air in an apparatus called an *ozonizer*. In this apparatus a small percentage of the oxygen is converted to ozone, as may be noted by the characteristic odor of the gas mixture produced.

Although ozone is composed exclusively of oxygen atoms, the atoms are bonded together in a different fashion than in ordinary diatomic oxygen molecules, and the molecules have quite different properties. These are summarized in Table 17.

Table 17.   Properties of Ozone

Molecular formula	O_3
Molecular weight	48.00
Boiling point, ° C	−111.5
Freezing point, ° C	−249.6
Weight, g/liter, 0°, atmospheric pressure	2.144
Relative density (air = 1)	1.658
Solubility in water, ml/liter, 18°, atmospheric pressure	45.4
Color	none (gas)
Odor	pungent

The ozone molecule is much less stable than the ordinary diatomic oxygen molecule and tends to rearrange spontaneously, even at ordinary temperatures, to diatomic oxygen.   This is the reverse of its formation.

$$2O_3 = 3O_2 + 69,000 \text{ cal}$$

Ozone is richer in energy than diatomic oxygen and is more reactive chemically.   It is a much more powerful oxidizing agent than ordinary oxygen, tending to inflame the mucous membranes of the throat and nose if it is breathed in high concentration.   The presence of ozone, even in traces, in a gas mixture can be readily detected by bubbling it through a solution of potassium iodide in water, with some starch present.   Iodine is formed, and this gives an intense blue color with the starch.

$$2I^- + H_2O + O_3 = 2OH^- + O_2 + I_2$$
$$I_2 + \text{starch} = \text{intensely blue substance}$$

This is an example of the powerful oxidizing effect of ozone.

The *uses of ozone* depend upon its power as an oxidizing agent.   By oxidation of the colored substances present, it bleaches oils and waxes, and it purifies air and water by killing bacteria.

The amount of ozone normally in the air about us is negligible, but there is more ozone in the higher reaches of the atmosphere.   The formation and subsequent decomposition of ozone there is caused by ultraviolet light.   Sunlight as it reaches the earth is very rich in ultraviolet energy. High-frequency ultraviolet quanta are absorbed by the diatomic molecules of oxygen, and ozone is formed.   In turn, the ozone molecules absorb low-frequency ultraviolet light, and diatomic oxygen is reformed. As a net result of these two processes in the upper atmosphere, most of the ultraviolet energy is removed from sunlight before it reaches us. When you recall the painful effects of overexposure to even the small amount of ultraviolet light that manages to get to us (sunburn), you will realize how fortunate we are to have the protection provided by the oxygen-ozone reactions in the upper air.

99. ALLOTROPY

Oxygen is said to exhibit *allotropy* because it can occur in more than one form, each form having its own characteristic structure and properties.   These different forms are called *allotropic forms* of the element. The diatomic molecule of oxygen has two atoms of oxygen closely associated, whereas the three atoms in the ozone molecule are arranged in a bent chain, as shown in Figure 26.   It is apparent that the two molecules should behave quite differently.   The unusual bonding in the ozone molecule will be discussed later in Chapter 14.

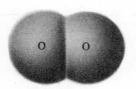
Diatomic oxygen molecule

Triatomic ozone molecule

Fig. 26.   Molecules of the allotropic forms of oxygen.

EXERCISES

1. Compare the number of moles of oxygen which would be produced for every 12 moles of reactant used in the changes represented by the equations which are given in Section 88c.

2. How many grams of oxygen will be obtained when 1 kg of KNO_3 is decomposed by heating, according to the equation given in Section 88c.   Solve this by the following steps:
 a) Write the equation.
 b) How many moles of O_2 are produced per mole of KNO_3?
 c) How many moles of KNO_3 are used?
 d) How many moles of O_2 then are expected?
 e) How many grams of O_2 are obtained?

3. What per cent by weight of the oxygen in manganese dioxide can be obtained as elementary oxygen by thermal decomposition according to the equation in Section 88c?

4. What is believed to be unusual about the bonding in the O_2 molecule, and what property of oxygen gas is thought to be associated with this?

5. From the position of each of the following elements in the Periodic Table, would you expect its oxides to be ionic or molecular: a) Li; b) I; c) K; d) N; e) S? In which cases would the oxides be basic anhydrides, which acidic anhydrides?

6. On the basis of the data given in Table 16, would you: a) expect NO to be more or less stable thermally than CO_2? b) expect to find gold oxide, Au_2O_3, persisting in the earth?

7. a) What is the gram-equivalent weight of copper in Cu_2O and in CuO, assuming oxygen has a gram-equivalent weight of 8.000 g in each of these oxides?
 b) What is the valence of copper in each oxide?

8. What is the gram-equivalent weight of oxygen in peroxides?   Remember that in peroxides each oxygen atom uses only one unit of combining capacity toward atoms of other elements.

9. Explain how it is possible for oxygen to form both oxides and peroxides in its efforts to achieve the electronic configuration of neon.

10. What is characteristic of the state of combination of oxygen in: a) ionic oxides; b) molecular oxides; c) ionic peroxides; d) molecular peroxides; e) ionic hydroxides; f) molecular hydroxides?

11. We write the formula for the hydroxide formed when phosphoric oxide, P_4O_{10}, combines with water as H_3PO_4, and that formed by MgO as $Mg(OH)_2$. Which of these hydroxides is an acid and which is a base?

12. A mixture of finely powdered carbon and $KClO_3$ explodes violently when heated. How can you account for this in terms of information given by certain equations in this chapter?

13. How do you account for the fact that peroxides and ozone are excellent oxidizing agents?

14. The pungent odor of ozone is sometimes apparent after thunderstorms. How do you account for this?

15. Give three different tests you could use to decide whether a sample of gas is ordinary oxygen or ozone.

Chapter 8

▶ **Hydrogen**

▶ **Reduction-Oxidation**

▶ **Oxidation States**

▶ **Acid-Base Neutralization**

The second element we shall consider in detail is hydrogen. This element by itself is of very considerable importance, and it enters into the composition of a great number of important compounds. Discussion of hydrogen at this time, directly following the chapter on oxygen, will allow us to introduce many new chemical concepts which are basic in organizing and understanding the chemistry of all of the elements. We have already seen how useful it is to use the combining capacity of the hydrogen atom as a standard for comparing the combining capacities of other elements.

100. THE ATOMIC STRUCTURE AND THE PLACE OF HYDROGEN IN THE PERIODIC TABLE

Hydrogen is unique among the elements. The three isotopic atoms, $_1H^1$, $_1H^2$, and $_1H^3$ are known, but, as indicated in Table 5, page 49, ordinary hydrogen is practically all $_1H^1$ atoms. These consist of a proton for the nucleus and one electron in the first shell, the atomic structure being the simplest of all of the elements. The hydrogen atom is relatively small. Its extraordinary position in the Periodic Table is emphasized in Table 10, page 62. Hydrogen is the only active element in Period I. It resembles the first element in each of the succeeding periods in that it has only one valence electron; accordingly, we can expect it to behave in some respects like the metals lithium and sodium of Group I. On the other hand, it is only one electron short of the electron configuration of the inert gas helium, and hence, should somewhat resemble the non-metals such as fluorine and chlorine, which just precede the inert gases in the succeeding periods. This dual nature of the hydrogen atom is reflected in the great versatility it shows in chemical behavior.

120

101. OCCURRENCE OF HYDROGEN

Hydrogen constitutes only about 1 per cent of the mass of the earth. This is not very great compared to that of oxygen, but because hydrogen atoms are so light, we have a tremendous number of atoms of this element. These atoms are easily available because they are found combined in many common and cheap materials, and there is a large turnover of them in nature. The free element is so reactive toward the oxygen of the air that it has little chance to accumulate in nature. We have already noticed that 11.1 per cent of water by weight is hydrogen. All animal and plant materials contain considerable amounts of combined hydrogen. Natural gas and petroleum are made up of compounds of hydrogen, and all acids contain this element. There is considerable hydrogen in many minerals, in combination with other elements.

102. PREPARATION AND PRODUCTION OF HYDROGEN

To obtain elementary hydrogen, we use its more common compounds, which can be decomposed in many different ways to yield the free element.

a. From water. The *electrolysis* of water, containing small amounts of other substances such as sulfuric acid, is perhaps the best method for the production of pure hydrogen. This is discussed in detail in Chapter 19. Because other substances of considerable value are produced at the same time, and these may actually be the products of primary importance to industry, much hydrogen accumulates as a by-product in electrochemical operations. Such hydrogen is available quite cheaply and is marketed in steel cylinders under high pressure. The endothermic nature of the decomposition of water has already been discussed quantitatively in Section 83.

Many *metals react directly with water*, liberating part or all of the hydrogen and forming the hydroxides or oxides of the metals. Very active metals, such as sodium, react rapidly with water even at room temperature.

$$2Na + 2H_2O = 2NaOH + H_2$$

Other less active metals will react with water at reasonable rates only if the temperature is raised. Thus, magnesium does not react appreciably with water at room temperature but does displace hydrogen rapidly from boiling water.

$$Mg + 2H_2O \overset{100°}{=} Mg(OH)_2 + H_2$$

Iron reacts very slowly even with boiling water, but when steam is passed over red-hot iron, the formation of hydrogen occurs rapidly.

$$3Fe + 4H_2O \overset{600°}{=} Fe_3O_4 + 4H_2$$

Carbon is found to react with steam at high temperatures.

$$\overset{1000°}{C + H_2O \ = \ CO + H_2}$$

This reaction gives a mixture of the two gases, carbon monoxide and hydrogen, which is known as *water gas.* Since both of these gases will burn with oxygen to produce much heat, the water-gas mixture is a very good fuel. It can be produced cheaply, but separation of the hydrogen from the carbon monoxide is difficult and, therefore, this process is not a good one to use when pure hydrogen is desired. However, the water-gas process is widely used to provide both hydrogen and carbon monoxide for industrial operations. It will be considered in greater detail when carbon monoxide is discussed.

b. From acids. *Certain metals* are effective also in liberating hydrogen from solutions of acids in water. In general, metals attack acids more readily than they do water. Thus, sodium reacts violently with acids, while zinc, which shows no appreciable rate of reaction with water at room temperature, will react with dilute acids under the same conditions to give a steady evolution of hydrogen.

$$Zn + 2HCl = ZnCl_2 + H_2$$
$$Zn + H_2SO_4 = ZnSO_4 + H_2$$
$$Fe + H_2SO_4 = FeSO_4 + H_2$$

The *order of activity of the metals* toward water and acids to produce hydrogen is, in general, much the same as that of their activity toward oxygen. The Electromotive Series, as given in Table 68, page 436, lists the common metals in order of decreasing activity. This is found to vary periodically with atomic number, decreasing across the periods and increasing down the groups.

c. From basic hydroxides. Certain elements are able to liberate hydrogen from the basic hydroxides. Aluminum and silicon are corroded by solutions of strong bases to give hydrogen and aluminates or silicates, respectively.

$$2Al + 2NaOH + 2H_2O = 2NaAlO_2 + 3H_2$$
$$Si + 2NaOH + H_2O = Na_2SiO_3 + 2H_2$$

The alloy ferrosilicon is particularly effective for producing hydrogen from basic solutions and has afforded a convenient way to make hydrogen under special conditions, such as providing hydrogen for inflating barrage balloons in the field.

d. From hydrocarbons. Petroleum oil cracks or decomposes when heated to yield hydrogen and other substances. Large amounts of hydrogen are produced in the refining of petroleum when such cracking takes place, providing a cheap industrial supply of hydrogen.

Heating the methane in natural gas with steam affords another cheap way of producing hydrogen.

$$CH_4 + H_2O = CO + 3H_2$$

e. From ammonia.   Ammonia, NH_3, can be manufactured readily. When this compound is heated, it tends to crack, or decompose, into hydrogen and nitrogen.

$$2NH_3 = 3H_2 + N_2$$

Liquid ammonia stored in steel cylinders can be transported readily, and its thermal decomposition may be, under special conditions, a very convenient way to provide hydrogen if contamination with nitrogen does not interfere with its use.

f. From compounds of hydrogen with the metals.   Some metals, such as calcium, form compounds with hydrogen, and these compounds react readily with water to give hydrogen.

$$CaH_2 + 2H_2O = Ca(OH)_2 + 2H_2$$
$$LiH + H_2O = LiOH + H_2$$

hydrides

Such reactions yield a very large volume of hydrogen gas from a small weight of the hydride of the metal and are very satisfactory for producing the gas when the high cost of the method is not so important a consideration as is convenience.

103. MOLECULAR STRUCTURE AND PROPERTIES OF HYDROGEN

Table 18.   Properties of Hydrogen

Atomic number	1
Atomic weight	1.008
Molecular formula	H_2
Molecular weight	2.016
Valence	1
Boiling point, ° C	−252.7
Freezing point, ° C	−259.14
Weight, g/liter, 0° atmospheric pressure	0.0899
Relative density (air = 1)	0.069
Solubility in water, ml/liter, 18°, atmospheric pressure	18.4
Color	none
Odor	none

Under ordinary conditions hydrogen is a colorless, odorless, tasteless gas consisting of hydrogen molecules, which are built up of two atoms firmly united by one covalent bond (see Figure 18, page 83).   Because of the very low atomic weight of hydrogen, its molecule is the lightest known, and hydrogen gas is less dense than any other gas under comparable conditions. Its use for inflating balloons is based upon the fact that it is so much lighter than air.

Because it boils at $-252.7°$ and freezes at $-259.14°$, liquid hydrogen is used as a refrigerating liquid for cooling other materials to extremely low temperatures.

Hydrogen is not very active chemically at ordinary temperatures, but it reacts readily with many substances at higher temperatures. The highly exothermic reaction of hydrogen with oxygen has already been considered in some detail.

$$2H_{2(g)} + O_{2(g)} = 2H_2O_{(g)} + 115{,}600 \text{ cal}$$

Under certain conditions this reaction goes with tremendous speed, and a violent explosion results, owing to the enormous amount of energy suddenly made available. *One should always use great caution in handling hydrogen or similar combustible gases.* While the most powerful explosions

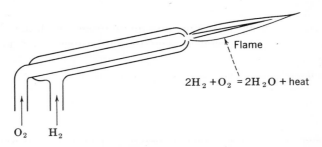

Fig. 27. Oxyhydrogen burner.

are obtained when the ideal ratio of two moles of hydrogen per mole of oxygen is used, explosions may occur also with mixtures of the two gases varying over a wide range of concentration.

Hydrogen can be caused to burn quietly with air or with oxygen if a proper device, such as the oxyhydrogen burner, is employed. This burner makes it possible to heat bodies up to temperatures of 2800° or more.

The *heating value* (the heat liberated per unit weight of fuel) of hydrogen is very large compared to the values for other elements. The heating values given in Table 19 may be calculated from the data on the heats of reaction such as those given in Table 16, page 112.

When sufficient energy is added to the hydrogen molecule, it breaks up into the individual atoms to give *monatomic hydrogen*.

$$H_2 + 103{,}800 \text{ cal} = 2H$$

This dissociation is accomplished in the atomic hydrogen torch, invented by Langmuir. Hydrogen gas is passed through an electric arc, which provides the energy for breaking up the molecules to give monatomic hydrogen.   These single atoms of hydrogen have a great tendency to recombine, when they collide, to give the diatomic molecules again. This recombination is highly exothermic, liberating the same amount

Table 19.   Heating Values of Common Elements

	Cal per g Burning
Zn (to ZnO)	1,277
Fe (to Fe_2O_3)	1,776
Na (to Na_2O)	2,162
P (to P_4O_{10})	5,813
Al (to Al_2O_3)	7,040
C (to CO_2)	7,865
H (to H_2O)	33,910

of energy that was absorbed when monatomic hydrogen was formed.   It is catalyzed by contact of the monatomic hydrogen with metal surfaces, and, by directing the stream of monatomic hydrogen at a metal, very high temperatures (4000 to 5000°) may be attained.   The atomic hydrogen torch may be used for cutting high-melting-point metals.

104.   REDUCTION.   CONCURRENCE OF OXIDATION-REDUCTION

Hydrogen has such a strong tendency to combine with oxygen that it can remove oxygen from certain compounds under the proper conditions.   If iron rust (ferric oxide) is heated with hydrogen, elementary iron and water are formed.

$$Fe_2O_3 + 3H_2 = 2Fe + 3H_2O$$

When oxygen is removed from a compound, *reduction* is said to occur, the compound is *reduced*, and the substance removing the oxygen acts as the *reducing agent* (using these terms in a very restricted sense).

Now, let us consider the reaction of iron oxide and hydrogen in greater detail.   The ferric oxide is *reduced* by the *reducing agent* hydrogen, while the hydrogen is *oxidized* by the *oxidizing agent* ferric oxide.   Oxidation must always be accompanied by an equivalent amount of reduction, the two effects always proceeding simultaneously.   In the reaction of iron oxide with hydrogen, the oxygen removed from the iron oxide must combine with the hydrogen to form water.

All of the examples of oxidation we have discussed in considering the formation of oxides from the elements must also involve reduction. When magnesium unites with oxygen to form MgO, the magnesium is oxidized and the oxygen is said to be reduced.   Magnesium is the reducing agent because it effects the reduction of oxygen.   Oxygen is the oxidizing agent because it effects the oxidation of magnesium.

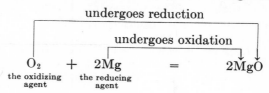

$$O_2 \;\; + \;\; 2Mg \;\;\;\; = \;\;\;\; 2MgO$$

the oxidizing agent   the reducing agent

105.   THE ELECTRONIC INTERPRETATION OF OXIDATION-REDUCTION

In oxidation-reduction reactions electronic rearrangements take place when the atoms change their state of combination with other atoms. When magnesium metal combines with oxygen and is oxidized, each magnesium atom loses two electrons and forms a positively charged ion.

$$Mg = 2e^- + Mg^{2+}$$

The magnesium atom goes to a *more electropositive condition*.   At the same time the electrons lost by the magnesium atoms are gained by oxygen atoms which form negative oxide ions.

$$O_2 + 4e^- = 2O^{2-}$$

The oxygen atoms go to a *more electronegative condition*.

This is typical of oxidation-reduction reactions.   *The material that is oxidized always goes to a more electropositive condition, while the material that is reduced always goes to a more electronegative condition.*   In the process, the material that is oxidized becomes less associated with electrons, and the material that is reduced becomes more associated with electrons.   Chemists have now extended the use of the term *oxidation-reduction* to include all reactions in which such electronic changes occur. In the broad use of the term, it is not necessary that an oxidation-reduction reaction involve oxygen.   For instance, when sodium metal reacts with chlorine, sodium forms Na^+ ions and is oxidized, while chlorine forms Cl^- ions and is reduced.   The formation of NaCl from the elements is an oxidation-reduction reaction.

106.   OXIDATION STATES

The use of the concept of oxidation states helps to make clear the changes atomic systems undergo when oxidation-reduction takes place. An element in the free condition, where its atoms are not combined with those of any other element, is said to be in the *oxidation state of zero*.   Its atoms may or may not be chemically bonded to each other, but none of the electrons associated with its atoms is involved in chemical bonding to atoms of another element.   Thus, monatomic hydrogen and the diatomic

molecules of ordinary hydrogen gas are both considered to involve hydrogen in the oxidation state of zero.   Notice that, although in the H—H
molecule each hydrogen is using its electron to form a bond to the other
hydrogen atom and so has a combining capacity of one, the oxidation
state of the hydrogen is taken as zero.   When an element combines with
another to form a compound and its atoms go to a more electropositive
condition because they become less associated with electrons, they go
to a *positive oxidation state*.   When an element, in forming a compound,
becomes more associated with electrons, it goes to a negative condition,
and we say that it goes to a negative *oxidation state*.   The number of the
oxidation state depends upon the number of electrons per atom involved
in the bonding to the atoms of other elements.   It will be positive if the
atom is less associated with electrons than when it is neutral, negative if
more associated with electrons.

We see how this works for magnesium and oxygen and their reaction
product MgO.

Oxidation State	
0	Magnesium in magnesium metal
0	Oxygen in O_2 or O_3 molecules
+2	Magnesium as Mg^{2+} ions
—2	Oxygen as O^{2-} ions
+2	Magnesium in MgO
—2	Oxygen in MgO

It is conventional to indicate the oxidation state of an atom by placing
the proper sign and number over its symbol.   By writing

$$\overset{0}{Mg} \quad and \quad \overset{0}{O_2}$$

we indicate that magnesium and oxygen are in the zero oxidation state.

$$\overset{+2}{Mg}\,\overset{-2}{O}$$

indicates that in magnesium oxide, magnesium is in the **+2** oxidation
state and oxygen is in the **—2** oxidation state.

In calcium metal and in chlorine gas the atoms are in the zero oxidation state.

$$\overset{0}{Ca} \qquad \overset{0}{Cl_2}$$

They combine to form the ionic compound calcium chloride, which is
composed of Ca^{2+} and Cl^- ions.   In $CaCl_2$, therefore, calcium is in the
+2 oxidation state and chlorine is in the **—1** oxidation state, and we can
indicate this by writing

$$\overset{+2}{Ca}\,\overset{-1}{Cl_2}$$

The oxidation state of an atom in a simple ion is always the same in sign and number as the charge on the ion.

Oxidation-reduction is not restricted to ionic reactions. In forming molecules an atom may go to a more electropositive condition by forming an electron-pair bond to a more electronegative atom. This more electronegative atom has a greater share in the pair of bonding electrons and has gone to a more negative oxidation state. There is no complete transfer of electrons from one atom to another. The number of the oxidation state of each atom in the molecule is equal to the number of its electrons it has used in forming covalent bonds to atoms of other elements.

In elementary hydrogen and oxygen the atoms are in the zero oxidation state

$$\overset{0}{H_2} \qquad \overset{0}{O_2}$$

When they combine to form molecules of water, each of two hydrogen atoms forms one covalent bond to the more electronegative oxygen atom. Accordingly, we say the hydrogen goes to the **+1** oxidation state and the oxygen goes to the **—2** oxidation state, and to show the oxidation states of the atoms in the water molecule we write

$$\overset{+1\ -2}{H_2\ O}$$

In the formation of water, hydrogen is oxidized and oxygen is reduced, although there has been no complete transfer of electrons.

By specifying the oxidation state of an atom, we indicate whether the element is free (uncombined with other elements) or whether it is combined with other elements. When it is combined with other elements, the sign of its oxidation state depends upon whether it has gone to a more electropositive or a more electronegative condition, and the number indicates how many electrons the atom has lost or gained in forming ions or has furnished for the formation of covalent bonds to other elements.

By listing the oxidation states which atoms of an element can assume, we describe the complete range of its combining capacity toward other elements. The only oxidation states known for magnesium are **0** and **+2**. Whenever magnesium combines with other elements it is oxidized to the **+2** oxidation state, usually by forming Mg^{2+} ions. Tin has oxidation states of **0**, **+2**, and **+4**. We accordingly can expect to work with this element either as the metal or combined in compounds such as $SnCl_2$ or $SnCl_4$.

$$\overset{+2\ -1}{Sn\ Cl_2} \qquad \overset{+4\ -1}{Sn\ Cl_4}$$

As mentioned in Section 62, in the names of compounds of the metals we can use Roman numerals to indicate the charge of the ion of the metals. This will also be the oxidation state of the metal.   The names *tin(II) chloride* and *tin(IV) chloride* refer respectively to $SnCl_2$ and $SnCl_4$. The older and still frequently used names, *stannous chloride* and *stannic chloride*, use the endings *-ous* and *-ic* to indicate the two different oxidation states of tin.   The ending *-ic* is always used for the higher oxidation state.

107. DEDUCTION OF OXIDATION STATES

In order to assign the correct value for the oxidation state of an element in a given compound, we must know which atoms are bonded together and how the electrons are involved in the bonding. We have seen that when oxygen combines with other elements, the oxygen atom usually becomes associated with two more electrons and goes to a more electronegative condition.   Hence, it usually is safe to assign the **−2** oxidation state to this element in its compounds, with the exception of the peroxy systems.   Hydrogen is in the **−1** state when it is combined with the more active metals and in the **+1** state when it is combined with the nonmetals.   The metals almost invariably go to positive oxidation states when they combine with nonmetals.   The oxidation state of an atom forming a simple ion is equal to the charge of the ion.

It is possible to derive the probable oxidation state of an element in a compound whose correct formula is known by assuming probable values for the oxidation states of the other elements that are present. *In a given compound the sum of the units of positive oxidation state must be just equal to the sum of the units of negative oxidation state.*   In water, H_2O, each hydrogen atom contributes one unit of positive oxidation state to give a total of two positive units that are just balanced by the two units of negative oxidation state of the oxygen.

The correct formula for ferric oxide is Fe_2O_3.   Assuming that oxygen is in the oxidation state of **−2**, the formula indicates a total of six units of negative oxidation state.   This requires that the iron atoms present contribute six units of positive oxidation state, and each iron atom must be in the oxidation state of **+3**.   Similar reasoning for the compound FeO indicates that in this oxide iron is in the oxidation state of **+2**.   The correct formula for sulfuric acid is H_2SO_4.   We can deduce the oxidation state of the sulfur by assuming that each oxygen atom is in the **−2** state and each hydrogen atom is in the **+1** state.   The four oxygen atoms then contribute eight negative units; the two hydrogen atoms, two positive units.   Therefore, the sulfur atom must account for six positive units and be in the oxidation state of **+6**.

In a complex ion the sum of the positive units must differ from the sum of the negative units by the charge of the ion.   Thus, in the sulfate ion, SO_4^{2-}, the four oxygen atoms contribute eight negative units.   Two of these are accounted for by the charge of 2− of the ion.   Therefore, **the sulfur atom is in the oxidation state of +6.**

108.   PERIODICITY OF OXIDATION STATES

The oxidation states that can be realized by elements in forming compounds are associated with the electron configuration of their atoms, being closely associated with the number of valence electrons.   Because the electron configurations vary periodically with increasing atomic number, it is to be expected that the oxidation states of the elements will also change periodically.   In Table 20 the first 20 elements are listed in order of their atomic numbers, and their maximum negative and positive oxidation states are indicated.

Table 20.   Periodicity of Oxidation States

Element	H							He
Atomic no.	1							2
Max. oxid.	**−1**							
states	**+1**							**0**
Electrons in								
shells	1							2

Element	Li	Be	B	C	N	O	F	Ne
Atomic no.	3	4	5	6	7	8	9	10
Max. oxid.				**−4**	**−3**	**−2**	**−1**	0
states	**+1**	**+2**	**+3**	**+4**	**+5**			
Electrons in								
shells	2, 1	2, 2	2, 3	2, 4	2, 5	2, 6	2, 7	2, 8

Element	Na	Mg	Al	Si	P	S	Cl	A
Atomic no.	11	12	13	14	15	16	17	18
Max. oxid.				**−4**	**−3**	**−2**	**−1**	0
states	**+1**	**+2**	**+3**	**+4**	**+5**	**+6**	**+7**	
Electrons in								
shells	2, 8, 1	2, 8, 2	2, 8, 3	2, 8, 4	2, 8, 5	2, 8, 6	2, 8, 7	2, 8, 8

With each unit increase in atomic number, there is a change in maximum oxidation state, usually by one unit, but this change proceeds in cycles.   Every so often, inert elements having only the zero oxidation state appear, succeeded by elements having the oxidation state of **+1,** and these in turn are followed by elements having the oxidation state of **+2,** and so forth.   Such periodic fluctuation of oxidation state continues through the rest of the elements.   In the long periods, starting with IV, the maximum positive state that is possible increases regularly up through Group VII, then falls back to low values for the 1B subgroup elements, and then begins to build up again.   Negative states are usually exhibited only by the elements in the four places preceding the inert gases, decreasing with increasing atomic number across the period.

109. OXIDATION-REDUCTION AND CHANGES IN OXIDATION STATES

We have extended the use of the term *oxidation* to include all changes of atoms to a more positive condition, that is, to a more positive oxidation state. And the term *reduction* has been broadened to include all changes of atoms to a more negative condition, to a more negative (less positive) oxidation state. It is clear that in oxidation and reduction the changes to more positive or negative states will involve electronic rearrangement, such that the gain in positive oxidation state will be accompanied by a corresponding gain in negative oxidation state. Each electron that is lost or that becomes less associated with one atom must be gained or become more associated with another atom.

Applying this to the reaction between ferric oxide and hydrogen, suppose we indicate above each element in each formula the oxidation state of its atoms and trace the changes in oxidation states which are involved in the chemical change.

Reduction: $2 \times 3 = 6$ units of change to less positive oxidation state

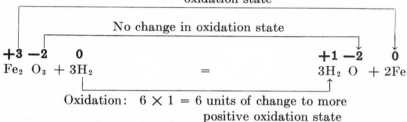

Oxidation: $6 \times 1 = 6$ units of change to more positive oxidation state

The total number of units of change to a more positive oxidation state undergone by the atoms of hydrogen is just balanced by the total number of units of change to a more negative (less positive) oxidation state experienced by the iron. *In any properly balanced equation for a chemical change involving oxidation-reduction, the total units of change involved in the oxidation are always equal to the total units of change involved in the reduction;* the amount of oxidation is always equivalent to the amount of reduction. In fact, one of the best ways to balance a complicated equation involving oxidation-reduction is to do so by balancing the changes in oxidation states.

Take the case of the reaction of sodium with chlorine to form sodium chloride.

Oxidation: $2 \times 1 = 2$ units of change to more positive oxidation state

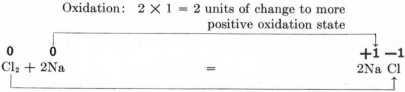

Reduction: $2 \times 1 = 2$ units of change to less positive oxidation state

Chlorine is reduced and acts as an oxidizing agent.   Sodium is oxidized and acts as a reducing agent.

110.   COMPOUNDS OF HYDROGEN

Hydrogen forms simple binary compounds with many elements, the properties of the compounds reflecting the nature of the second element.

a. With metals.   When hydrogen is brought together with many of the very active metals at somewhat elevated temperatures and especially at high pressures, direct combination occurs to give compounds that are ionic and in which the hydrogen is present as the negative ion.   In these reactions hydrogen is reduced to the oxidation state of **—1**, and the metals are oxidized.   Such compounds are known as *ionic hydrides.*

$$Ca + H_2 = CaH_2$$
$$2Na + H_2 = 2NaH$$
$$2Li + H_2 = 2LiH$$

At ordinary temperatures these hydrides are colorless solids; they decompose into the elements if heated vigorously.   As indicated in Section 102*f*, they react vigorously with water to give hydrogen and the hydroxides of the metals.   They are highly combustible and must be stored and handled in the absence of air.   Since the hydrogen is present in the oxidation state of **—1** and has a strong tendency to change to the oxidation state of **0** or **+1,** these hydrides are very powerful reducing agents.   Calcium, lithium and sodium hydrides are the more stable ones and are available commercially.   Rust scale, Fe_2O_3, can be removed from steel by dipping it into molten sodium hydride which reduces the oxide to iron.

$$Fe_2O_3 + 3NaH = 3NaOH + 2Fe$$

The steel is subsequently immersed in water to wash off the sodium hydroxide that adheres.

Many of the less active metals, such as iron, palladium, and tungsten, absorb considerable quantities of hydrogen under certain conditions to give hard, brittle materials that have the general properties of metals and are usually referred to as *metallic hydrides.*   Apparently, in these cases the hydrogen atoms are able to behave somewhat like atoms of metals.

b. With nonmetals.   Hydrogen unites with the nonmetallic elements to give *molecular compounds*, which, in most cases, are gases or liquids under ordinary conditions.   Thus, hydrogen and chlorine combine in a highly exothermic fashion to form hydrogen chloride, hydrogen being oxidized while chlorine is reduced.

$$H_2 + Cl_2 = 2HCl$$

In these compounds the hydrogen is in the oxidation state of **+1.**   Many of them furnish hydrogen ions readily and may be classified as *acids*, exhibiting the characteristic properties already described for such compounds. We distinguish between *hydracids*, such as HCl, which have no oxygen present, and *oxyacids*, such as H_2SO_4, which contain oxygen and which are acidic hydroxides. The molecules of the hydracids of the very highly electronegative elements, such as fluorine and chlorine, are very stable thermally, but those of the less electronegative elements, such as iodine and arsenic, break up rapidly when they are heated. The compounds of hydrogen with oxygen are so important that we will consider them in detail.

111. WATER

It is impossible to overestimate the importance of this compound, since it usually is present at least in traces in the chemical systems we normally handle, and because it affects the behavior of these systems in such deep-seated ways. Its direct synthesis and analysis and the accompanying energy changes already have been considered. Pure water is colorless, tasteless, and odorless. Its more important properties are summarized in Table 21.

Table 21.   Properties of Water

Molecular formula, as steam	H_2O
Molecular weight, as steam	18.016
Boiling point, ° C	100.000
Freezing point, ° C	0.000
Density, g/ml, 4°	1.000
Heat of vaporization, cal/g, 100°	539.55
Heat of fusion, cal/g, 0°	79.76
Specific heat, cal/g, 14.5–15.5°	1.000
Color	none
Odor	none

The chemical bonding in the water molecule and its spatial configuration have already been discussed in detail in Sections 66, 67, and 69. The nonlinear, bent-chain shape of the molecule plays an important part in determining the behavior of water and illustrates how important it is to know something about the spatial configurations of molecules if we wish to understand their properties. The highly polar nature of the molecules of water, as described in Section 70, makes this compound outstanding as a solvent, as we shall see later.

The changes in density of water with change in temperature are unusual and of considerable interest because they affect our environment in many ways. As water is cooled from 100°, its density in grams per milliliter gradually increases from 0.9584 until it reaches a maximum of 1.0000 at 4°. With further cooling, the effect reverses, and the density now decreases, reaching the value 0.9998 at 0°.   When water freezes, there is a very great decrease in density to 0.917.   The decrease in density below 4° is due to weak chemical association of the water molecules in such a fashion as to produce less compact structure.   (See Section 181.)

When the surface layer of a quiet body of water is cooled below 4°, it tends to remain on top, owing to its lower density, and it eventually freezes to ice, which floats on the denser liquid water.   Hence, rivers, lakes, and oceans usually freeze at the surface and do not freeze solid. When water freezes, there is an expansion of about 9 per cent in volume, and if the freezing takes place in a limited spaced filled with the water, tremendous pressure will be developed.   This is sufficient to break glass bottles, make roads "heave" and crack, and split massive rocks.   The disintegration resulting from the freezing of water in cracks in rock formations plays a major role in the weathering of mountains and the formation of soils.

With increase in population and expansion of industry and farming, our supply of water becomes more and more critical.   The purification of water for domestic and industrial use and the softening of hard water are chemical problems that will be considered later.   Because we will use water to illustrate much of the general discussion as we go along, it will not be discussed further at this time.

112. HYDROGEN PEROXIDE

In Sections 91 and 92 it was pointed out that hydrogen forms two compounds with oxygen, namely water and hydrogen peroxide.   Hydrogen peroxide may be obtained in many different ways but is produced most conveniently by the action of water or acids on peroxides or other peroxy compounds.   When sodium peroxide is dropped into ice water, a dilute solution of hydrogen peroxide is formed.

$$Na_2O_2 + 2H_2O = 2NaOH + H_2O_2$$

But it is very difficult to purify and concentrate the solution.   A more satisifactory laboratory method involves adding barium peroxide to dilute sulfuric acid.

$$BaO_2 + H_2SO_4 = BaSO_4 + H_2O_2$$

The barium sulfate precipitates and can be filtered off, leaving a dilute solution of hydrogen peroxide.   Large scale production of hydrogen peroxide is usually accomplished by electrolyzing concentrated sulfuric acid to make peroxysulfuric acid, and then treating this with water.

$$2H_2SO_4 \overset{\text{electrolysis}}{=} H_2 + H_2S_2O_8$$
$$H_2S_2O_8 + 2H_2O = H_2O_2 + 2H_2SO_4$$

Hydrogen peroxide is commonly marketed as a 3 per cent solution of the compound in water. By special techniques, more concentrated aqueous solutions containing as much as 90 per cent H_2O_2 can be made. If the hydrogen peroxide solutions are concentrated too much, they become dangerously explosive, but, by keeping impurities to a minimum, it is possible to produce highly concentrated solutions. Hydrogen peroxide is very low in stability compared to water, tending even at room temperature to decompose exothermally.

$$2H_2O_2 = 2H_2O + O_2 + 46,340 \text{ cal}$$

The bonding and configuration of the H_2O_2 molecule have been compared with that of H_2O in Figure 23, page 88. The formation of these two different molecules by hydrogen and oxygen arises because an oxygen atom can form two covalent bonds in two different ways. Each of the two bonds may be toward a hydrogen atom, in which case water molecules are formed; or it may form one bond toward a hydrogen atom and another toward a second oxygen atom to give hydrogen peroxide. The structure of the molecule of hydrogen peroxide is believed to be a bent chain with the centers of the four atoms probably not in the same plane.

When two oxygen atoms appear bonded together in a substance in this fashion, we say that the peroxy group is present and the substance is a *peroxy* compound. The oxygen atom is in the oxidation state of -1 in such peroxy compounds because each oxygen atom has made use of only one of its electrons in bonding to hydrogen. The bond between the oxygen atoms does not count in determining the number of the oxidation state. Notice that each oxygen atom in the H_2O_2 molecule has two covalent bonds and therefore has a total combining capacity of two, but that only the combining capacity toward atoms of another element determines the number of the oxidation state.

113. HYDROGEN PEROXIDE AS OXIDIZING OR REDUCING AGENT

Hydrogen peroxide acts as a powerful *oxidizing agent* when it is mixed with suitable reducing agents. When it is added to a solution of iodide and hydrogen ions, the solution turns brown because iodine is formed.

Reduction: 2 × 1 units of change of oxidation state

Oxidation: 2 × 1 units of change
of oxidation state

$$\overset{+1}{H_2}\ \overset{-1}{O_2} + \overset{-1}{2I^-} + \overset{+1}{2H^+} = \overset{0}{I_2} + \overset{+1}{2H_2}\overset{-2}{O}$$

By adding starch to the solution, the appearance of the blue color characteristic of the combination of starch and elementary iodine can be used to test for the presence of very small amounts of hydrogen peroxide. The familiar uses of hydrogen peroxide as a *bleaching agent* and as an

antiseptic exploit its strong oxidizing action. It is a very satisfactory oxidizing agent in that, when it decomposes, water usually is formed. Since water already is present in the solution, there are no complications due to the introduction of new substances to the system.

Hydrogen peroxide acts as a *reducing agent* when brought in contact with a suitable oxidizing agent. Thus, when hydrogen peroxide is added to a solution of potassium permanganate, which has some sulfuric acid present, the purple color characteristic of the permanganate ion disappears, and bubbles of oxygen gas form. The oxygen in the hydrogen peroxide goes to the zero oxidation state, and manganese goes from **+7** to **+2,** being reduced.

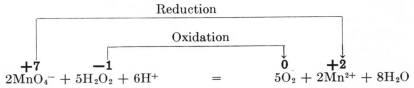

Reduction

Oxidation

$$\overset{+7}{2MnO_4^-} + \overset{-1}{5H_2O_2} + 6H^+ = \overset{0}{5O_2} + \overset{+2}{2Mn^{2+}} + 8H_2O$$

Because of the low stability of hydrogen peroxide, certain points must be kept in mind in the storage of its solutions. The rate at which it decomposes is accelerated by the action of light or heat. Manganese dioxide, platinum, bases, and certain enzymes strongly catalyze its decomposition. To preserve solutions of hydrogen peroxide, it is important to keep them cool, protect them from light, and keep them from contact with catalysts. In fact, negative catalysts (inhibitors or stabilizers), such as acids, are usually added to stabilize these solutions.

114. EQUIVALENT WEIGHTS OF OXIDIZING AND REDUCING AGENTS

The concept of equivalent weights can be extended to the reactants in oxidation-reduction reactions. *A gram-equivalent weight of a reducing or oxidizing agent in a given reaction is that weight which undergoes 6.02 × 10^{23} units of change in oxidation state in the reaction.* When one gram-equivalent weight of a reducing agent reacts with one gram-equivalent weight of an oxidizing agent, one mole of electrons is lost completely by, or becomes less associated with, the reducing agent, and this mole of electrons is gained completely by, or becomes more associated with, the oxidizing agent.

In the reaction of chlorine with hydrogen to form hydrogen chloride, one mole of chlorine is reduced by one mole of hydrogen.

Reduction: 2 × 1 units of change in oxidation state

Oxidation: 2 × 1 units of change in oxidation state

$$\overset{0}{Cl_2} + \overset{0}{H_2} = 2\overset{+1}{H}\,\overset{-1}{Cl}$$

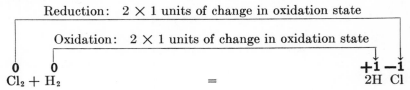

In this reaction one gram atom, 35.46 g, of the oxidizing agent, chlorine, will provide 6.02×10^{23} atoms of chlorine, each of which undergoes one unit of change to a more negative oxidation state.   The gram-equivalent weight of chlorine as the oxidizing agent in this reaction, therefore, is 35.46 g.   The gram-equivalent weight of the reducing agent hydrogen is 1.008 g.

In the reaction in Section 113, where hydrogen peroxide oxidizes iodide ions in the presence of hydrogen ions, each molecule of hydrogen peroxide is responsible for two units change in oxidation state.   In this reaction the gram-equivalent weight of hydrogen peroxide as an oxidizing agent is 17.008 g, half the molecular weight.   Each iodide ion changes one unit to a more positive oxidation state, and therefore the gram-equivalent weight of the iodide ion as a reducing agent is 126.9 g, the gram-ionic weight.

In the oxidation-reduction reaction of hydrogen peroxide with permanganate ions in the presence of hydrogen ions, each molecule of hydrogen peroxide is responsible for two units of reducing action.   In this case the gram-equivalent weight of hydrogen peroxide as a reducing agent is 17.008 g.   Each manganese atom in a permanganate ion is reduced five units in oxidation state, and the gram-equivalent weight of permanganate ion as an oxidizing agent in this reaction is 23.78 g, one-fifth the gram-ionic weight.

$$\frac{\text{One gram equivalent of any}}{\text{oxidizing or reducing agent}} = \frac{\text{the gram-molecular or ionic weight}}{\substack{\text{number of units change in oxidation} \\ \text{state per molecule or ion}}}$$

115. ACID-BASE NEUTRALIZATION. SALTS

One of the very characteristic properties of all acids, whether hydracids or oxyacids, is that they react readily with all bases.   When a solution of hydrochloric acid is mixed with a solution of sodium hydroxide, a vigorous reaction occurs.   In the process, the acidic and basic qualities vanish; we say that the acid and base have been *neutralized* and that the reaction involves *neutralization.*   The sour taste common to all acids and the bitter taste common to all bases disappear.   In this acid-base neutralization, the hydrogen ions furnished by the acid combine with the hydroxide ions furnished by the base, and water is formed.   When the solution produced by the neutralization of hydrochloric acid by sodium hydroxide is evaporated, a colorless solid is left.   This solid can be identified as sodium chloride, ordinary table salt.   The over-all reaction, starting with pure HCl and NaOH, may be summarized in the equation

$$HCl + NaOH = H_2O + NaCl$$

Any acid will react with any base in a similar fashion to produce water.   When the resulting solution is evaporated, crystals are formed by the combination of the residues left when hydrogen ions split out of the acid and hydroxide ions leave the base.   These crystalline products are called *salts* because sodium chloride is the most familiar example of this class of substances.   The following equations describe a number of such neutralization reactions of some of the more common acids by basic hydroxides to produce water and the salt of the acid and base.

$$H_2SO_4 \;+\; 2NaOH \;=\; 2H_2O \;+\; Na_2SO_4$$
sulfuric acid   sodium hydroxide   sodium sulfate

$$2HCl \;+\; Ca(OH)_2 \;=\; 2H_2O \;+\; CaCl_2$$
hydrochloric acid   calcium hydroxide   calcium chloride

$$HF \;+\; KOH \;=\; H_2O \;+\; KF$$
hydrofluoric acid   potassium hydroxide   potassium fluoride

$$H_2SO_4 \;+\; Mg(OH)_2 \;=\; 2H_2O \;+\; MgSO_4$$
sulfuric acid   magnesium hydroxide   magnesium sulfate

$$2HNO_3 \;+\; Ba(OH)_2 \;=\; 2H_2O \;+\; Ba(NO_3)_2$$
nitric acid   barium hydroxide   barium nitrate

$$HC_2H_3O_2 \;+\; NaOH \;=\; H_2O \;+\; NaC_2H_3O_2$$
acetic acid   sodium hydroxide   sodium acetate

Note that in some acids, such as acetic, $HC_2H_3O_2$, not all the hydrogen atoms can take part in the neutralization reaction, the rest being combined differently in the molecule and held so firmly that they are not available for neutralization.   We indicate this difference by the way in which we write the formula for the acid.

Acid-base neutralization will be considered in greater detail later, and the use of the terms *acid* and *base* will then be expanded to include recent developements in the theory dealing with such systems.

116.   EQUIVALENT WEIGHTS OF ACIDS AND BASES

From the equation for a neutralization reaction, the amount of the base needed to neutralize a given amount of the acid and the amounts of water and salt formed can be calculated, using the method outlined in Section 81.   By calculations of this kind, the quantities of different acids that will react with a given amount of a given base can be estimated and compared.   The equations tell us that to neutralize one mole of sodium hydroxide (40.01 g), one mole of hydrochloric acid (36.47 g) or one-half mole of sulfuric acid (49.04 g) is required.   These respective amounts of the acids furnish one mole of hydrogen ion (1.008 g); this is just the amount needed to combine with the one mole of hydroxide ions from one mole of sodium hydroxide to produce one mole of water.   One mole of hydrochloric acid is *chemically equivalent* to one-half mole of sulfuric acid in neutralizing sodium hydroxide or any other base.   The amount of any acid that will furnish one mole of hydrogen ions in neutralizing a base is called the *gram-equivalent weight of the acid*.   The gram-equivalent weight of any acid is equal to the weight of one mole of the acid divided by the number of atoms of hydrogen per molecule of acid which take part in neutralization.

Similarly, one mole of sodium hydroxide or one-half mole of calcium hydroxide is needed to neutralize one mole of hydrochloric acid, and these quantities of the two bases therefore have equivalent basic action. These quantities of the respective bases furnish one mole of hydroxide ions to neutralize one gram-equivalent weight of the acid and are the *gram-equivalent weights of these bases*. A gram-equivalent weight of a base contains one gram-equivalent weight of hydroxyl groups available for neutralization.

EXERCISES

1. How does the element hydrogen differ from every other element with respect to its position in the Periodic Table?

2. a) What two groups of elements does hydrogen resemble to some extent?
b) How do you account for this in terms of electronic configuration?

3. a) Recalling that hydrogen has three isotopes, how many different molecules of water all containing $_8O^{16}$ can you think of?
b) What is the molecular weight of each of these molecules?
c) Why is the average molecular weight of steam very close to 18.016?

4. Using the weight percentages of oxygen and hydrogen occurring in the earth as given in Table 2, page 15, calculate the relative abundance of the atoms of these two elements.

5. Write balanced equations for five different chemical changes which can be used to prepare hydrogen.

6. Making use of simple chemical reactions of oxygen and hydrogen, distinguish between: a) oxidation and reduction in the narrow sense; b) oxidation and reduction in the broad sense; c) oxidizing agents and reducing agents.

7. a) Describe the operation of the oxyhydrogen burner.
b) How much energy will the combustion of five moles of hydrogen in the burner provide?
c) What other device described in this chapter is very effective for producing high temperatures? Explain the principle upon which this device operates.

8. Potassium metal combines with violence with chlorine.
a) Making use of the positions of these elements in the Periodic Table and of what you know about chemical bonding, predict the oxidation states each will assume when they combine.
b) Write the equation for the reaction and indicate clearly how oxidation-reduction is involved.
c) What is the gram-equivalent weight of potassium in this reaction?
d) Will the compound that is formed have a low or a high melting point?

9. If you wish to select an element that will be a very strong reducing agent, where would you look in the Periodic Table?

10. Assuming oxygen to be in the -2 oxidation state, what is the oxidation state of manganese in: a) MnO; b) Mn_2O_3; c) MnO_2; d) MnO_4^{2-}; e) MnO_4^{-}?

11. If hydrogen is in the oxidation state of $+1$, what is the oxidation state of the other element in: a) NH_3; b) H_2S; c) HI?

12. What is the oxidation state of arsenic in H_3AsO_3?

13. Indicate the oxidation states of the elements and the changes in oxidation state that take place in the oxidation-reduction that occurs in:
  a) $H_2 + Ca = CaH_2$
  b) $Cl_2 + H_2 = 2HCl$
  c) $2NH_3 = 3H_2 + N_2$
  d) $CaH_2 + 2H_2O = Ca(OH)_2 + H_2$
  e) $Fe_2O_3 + 3NaH = 3NaOH + 2Fe$

14. In what respects do the compositions of hydracids resemble and differ from the composition of oxyacids?

15. Hydrogen enters into the composition of both HCl and KOH. What happens to the hydrogen atoms when each of these substances take part in acid-base neutralization?

16. What are the gram-equivalent weights of nitric acid and barium hydroxide when they neutralize each other according to the equation given in Section 115?

17. a) What is the gram-equivalent weight of calcium as a reducing agent when it combines with hydrogen to form CaH_2?
  b) What is the gram-equivalent weight of Fe_2O_3 when it is reduced by hydrogen to give iron?

18. Compare the water and hydrogen peroxide molecules with respect to: a) spatial configuration; b) chemical bonding; c) total combining capacity of the atoms of oxygen in each; d) oxidation states of the atoms; e) thermal stability; f) effectiveness as oxidizing agents.

Chapter 9

▶ The Gaseous State

117. THE DIFFERENT STATES OF MATTER

As mentioned in Section 17, matter exists in the gaseous, liquid, and solid states, depending upon the conditions. (The term *vapor state* is now generally used as synonomous with gaseous state.) Each state is identified with certain characteristics which allow us to distinguish between these states. The substance water can exist as gaseous steam, as ordinary liquid water, and as solid ice. When cooled (heat energy withdrawn), steam tends to form liquid water, and when water is cooled it tends to freeze to ice. When heat energy is added to ice, it tends to change to the liquid state; and when liquid water is heated, it tends to turn into steam. When a substance undergoes such changes in state, we say that *transitions* occur. Adding heat to a substance favors transition from the solid to the liquid state, and from the liquid to the gaseous state. Cooling the substance tends to reverse these transitions.

The gaseous state of matter is the easiest state to study with simple apparatus and was the first that the early scientists were able to investigate successfully. It is, for the same reason, the easiest state of matter for the student to consider. We shall apply the scientific method to the study of gases, first accumulating by observation some facts about the behavior of gases in general, then summarizing these facts, and finally considering theories as to the structure that all gases are believed to have. These theories should account for and allow us to predict the behavior of all matter in the gaseous state. We shall try to answer the questions what, how, and why.

118. WHAT IS THE QUALITATIVE BEHAVIOR OF GASES?

In order to study gases, we must be able to select and isolate samples of gases so that we can observe their behavior under varying conditions. The *gas burette*, shown in Figure 28a, is a simple apparatus that allows us to collect samples of gases and to measure accurately their volumes and pressures. The glass tube A, surmounted by the stopcock C, is graduated in terms of cubic centimeters or milliliters of volume and is connected by the rubber tube D to the glass leveling tube B. The latter is open to the atmosphere. Mercury is added until the apparatus is about half full.

When stopcock *C* is open, air can enter tubes *A* and *B* freely, and the mercury will be at the same level in both tubes.   When *B* is raised, mercury flows from *B* into *A* and can be caused to fill it.   If stopcock *C* is then closed, and tube *B* is lowered sufficiently, the level of the mercury drops in *A*, leaving above the mercury in the tube a space in which there is nothing.   We say that a *Torricellian vacuum* has been set up in *A*, as shown in Figure 28*b*.   (At room temperature there will be a very small

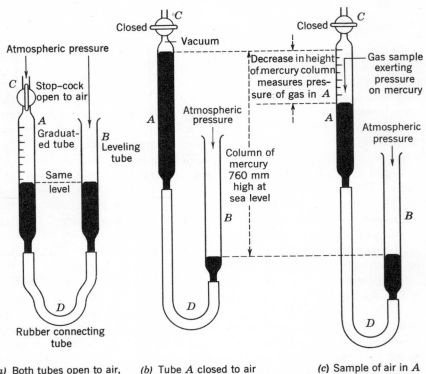

(*a*) Both tubes open to air,   (*b*) Tube *A* closed to air   (*c*) Sample of air in *A*
mercury at same level   with vacuum over mercury   above mercury

Fig. 28.   Gas burette.

amount of gaseous mercury present, but this is so small that we will ignore it.)   The level of the mercury in *A* is now observed to be 760 mm above the level in *B*, if the apparatus is at sea level at a latitude of 45° under normal atmospheric conditions.   Since the liquid mercury is free to flow between the two tubes, it is obvious that some force must be acting upon the mercury so that its level in *A* is maintained above that in *B*.   This force must be just equal, but opposite in direction, to the force of attraction to the earth of the mercury in the column between the two levels.   The air exerts on the mercury in *B* a pressure that is transmitted in all directions through the liquid and therefore operates to support the column of mercury in *A*. The height of the column of mercury between the two levels is a measure of the pressure of the atmosphere. An apparatus that measures atmospheric pressure in this fashion is known as a *mercury barometer;* Figure 29 shows two simple types of mercury barometers. The pressure of gases is usually given in terms of millimeters (mm) of mercury, indicating that the pressure is equal to the weight per square centimeter cross-sectional area of a column of mercury that number of millimeters high.

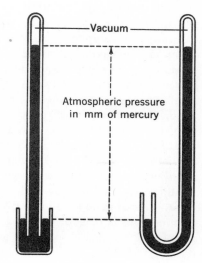

Fig. 29.   Simple mercury barometers.

In handling gases it is frequently convenient to refer to their behavior under *standard conditions of temperature and pressure*, which we will designate by STP. Standard temperature is 0°, and standard pressure is 760 mm of mercury, sometimes called *one atmosphere.*

Suppose that we use the gas burette to study a given sample of gas. We can trap a portion of gas in the apparatus by opening stopcock *C* so that air is free to flow into the Torricellian vacuum. We notice that, as air rushes in above the mercury, the level of the mercury drops, the mercury being forced down by the air. If the stopcock is then closed, we have secured a given quantity of gas in *A*, as shown in Figure 28c. As long as we keep stopcock *C* closed, we will be dealing with this fixed quantity of air, since it cannot escape through the glass walls or through the mercury, and since no more air can get in. By observing the behavior of this sample of gas, we can establish certain facts, and by substituting other gases in place of the air, we can demonstrate that these facts are true for all substances in the gaseous state.

We can then summarize these observed facts in the following generalizations:

a. All gases exert pressure. When the gas sample enters the burette, it forces down the mercury against the atmospheric pressure in *B*. The amount by which the column of mercury between the levels in *A* and *B* decreases in height, when the gas sample enters *A*, is a measure of the pressure exerted by the gas sample.

b. All gases expand by diffusion. When we had a vacuum in *A* and opened the stopcock *C*, we found that the air rushed in to occupy all of the available space above the mercury. Suppose we then close stopcock *C*. By lowering *B*, we can withdraw mercury from *A*, and the air in *A* expands to occupy the additional space. This is typical of all gases. When released in a given space, they spread rapidly throughout the space to occupy it completely, the movement being referred to as *diffusion*. *Gases have no definite shape or volume but assume that of the container.*

c. All gases are compressible. By raising *B*, we can force more mercury into *A*, and the volume occupied by the gas sample becomes smaller. Gases may be compressed readily to occupy smaller volumes.

d. Gases mix in all proportions. If we introduce some hydrogen into the space above the mercury in *A* when air is already present, we find that the hydrogen diffuses and distributes itself uniformly in the available space. The hydrogen behaves just as it would if the air were not there, except that the effective rate of diffusion is slower. Gases mix in all proportions and are said to be *completely miscible* in each other.

e. All gases confined in a given space exert more pressure when the temperature is raised. If we apply heat to tube *A* containing the sample of gas, the gas is found to exert a greater pressure on the mercury, tending to force it down in the tube. In order to keep the volume of the gas the same, we must raise *B* so that the level of mercury in *B* becomes higher with respect to the level in *A*.

f. Brownian movement is observed for small particles of solid or liquid when these are suspended in a gas. For example, cigar smoke consists

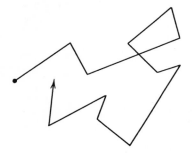

Fig. 30.   Kind of random path followed by particle undergoing Brownian movement.

of tiny particles of solid suspended in air. These particles can be demonstrated, by the use of the ultramicroscope, to be continuously jiggling around, as shown in Figure 30, undergoing erratic motion which is called

Brownian movement. The particles show very little tendency to settle out of the air.

These generalizations are *laws* governing the behavior of all gases. They are truths of nature that can be demonstrated experimentally as often as we wish, using any kind of matter in the gaseous state.

What model can be suggested for the structure of all substances in the gaseous state that will account satisfactorily for these facts?

119. KINETIC-MOLECULAR THEORY OF GASES

The kinetic-molecular theory of the structure of gases has been developed to explain their behavior. In the early days, this theory was very crude and frequently was found to be inadequate for predicting the way gases should perform. Accordingly, the theory was modified and gradually took the form of the modern version, which may be summarized as follows:

a) *A substance in the gaseous state is a collection of discrete particles, its molecules. These molecules have fixed average mass and are extremely small compared with the average distances which separate them under ordinary conditions.*

b) *The molecules are in continuous, rapid, straight-line motion in random directions, colliding with each other and with the walls of the container.*

c) *The average kinetic energies of the molecules of different gases are the same at a given temperature and increase with increase in temperature.*

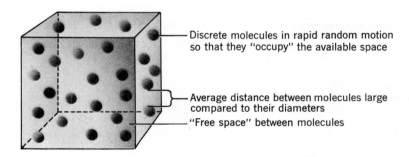

Discrete molecules in rapid random motion so that they "occupy" the available space

Average distance between molecules large compared to their diameters

"Free space" between molecules

Fig. 31. The molecular concept of a gas.

Figure 31 indicates the molecules of a gas in a given space. The molecules are highly magnified in size and, for convenience, are drawn as spheres. Remember that most real molecules have much more complicated shapes.

The kinetic-molecular theory has been very successful in accounting for the observed behavior of gases; in fact, it is now generally accepted as the truth. We now have strong experimental evidence for the existence of molecules and can measure their numbers, effective sizes, shapes, speeds, and masses.   Some specific figures for gases under standard conditions will help to establish a conception of the magnitudes involved and a feeling for the reality of molecules.   One milliliter of a gas under standard conditions contains, on the average, approximately 3×10^{19} molecules; yet the total actual volume of the molecules is negligible compared to the space they "occupy" because of their molecular motion.   The average distance between these molecules at standard conditions is approximately 13 times the average molecular diameter, and the total actual volume of the molecules is less than 0.1 per cent of the total volume "occupied" by the gas.

The hydrogen molecule weighs 3.348×10^{-24} g, has a diameter of about 2.2×10^{-8} cm, and at 0° has an average velocity of 1.84×10^5 cm or about 1 mile per sec.   In a sample of hydrogen gas at standard conditions, a molecule has on the average about 1.1×10^{10}, or 11 billion, collisions per second with other molecules and travels an average of about 16.6×10^{-6} cm between collisions.   At standard conditions the average velocity of oxygen molecules is 0.46×10^5 cm or about $\frac{1}{4}$ mile per sec, and the average distance traveled by an oxygen molecule between collisions is about 9.4×10^{-6} cm.

By virtue of its mass m and its velocity v, a molecule of a gas possesses *kinetic energy* according to the expression

$$\text{K.E.} = \tfrac{1}{2}mv^2$$

Heat is the total kinetic energy that the molecules of the system possess because of their motion.   The *temperature* of the gas is a measure of the average kinetic energy of the molecules.

The kinetic-molecular theory accounts for the general behavior of gases:

a. The pressure which a gas exerts is due to the bombardment of a given area by the molecules of the gas.   Because each molecule has mass and velocity, when it strikes a surface it will exert on that surface an *impulse* (pressure) which is dependent on the mass and velocity of the molecule and the time it acts on the surface.   The total pressure per unit area is proportional to the number of molecular impacts per unit of time and to the average impulse per impact.   The molecules of air in an automobile tire are continually colliding in tremendous numbers with the walls of the tire, forcing it to maintain its shape.

b. The diffusion and expansion of gases are consequences of the very rapid random motion of the molecules and of the possibility of increasing the average distance and the "free space" between them.   The term *free space* refers to the total space available to the gas minus the actual volume of the molecules.   Each molecule is relatively incompressible, compared to the sample of gas as a whole.

c. The compressibility characteristic of gases is explained by the idea that the amount of "free space" may be decreased and the average distances between molecules reduced until they come into close contact.

d. Gases mix freely because the molecules of one gas can diffuse among the molecules of another, owing to their random rapid motion and the enormous amount of "free space" between the molecules, irrespective of their species.

e. The increase of pressure of a gas with increase in the temperature reflects the increase in average kinetic energy of the molecules when they are heated. Since their average mass m is fixed and K.E. $= \frac{1}{2}mv^2$, as the temperature increases, they must move faster, and, because of their increased speed, they will hit the walls oftener and harder, exerting a greater pressure per unit area.

f. Brownian movement is due to the bombardment of the very small suspended particles by the gas molecules. Inequality in the number of collisions per unit time on unit areas of opposite sides of the particle produces erratic motion of the particle.

120. THE QUANTITATIVE BEHAVIOR OF GASES

So far, we have considered only the general or qualitative properties of gases and have shown how these are consistent with the kinetic-molecular theory. It is important to extend our discussion to the quantitative behavior of gases, in an effort to define the relationships between the number of molecules, molecular weight, rate of diffusion, volume, pressure, and temperature of gases. To do this, we must set up experiments in such a manner that only two of these quantities change and the others are held constant. We then can determine quantitatively, within the limits of the experiments, the relation between the two which are changing. By repeating this procedure, varying each pair of quantities in turn, the behavior of gases can be completely catalogued.

121. MOLECULAR WEIGHT AND RATE OF DIFFUSION

Thomas Graham in 1833 studied the effective rates of diffusion of various gases by comparing the rates at which samples, held at the same temperature and pressure, escaped through a hole in the container. He summarized his observations in what is usually known as *Graham's Law*. *At the same conditions of temperature and pressure, the rates of diffusion of gases are inversely proportional to the square roots of their average molecular masses (molecular weights).* By letting R_1 be the rate of diffusion of a gas having molecular weight m_1 and R_2 be the rate of diffusion of a gas having molecular weight m_2, Graham's Law may be stated mathematically as

$$\frac{R_1}{R_2} = \sqrt{\frac{m_2}{m_1}}$$

EXAMPLE: Calculate the relative rates of diffusion of hydrogen and oxygen. For oxygen and hydrogen at the same temperature and pressure,

$$\frac{R_{\text{oxygen}}}{R_{\text{hydrogen}}} = \sqrt{\frac{\text{molecular weight hydrogen}}{\text{molecular weight oxygen}}} = \sqrt{\frac{2}{32}} = \frac{1}{4}$$

Hydrogen diffuses four times as fast as oxygen under comparable conditions.

The kinetic-molecular theory accounts for this relationship between molecular mass and rate of diffusion. The kinetic energies of oxygen and hydrogen molecules are given by the expressions

$$\text{K.E.}_{\text{oxygen molecule}} = \tfrac{1}{2}m_O v_O{}^2$$
$$\text{K.E.}_{\text{hydrogen molecule}} = \tfrac{1}{2}m_H v_H{}^2$$

According to the theory, at a given temperature, the average kinetic energies of all kinds of molecules are equal.   Hence, at a given temperature

$$\text{K.E.}_{\text{oxygen molecules}} = \text{K.E.}_{\text{hydrogen molecules}}$$

Therefore,

$$\tfrac{1}{2}m_O v_O{}^2 = \tfrac{1}{2}m_H v_H{}^2$$
$$\frac{v_O{}^2}{v_H{}^2} = \frac{m_H}{m_O}$$
$$\frac{v_O}{v_H} = \sqrt{\frac{m_H}{m_O}}$$

The effective rate of diffusion R of a gas must be proportional to the absolute velocity v of its molecules, and, therefore,

$$\frac{R_{\text{oxygen}}}{R_{\text{hydrogen}}} = \sqrt{\frac{m_{\text{hydrogen}}}{m_{\text{oxygen}}}}$$

At a given temperature, the lighter the molecule is, the faster will be its average speed.   In order to possess as much kinetic energy as a heavier molecule, the lighter molecule must be traveling faster.

122. VOLUME AND PRESSURE OF A GIVEN NUMBER OF MOLECULES AT CONSTANT TEMPERATURE

The relation between volume and pressure can be established by trapping a given number of molecules of gas in the gas burette, holding the temperature constant, and measuring the pressure of the gas when it is expanded or compressed to various volumes.   It is found that when the volume is doubled, the pressure is halved, and that when the volume is halved, the pressure is doubled.   From such experiments it is clear that, *at constant temperature, the pressure of a given number of molecules of a gas is inversely proportional to the volume.*   This is *Boyle's Law,* discovered in

1662.   We can express this mathematically, letting p be the pressure at volume V, and p' being the pressure at volume V'.

$$\frac{p}{p'} = \frac{V'}{V}$$

or

$$pV = p'V' = K, \quad \text{and} \quad V = \frac{K}{p},$$

where the value of the constant K depends upon the number of molecules of the gas and the temperature.   For a given number of molecules of a gas at constant temperature, the product of pressure and volume is fixed. If the volume increases, the pressure must decrease accordingly; if the volume decreases, the pressure increases accordingly.

Boyle's Law can be deduced from the kinetic theory.   Suppose that we have a certain sample of gas in the gas burette A as shown in Figure 32, the circles representing the molecules.

According to the theory, the sample of gas consists of a certain fixed number of molecules having a certain fixed average molecular weight.   At a given temperature the molecules are moving in an erratic fashion and have a certain average kinetic energy, which is characteristic of that temperature and which remains the same as long as the temperature is held constant.   Because K.E. $= \frac{1}{2}mv^2$ and the average molecular weight and kinetic energy are not changed, the average speed of the molecules remains the same at constant temperature. If we decrease the volume of the gas

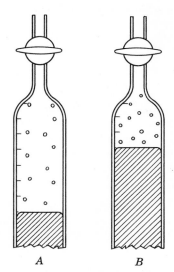

A   *B*

Fig. 32.   Relation between volume and pressure of gases.

to half the original volume by running in more mercury, as shown at B, the total number of molecules of gas in the burette remains the same, but the number of molecules per unit of volume is doubled.   This means that the total number of impacts of molecules per unit area of the surfaces confining the gas per unit of time is doubled.   The pressure exerted by the gas is therefore doubled because, on the average, each molecule is still hitting as hard as originally.

Relying upon the accuracy of Boyle's Law, we can calculate the change in pressure that should result if the volume of a given sample of gas undergoes a given change.

EXAMPLE: Suppose that a sample of hydrogen occupies a volume of 100 ml and its pressure is 50 mm. What will be its pressure if it expands to 200 ml, the temperature remaining the same?

Expansion of the gas means fewer impacts per unit area per unit time, and the pressure must decrease according to the inverse relationship. The pressure of the hydrogen at 200 ml volume will be equal to the original pressure multiplied by the fraction made up of the two volumes, the fraction being less than 1 because the pressure decreases.

$$\text{Pressure of sample of hydrogen at 200 ml} = 50 \text{ mm} \times \frac{100}{200} = 25 \text{ mm}$$

Inspection of this solution to the problem shows that the answer is consistent with the way the kinetic theory tells us hydrogen gas should behave.

In working gas problems, always go back to the kinetic theory and deduce the expression which will provide the answer desired. Do not memorize the mathematical expressions for the gas laws and substitute blindly in them. One of the purposes of assigning problems dealing with the behavior of gases is to give you practice in applying the theory of their structure.

123. TEMPERATURE AND PRESSURE OF A GIVEN NUMBER OF MOLECULES AT CONSTANT VOLUME

The relation between the temperature and pressure of a sample of a given number of molecules of gas, held at constant volume, can be studied in a gas burette, if the apparatus is modified so that the temperature of the gas may be changed. With proper care, it is possible to obtain data such as those given in the first two columns in Table 22, starting with the sample of gas at 100°C and a pressure of 373 mm of mercury.

Table 22. Variation of Pressure of a Sample of Gas with Temperature

Temperature t, °C	Pressure of Gas, Mm Hg	Temperature T, ° A
100	373	373
10	283	283
1	274	274
0	273	273
−1	272	272
−10	263	263
−100	173	173

From these data we can conclude that the pressure of a gas increases 1/273 of its pressure at 0° C for each degree rise in temperature. The pressure decreases the same fraction for each degree that the temperature is lowered. By plotting the temperature in ° C against the pressure, we get the straight line *AB* shown in Figure 33.

By extrapolation, we see that if the gas could be cooled to −273° C and stay as a gas, its pressure should become zero. This would mean that the velocity of the molecules would be reduced to zero, and that all the heat energy associated with the movement of the molecules would have been removed. Obviously, the gas could be cooled no further, and $-273°$ C is therefore referred to as *absolute zero*, the lowest temperature theoretically obtainable. It is interesting that, while no one has ever been able to cool matter down to absolute zero in the laboratory, experi-

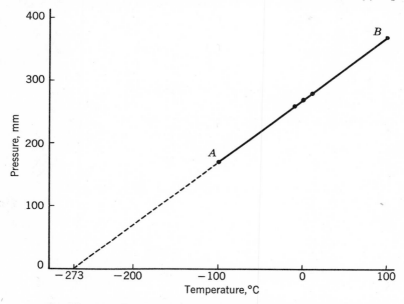

Fig. 33. Relation between pressure and temperature of gases.

menters have gotten to within 0.001° of it by using very special methods. But in these cases the matter was no longer in the gaseous state. Absolute zero has been shown recently to be a little lower than $-273°$ C. In 1955 an international committee adopted the value $-273.16°$ C as absolute zero, but in the discussion that follows, the value $-273°$ C will be more convenient and sufficiently accurate to use.

The absolute, or Kelvin, temperature scale is set up with absolute zero as the zero point, one degree on the absolute scale being of the same magnitude as one degree on the centigrade scale, and the readings usually being indicated as ° A or ° K. The symbol t is commonly used to indicate a temperature given on the centigrade scale, and T indicates a temperature given on the absolute scale. Conversion of centigrade to absolute readings involves the following realtionship:

$$\text{Degrees centigrade} + 273 = \text{degrees absolute}$$
$$°\,\text{C} \qquad + 273 = \qquad °\,\text{A}$$
$$t \qquad + 273 = \qquad T$$

Engineers in the United States and in England usually measure temperatures on the *Fahrenheit scale*, where the freezing point of water is taken as 32° F and the boiling point of water is 212° F.   Conversion of readings in degrees Fahrenheit to degrees centigrade are accomplished by making use of the expression

$$° C = \tfrac{5}{9}(° F - 32)$$

The relationship between the three temperature scales is shown in Figure 34.

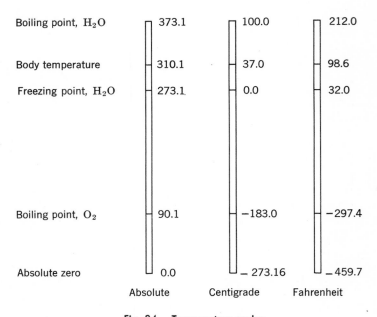

	Absolute	Centigrade	Fahrenheit
Boiling point, H_2O	373.1	100.0	212.0
Body temperature	310.1	37.0	98.6
Freezing point, H_2O	273.1	0.0	32.0
Boiling point, O_2	90.1	−183.0	−297.4
Absolute zero	0.0	−273.16	−459.7

Fig. 34.   Temperature scales.

Converting the temperature readings in centigrade, given in the first column of Table 22, to the absolute scale, we get the values given in the third column.   Comparing the values for pressure with those for temperature on the absolute scale, we note a simple relationship.   *At constant volume, the pressure of a given sample of gas is directly proportional to the absolute temperature.*   *Mathematically, we state this as*

$$\frac{p}{p'} = \frac{T}{T'}, \quad \text{or} \quad p = KT$$

where K is a constant whose value depends upon the number of molecules of the gas and the volume.   *In applying this law, be sure to remember to convert the temperature reading to the absolute scale.*

This law is consistent with the kinetic theory.   A given sample of gas is composed of a given number of molecules.   The theory postulates that the average kinetic energy of the molecules is directly proportional to the absolute temperature.   If the volume is kept constant, as the temperature is raised and the speed and kinetic energy of the molecules increase, the pressure developed must increase.

With the above relationship in mind, we can calculate what change in the pressure of a given sample of gas will result for a given change in temperature, and vice versa.

EXAMPLE: Suppose a sample of hydrogen occupies a volume of 100 ml at a pressure of 50 mm and a temperature of 20°.   What will be its pressure if the temperature is changed to 100°?

Since the temperature is increased, the kinetic energy of the molecules is increased, and the average velocity per molecule is increased.   This means that there will be more impacts per unit area per unit time and the molecules will be hitting harder; the pressure must increase.   The pressure of the hydrogen at 100° will be equal to the original pressure multiplied by the fraction made up of the two absolute temperatures, the fraction being greater than 1 because the pressure increases.

$$\text{Pressure of sample of hydrogen at } 100° = 50 \text{ mm} \times \frac{373}{293} = 63.7 \text{ mm}$$

124. TEMPERATURE AND VOLUME OF A GIVEN NUMBER OF MOLECULES AT CONSTANT PRESSURE

By selecting a sample of gas, changing its temperature, and measuring the change in volume that it undergoes when the pressure is kept constant, we can establish *Charles' Law: At constant pressure, the volume of a given number of molecules of a gas is directly proportional to the absolute temperature.*   Stated mathematically

$$\frac{V}{V'} = \frac{T}{T'}, \quad \text{or} \quad V = KT$$

The theory tells us that, as a gas is heated, the average kinetic energy of its molecules increases in proportion to the absolute temperature.   Therefore, the average velocity of the molecules increases, and the number of impacts and the impulse per impact will increase.   If the pressure per unit area is to be kept constant, the gas must expand to a larger volume so that the number of impacts per unit area will decrease sufficiently to offset the increase in impulse per impact.

EXAMPLE: Suppose that a sample of hydrogen occupies a volume of 100 ml at a temperature of 20°.   What will be its volume at 100°?

Since the temperature increases, the kinetic energy of the molecules must increase, and the number of impacts per unit area and the impulse per impact must increase.   The gas must expand to a larger volume if the pressure is to remain constant.   The volume of hydrogen at 100° will be equal to the original volume multiplied by a fraction made up of the absolute temperatures, the fraction being greater than 1 since the volume increases.

$$\text{Volume of sample of hydrogen at } 100° = 100 \times \frac{373}{293} = 127.3 \text{ ml}$$

Since the volume of a sample of gas varies with temperature and pressure, to compare different samples of gas it is necessary to consider them at the same conditions of temperature and pressure, usually under standard conditions. Problems correcting the volume of a given gas sample to standard conditions (STP) are worked by combining the effect due to temperature change with that due to pressure change.

EXAMPLE: Suppose we have a sample of hydrogen at 100° occupying a volume of 100 ml at a pressure of 700 mm. What will be the volume of this quantity of hydrogen under standard conditions?

The volume of the hydrogen under standard conditions will be equal to the original volume multiplied by a fraction made up of the two pressures, and also by a fraction made up of the two temperatures. The pressure fraction will be less than 1, since the pressure increases, and with this increase in pressure the volume must decrease. The temperature fraction will be less than 1, since the temperature decreases, and with this decrease in temperature the volume will become smaller.

$$\text{Volume of hydrogen STP} = 100 \times \frac{700}{760} \times \frac{273}{373} = 67.4 \text{ ml}$$

125. THE PRESSURE OF A MIXTURE OF GASES

Suppose we have hydrogen at a pressure of 50 mm in a 1-liter container, and oxygen at a pressure of 150 mm in a second 1-liter container. If the temperature is held constant and the oxygen is transferred to the 1-liter vessel holding the hydrogen, the total pressure of the mixture is found to be 200 mm. Experiments such as this lead to *Dalton's Law of Partial Pressures: The total pressure of a mixture of gases is equal to the sum of the partial pressures of the gases present.* The *partial pressure* of a gas is the pressure that the gas would exert if it were alone in the available space. If P is the total pressure of the mixture, and $p_1, p_2, p_3, \ldots$ are the partial pressures of gases 1, 2, 3, $\ldots$, then

$$P = p_1 + p_2 + p_3 + \cdots$$

Thus, since the atmosphere is a mixture of nitrogen, oxygen, water, carbon dioxide, and the inert gases,

$$P_{\text{atm}} = p_{N_2} + p_{O_2} + p_{H_2O} + p_{CO_2} + p_{\text{inert gases}}$$

When hydrogen is collected over water, water molecules will be present in the gas phase and

$$P_{\text{total pressure measured}} = p_{H_2} + p_{H_2O}$$
$$p_{H_2} = P - p_{H_2O}$$

Dalton's Law of Partial Pressures is in line with the kinetic-molecular theory. All kinds of molecules have the same average kinetic energy at a given temperature, and, on the average, each molecule, irrespective of kind, will make the same contribution to the total pressure. The total gas pressure in a given space is determined by the total number of molecules and by the temperature; the pressure is independent of the species of the molecules. The pressure that 100 molecules will exert in a flask of given capacity at a given temperature will be fixed, whether there are present 100 molecules of hydrogen, or 50 molecules of hydrogen and 50 molecules of oxygen, or 100 molecules of carbon dioxide.

126. REACTING VOLUMES OF GASES. AVOGADRO'S PRINCIPLE

You probably are now rather puzzled that, in this chemistry book, we have spent so much time describing the physical behavior of gases, a topic that is really in the domain of physics. We have done so because, by making use of the quantitative laws governing gases, the chemist can correlate the volumes and pressures of the gases reacting and formed in chemical changes with the masses of the substances involved. By means of the kinetic-molecular theory, we can arrive at an understanding of the structure of materials and of the way in which they participate in chemical change.

The early chemists were able, by simple methods, to determine the volumes, at constant pressure and temperature, of gases that take part in chemical reactions. In the electrolysis of water, for every two volumes of hydrogen produced, one volume of oxygen accumulates. In the synthesis of steam, two volumes of hydrogen combine with one volume of oxygen to give two volumes of steam.

$$2H_{2(g)} + O_{2(g)} = 2H_2O_{(g)}$$

2 volumes   1 volume   2 volumes

Such experimental observations were summarized in 1808 by Gay-Lussac as the *Law of Combining Volumes: Gases react and are produced in simple definite volume ratios.* These volume ratios are the mole ratios indicated by the balanced equations. Once the correct equation for a chemical change in which substances participate as gases is written, it is possible to calculate the actual volumes involved.

EXAMPLE: Suppose 5 liters of hydrogen STP combine with chlorine to form hydrogen chloride. What volume of chlorine will be used and what volume of hydrogen chloride will be formed?

$$H_{2(g)} + Cl_{2(g)} = 2HCl_{(g)}$$

The equation above tells us that, measured at the same temperature and pressure, when one volume of hydrogen reacts, one volume of chlorine combines with it to give two volumes of hydrogen chloride. Therefore 1 liter of hydrogen will combine with 1 liter of chlorine, and 5 liters of hydrogen STP will combine with 5 liters of chlorine STP.   One liter of hydrogen reacts to give 2 liters of hydrogen chloride; 5 liters of hydrogen STP will react to give $2 \times 5 = 10$ liters of hydrogen chloride.

To account for the Law of Combining Volumes, *Avogadro's Principle* was advanced in 1811.   *Equal volumes of all gases, under the same conditions of temperature and pressure, contain the same number of molecules.* This can be deduced from the kinetic-molecular theory.   Since all molecules, regardless of kind, have the same average kinetic energy at a given temperature, they all make the same contributions to volume at a given pressure.   The total volume of gas at a given temperature and pressure is determined by the number of molecules present.   *All molecules, irrespective of kind, have the same ability to occupy space.*   At given conditions, 100 molecules of hydrogen will occupy the same volume as 100 molecules of oxygen, 100 molecules of hydrogen chloride, or a mixture of 95 molecules of hydrogen and 5 molecules of water.   Avogadro's Principle gives the chemist a very convenient method for selecting equal numbers of molecules of different substances; he simply takes equal volumes of the gases under the same conditions of temperature and pressure.   At the time Avogadro suggested his principle, it was merely a guess.   However, we can now prove experimentally the truth of this statement, and Avogadro's Principle is accepted as a law.

It follows from Avogadro's Law and the kinetic-molecular theory that the weights of equal volumes of different gases under the same conditions of temperature and pressure must be different.   One liter of oxygen STP weighs 1.429 g, whereas 1 liter of hydrogen STP weighs only 0.0899 g.   Note that the ratio of these weights of equal volumes of the two gases is the same as the ratio of their molecular weights.

$$\frac{1.429 \text{ g of oxygen}}{0.0899 \text{ g of hydrogen}} = \frac{\text{molecular weight of oxygen}}{\text{molecular weight of hydrogen}} = \frac{32.00}{2.016}$$

127.   MOLAR VOLUMES AND MOLECULAR WEIGHTS

What volume under standard conditions will one mole of a gas occupy? We can calculate this for any substance if we know the weight of 1 liter STP of that substance and its molecular weight.

$$\begin{aligned} \text{Volume of one mole} \atop \text{of oxygen STP} &= \frac{\text{gram-molecular weight of oxygen}}{\text{weight of 1 liter of oxygen STP}} \\ &= \frac{32.00 \text{ g}}{1.429 \text{ g}} \\ &= 22.4 \text{ liters} \end{aligned}$$

The *gram-molecular volume*, or *molar volume*, is the volume STP of one mole of any substance as a gas.   The value 22.4 liters as calculated above is the molar volume of oxygen. According to the kinetic-molecular theory, the molar volume of any other gas should also be 22.4 liters. One mole of any gas contains, on the average, 6.02×10^{23} molecules, and every molecule, irrespective of kind, makes the same average contribution to volume under the same conditions of temperature and pressure.

We thus have a relationship between weight and volume which is very convenient to use. For any molecular substance,

$$\frac{\text{Gram-molecular weight}}{\text{Weight of 1 liter STP}} = 22.4 \text{ liters STP (its molar volume)}$$

If we know the molecular weight of any gas and remember that one mole will occupy 22.4 liters STP, we can calculate the volume STP of any weight of that gas. By applying the gas laws we can calculate what the volume will be under any other conditions of temperature and pressure.

EXAMPLE: What will be the volume of 11 g of CO_2 measured at 20° and 700 mm pressure? The molecular weight of CO_2 is 44.

$$\text{Volume of 11 g of } CO_2 \text{ STP} = 22.4 \times \frac{11}{44} = 5.6 \text{ liters}$$

Since the temperature specified in the problem is higher than 0°, the volume accordingly must be greater. Therefore, the volume STP must be multiplied by a fraction composed of the two absolute temperatures, and this fraction will be greater than 1. The pressure specified is less than 760 mm, and the volume accordingly must be greater. Therefore, the volume must be multiplied by a fraction composed of the two pressures, the fraction being greater than 1.

$$\text{Volume of 11 g of } CO_2 \text{ at } 20° \text{ and } 700 \text{ mm} = 5.6 \times \frac{293}{273} \times \frac{760}{700} = 6.5 \text{ liters}$$

The relation between gram-molecular weight, the weight of 1 liter STP, and the molar volume gives us an elegant experimental method for *determining the molecular weight* of any substance which can be handled as a gas. The weight and volume of a given sample of the gas are measured at a given temperature and pressure. Then the weight of 22.4 liters STP of the gas is calculated. This is the gram-molecular weight of the substance.

EXAMPLE: 200 ml of acetylene at 740 mm and 20° is found to weigh 0.2105 g. What is its molecular weight?

The volume of this sample of acetylene STP can be found by multiplying the known volume by fractions determined by the pressure change and the temperature change. The temperature is decreasing from 20 to 0°, which will cause the volume to decrease; the temperature fraction will be less than 1. The pressure increases from 740 to 760 mm, which will cause the volume to decrease; the pressure fraction will be less than 1.

$$\text{Volume of 0.2105 g acetylene STP} = 200 \times \frac{740}{760} \times \frac{273}{293} = 182 \text{ ml}$$

The weight of 182 ml of acetylene STP is 0.2105 g. Therefore,

$$\text{Weight of 1 liter STP} = 0.2105 \times \frac{1000}{182} = 1.16 \text{ g}$$
$$\begin{aligned} \text{The molecular weight} &= \text{weight of 22.4 liters} \\ &= 1.16 \times 22.4 \\ &= 26.0 \text{ g} \end{aligned}$$

Therefore the correct molecular formula for acetylene is C_2H_2, not CH.

128. THE GENERAL GAS LAW

The various quantitative relationships between the four factors—pressure, volume, number of molecules, and temperature—can be combined to give one general gas law that summarizes the behavior of all gases. For a given sample of gas

p is proportional to T, to $1/V$, and to the number of molecules

Therefore,

pV is proportional to T and to the number of molecules

We can use n to designate the number of moles, and this will indicate the total number of molecules, there being 6.02×10^{23} molecules per mole. Hence,

pV is proportional to $n \times T$

If we let R be the proportionality constant, then

$$pV = nRT$$

This is known as the *general gas law* and it summarizes the behavior of all gases.

The proportionality constant R, usually referred to as the *gas constant*, may be calculated from what we already know about gases. Its numerical value, irrespective of the kind of gas, will depend upon the units in which we express the pressure, volume, number of molecules, and temperature. Suppose we express p in atmospheres, V in liters, n in moles, and T in degrees absolute. We have learned that 1 mole of any gas at 273° A in a volume of 22.4 liters exerts a pressure of 1 atm. Substituting these values in

$$pV = nRT$$

we get

$$1 \text{ atm} \times 22.4 \text{ liters} = 1 \text{ mole} \times R \times 273° \text{ A}$$

Therefore

$$R = \frac{1 \text{ atm} \times 22.4 \text{ liter}}{1 \text{ mole} \times 273° \text{ A}} = 0.0820 \text{ atm liter/mole } °\text{A}$$

Knowing the value of R, and specifying the values for any three of the other terms, we can calculate the value for the remaining term.

EXAMPLE: What will be the volume in liters of 64.0 g of oxygen at 380 mm of pressure and 273° C?

First the weight, pressure, and temperature of the gas must be converted to moles, atmospheres, and degrees absolute; these are the units for which R equals 0.0820.

$$\frac{64.0 \text{ g of oxygen}}{32.0 \text{ g of oxygen per mole}} = 2.00 \text{ moles of oxygen}$$

$$\frac{380 \text{ mm}}{760 \text{ mm per atm}} = 0.500 \text{ atm}$$

$$273° \text{ C} + 273° = 546° \text{ A}$$

Substituting these values in the equation $pV = nRT$

$$0.500 \text{ atm} \times V \text{ liters} = 2.00 \text{ moles} \times 0.0820 \times 546° \text{ A}$$

$$V = \frac{2.00 \times 0.0820 \times 546}{0.500} = 179 \text{ liters}$$

EXAMPLE: How many moles of any gas must be introduced into a container having a volume of 1,120 ml in order that the pressure of the gas be 190 mm at 0° C?

$$\frac{1120 \text{ ml}}{1,000 \text{ ml per liter}} = 1.12 \text{ liters}$$

$$\frac{190 \text{ mm}}{760 \text{ mm per atm}} = 0.250 \text{ atm}$$

$$0° \text{ C} + 273° = 273° \text{ A}$$

Substituting in the equation $pV = nRT$

$$0.250 \text{ atm} \times 1.12 \text{ liters} = n \text{ moles} \times 0.0820 \times 273° \text{ A}$$

$$n = \frac{0.250 \times 1.12}{0.0820 \times 273} = 0.0125 \text{ moles of any gas}$$

129. DEVIATIONS FROM THE IDEAL-GAS LAWS

The gas laws described above were based on limited and not very precise observations of gases at temperatures and pressures in the neighborhood of ordinary conditions. These laws hold reasonably well for gases at relatively low pressures and at relatively high temperatures, that is, when the average intermolecular distance is large and the average kinetic energy is high. They do not hold so well when the gases are observed at high pressures and at low temperatures, when the intermolecular distances are small and the average kinetic energy of the molecules is low.

According to Boyle's Law, at constant temperature, pV should remain constant as the pressure of a sample of gas is varied. In Figure 35, where pV is plotted against p, and the number of molecules and the temperature are such that pV is unity at 1 atm, any gas behaving "ideally" (strictly according to Boyle's Law) should give the horizontal line labeled "Ideal gas" at constant temperature.   The actual values measured for hydrogen, oxygen, and carbon dioxide give the curves shown, which at high pressures deviate considerably from the ideal case.

All actual gases show deviations from the ideal-gas laws.   These are new facts, the discovery of which requires us to modify the kinetic-molecular theory, which we have found to account so nicely for the ideal-gas laws.   How can the deviations from the laws be accounted for?

If we consider the molecular systems more carefully, we will discover two reasons why we may expect the laws to break down at low tempera-

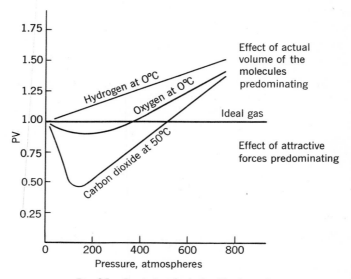

Fig. 35.   **Deviation from the ideal-gas laws.**

tures and high pressures.   In our discussion so far, we have neglected to take into account the *actual volume of the molecules* and any *attractive forces that may exist between them*.   We have dealt with so-called *ideal gases*, those whose molecules have zero volume and no attraction for each other.   But with real gases, we should expect deviations due to actual molecular volumes and to actual intermolecular attractive forces, as indicated in Figure 36.

When we measure the volume of a gas, we actually measure not only the free space between the molecules, but also the volume of the molecules.   In the ideal-gas laws, *V* should apply only to the free space. The changes in volume calculated by use of Boyle's Law are the changes in the free space.   At low pressures, the volume of the free space is so huge compared to the actual volume of the molecules that we can neglect the latter, and the total volume will be a reasonably good measure of the free space.   But at high pressures the molecules, on the average, get very close together, and then their volume becomes appreciable compared to the free space. The total volume measured will tend to be greater than that calculated by means of the gas laws. Because of the volume of the molecules, the pV measured will tend to be greater than that calculated by Boyle's Law, and the curve for the real gas will tend to rise above the ideal curve.

Attractive forces do exist between real molecules, and these attractive forces increase rapidly as the molecules approach each other. The attraction is negligible at very low pressures because of the great average distance between molecules. But when the gas is compressed and the molecules get closer, the attractive forces become significant with respect to the kinetic energy of the molecules. The motion of the molecules

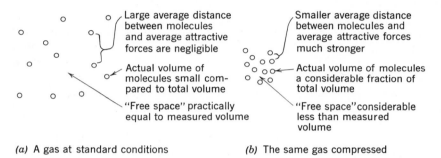

(a) A gas at standard conditions   (b) The same gas compressed

Fig. 36.   A real gas at low and high pressures.

becomes restricted. The pressure they exert and their ability to occupy space becomes less because of this attraction. The effect will be to make the product pV actually less than that calculated, and the curve for the real gas will tend to fall below the ideal curve. At lower temperature the average kinetic energy of the molecules is smaller and the deviation due to intermolecular attraction is greater.

The two factors causing deviation will tend to counterbalance each other, but the net effect still may be a considerable variation. This net deviation varies with different gases at a given temperature, reflecting the differences in attractive forces between the molecules and their differences in volume as the kind of molecule changes. Obviously, a careful study of the deviations shown by a given gas may be useful in giving us information as to the nature of its molecules. Deviations become more pronounced at lower temperatures because the effect of the attractive forces becomes relatively greater as the average kinetic energy of the molecules decreases.

Because of the attractive forces between molecules, when a real gas, such as oxygen or carbon dioxide, is allowed to expand from a highly compressed state into a vacuum, the gas cools. This cooling effect is due to the fact that work must be done against the attractive forces to increase the average intermolecular distance. This work increases the potential energy of the system at the expense of the kinetic energy of the molecules, and the temperature is lowered. Thus, carbon dioxide may cool so much on rapid expansion, when it escapes from a storage cylinder, that it may freeze to dry ice. If the gas were ideal, it would not cool down when it expanded into a vacuum. When a gas is compressed, it heats up because the loss of potential energy and gain of kinetic energy by the molecules.

It is important to remember that in the kinetic-molecular theory of gases the specification is made that the molecules of a gas have a fixed average mass, and the ideal-gas laws assume that these molecules persist unchanged in mass through changes in pressure and temperature. The number of molecules in a given sample of gas therefore is assumed to remain constant. Actually, however, in many cases when the pressure and temperature of a real gas are changed, its molecules undergo chemical change splitting up to give a larger total number of molecules or uniting to give a smaller total number of molecules. It is obvious that in such a case the sample of gas will not obey the ideal-gas laws and that the deviation from these may be used to follow the chemical changes which occur.

The observed deviations from the gas laws might have led us to discard them and the kinetic theory devised to explain them. However, the deviations turn out to be just what we would predict if we consider more carefully the properties of real molecules and apply the theory accordingly. The net effect has been to give us better understanding of the nature of real gases. We can continue to use the ideal-gas laws at relatively low pressures and relatively high temperatures, such as standard conditions, knowing that they describe the actual behavior of gases under these conditions with reasonable accuracy, provided that no chemical changes occur.

EXERCISES

1. How does the kinetic-molecular theory account for the fact:
a) That when a small bottle of hydrogen sulfide gas is opened in a large room, the disagreeable odor of this gas very soon becomes apparent in all parts of the room?
b) That one mole of oxygen in a given container at a given temperature exerts the same pressure as does one mole of hydrogen under the same conditions?
c) That although 1 liter of oxygen STP weighs only 1.429 g, steel cylinders containing over 200 g of oxygen per liter capacity are available on the market?
d) That an automobile tire is much more likely to blow out on a hot summer day than in cold winter weather?
e) That a toy rubber balloon filled with hydrogen will rise rapidly when released in the air?

2. Will there be an increase or decrease in: a) the number of molecular impacts per unit surface, b) the average kinetic energy per molecule, c) the number of molecules per unit volume, d) the average molecular velocity, and e) the weight per unit volume,

1) When the temperature of a sample of gas in a container is raised?
2) When the volume of a sample of gas is increased, the temperature remaining constant?
3) When the number of moles per unit volume of a given gas is increased, the temperature remaining constant?

3. a) Which will diffuse the faster at the same temperature, molecules of CH_4 or molecules of HCl?

   b) How will the average kinetic energies of the molecules of these two gases compare?

4. Substance A has a molecular weight of 36 and substance B has a molecular weight of 81. Compare the rates at which molecules of these substances diffuse at room temperature. What will happen to their rates of diffusion if the temperature is raised to 100°, and how will their diffusion rates compare at this new temperature?

5. A sample of hydrogen measures 20 ml at 20° and a pressure of 1 atm. What will be the volume of this hydrogen if the pressure is increased to 4 atm, the temperature remaining constant?

6. 100 ml of air at 25° exerts a pressure of 300 mm. If the volume is kept constant and the air is heated to 596°, what will be the pressure?

7. A sample of oxygen has a volume of 250 ml at 23° and 500 mm pressure.
   a) What will be its volume at 319°, the pressure remaining at 500 mm?
   b) What will be its volume if the pressure is increased to 2,500 mm, the temperature remaining at 23°?
   c) At what temperature will its volume be 500 ml at a pressure of 500 mm?
   d) What will be its pressure at 319° if its volume is 250 ml?

8. A given quantity of gas has a volume of 40 liters at 273° and 100 atm pressure.
   a) What will be the volume of this gas at standard conditions?
   b) How many moles are there of this gas?

9. At what temperature will the pressure of a given amount of air in an automobile tire rise to 40 lb per sq in. if it is 30 lb per sq in. at 20°, assuming the volume of the tire does not change?

10. Calculate the weight of 1 liter of SO_2 gas STP. Will the weight per liter increase or decrease: a) with rise in temperature? b) with rise in pressure?

11. Compute the molecular weight of a gas if 67.2 liters of it STP weighs 96 g. The simplest formula for this gas is NH_2. What is its true molecular formula?

12. The following data were obtained for a certain gas. 1.060 g occupied a volume of 1 liter when collected over water at a pressure of 742 mm at 29°. Its

weight composition was found to be 85.63 per cent carbon and 14.37 per cent hydrogen. The partial pressure of water in the gas was 30 mm.
   a) What is the weight of one mole of the gas?
   b) What is its simplest formula?
   c) What is its molecular formula?

   13. What is the pressure in a 1-liter tank that contains two moles of oxygen and four moles of hydrogen at 0°?

   14. What will be the volume STP of 64 g of CH_4?

   15. 12.04×10^{23} molecules of hydrogen are in a container having.a capacity 11.2 liters. What will be the pressure in the container at 32° F?

   16. The weight of 1 liter of oxygen at 0° and 760 mm pressure is 1.429 g.
   a) What will be the weight of 1 liter of oxygen at 0° and a pressure of 1,520 mm?
   b) What will be the weight of 1 liter of oxygen at 273° and a pressure of 760 mm?

   17. Ten liters of hydrogen is reacted with oxygen gas to form steam. At the same conditions of temperature and pressure, what volume of oxygen is needed for this reaction and what volume of water vapor is formed?

   18. If five moles of zinc reacts with hydrochloric acid, according to the equation

$$Zn + 2HCl = H_2 + ZnCl_2$$

what will be the volume STP of the hydrogen gas that is formed?

   19. You wish to prepare five moles of HCl by the reaction

$$H_2 + Cl_2 = 2HCl$$

What volumes STP of hydrogen and chlorine will be required?

   20. Which can be expected to show the larger deviation from the ideal-gas laws, other factors being similar:
   a) A gas that has weak intermolecular attractive forces or a gas that has strong forces of attraction between its molecules?
   b) A gas composed of small molecules or one made up of large molecules?

Chapter 10

▶ The Liquid State

130. CONDENSED STATES OF MATTER

When gases are cooled and compressed they tend to condense to the liquid state. Upon further cooling, liquids tend to freeze and change to the solid state. We have seen that in gases, matter is in a highly dispersed form, the particles being widely separated. When a gas condenses to a liquid, its particles come into close contact. Such close contact

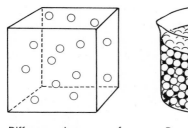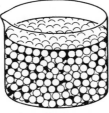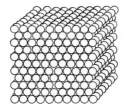

Diffuse random array of molecules in gas phase

Densely packed but random array of molecules in liquid phase

Dense and ordered array of molecules in solid phase

Fig. 37. Comparison of molecules in gaseous, liquid, and solid states.

between the constituent particles is also characteristic of the solid state. Figure 37 compares the way in which molecules are arranged in the three states. Accordingly, the liquid and solid states are referred to as condensed states of matter. We will consider the liquid state in this chapter and continue in the next chapter with a discussion of the solid state.

131. THE GENERAL PROPERTIES OF LIQUIDS

Liquids are observed to be mobile, having no fixed shape; they flow readily to assume the shape of the container. Unlike gases, liquids are relatively *incompressible*, and a given mass of liquid has a fixed volume at a given temperature. Liquids undergo only small changes in volume with change in temperature. A liquid, if its total volume is less than that of its container, will occupy only a portion of the available space.

It flows to the lower part of the container and *maintains a definite, horizontal, upper surface*, or boundary.

132. LIQUEFACTION OF GASES

The kinetic-molecular theory can be extended to cover the conversion of gases to liquids. When we cool a gas, we lower the average kinetic energy of its molecules; and when we compress it, we force its molecules, on the average, closer together. In a real gas, the attractive forces between the molecules will increase with compression. Eventually the attraction may become greater than the tendency, owing to their kinetic energy, for the molecules to move apart, especially if the gas is cooled at the same time. The molecules will then coalesce and form a liquid.

It is not enough, in all cases, simply to compress the gas in order to achieve liquefaction. A temperature exists for each gas above which the substance does not liquefy, no matter how much the molecules are crowded together, no matter how much the gas is compressed. This is called the *critical temperature*. Above this temperature the average kinetic energy of the molecules is sufficient to overcome the attractive intermolecular forces, and the molecules do not coalesce. At, and below, the critical temperature, the forces of attraction are sufficient to overcome the tendency for the molecules to separate only if the average distance between the molecules is small enough, that is, only if the gas is compressed sufficiently. The pressure necessary to liquefy the gas at the critical temperature is called the *critical pressure*. Each substance has its own characteristic critical temperature and critical pressure. These are given in Table 23 for some common substances.

Table 23.   Thermal Properties of Some Common Substances

Substance	Critical Temperature, °A	Critical Pressure, Atm	Molar Heat of Vaporization, Cal/Mole	Normal Boiling Point, °A
Helium	5.2	2.26	23.9	4.2
Hydrogen	33.24	12.8	216	20.3
Nitrogen	126.0	33.5	1,338	77.2
Oxygen	154.3	49.7	1,636	90.0
Carbon dioxide	304.2	73.0		
Ammonia	405.5	111.5	5,561	239.6
Ether	466.9	35.5	6,210	307.5
Alcohol	516.2	63.1	9,384	351.4
Water	647.1	217.7	9,712	373.0

The values for the critical temperatures reflect the magnitude of the attractive forces between the molecules. Substances with strong intermolecular attraction, such as water, alcohol, ether, and ammonia, can be liquefied at relatively high temperatures if they are compressed sufficiently. Hydrogen molecules are not attracted strongly to each other, and hydrogen must be cooled very much before it liquefies, regardless of how high the pressure is.

133. THE STRUCTURE OF LIQUIDS

The liquid state for a *molecular substance* consists of molecules held in close contact by their attractive forces. Because the molecules themselves are not easily distorted, and because they must maintain contact in order to be in the liquid state, the liquid changes only very slightly in volume when the pressure is changed; liquids are relatively incompressible and undergo only small change in volume when the temperature is changed. The molecules in a liquid still possess kinetic energy and are able to move past each other in random fashion, undergoing diffusion. A given molecule in a beaker of water is continually moving around and has the possibility of being anywhere in the space occupied by the liquid. The structure of a liquid is a *random structure*, a given molecule having no fixed neighboring molecules.

Ionic substances in the liquid state are made up of ions that behave much as do the molecules in a molecular liquid. Liquid sodium chloride is made up of Na^+ and Cl^- in equal numbers. The structure is random, the ions undergoing diffusion. By modifying the kinetic theory to take into account the effect of the electrical charges of the ions, it is possible to explain satisfactorily the behavior of ionic liquids. The attractive forces between ions of opposite charge are much stronger than the forces of attraction between molecules.

134. EVAPORATION OF LIQUIDS

A sample of liquid, such as water, when exposed to the air and allowed to stand, is observed to decrease in volume. This decrease can only be due to the escape of water molecules from the liquid to the gaseous state. *Evaporation* is said to occur. Why do liquids evaporate?

Suppose that in Figure 38 the circles indicate, on a considerably magnified scale, the molecules comprising the surface of the liquid and some of those below the surface. The intermolecular forces of attraction hold the molecules together in the liquid so that they cannot leave freely. The molecules in the surface layer are held down by attraction to the molecules below and beside them. If a molecule is to escape to the gaseous state above the liquid, it must have enough kinetic energy to overcome the net attractive force to the other molecules of liquid. So far, we have been very careful to speak of the "average" kinetic energy that molecules have at a given temperature. We have specified "average" because it can be shown that the actual kinetic energies of individual molecules of a substance at a given temperature do vary. At a given instant some molecules have more energy, some have less, than the average. And because, when collision occurs, kinetic energy may be transferred from one molecule to another, the kinetic energy of a given molecule changes. However, as long as the liquid as a whole remains at the

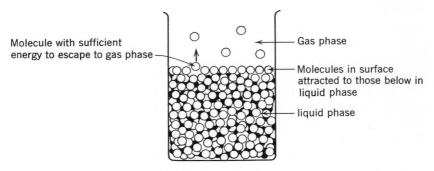

Molecule with sufficient energy to escape to gas phase

Gas phase

Molecules in surface attracted to those below in liquid phase

liquid phase

Fig. 38.   Evaporation of a liquid.

same temperature, the average kinetic energy of its molecules remains the same. The distribution of kinetic energy among the molecules of a liquid at a given temperature can be demonstrated to conform to the curve shown in Figure 39.

Each point on the curve represents the percentage of molecules in the liquid having a given actual kinetic energy. Most of the molecules have kinetic energies near that of A, the average for the liquid. The

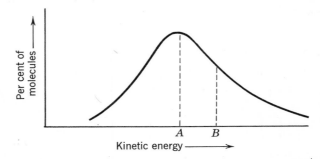

Fig. 39.   Distribution of kinetic energy among molecules of a liquid at a given temperature.

points on the curve to the left of A represent molecules that have less than the average kinetic energy of the system. The points on the curve to the right of A represent the molecules that have more kinetic energy than the average for the system. If B is the kinetic energy that is just sufficient for a molecule to escape from the liquid, then the molecules represented on the curve as having kinetic energies of this value or greater will be the ones in the liquid that have the possibility of escaping to the gaseous state.   Each liquid has a specific molecular-energy distribution curve at a given temperature.   At that temperature a certain fixed percentage of the molecules will have enough kinetic energy to escape.   The escape of these more energetic molecules will lower the average kinetic energy of those remaining, and the temperature of the liquid will be lowered, the curve being displaced to the left.   This displacement accounts for the cooling effect observed when evaporation occurs.

When the molecules change from the liquid to the gaseous state, they separate against the intermolecular forces of attraction.   This means that work is done, the molecules losing kinetic energy and gaining potential energy.   Heat may be supplied in sufficient amounts from the surroundings to counteract this cooling effect and allow the liquid to evaporate at a fixed temperature.

The energy that must be supplied to evaporate a given mass of liquid at a given temperature is known as the *heat of vaporization*.   If the quantity of liquid evaporating is one mole, then we speak of the *molar heat of vaporization*.   The value of the molar heat of vaporization should vary as we change the type of molecule.   The same number of molecules, 6.02×10^{23}, is involved per mole of all molecular liquids, but the forces of intermolecular attraction vary.   Table 23 shows the molar heats of vaporization of some common substances at their normal boiling points.   Here, as in the case of the critical temperature, there is a correlation with the forces of attraction; the greater the attractive forces between the molecules, the larger is the amount of kinetic energy needed for vaporization and the more endothermic is the transition from liquid to gas.   Since the forces holding ions in the liquid state are much larger than intermolecular forces, ionic liquids do not vaporize readily.

135. EQUILIBRIUM VAPOR PRESSURE

At a given temperature, the percentage of molecules of a liquid that have kinetic energy enough above the average to allow them to escape is fixed.   Hence, the *escaping tendency*, the tendency for the molecules of the liquid to evaporate, will be fixed for a given temperature and will be a specific property of the substance.   How can this be measured?

Suppose we place a beaker of a liquid, such as water, under a bell jar, as in Figure 40.   The water is free to evaporate, but the molecules that escape into the gaseous state are trapped in the bell jar.   If we allow the system to stand at constant temperature, we observe that at first the level of water in the beaker goes down, but that eventually the volume of liquid remaining in the beaker becomes constant.   Why?

The molecules, as they evaporate, cannot escape from the bell jar, and they accumulate as a vapor in the limited space above the liquid.   In the gaseous state they exert pressure, the *partial aqueous vapor pres-*

sure, the magnitude of this pressure being determined by the concentration of molecules and the temperature.   The molecules of the vapor are moving in a random fashion and, sooner or later, will travel back to the surface of the liquid.   There, the attraction to the other molecules in the liquid may cause the vapor molecules to enter the liquid, and they may *condense.*   As evaporation progresses at constant temperature (and, therefore, at constant rate per unit surface area) and the concentration of molecules in the vapor state increases, the number of molecules condensing per unit of time increases.   Eventually the *rate of condensation becomes equal to the rate of evaporation,* and *equilibrium* is reached by the system.   This is spoken of as a case of *dynamic equilibrium.*   It involves the reversible change of state, in which the opposing changes, evaporation and condensation, continue, but the rates of these opposing changes have become equal.   Once equilibrium has been established, the total number of molecules in each state remains constant, although there is a continual interchange of molecules between the two states.   A given molecule has the possibility of traveling back and forth between the two states.

As equilibrium between the liquid and gaseous states is approached the vapor pressure approaches a maximum.   *At equilibrium the vapor phase is* said to be *saturated,* and the pressure of the vapor is called the *saturation, or equilibrium, vapor pressure.*   This equilibrium vapor pressure for the substance will be a measure of the escaping tendency of the liquid at that temperature.   Frequently, just the term *vapor pressure* is used when the term equilibrium vapor pressure is meant.   This usage is regrettably loose, since the term *vapor pressure* may refer to the actual

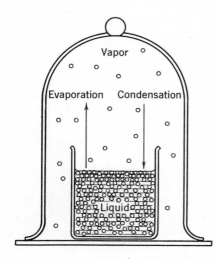

Fig. 40.   Evaporation and condensation.

Table 24.   Equilibrium Vapor Pressures in Millimeters of Mercury at Various Temperatures

Sub-stance	0°	20°	40°	60°	80°	100°	120°
Water	4.58	17.5	55.3	149.4	355.1	760.0	1490
Alcohol	12.2	43.9	135.3	352.7	812.6	1693.3	3225
Ether	185.3	442.2	921.3	1730.0	2993.6	4859.4	7494

pressure of vapors when the vapor phase is not saturated and not at equilibrium with the liquid phase.   (The term *vapor tension* is also sometimes used to refer to the escaping tendency of a liquid.)

We can easily measure the equilibrium vapor pressure of various liquids at various temperatures by determining the height of a column of mercury that the vapor pressure will support.   Some data thus obtained are given in Table 24 for water, alcohol, and ether.

Study of these data shows that *two factors determine the equilibrium vapor pressure:*

a. The nature of the liquid.   At a given temperature the equilibrium vapor pressure of water is less than that of alcohol, which, in turn, is less than that of ether.   The molecules of water have the lowest escaping tendency, and those of ether have the highest escaping tendency.   This factor is in accordance with the decrease in intermolecular forces of attraction as we go from water to alcohol and then to ether.   The equilibrium vapor pressure of a liquid is characteristic of its particular kind of molecule.   In general, polar substances are less volatile than nonpolar substances of comparable molecular weight.   With substances having similar polarity and structure, the volatility usually decreases with increase in molecular weight.

b. The temperature.   The data in Table 24 show that in the case of each substance, as the temperature increases, the equilibrium vapor pressure increases.   With increase in temperature there is an increase in the average kinetic energy of the molecules.   This means that the curve for the distribution of energy among the molecules of the liquid will be displaced to the right, and a higher percentage of the molecules will have sufficient energy to escape to the gas phase.   The escaping tendency and the equilibrium vapor pressure increase with rise in temperature.   More energy is available in the system for doing the work of separating the molecules.

By plotting the equilibrium vapor pressure against the temperature, the curves shown in Figure 41 may be constructed.   Each pure liquid has its own characteristic equilibrium vapor pressure–temperature curve on which any point defines the saturation vapor pressure of the liquid at the temperature indicated.

A liquid is said to *boil* when bubbles of its vapor form in the liquid and rise to the surface to release the vapor.   If the liquid is exposed to the air, the liquid will boil when the equilibrium vapor pressure becomes equal to atmospheric pressure.   The *normal boiling point* of a liquid is the temperature at which its equilibrium vapor pressure is 760 mm, that is, standard pressure.   If the equilibrium vapor pressure–temperature curve for a given liquid is available, it is a simple matter to read off the normal boiling point of the substance.   Thus, in Figure 41, ether is seen to have a normal boiling point of 34.5°, alcohol 78.4°, and water 100°.   Because local atmospheric pressures vary with atmospheric conditions, and because these, for places above sea level, are usually less than 760 mm, liquids often "boil" below their normal boiling points.   At 2.7 miles above sea level, as on Pike's Peak, the atmospheric pressure is commonly only about 450 mm, and there water boils at 86°; at the shore of the Dead Sea, 1,300 ft below sea level, water boils at 101.14°.   At high

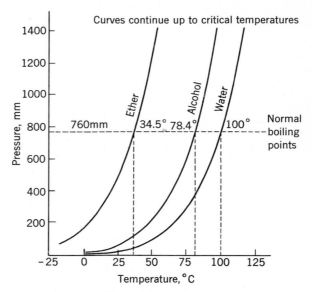

Fig. 41.   Equilibrium vapor pressure-temperature curves.

elevations boiling water does not make available such high temperatures for cooking as it does at sea level, and food cooks more slowly.   Pressure cookers make it possible to cook faster by maintaining higher vapor pressures above the water.   These pressures raise the boiling point of the water and the temperature to which the food is heated.   By controlling the vapor pressure above a liquid, we can control the temperature at which equilibrium is set up between the liquid and vapor phases.

Inspection of the normal boiling points for some common substances given in Table 23 shows clearly that the values increase in the same general order as do the critical temperatures and the heats of vaporization.   This is to be expected, since all these quantities should increase with an increase in the forces of attraction between molecules.

136. DISTILLATION OF LIQUIDS

We have seen that liquids tend to evaporate to give vapors, and that vapors tend to condense to form liquids.   Evaporation is an endothermic change, and the addition of heat to the system speeds up the rate of evaporation.   Condensation is an exothermic change, and cooling the vapor will favor such condensation.   We take advantage of these facts in *distillation*, which is employed so frequently in the laboratory and in industry.   When a liquid is distilled, its molecules are given a round trip from the liquid state to the vapor state and back to the liquid state, as shown in Figure 42.

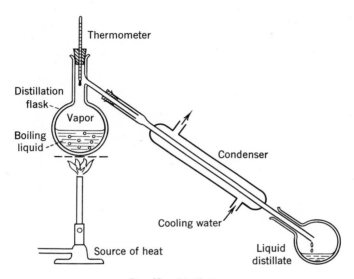

Fig. 42.   Distillation.

By heating the liquid in the distillation flask, the liquid is converted to vapor, which flows over into the condenser.   When the vapor is chilled by contact with the walls of the condenser, the molecules condense to the liquid distillate, which flows into the collecting vessel.

137.   LIQUID AIR

The principles that we have found to govern the relations of gases and liquids are well illustrated in the liquefaction of air and the behavior of this and other refrigerating liquids.   Figure 43 shows schematically the essential steps in the liquefaction of air.

Air is compressed, after water vapor and carbon dioxide have been removed.   The heat developed by the compression of the gas is removed by cooling.   The cool compressed gas is then allowed to pass through the valve of the liquefier into a region of lower pressure.   The gas expands at the expense of its kinetic energy, and the temperature is lowered. This cold expanded air is allowed to flow back around the coils containing the compressed gas, and the temperature of the latter is lowered.   As a result, a portion of the original air condenses to the liquid state.   This liquid air is stored in Dewar vessels, double-walled glass containers of the vacuum-bottle type which give good thermal insulation.

Liquid air is a mixture of oxygen, nitrogen, and small amounts of the more condensable inert gases. At atmospheric pressure, the liquid mixture boils at about $-190°$. It is a mobile, almost colorless liquid and is very useful as a refrigerant for cooling other materials.

Since liquid air is principally a mixture of oxygen and nitrogen, it serves as an excellent source of these elements. The normal boiling point of nitrogen is $-195.8°$, whereas that of oxygen is $-183°$. The nitrogen

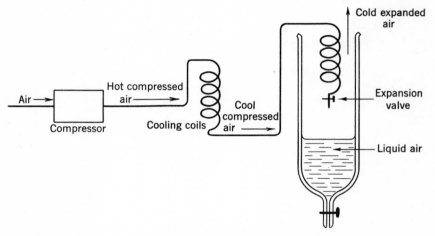

Fig. 43.   Liquefaction of air.

molecules thus have a greater escaping tendency than the molecules of oxygen and will tend to evaporate first, the residual liquid becoming richer in oxygen. If proper methods of fractional evaporation are used, the first fractions of gas obtained will be relatively pure nitrogen, while the last fractions will be relatively pure oxygen. The liquefaction and fractional evaporation of air are used to provide cheap supplies of nitrogen and oxygen for large-scale use. The process can be refined so that the inert gases of the atmosphere also can be extracted. The neon used in neon electric lighting tubes is obtained in this fashion.

EXERCISES

1. Classify each of the following as exothermic or endothermic: a) evaporation of a liquid; b) the transition from the gaseous to the liquid state; c) raising the temperature of a gas; d) lowering the temperature of a liquid.

2. Compare the structure and general properties of a molecular substance in the liquid state with its structure in the gaseous state.

3. a) Why do compression and cooling of a gas lead to its liquefaction?

b) Why is it not always sufficient only to compress a gas in order to effect its transition to the liquid state?

4. Ether is sometimes used to produce local anesthesia by spraying the liquid on the skin and allowing the ether to evaporate, the nerves in the vicinity becoming chilled and numb.

a) How do you account for the effectiveness of ether for this use?

b) Why will water be less effective?

5. How many calories of heat must be added to keep the temperature of the system constant when 37.06 g of ether, $(C_2H_5)_2O$, evaporates at the normal boiling point?

6. If at one time the atmospheric pressure at a given point is 750 mm and at another time it is 720 mm, at which time would water have the lower boiling point?

7. Why do people in hot arid regions frequently store drinking water in porous earthenware jars in spite of the fact that there is some loss of water during such storage?

8. The attractive forces between molecules of sulfur dioxide, SO_2, are much greater than the attractive forces between molecules of methane, CH_4. Which of these two substances will have: a) the higher critical temperature? b) the lower molar heat of vaporization? c) the lower equilibrium vapor pressure at a given temperature? d) the lower normal boiling point?

9. From the thermal data given in Table 23, account for the fact that ammonia has been widely used as a refrigerant in liquid-gas refrigerating systems.

10. A sample of hydrogen is collected at 20° over water, the gas phase having a volume of 2 liters and being at equilibrium with the liquid phase. The total pressure of the gas phase is found to be 93.5 mm. What would be the volume of the hydrogen if it were dry and its pressure were 152 mm at 20°? (Make use of Table 24.)

11. a) What changes in state take place in the process of distillation?

b) How is the apparatus shown in Figure 42 designed to cause each of these changes to occur?

12. Making use of Figure 41, predict the order in which the compounds water, ether, and alcohol will appear in the distillate if a mixture of the three is distilled.

Chapter 11

▶ The Solid State

138. FREEZING OR CRYSTALLIZATION

When water is cooled to 0° and more heat is removed, the liquid freezes and forms ice crystals which are hard and rigid. The system no longer flows readily. In order to freeze water, we must withdraw considerable amounts of heat from the system.

This behavior is what may be expected from the kinetic theory. When molecules or ions in the liquid state are cooled, they lose kinetic energy and move more slowly. If they lose sufficient kinetic energy, their random motion and ability to change position with respect to each other become so small, compared with the forces of attraction between the particles, that they tend to take up fixed positions in space relative to each other. They pack together in a regular three-dimensional pattern, and we say the liquid *freezes*, or *crystallizes*, to give a *solid*, or *crystalline material*. This material may be a solid chunk made up of many interlocking crystals, or it may be a collection of separate single crystals.

139. THE GENERAL PROPERTIES OF SOLIDS

Solids are rigid and maintain their own shapes. They show very little tendency to expand or contract in volume, tremendous pressure being necessary to produce appreciable compression. They change only slightly in volume when the temperature is changed. The crystals making up solids are bounded by *plane surfaces*, or *faces*, which meet at *fixed angles*. Each substance in the solid state is characterized by a

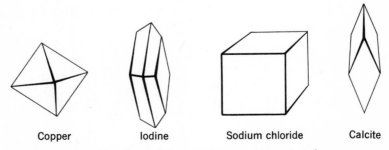

| Copper | Iodine | Sodium chloride | Calcite |

Fig. 44. External shapes of some common crystals.

The Greek philosophers, 600–1 B.C., observed nature and collected many facts. They speculated about the nature of matter, elements, and atoms. Aristotle suggested the possibility of the transmutation of matter. But the conflicting ideas that arose were not tested by experiment, and scientific thought stagnated. This detail from Raphael's painting, "School of Athens," is thought to be a representation of Aristotle, though some scholars believe it represents St. Paul. (Bettmann Archive)

From about A.D. 1 to 1700, the alchemists undertook crude experimentation in the hope of transmuting the baser metals to gold and of discovering the Grand Elixir, a cure-all which would confer eternal life. Chemical apparatus and experimental methods slowly evolved and considerable basic chemical information accumulated. This seventeenth-century painting, "The Alchemist," depicts the most famous and typical alchemical scene. (Courtesy of Fisher Scientific Company)

Roger Bacon, 1214–1292. This English monk and medieval alchemist was one of the first exponents of scientific reasoning based upon accurate observation and experiment. (Courtesy of Fisher Scientific Company)

Left: Paracelsus, 1490–1541. Swiss physician and astrologer, Paracelsus founded the school of iatrochemistry which advocated the administration of chemicals to cure disease and promote health. Random experimentation inevitably led to discovery of much qualitative chemical knowledge. The work of Paracelsus and his followers laid the foundation for modern medicine and chemotherapy. (Courtesy of Fisher Scientific Company)

Right: Robert Boyle, 1627–1691, England. Last of the alchemists and first of the modern chemists. Elaborating the views earlier proposed by Roger Bacon, da Vinci, and Francis Bacon, he insisted on the necessity of testing every theory by experiment, the theory to be modified or rejected if it were found to be inconsistent with the experimental facts. He gave the first clear-cut definition of chemical elements and spread his views by publishing *The Skeptical Chemist* in 1661. His experiments on the behavior of gases and the nature of the atmosphere were outstanding. (Courtesy of Fisher Scientific Company)

Left: G. E. Stahl, 1660–1734, Germany. The phenomena of flame and combustion puzzled man from the earliest times. Stahl, elaborating earlier suggestions, developed the erroneous theory that when bodies burned a mysterious something called "phlogiston" escaped into the atmosphere. The corrosion of metals likewise was supposed to involve the escape of phlogiston, and charcoal was assumed to furnish phlogiston for the reduction of minerals to metals. Although wrong, the theory was useful because it associated these three important chemical processes. It dominated chemical thought for 150 years and was supported by such eminent chemists as Boyle, Black, Priestley, Scheele, and Cavendish.

Right: Joseph Black, 1728–1799, Scotland. He identified many substances and catalogued their properties; distinguished mild alkalis (carbonates) from caustic alkalis (hydroxides) and showed their relationship to carbon dioxide; worked with the concept of specific heat.

Left: Joseph Priestley, 1733–1804, England. A clergyman who made chemistry his hobby, Priestley was a gifted experimenter with gases and invented apparatus and methods for their study. He isolated oxygen in 1774 by heating mercuric oxide. He explained the behavior of oxygen in terms of the phlogiston theory. Worked with hydrogen, carbon dioxide, and many other gases. Persecuted as a dissenting clergyman, he emigrated to Pennsylvania in 1794. (Courtesy of Fisher Scientific Company)

Right: Carl Wilhelm Scheele, 1742–1786, Sweden. Statue by Börjeson. He experimented widely with chemical changes and the composition of minerals and other materials, work much needed if progress in chemical theory was to go forward. He wrote a treatise on "Air and Fire," applying the phlogiston theory to account for his facts; discovered chlorine, molybdenum and tungsten, and isolated oxygen independently of Priestley.

Left: Henry Cavendish, 1731–1810, England. A "human measuring machine," he made an astonishingly accurate analysis of water, referring to hydrogen as phlogiston.

$$\text{Water} = \text{phlogiston} + \text{dephlogisticated air}$$
$$\text{(hydrogen)} \qquad \text{(oxygen)}$$

Cavendish analyzed air and found a small amount of chemically inert gas, which later was shown to be impure argon. (Courtesy of Fisher Scientific Company)

Left: Antoine Laurent Lavoisier, 1743–1794, France. He stressed the use of the chemical balance to follow the weight relations in chemical change, and verified the laws of conservation of matter and definite composition. He showed that when metals are heated in air they combine with atmospheric oxygen in definite weight ratios. Combining his experimental data with that of Cavendish on the composition of water and the air, Lavoisier developed the correct explanation of the part played by the atmosphere in combustion, discrediting the false phlogiston theory. He drew up a list of elements, applying Boyle's definition, and laid the foundation for chemical nomenclature. His many contributions set the stage for the remarkable chemical developments of the nineteenth century. (Courtesy of Fisher Scientific Company)

Below: John Dalton, 1766–1844, England. Study of the qualitative laws of chemical change and the behavior of gases convinced Dalton that elements must be made up of collections of discrete particles, atoms, that are the units of the elements that take part in chemical change without loss in weight. He introduced the concept of relative atomic weights and used symbols to designate atoms and how they might be involved in forming compounds. He was unable to distinguish clearly between atoms and molecules. At the right is an excerpt from Dalton's Notebook, showing the list of elements.

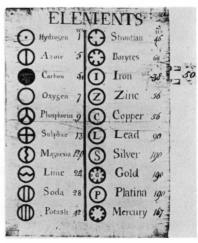

Left: Gay-Lussac, 1778–1850, France; *center:* Avogadro, 1776–1856, Italy; *right:* Canniz-zaro, 1826–1910, Sicily.   Gay-Lussac's discovery that gases react in definite ratios by volume clearly pointed to the particle nature of gases.   Avogadro was convinced that gases are made up of particles and postulated that equal volumes of all gases under the same condition contain equal numbers of molecules.   We honor his memory whenever we make use of the Avogadro Number.   The significance of the work of Gay-Lussac and Avogadro was ignored for fifty years and there was great confusion about equivalent weights, atomic weights, and molecular weights.   Cannizzaro in 1860 pointed out cont clusively how Gay-Lussac's law and Avogadro's principle could be used to resolve this confusion and establish true atomic weights.   (Picture of Cannizzaro, courtesy of Fisher Scientific Company)

Right: Humphry Davy, 1778–1829, England. Davy observed the anesthetic effect of inhaling nitrous oxide.   Making use of the newly in-vented electric battery, he discovered how to use electrolysis to break up compounds into their elements, and thus first isolated the alkali metals, potassium and sodium, and the alkali earth metals, magnesium, calcium, strontium, and barium.   He demonstrated that chlorine and iodine were elements and predicted the existence of fluorine.   He burned the diamond in oxygen to form carbon dioxide.   Davy sug-gested that the chemical combination of atoms might be due to electrical forces.

Left: Michael Faraday, 1791–1867, England. The pupil of Davy, Faraday continued the work with electrolysis, measuring the amounts of chemical changes that occurred when given amounts of electricity traversed a cell. This demonstrated the atomicity of both matter and energy and the close relationship of chemical and electrical phenomena.

Right: Jons Jacob Berzelius, 1779–1848, Sweden. He developed exact quantitative procedures and applied these to the analysis of a vast array of materials and to the determination of atomic weights. He and his students isolated many elements and established the composition of a host of substances. This led to the general acceptance of Dalton's Atomic Theory. Berzelius set a pattern for careful quantitative experimentation and organized chemical education. He played a key role in developing the use of modern chemical symbols, formulas, and equations, and the acid-base-salt classification of substances.

Left: Fredrick Wöhler, 1800–1882, Germany; *right:* Justus von Liebig, 1803–1873, Germany. Organic compounds originally were believed to be formed only by living organisms. Wöhler discovered how to change ammonium carbonate into urea and this inaugurated the synthesis in the laboratory and in industry of a vast number of compounds of carbon. Liebig found out that the percentage of carbon in such compounds could easily be determined by burning them and measuring the carbon dioxide formed. In 1832 he began the publication of the *Annalen*, a chemical journal which did much to spread scientific knowledge throughout the world.

Left: Robert Wilhelm Bunsen, 1811–1899, Germany; *right:* Gustav Kirchhoff, 1824–1887, Germany. They invented spectroscopic analysis and used this to discover cesium and rubidium. Other chemists soon utilized this new technique to isolate other elements such as thallium, indium, and others, adding materially to the list of recognized chemical elements.

Left: Lothar Meyer, 1830–1895, Germany; *center:* Dimitri Mendeléeff, 1834–1907, Russia; *right:* part of Mendeléeff's Periodic Table, 1869. As the list of known elements expanded and reliable atomic weights became known, chemists became greatly interested in the relationships between these elements. By the 1860's the time was ripe for conclusive work and, simultaneously but independently, two chemists developed the concept of periodic variation of the properties of elements with increasing atomic weight. Meyer emphasized this periodicity and Mendeléeff was very successful in developing the essential features of the Periodic Table. He used this table to predict new elements and their properties. This stimulated others to search for these, and the discovery of scandium, gallium, and germanium convinced the scientific world of the fundamental worth of the Periodic Classification.

H 1		
	Be 9.4	Mg 24
	B 11	Al 27.4
	C 12	Si 28
	N 14	P 31
	O 16	S 32
	F 19	Cl 35.5
Li 7	Na 23	K 39

Left: Svante Arrhenius, 1859–1927, Sweden; *right:* Jacobus van't Hoff, 1852–1911, Holland. Arrhenius in 1887 suggested the revolutionary theory of electrolytic dissociation in solution which was generally greeted with abusive skepticism. Wilhelm Ostwald (1853–1932, Germany) simultaneously pointed out that a substance in solution behaves much like a gas, occupying a volume equal to the solution. Van't Hoff contributed to the theory of solutions, and the work of these three laid the foundation for the new science of physical chemistry. Van't Hoff also introduced the concept of tetrahedral bonding for carbon atoms which afforded an explanation for isomerism and marked the beginning of stereochemistry. He studied the velocity of oxidation reactions and carried out phase-rule studies of the Stassfurt salts. Ostwald also pioneered in catalysis. (Bettmann Archive)

Left: Henri Moissan, 1852–1907, France. He isolated fluorine by electrolysis, vindicating Davy's suggestion of the existence of this element; developed the electric furnace for carrying out chemical reactions at high temperatures, thus opening up a great new area for work in synthetic inorganic chemistry. (Bettmann Archive)

Right: William Ramsay, 1852–1916, Scotland. He collaborated with Rayleigh to discover argon in the atmosphere. His subsequent isolation of helium, neon, krypton, and xenon from the air added the whole zero group of chemically inert elements to the Periodic Table.

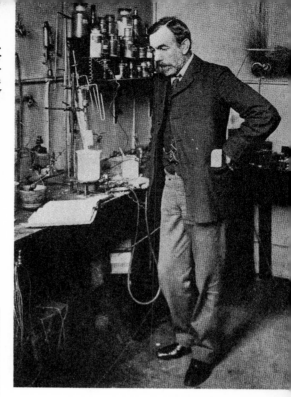

Left: William Crookes, 1832–1919, England. Crookes studied the electrical discharge in gases at low pressures and the qualitative nature of cathode rays. Wilhelm Röntgen (1845–1923, Germany) showed that when the cathode rays in such tubes strike surfaces, X-rays are generated. (Courtesy of Fisher Scientific Company)

Right: J. J. Thomson, 1856–1940, England. He studied the mass and charge of cathode particles in gas-discharge tubes and discovered and characterized the electron as a component of all atoms. This confirmed the complexity of atomic structure, and Thomson suggested his "corpuscular model" of the atom.

Left: Marie and Pierre Curie in 1896, France. Becoming interested in the discovery of radio-activity by Becquerel in 1896, Mme. Curie, assisted by her husband Pierre, isolated the two new radioactive elements, polonium and radium, from pitchblende ore. This brilliant work, done with the most meager equipment under great financial insecurity, laid the foundation for modern radiochemistry.

Right: Ernest Rutherford, 1871–1937, New Zealand, Canada, England. His study of the nature of radioactive change led to elucidation of the complex structure of atoms and the development of the nuclear model of the atom. He discovered the proton and was the first to accomplish the artificial transmutation of elements by nuclear reaction. (Courtesy of Central Scientific Company)

Left: Niels Bohr, 1885—, Denmark. In 1913, by assuming a series of orbital energy levels for the electrons in the hydrogen atom, Bohr was able to develop a quantum mechanical model of the atom which could account for the absorption or emission of energy by the atom. He suggested electronic configurations for the elements which are consistent with the periodic variations of properties with increasing atomic number. In 1926 Erwin Schrödinger (in Germany) applied the concept that electrons act not only as particles but also have some of the characteristics of waves. This forces the realization that atomic systems can never be adequately represented by mechanical models. Wave mechanics attempts to describe the behavior or atoms mathematically in terms of wave equations. (Bettmann Archive)

Left: G. N. Lewis, 1875–1946; *center:* Irving Langmuir, 1881—; *right:* Linus Pauling, 1901—; all United States. In 1916, Lewis developed the concept of the shared-electron-pair bond and Kossel explained ionic bonding in terms of complete transfer of electrons to produce charged ions. Langmuir elaborated on the use of these bonding ideas to account for the spatial configurations of molecules. Pauling has applied wave mechanics and the concepts of electronegativity and resonance to the problem of accounting for the structure and bonding of substances. (Lewis, by Johan Hagemeyer; Langmuir, courtesy of General Electric Research Laboratory; Pauling, courtesy of California Institute of Technology)

Right: Peter Debye, 1884—, Holland, Germany, United States. He proposed that strong electrolytes are completely ionized in solution; studied the polarity of molecules and the diffraction of X-rays by crystalline powders. W. H. Bragg (1862–1942, England) earlier had developed the X-ray–diffraction method for determining the arrangement of atoms in crystals and worked out the crystal structures of many of the silicates. Debye developed the electron-diffraction method for studying the structure of molecules of gases and the use of light scattering for the investigation of very large molecules of high polymers; suggested the magnetic technique for obtaining extremely low temperatures. (Courtesy of Cornell Photo Science)

Left: Otto Hahn, 1879—, Germany; *right:* Lise Meitner, 1878—, Austria, Germany, Sweden. Hahn and Meitner collaborated in the study of nuclear reactions. In 1939 Hahn and Strassman discovered the fission of the uranium atom under neutron bombardment, and Meitner and Frisch suggested an explanation of the phenomenon. (Meitner, Black Starr Photograph)

Left: Enrico Fermi, 1901–1954, Italy, United States. Developed the first nuclear reactor by using the fission of uranium in a controlled chain reaction. This has been exploited in the atomic bomb and in power reactors. (Town and Country Photographers)

Right: G. T. Seaborg and E. M. McMillan, United States. In 1940 McMillan and Abelson artificially produced element 93 (neptunium) by bombarding the nuclei of uranium^{238} with neutrons. Extension of this technique has enabled Seaborg and collaborators to synthesize the additional transuranium elements—plutonium, americium, curium, berkelium, californium, fermium, einsteinium, and mendeleevium. (Photograph from *Chemical and Engineering News*)

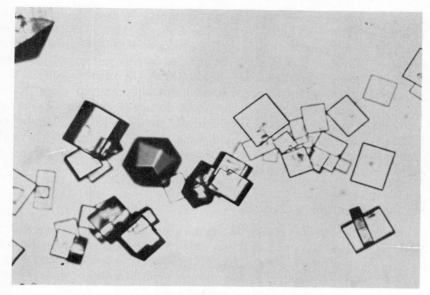

(a) Sodium chloride, NaCl

(b) Hydrated copper sulfate, CuSO$_4$·5H$_2$O

Fig. 45. Photographs of crystals formed from solution. Highly magnified.

definite and peculiar crystal pattern, which may be used to identify that substance. Figure 44 indicates the characteristic external shapes of crystals of some common substances. These are drawn as perfectly developed or "ideal" crystals. Actually, real crystals usually are not so perfectly formed. They may be irregularly developed and often are joined to other crystals to form irregular aggregates. But the external surfaces are planar, and the angles between the planar faces are characteristic of the particular crystalline substance. Figure 45 shows photographs, obtained by the use of a microscope, of collections of crystals formed by crystallization from aqueous solutions. Ordinary table salt is such a random collection of crystals of sodium chloride.

140. THE STRUCTURE OF CRYSTALS

While the external shapes of crystals are important, the chemist is more interested in finding out just how the atoms of a substance take part in building up crystals. We want to pry into the interior of crystals and find out what neighbors a given atom has and how close these neighboring atoms are. This investigation will tell us which atoms are bonded chemically together and something about the nature of these bonds. The interior structure of crystals can be studied by X-ray diffraction methods. When a beam of X-rays traverses a crystal, the X-rays are diffracted or scattered by the atoms in the crystal. Elaborate study of the way in which a given crystalline substance affects an X-ray beam makes it possible to determine the actual arrangement in space of the atoms in the crystal. This arrangement is always found to involve some regular pattern which is repeated in three dimensions to give the massive crystal. The regular unit of pattern of the atoms in the crystal is called its *unit cell*. By repetition in three-dimensional space of the unit cell, the extended pattern of the crystal, its *space lattice*, is built up. Each substance as a solid under given conditions has its own characteristic unit cell and space lattice, its own particular spatial arrangement of atoms. The unit cell and space lattice of a given crystal specify exactly the position of the center of each atom relative to the centers of the neighboring atoms. The number of nearest neighboring atoms of an atom in the interior of a crystal is referred to as its *coordination number*. The external shape of a crystal and the way it cleaves (breaks) reflect the way the atoms are arranged in the crystal pattern and are characteristic of the substance.

141. CRYSTALS OF METALS

In a crystal of copper the atoms are packed together as shown in Figure 46*a*. The position of the center of each atom at a point in the space lattice is indicated by the symbol Cu. The massive crystal is

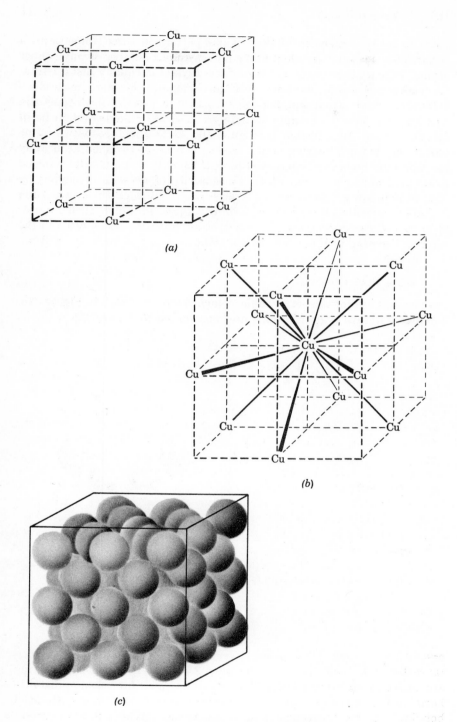

(a)

(b)

(c)

Fig. 46.   The crystal structure of copper.

built up by the extension of this regular pattern in three dimensions, a crystal of appreciable size containing a tremendous number of tiny copper atoms.   Each atom in the interior of the crystal is equally distant from 12 neighboring atoms, as shown in Figure 46b, and therefore has a characteristic coordination number of 12.   In the crystal the atoms are usually considered to be approximately spherical in shape and to be in direct contact, as indicated in Figure 46c.   The distance between the centers of two neighboring copper atoms can be determined accurately by X-ray methods and is observed to be 2.52×10^{-8} cm, usually referred to as 2.52 angstrom units (Å).   Thus, study of crystals of copper by X-ray techniques has given us precise knowledge of their structure. Metallic elements crystallize in *metallic lattices,* in which each interior atom has a large coordination number, either 8 or 12.   Each atom in the interior has exactly the same environment as every other interior atom.

142. MOLECULAR CRYSTALS

The unit cell for the nonmetallic element iodine is shown in Figure 47a, and two adjacent pairs of atoms are represented in Figure 47b.   In the

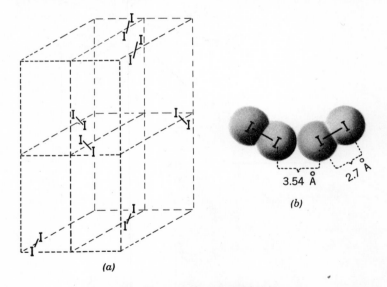

3.54 Å   2.7 Å

(b)

(a)

Fig. 47.   The crystal structure of iodine.

crystal lattice each iodine atom is very close to a second atom, the distance between their centers being only 2.7 Å.   The other neighboring atoms are much farther away, 3.54 Å.   The small interatomic distance between the atoms in a pair is believed to be due to covalent chemical bonding, the two sharing a pair of electrons.   Hence, the two atoms interpenetrate or overlap. Each pair constitutes a molecule of iodine, I_2. The distance between the centers of iodine atoms in adjacent molecules is much greater because there is no chemical bonding between them; the molecules are held together in the crystal merely by intermolecular attractive forces which are small compared with the covalent bonding forces holding the two atoms together in the molecule. The massive crystal of iodine is built up of diatomic molecules packed together in a regular pattern.

Figure 48a shows the crystal structure of carbon dioxide, and Figure 48b indicates a molecule of this substance. As can be seen, in solid carbon dioxide (dry ice) the CO_2 molecules are the building units, and the state of chemical combination of carbon and oxygen is clearly indicated.

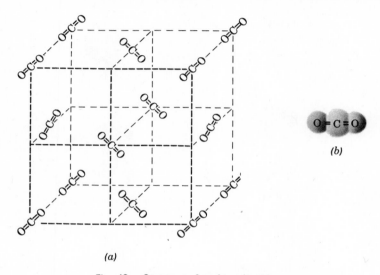

(b)

(a)

Fig. 48.   Structure of carbon dioxide.

Molecular substances form crystals in which the molecules are packed in some regular pattern throughout the crystal. The molecules may be small, such as the monatomic molecules of helium, the diatomic molecules of iodine, hydrogen, and hydrogen chloride, or the triatomic molecules of carbon dioxide. The molecules may have much more extended structures, such as $C_{12}H_{22}O_{11}$ for sugar. In some solids, the molecules have no finite size but consist of endless chains, bands, or sheets of atoms that are covalently bonded together. These giant molecules are packed together to form the crystal pattern. In the most extreme case, such as that of diamond crystals, and of silicon carbide, the molecule extends endlessly in three dimensions so that the single crystal is one giant molecule. Nonmetallic elements and compounds where the bonding is covalent form *molecular crystals*.

143. IONIC CRYSTALS

The structure of crystals of sodium chloride has already been discussed in detail in Section 64.   You will recall that in the interior of the crystal, each sodium atom has six chlorine atoms as near neighbors, and each chlorine atom has six sodium atoms as near neighbors.   Each sodium and chlorine atom has a coordination number of 6, six near neighbors all of which are equivalent; whereas if definite molecules of NaCl existed in the solid, we would expect to find one sodium atom most closely associated with only one chlorine atom.

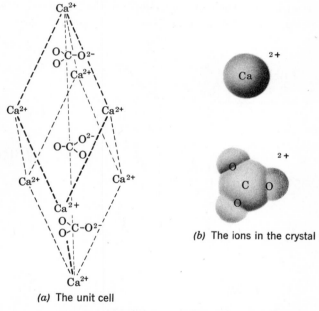

(a) The unit cell

(b) The ions in the crystal

Fig. 49.   The unit cell and the ions of calcite, Ca CO₃.

In such a case we are forced to conclude that no molecules exist in the crystal but that the atoms are the units making up the crystal lattice. There is good reason to believe that each atom bears an electrical charge, the sodium positive and the chlorine negative; that they exist in the crystal as *ions;* and that the crystal is an *ionic solid*.   The strong electrostatic forces of attraction between the neighboring ions of opposite charge hold the ions firmly together in the crystal lattice.   The formula NaCl is merely the simplest formula, giving the correct atom ratio, there being no molecular formula, because there are no molecules.   The total number of positive charges on the ions must be equal to the total number of negative charges to produce the crystals of salt, which are electrically neutral as a whole.   This determines the 1:1 ratio between sodium and chlorine atoms in the crystalline substance.

Ionic substances always form *ionic crystals* in which positive and negative ions are the building blocks.   Figure 49 shows the structure of calcite crystals, which constitute the common mineral, limestone.

Calcium ions, Ca^{2+}, are packed together in a regular pattern with an equal number of carbonate ions, $CO_3{}^{2-}$.   The close association of three oxygen atoms with one carbon atom to produce the *complex ion*, $CO_3{}^{2-}$, is quite apparent.   The bonding in this ion will be discussed in Chapter 14.   Crystal-structure studies afford the best means we have of determining the composition and spatial configuration of complex ions.

144. POLYMORPHISM

A substance may exist in more than one crystalline form and, in this case, is said to show *polymorphism*.   Thus, carbon is found either as diamond crystals or in the form of graphite.   Polymorphism arises because it is possible for the particles of the substance to pack together in different ways in the solid state.   One crystalline form will be favored by certain conditions.   When the conditions are changed, another crystalline form may be more stable.   Polymorphism is quite common, and we shall encounter it frequently in our study of solids.

145. APPLICATION OF KINETIC THEORY TO SOLIDS

We can extend the kinetic theory to explain the behavior of solids, taking into account the fact that in crystals the particles building up the massive material may be atoms of the metals in metallic lattices, molecules or molecular substances in molecular lattices, or positive and negative ions in the ionic lattices.   These units are at close quarters.   At any temperature above absolute zero, these particles must possess a given average kinetic energy of motion.   Accordingly, they are considered to be oscillating in a very restricted fashion about their lattice points, maintaining their average relative positions in space.   Changing the temperature of a solid involves reducing or increasing the average kinetic energy of its particles.

146. MELTING OR FUSION OF SOLIDS

When a solid is heated, sufficient energy may be imparted to the particles to overcome the attractive forces that hold them in their positions in the crystal lattice, and *melting* (*fusion*) to the liquid state occurs. Thus, when ice is warmed to 0° and the heating process is continued, the crystals of ice melt to liquid water.   If the crystals are molecular, the liquid formed will be *molecular*.   If the crystals are ionic, the liquid formed upon fusion will be composed of *ions*.   In any case, the particles in the liquid phase stay in close contact but are able to slide past each other and are free to exchange neighbors. The particles have random motion and random position.

Melting (fusion) is the reverse of freezing (crystallization), the transition between the solid and liquid states being reversible, as indicated in the general expression

$$\text{Solid} + \text{heat} \underset{\text{freezing, crystallization}}{\overset{\text{fusion, melting}}{\rightleftharpoons}} \text{liquid}$$

Figure 50 shows, in two dimensions, how the particles in ordered array in a crystalline phase change to the random arrangement of the liquid phase when melting occurs, and how freezing involves the addition of particles from the liquid phase to positions in the crystal lattice. (The particle structure of the liquid phase is not shown.)

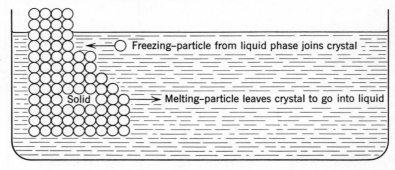

Fig. 50.   Melting and freezing.

When the liquid is in contact with the solid, the rate of melting may be just balanced by the rate of freezing and the system will be at equilibrium, the changes continuing but the quantities of solid and liquid remaining constant. The *melting point* of a solid, or the *freezing point* of a liquid, is the temperature at which both solid and liquid coexist at equilibrium at a given pressure. This temperature is characteristic for each substance and is usually measured at standard pressure, in which case it is designated as the *normal melting point*. It changes only slightly with change in pressure. The normal melting point for ice (or the freezing point of water) is 0°. At this temperature, chunks of ice can exist in contact with liquid water at 1 atm pressure.

The melting points given in Table 25 for a number of substances are found to vary over a wide range. The magnitude of the melting point of a solid is a function of the forces of attraction between the units that are present and of their ordered packing in the crystal. The attractive forces between molecules are not large, and molecular solids built up of small, symmetrical molecules, such as H_2, N_2, and O_2, have low melting points. Substances having heavier and less symmetrical molecules, such as sugar, have higher melting points. Substances made up of giant endless molecules are normally solids with high melting points; the diamond does not melt when heated to 3800° A, and the melting point of silicon carbide is about 3000° A. The forces of attraction in ionic solids

Table 25. Melting Points and Heats of Fusion

Substance	Melting Point, ° A	Molar Heats of Fusion, Cal/Mole
Hydrogen	13.9	28
Oxygen	54.23	106.3
Nitrogen	63.1	172.3
Alcohol	158.7	1145.4
Ammonia	195.3	1426.3
Water	273	1434.1

are very great, and ionic substances are invariably solids at room temperature and have relatively high melting points (NaCl melts at 1077° A). The interatomic forces of metals vary over wide limits; mercury melts at 234.1° A, and tungsten has a melting point of 3643° A.

147. HEAT OF FUSION

The process of fusion is endothermic, whereas freezing is exothermic. Energy must be added to a solid in sufficient amount to overcome the attractive forces which anchor the particles in their fixed positions with respect to each other, so that they become able to slide past each other. The amount of energy necessary to break down the orderly arrangement of particles in a crystal lattice to give the random, mobile structure characteristic of the liquid state varies from substance to substance. It depends upon the substance, and it is fixed for a given amount of the substance. The *molar heat of fusion* is the heat required to convert one mole of the solid to liquid at its normal melting point, without change in temperature. The same amount of heat must be removed from the liquid to convert it to the solid state at its freezing point. Note the molar heats of fusion listed in Table 25. In general, the magnitudes of the molar heats of fusion are found to vary in the same fashion as the melting points. These are functions of the attractive forces between the particles of the substance. The molar heats of fusion increase, in general, with the molecular weights of molecular substances, and are high for ionic crystals. They vary with the melting points of the metals.

148. VAPORIZATION OF SOLIDS

Ice on the sidewalk diminishes in amount slowly in cold weather, even when the temperature never gets up to 0°. Under these conditions no liquid is observed. When exposed freely to the air, crystals of iodine in a short time disappear without any evidence of changing to the liquid state. If the temperature of solid iodine is raised carefully, so that the system is not heated to the melting point, the purple vapor of this substance can be seen to form directly from the solid. When this vapor is cooled, crystals of iodine are formed directly. A strong odor of camphor becomes noticeable when crystals of this substance are exposed to the air at room temperature, although the crystals do not melt. Such observations can be accounted for only by assuming that, at a given temperature, a solid has a certain tendency to vaporize, changing directly to the gaseous state, and that the reverse transition is also possible, as illustrated in two dimensions in Figure 51.

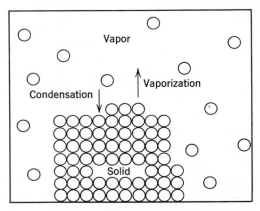

Fig. 51. Solid-vapor transition.

The vaporization of solids is to be expected from the kinetic model of the structure of solids which we have described. The units in a crystal, by virtue of their kinetic energy, have a certain tendency to escape from the surface of the vapor phase at a given temperature. There will be a corresponding tendency for the particles of the vapor to condense on the surface of the crystal. When the solid is allowed to stand in a closed space, it will tend to come to equilibrium with its vapor. The vapor will eventually become saturated, if enough of the substance is present to establish equilibrium. The equilibrium vapor pressure is a measure of the tendency to vaporize, that is, it is a measure of the escaping tendency of the solid. As the temperature of the solid is raised and the average kinetic energy of its particles increases, there will be a corresponding increase in its equilibrium vapor pressure. The equilibrium vapor pressures of most substances, such as water, are small in the temperature range below their melting points. However, some solids, such as iodine and camphor, vaporize readily and develop high vapor pressures.

The equilibrium vapor pressures of solids may be measured by the same methods that are effective for liquids. We can determine the height of a column of mercury that is supported by the saturated vapor in contact with some of the solid at a given temperature. By repeating this procedure at various temperatures below the melting point of the solid, we can completely catalogue the relation between equilibrium vapor pressure and temperature for the solid substance. Such data for ice, plotted in Figure 52, give the line *OB*. (The temperature scale used here is distorted considerably.) A given point on this line indicates the

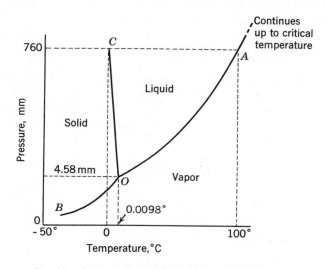

Fig. 52.   Pressure-temperature diagram for water.

equilibrium vapor pressure of ice at a given temperature. Each solid is found to have a characteristic equilibrium vapor pressure-temperature curve, along which the solid phase is at equilibrium with the vapor phase.

In Figure 52, data for the equilibrium between the liquid and vapor have been plotted along *OA*. Line *OC* represents the variation of the melting point of the solid with pressure; at any point on this line the solid is at equilibrium with the liquid. The three equilibrium curves intersect at *O*. At this point, solid, liquid, and vapor are in equilibrium, and the temperature and pressure at *O* are fixed. The solid, liquid, and vapor forms of a substance can coexist at only one temperature and only one pressure, this point being referred to as the *triple point* for the system. This is the melting point of the solid when it is at its equilibrium vapor pressure. For water, the temperature of the triple point is +0.0098°, and the pressure is 4.58 mm. The normal melting point of a solid is the temperature at which the solid is at equilibrium with the liquid at 760 mm total pressure. This will be 0° for ice, the temperature corresponding to point C in Figure 52. The melting point of ice decreases slightly with increase in pressure. (This decrease has been exaggerated in the diagram to make the effect apparent.) Ice skaters take advantage of this. Under the high pressure developed locally where the edge of the skate is in contact with the ice, the ice melts, the rest of the ice under atmospheric pressure maintaining its solid state. The liquid water formed between the skate and the ice allows the edge to move with very little friction, and the skater is able to glide along without doing much work. As soon as the pressure of the skate on the ice is released, the water freezes. On very cold days, the pressure of the skate on the ice is not sufficient to melt it, and we find that skating becomes more difficult.

149. SUMMARY OF CHANGES IN STATE

Figure 53 summarizes the changes of state which are observed for matter. *Distillation* of liquids involves the evaporation of the liquid and then the liquefaction of the vapor. *Sublimation* of solids is the round trip made up of vaporization to the gaseous state and the subsequent condensation of the vapor to reform the solid.

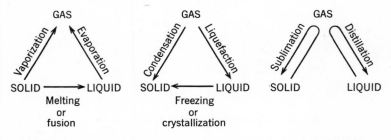

(a) Endothermic transitions   (b) Exothermic transitions   (c) Round trips

Fig. 53.   Summary of changes of state.

The chemist often uses distillation to purify liquids and sublimation to purify solids. He takes advantage of the fact that the desired substance will usually differ in volatility from the impurities so they can be separated.

150. UNDERCOOLED LIQUIDS. GLASSES

Liquids sometimes undercool, that is, they stay in the liquid state at temperatures below their freezing points. In this case the system is said to be in a *metastable* condition; it is not at equilibrium. The tendency to undercool varies with the nature of the substance. In general, liquids made up of large particles with extended structures are quite viscous (do not flow readily) at temperatures near their freezing points, and such cumbersome units do not easily orient themselves into the regular pattern of a crystal lattice. So, especially if the rate of cooling is fast, the liquid may be carried below its freezing point without the formation of crystals. Since such an undercooled liquid is not stable, there is always the possibility that it will attain equilibrium by crystallizing. Mechanical agitation frequently starts this crystallization. Addition of crystals (seeding) to act as nuclei for crystallization will tend to produce solidification.

Even such a mobile liquid as water may be undercooled if it is kept very still during the cooling process, but undercooled water is very unstable, and a slight jar will suffice to start the formation of ice. Materials with huge particles or extended structures, such as window glass, rubber, and plastics, show remarkably strong tendencies to undercool. As the temperature is lowered, the undercooled liquids become less and

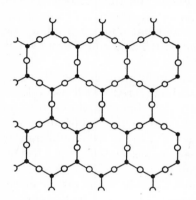

(a) Repeated pattern of a crystal   *(b)* Random structure of a glass

Fig. 54. Structures of crystals and glasses (after Zachariasen).

less mobile, and finally become quite rigid, forming *glasses*. Because such highly undercooled systems are rigid, they frequently are spoken of as solids. *Strictly speaking, the term solid is synonymous with crystalline,* and it is probably better to consider glasses as liquids in a highly undercooled condition. A crystalline substance is characterized by a regular arrangement of its atoms in a space lattice as shown in two dimensions in Figure 54a, whereas the same substance as a glass has a random structure such as that indicated in Figure 54b.

151. REVERSIBLE PHYSICAL CHANGE, EQUILIBRIUM, AND LE CHÂTELIER'S PRINCIPLE

We have found that the changes in the states of matter are *reversible* and that dynamic equilibrium may be set up between these states. Such equilibrium is established when the rates of the opposing changes become equal. Extensive study of reversible changes and the equilibria associated with them has led to a simple generalization, first enunciated by van't Hoff but commonly referred to as *Le Châtelier's Principle or Law: A system at equilibrium, when subjected to any stress (such as change in temperature, pressure, or concentration of matter) so that equilibrium is upset, will tend to adjust itself so as to remove the stress and re-establish equilibrium.* In any system not at equilibrium, that change will be favored which will bring the system to equilibrium. Suppose that we see how this works out with the reversible changes in states of matter.

If a liquid is in equilibrium with its vapor at a given temperature, and if the system is heated, the system will no longer be at equilibrium and will tend to readjust itself by changing in such a way that heat is absorbed. Heating raises the average kinetic energy of the molecules of liquid, and there will be an increased tendency to vaporize and thus absorb some of the kinetic energy. This will give rise to an increased rate of evaporation, but eventually, if the temperature is maintained at a higher level, a new equilibrium will be set up with a correspondingly higher equilibrium vapor pressure for the system.

Similarly, if a vapor-liquid system at equilibrium is cooled, equilibrium will be upset, and that change will be favored which will release heat; the rate of condensation will increase, and the rate of evaporation will decrease. The concentration of molecules in the vapor state will decrease, and the vapor pressure will go down until a new equilibrium is set up at a lower temperature. This will be associated with a correspondingly lower equilibrium vapor pressure.

In general, in any system in which reversible change is taking place, the addition of heat will favor an endothermic change, and the removal of heat will favor an exothermic change. Increasing the pressure will favor a change that will reduce the pressure. Increasing the mass per unit volume of a substance involved in a reversible chemical change will favor the chemical change that will reduce the mass per unit volume of the substance.

Le Châtelier's Principle is very important because it allows us to predict what will happen to a system undergoing reversible change if it is not in equilibrium. It enables us to deduce how conditions should be arranged so that we can force a system to change in a given direction. To melt a solid, an endothermic process, we supply heat to the system. To liquefy air, an exothermic process which involves also a very considerable increase in mass per unit volume, we cool the system and increase the pressure. To produce ozone, an endothermic change, we must supply energy to the system. A clear understanding of the concept of reversible change, of dynamic equilibrium, and of Le Châtelier's Principle is fundamental to success in the study of chemistry.

EXERCISES

1. Show how the terms, *unit cell, space lattice,* and *coordination number* are useful in the description of the details of the structures of solids.

2. Compare the crystal structures of metals, molecular substances, and ionic substances in terms of the kinds of units which build up the crystals.

3. How do the forces holding molecules together in a crystal lattice compare in strength with the covalent bonding forces between the atoms in each molecule?

4. What evidence can you cite for the statement that crystals of iodine are built up of I_2 molecules?

5. Consider 1 g of carbon dioxide in the solid, liquid, or gaseous state at a given temperature. In which state will this sample of carbon dioxide have: a) the most regular structure? b) the lowest density? c) the most energy? d) the greatest compressibility? e) the highest percentage of oxygen?

6. How much heat must be added a) to 8.064 g of crystalline hydrogen at 13.9° A to convert it to liquid at the same temperature? b) to 8.064 g of liquid hydrogen at 20.3° A to convert it to hydrogen gas at the same temperature? c) to 72.064 g of ice at 0° C to convert it to steam at 100° C?

7. The normal melting points of chlorine and bromine, both of which occur as diatomic molecules, are −101.6° and −7.2°, respectively. Predict which has: a) the higher normal boiling point; b) the larger molar heat of fusion; c) the smaller molar heat of vaporization; d) the lower critical temperature; e) the higher equilibrium vapor pressure for the liquid at 0°.

8. a) In which state of matter does window glass belong?
b) Is window glass at equilibrium?
c) If window glass crystallizes, will the change be exothermic or endothermic?
d) Does window glass have an appreciable vapor pressure at room temperature?

9. Two grams of water vapor is at equilibrium with 4 g of liquid water in a given cylinder at 20°. Apply the Principle of Le Châtelier, and predict how the relative amounts of water in the liquid and gaseous phases will change if: a) the temperature of the system is lowered; b) the volume of the system is increased.

10. Describe the endothermic and exothermic changes involved in: a) distillation; b) sublimation.

11. You wish to sublime iodine crystals. How do you apply the Principle of Le Châtelier in carrying out this process?

Chapter 12

▶ Solutions

152. PREPARATION AND GENERAL PROPERTIES OF SOLUTIONS

So far in our discussion of the states of matter, we have usually concerned ourselves with the behavior of pure substances. Actually, in practice, we more frequently deal with mixtures of substances, and one kind of mixture that is of particular interest in chemistry is a solution. In Section 18 we have already referred to *solutions* as being *homogeneous mixtures* of two or more substances.

If water is added to a mixture of sand and sugar, the crystals of sugar disappear. The sugar may now be shown to be dispersed uniformly throughout the water, as can be detected roughly by tasting various portions. The fragments of sand remain unchanged and can be separated from the liquid phase by filtration, but the sugar goes through the filter paper with the water. Sugar is said to be *soluble* in water, and sand is said to be *insoluble* (not appreciably soluble). The *solution* formed by the dispersion of the sugar in the water consists of the *solute* (the dissolved sugar) and the *solvent* (water).

In the solution of sugar the molecules of sugar are scattered among the molecules of the water. These molecules of sugar continually *diffuse* through the water and *do not settle out*. The solution is *homogeneous*, there being no boundaries between its parts. However, *its composition*, the ratio of sugar to water, *may be varied* through certain limits. It does not obey the law of definite composition, differing in this respect from a pure compound. The behavior of the sugar is typical of molecular solutes in general when they go into solution and their molecules persist as such in solution. As we shall see later in Chapter 16, some very polar molecules tend to break up into ions when they dissolve in polar solvents.

When an *ionic substance*, such as sodium chloride, dissolves in water, the ions of the solute become dispersed among the molecules of the water to give a salt solution, commonly called *brine*. Ions in solution behave in much the same fashion as we have described for the molecules of sugar, except that the charges on the ions will modify their behavior in certain ways. Solutions of ions become homogeneous because of diffusion. A solution of ions is always electrically neutral, the total number of units of positive ionic charge being just equal to the total number of units of negative ionic charge.

153. KINDS OF SOLUTION PHASES

Three general kinds of solution phases, involving different combinations of substances in different states, are possible.

a. Gaseous solution phases.   These consist of gases dispersed in each other; such systems were discussed in Section 125, when we considered the total pressure of a mixture of gases as summarized in Dalton's Law of Partial Pressures.   Any mixture of gases is a solution, since all gases are *completely miscible* (mix in all proportions).   Air is a good example of such a gaseous solution.

b. Liquid solution phases.   In this case the solution is a liquid phase and exhibits the general properties characteristic of liquids.   Liquid solutions may be obtained by the mixture of a liquid solvent with gaseous, liquid, or solid solutes.   We find that oxygen gas will dissolve in water, that liquid alcohol forms a solution when mixed with water, and that solid sugar goes into solution in water.   In all these cases, the homogeneous solutions which are formed are in the liquid state.   Liquid solutions are perhaps the most important class of solutions with which we work in chemistry.   The most common liquid solvent is water, which has a remarkable ability to dissolve a great variety of solutes.   *Aqueous solutions* are those in which water is the solvent.

c. Solid solution phases.   Here we have the particles of one substance dispersed in the crystal lattice of a second substance in a homogeneous fashion.   When metals are heated together in the formation of alloys, the products frequently consist of solid solutions.   Many complex minerals are solid solutions of ionic substances.   Crystals of compounds such as oxides sometimes have an excess of one of the elements in solid solution so that the composition of the phase varies.

154. IMPORTANCE OF SOLUTIONS

By employing solutions we can set up conditions very favorable to carrying out and studying the nature of chemical change.   A large number of chemical changes proceed best if they take place in solution.   As highly dispersed individual molecules or ions in solution, reacting substances are in a very active and mobile condition.   These particles mix freely by diffusion and, when they collide, can react readily.   All of the particles of each solute are in a condition to take part in the reaction, and frequently the solvent acts as a powerful catalyst for the chemical change.   By understanding and taking advantage of the behavior of solutions, the chemist has the opportunity of controlling many chemical changes and forcing them in the direction he desires.   You will use solutions very frequently in the laboratory, and they are widely employed in industrial operations.   Solutions play a star role in the chemical changes involved in our bodily processes.   Much of our food, such as many of the substances present in milk, is provided in aqueous solution, and digestion proceeds by means of solution phenomena.   Our blood is an outstanding example of a complicated solution.   We must acquire a thorough knowledge of the fundamental nature of solutions in order to understand their behavior and to know how to exploit them most advantageously.

155. CONCENTRATION OF SOLUTIONS

The *concentration of a solution* defines the composition in terms of the amount of solute in a given amount of solvent or solution.   In a rough way, this may be done by using the terms *dilute* and *concentrated* to indicate, respectively, a small ratio or a large ratio of solute to solvent. To be more exact, it is common to state the concentration of solutions in such terms as the following:

> Grams of solute per gram of solvent
> Grams of solute per 100 g of solution, percentage
> Grams of solute per liter of solution
> Moles of solute per liter of solution, molarity
> Gram-equivalents of solute per liter of solution, normality
> Moles of solute per 1,000 g of solvent, molality

A *standard solution* is one of known content; the determination of the concentration of a solution is known as *standardizing* the solution.

A *molar (1M) solution* contains one mole of solute per liter of solution. Remember, as pointed out in Section 78, that one mole is the gram-molecular weight of a molecular substance where the formula we write is the true molecular formula; with ionic compounds where there are no molecules, one mole is the gram-formula weight, using the simplest formula.   Since the molecular weight of cane sugar, $C_{12}H_{22}O_{11}$, is 342.3, a 1M solution of cane sugar contains 342.3 g of sugar per liter of solution; a 3M solution of sugar contains 3×342.3 g of sugar per liter of solution. The molecular weight of H_2SO_4 is 98.08.   Hence, a 2M solution of sulfuric acid contains 196.16 g per liter of solution and a 0.1M solution contains 9.808 g per liter.

The formula weight of the ionic compound NaCl is 58.46.   A molar solution of sodium chloride contains 58.46 g of salt per liter of solution, and this solution is 1M with respect to Na^+ and Cl^- because there is one mole of each present per liter.

We use the molar system of specifying the concentration of solutions very frequently because, if the *molarity* (number of moles of solute per liter of solution) of a solution is known, it is easy to select a specific number of moles, or molecules, or ions of the solute by measuring out the proper volume of this solution.   For instance, if we wish to use 6.02×10^{23} molecules of sugar in a given reaction, we can add 1 liter of a 1M solution or 5 liters of a 0.2M solution.   *Equal volumes of equimolar solu-*

tions contain the same number of moles. Thus, 100 ml of a $5M$ solution of sugar contains the same number of moles of solute as does 100 ml of a $5M$ solution of alcohol.

EXAMPLE: a) How many grams of ethyl alcohol, C_2H_5OH, are there in 1 liter of a $1.000M$ solution of this solute?

A $1.000M$ solution of C_2H_5OH must contain 1.000 mole of alcohol per liter of solution.

$$1.000 \text{ mole of } C_2H_5OH = 2 \times 12.01 \text{ g} + 6 \times 1.008 \text{ g} + 16.00 \text{ g} = 46.07 \text{ g}$$

$$\text{Grams of } C_2H_5OH \text{ per liter of } 1.000M \text{ solution} = 46.07 \text{ g}$$

b) How many grams of C_2H_5OH are there in 500 ml of a $3.000M$ solution?

A $3.000M$ solution contains 3.000 moles per liter

$$500 \text{ ml of solution} = \frac{500 \text{ ml}}{1{,}000 \text{ ml per liter}} = 0.500 \text{ liters}$$

Moles of C_2H_5OH in
500 ml of $3.000M$ solution $= 3.000 \text{ moles} \times 0.500 \text{ liter} = 1.50 \text{ moles}$

Grams of C_2H_5OH in
500 ml of $3.000M$ solution $= 1.50 \text{ moles} \times 46.07 \text{ g per mole} = 69.1 \text{ g}$

c) How many molecules of C_2H_5OH will there be in 500 ml of $3.000M$ C_2H_5OH?

Number of molecules of
C_2H_5OH in 500 ml $= 1.50 \text{ moles} \times 6.02 \times 10^{23} \text{ molecules per mole}$
of $3.000M$ solution

$$= 9.03 \times 10^{23} \text{ molecules}$$

d) 800 ml of a solution contains 92.14 g of C_2H_5OH. What is the molarity of this solution?

Liters of solution $\quad = \dfrac{800 \text{ ml}}{1{,}000 \text{ ml per liter}} = 0.800 \text{ liters}$

Moles of C_2H_5OH in
0.800 liters of solution $= \dfrac{92.14 \text{ g}}{46.07 \text{ g per mole of } C_2H_5OH} = 2.00 \text{ moles}$

Moles of C_2H_5OH
per liter of solution $= \dfrac{2.00 \text{ moles}}{0.800 \text{ liters}} = 2.50 \text{ moles per liter}$

Therefore the solution is $2.50M$ with respect to C_2H_5OH.

A *normal* $(1N)$ *solution* contains one gram equivalent of the solute per liter of solution. For an acid, this will be the weight of acid which will furnish 1.008 g of hydrogen ion for neutralization of a base. Thus, a $1N$ solution of HCl has 36.465 g of HCl per liter of solution, whereas a $1N$ solution of H_2SO_4 will have one-half mole or 49.04 g of H_2SO_4 per liter of solution. Since in acetic acid, $HC_2H_3O_2$, only one of the four hydrogen atoms is easily furnished as an ion, a $1N$ solution will have one mole of the acid per liter of solution; it will also be a $1M$ solution. A normal solution of a base for neutralization of an acid must have that weight of base per liter of solution which will furnish one gram equivalent of OH^-, 17.008 g. Therefore, a normal solution of NaOH will have one mole or 40.005 g of NaOH per liter. A normal solution of $Ca(OH)_2$ will contain one-half mole of this substance per liter. It is convenient to deal in terms of *normality of solutions because equal volumes of equinormal solutions contain chemically equivalent amounts of solute.* Thus, 50 ml of a $1N$ solution of HCl will contain just enough HCl to neutralize completely 50 ml of a $1N$ solution of NaOH or 50 ml of a $1N$ solution of $Ca(OH)_2$. Because the size of the gram equivalent depends upon the reaction a reagent takes part in and may vary for different reactions, the normality of a solution defines the concentration only when the reaction is specified or understood.

EXAMPLE: How many grams of hydrogen peroxide will there be per liter of a solution that is $1.00N$ with respect to H_2O_2 when, as described in Sections 113 and 114, it is used in the reaction

$$H_2O_2 + 2I^- + 2H^+ = I_2 + 2H_2O?$$

The gram-equivalent weight of H_2O_2 in this reaction $= \dfrac{34.016 \text{ g per gram-molecular weight of } H_2O_2}{2 \text{ gram-equivalent weights per mole}} = 17.008$ g

Grams per liter of $1.00N$ H_2O_2 solution $= 17.0$ g

EXAMPLE: How many grams of H_2SO_4 must be diluted with water to prepare 5.00 liters of $0.100N$ H_2SO_4 as used in the neutralization reaction

$$H_2SO_4 + 2NaOH = 2H_2O + Na_2SO_4?$$

The gram-equivalent weight of H_2SO_4 in this reaction $= \dfrac{98.08 \text{ g per gram-molecular weight of } H_2SO_4}{2 \text{ gram-equivalent weights per mole}} = 49.04$ g

$0.100N$ H_2SO_4 contains 0.100 gram-equivalent weights per liter

Grams of H_2SO_4 per liter of $0.100N$ H_2SO_4 $= \dfrac{49.04 \text{ g per}}{\text{gram-equivalent weight}} \times \dfrac{0.100 \text{ gram-equivalent}}{\text{weights per liter}}$
$= 4.90$ g / lite

Grams of H_2SO_4 in 5.00 liters $0.100N$ H_2SO_4 $= 5.00$ liters $\times$ 4.904 g per liter $= 24.5$ g

The *molality system* is sometimes used, the *molal* concentration being the number of moles of solute per 1,000 g of solvent. This system has the advantage that in equimolal solutions of different solutes in a given solvent there will be the same number of moles or molecules of solute per mole of solvent. If the molality of a solution with respect to each solute present is known, it is easy to calculate the *mole fraction* of each component of the solution. This is equal to the number of moles of that component divided by the total number of moles of all components.   A 5 molal (5*m*) aqueous solution of sugar has five moles of sugar per 1,000 g of water.

$$\text{1,000 g of water} = \frac{1,000 \text{ g}}{18.016 \text{ g}} = 55.5 \text{ moles of water}$$

$$\text{The mole fraction of sugar in the solution} = \frac{5}{5 + 55.5} = 0.083$$

$$\text{The mole fraction of water in the solution} = \frac{55.5}{5 + 55.5} = 0.917$$

It is important to understand that the concentration of a solution is independent of the actual amount of the solution.   Five liters of a 2*M* solution has the same concentration as 20 ml of a 2*M* solution.

156.   THE PROCESS OF SOLUTION.   SOLUTION EQUILIBRIUM

In order to form a solution, the particles of solute must separate and disperse among the particles of solvent.   The process of solution of a solid solute in a liquid solvent will be an example to discuss in detail, so that we can see what factors are involved, in general, when solutions form.

Suppose that we consider what happens when sugar dissolves in water to give a sugar sirup.   In Figure 55 we have a large crystal of sugar in a beaker.   When water is added, the crystal begins to diminish in size, molecules of sugar leaving its surface and diffusing among the molecules of water to give a sweet solution.   In order that a molecule of sugar may be able to leave the crystal, the forces of attraction to other sugar molecules that anchor the molecule in the crystal must be overcome.   In order that the molecule of sugar may mix with the molecules of water, these molecules of water must be shoved apart against their intermolecular attraction.   A third kind of attractive force, that between molecules of sugar and molecules of water, operates in this system.   If this last force is sufficiently large to overcome the tendency of sugar molecules to cling together in the crystal lattice and the tendency of the water molecules to stay in contact, then solution will take place.

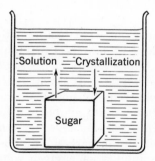

Fig. 55.   Solution of a crystal.

When the molecules of sugar leave the surface of the crystal, they diffuse among the water molecules, eventually distributing themselves uniformly throughout the liquid phase.   In their continual random travels they tend, sooner or later, to strike the crystal surface again, and there they may crystallize out, owing to the attraction to the molecules of the crystal. The rate at which the molecules leave the surface of the crystal is constant per unit area at a given temperature for a given solute and solvent. As the concentration of molecules in solution increases, the number of molecules depositing per unit surface per unit time increases. Eventually, *equilibrium* will be set up for the reversible change, and the number of molecules going into solution per unit of time will just be equal to the number crystallizing out. The concentration of the solution will then remain constant, and the solution is said to be *saturated.* *It contains the maximum amount of solute that it can hold in solution at equilibrium with the solid phase.* Note that this is another case of *dynamic equilibrium,* solution and deposition continuing at equal rates. If we put a crystal of imperfect shape into a solution saturated with respect to that crystalline material, the crystal will slowly "mend" its shape, owing to loss of particles from some areas and gain of particles by other areas. When a solution has less solute present than the equilibrium concentration, the solution is *unsaturated.*

157. SOLUBILITY

The *solubility* of a solute in a solvent under specific conditions is *measured by the concentration of the saturated solution.* This concentration defines accurately the tendency of the solute to go into solution in the solvent. By studying the solubilities of a variety of solutes in a variety of solvents, with change of pressure and temperature, we can find out what factors determine solubility and gain in understanding of how we may best manipulate these to our advantage.

The nature of the solute and the nature of the solvent affect solubility markedly. At room temperature, sugar is very soluble in water but is only slightly soluble in gasoline. Iodine is only slightly soluble in water but is quite soluble in alcohol or carbon disulfide. Sodium chloride goes into solution in water readily but will not dissolve to any appreciable extent in carbon disulfide or gasoline. These facts show us that the solubility of a given solute is different in different solvents and that different solutes have different solubilities in a given solvent.

The effect of the nature of the solute and the nature of the solvent on solubility is connected with the three kinds of attractive forces which operate on the particles involved in a solution. Solute-solute attraction and solvent-solvent attraction must be overcome by solute-solvent attraction in order that solution may take place. The relation between these different attractive forces under given conditions will fix the solubility of a given solute in a particular solvent.

In general, substances tend to be soluble in solvents that are similar. Polar compounds are likely to be more soluble in polar solvents than in nonpolar solvents. Ionic solutes may be soluble in a polar solvent such as water, but usually are not soluble in nonpolar solvents such as benzene.

Nonpolar substances are usually more soluble in nonpolar solvents than in polar materials.

The partial pressure of a gas above a solution is found to affect strongly the solubility of the gas.   The solubilities of oxygen, nitrogen, and carbon dioxide in water at different pressures of the gas above the liquid are plotted in Figure 56.   We see that at a given temperature the solubility of each gas increases in a very regular fashion as the pressure of the gas increases.   Such behavior is typical for the solution of all kinds of gases in liquids and is summarized in *Henry's Law: The solubility of a gas in a liquid is directly proportional to the partial pressure of the gas above the liquid.*   This relationship is exploited in the carbonation and use of soda

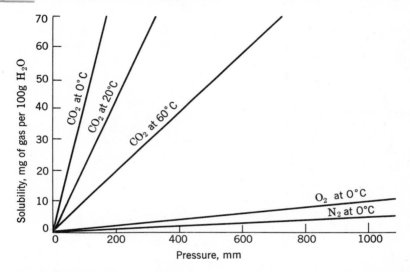

Fig. 56.   Variation of solubilities of gases with their partial pressures and with temperature.

water.   The water absorbs a large quantity of carbon dioxide when held in contact with that gas at high pressure.   It is bottled so that the high pressure is maintained and the carbon dioxide stays in solution.   When the bottle is uncapped, the pressure over the solution is lowered, and the solubility of carbon dioxide in water decreases.   The excess of the gas escapes to give the effervescence that we observe, but during the process, the carbon dioxide provides the slightly tingling taste that is desired in the beverage.

Changes in pressure, in the range that we normally work with, have only very little effect on the solubilities of solids and liquids.   The big effect of pressure on the solubility of gases and the small effect of pressure on the solubility of liquids and solids are accounted for nicely by applying the Principle of Le Châtelier.   The greater the pressure that the gas is under, the more it is compressed and the higher the concentration of its molecules in the vapor phase. The increase in the concentration of the gas favors the change that will lower it, the process of solution, and the solubility increases. Because liquids and solids are relatively incompressible, changing the pressure does not materially affect their concentration, and their solubilities therefore do not change appreciably.

In some kinds of solution, *changes in temperature may affect the solubility* considerably. The decrease of solubility with increase in temperature, shown by the curves for carbon dioxide in Figure 56, is typical of most gases. *Gases usually become less soluble in liquids with increase in*

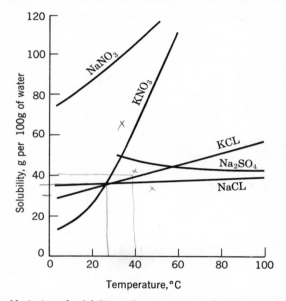

Fig. 57. Variation of solubility with temperature of solid solutes in water.

temperature. We can effectively free a solution of a dissolved gas by raising the temperature sufficiently. The small amount of oxygen normally present in water that has been in contact with the air can be removed by boiling the water for a few minutes.

It is not possible to generalize so satisfactorily about the change of solubility of liquids in liquids as the temperature is changed. Some liquid pairs, such as alcohol-water, are completely soluble (miscible in all proportions) over wide ranges in concentrations. Other liquid pairs, such as nicotine-water, show wide variations of solubility with temperature, there being in some temperature ranges an increase of solubility with increase in temperature, and in other ranges, the opposite effect. Many liquid pairs, such as water-gasoline, show little mutual solubility at any temperature.

Figure 57 gives the solubility-temperature curves for a number of solids in water at atmospheric pressure. Many solids, such as KCl, KNO₃, and NaNO₃, increase markedly in solubility with increase in temperature. Some substances, for example NaCl, show little change in solubility with change in temperature. In rarer cases, for instance Na₂SO₄, the solubility of a solid actually decreases with increase in temperature. We cannot predict the effect of change of temperature on the solubility of solids in liquids, but must check each solution experimentally.

158. HEAT OF SOLUTION

When a solute dissolves in a solvent, there always is an accompanying heat change, the *heat of solution*, which sometimes is of considerable magnitude. In some cases the process of solution is *exothermic;* in other cases it is *endothermic*. The quantity of heat involved in the change is a function of the nature and amounts of the solute and the solvent. Heats of solution are usually expressed in terms of the calories of heat evolved or absorbed when one mole of solute is dissolved in a specified number of moles of solvent. When concentrated solutions are diluted by the addition of more solvent, an energy change, either exothermic or endothermic, also is observed. Sometimes this *heat of dilution* may be in the opposite direction from the *heat of solution*. In order to determine experimentally whether the process of solution is exothermic or endothermic, we can add some of the solute to a solution which is very nearly saturated and thus eliminate any great change in concentration. If the system is observed to increase in temperature the process of solution is exothermic; if the temperature decreases, the process of solution is endothermic.

If we know whether the process of solution is exothermic or endothermic, we may predict, by applying Le Châtelier's Principle, how the solubility will change with temperature. The solubility is the concentration of the solution at a given temperature when equilibrium has been established between the solute and the solution. If we put a stress on this equilibrium system by increasing the temperature, that is, by adding heat, the change that uses up heat will be favored; the endothermic change will be favored. If the process of solution for the particular solute and solvent is endothermic, then more of the solute will tend to go into solution as the temperature is raised, and the solubility will increase. If the particular process of solution is exothermic, then the solute will tend to crystallize out, and the solubility will decrease as the temperature is raised.

159. RATE OF SOLUTION

The term *rate of solution* refers to the actual amount of solute entering the solution per unit of time. It *should not be confused with solubility*. Very finely divided sugar will dissolve faster in water than the same

amount in the form of large crystals.   The more finely divided the solute
is, the greater will be the amount of surface per gram exposed to the
solvent and the more rapid will be the total rate of solution.   The rate
of solution will also depend upon the effective movement of the solute
particles away from the surface of the solute.   The natural rates of diffusion of different particles vary under given conditions.   By stirring the
solution, we can speed up the mixing process.   If we wish to produce a
saturated solution of a solid solute as rapidly as possible, we should grind
the solute to a fine powder and agitate the mixture vigorously.   Heating
also increases the rate of solution.

160.   SEPARATION OF SOLUTE FROM SOLUTION

If the pressure or temperature of a saturated solution is changed so
that the solubility is lowered, or if some of the solvent is removed by
evaporation, the amount of solute in the solution will exceed the saturation value and the excess will *tend to separate*.   In the case of the solution
of a solid in a liquid, crystallization will occur, thus removing the stress
on the system.   The crystals continue to grow until equilibrium is established between them and the solution.   The solution then will be just
saturated, but the processes of dissolving and crystallizing continue at
equal rates.   The faster the rate of crystallization is, the smaller will be
the size of the crystals which are formed.   Dissolving a substance and
then recovering it by crystallization is a good procedure for purifying solids.   When the crystals grow from solution, impurities may be
entrapped, or *occluded*.   By redissolving these crystals and then recrys-
tallizing, the substance will be purified further, since the more soluble
impurities will tend to remain in solution.

161.   SUPERSATURATED SOLUTIONS

Certain solutes do not start to form crystals readily when their
concentration, in solutions not in contact with crystals, is increased
above the saturation value by changing the temperature or by evaporating the solvent.   *Supersaturated solutions* are then produced.   These
supersaturated solutions actually have more of the solute in solution
than can normally be held at equilibrium with the solid solute.   This is
an unstable condition, and mechanical shock or agitation may start
crystallization of the excess solute.   The addition of a small crystal, or
"seed," of the solute is sure to cause crystallization.   Apparently, it is
sometimes very difficult to start the building of a crystal, but once this
is started, further crystallization proceeds very rapidly, and equilibrium
is established.   To be sure that you are dealing with a *saturated* solution,
you should make certain that an excess of the solid has been in contact

with the solution for a long enough time so that equilibrium will have been achieved.

Figure 58 compares an unsaturated, a saturated, and a supersaturated solution in contact with a crystalline solute at the same temperature. The small circles indicate relative numbers of solute particles in solution, and the lengths of the arrows indicate the relative rates of dissolving and crystallization per unit area of crystal.

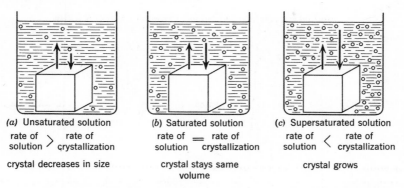

(a) Unsaturated solution
rate of > rate of
solution   crystallization

crystal decreases in size

(b) Saturated solution
rate of = rate of
solution   crystallization

crystal stays same
volume

(c) Supersaturated solution
rate of < rate of
solution   crystallization

crystal grows

Fig. 58. Comparison of unsaturated, saturated, and supersaturated solutions.

162. VAPOR PRESSURE OF SOLUTIONS

The presence of solute particles among the solvent particles will modify the behavior of the liquid solvent considerably, because of the solute-solvent forces of attraction and because the solute particles get in the way of the solvent particles and hinder their motion. The addition of particles of a nonvolatile solute to a volatile solvent lowers the tendency of the molecules of the solvent to escape to an extent which, for dilute solutions, is directly proportional to the number of particles of solute present in a given weight or given number of moles of solvent. In other words, the equilibrium vapor pressure of a given solvent will be lowered proportionally to the number of moles of solute particles in a given weight or given number of moles of solvent.

In Figure 59 the characteristic equilibrium vapor pressure curve for pure water is represented by the line OA. (The temperature scale is somewhat distorted, as already mentioned for Figure 52.) When a nonvolatile solute such as sugar is added, the equilibrium vapor pressure curve for the water is lowered to the line DE. This effect is very much exaggerated on the plot so that it may be more apparent. As can be seen, this lowering of the equilibrium vapor pressure of the solvent will be accompanied by a proportional increase in the boiling point and a proportional lowering of the freezing point of the solvent. The effect on a given weight of a given solvent is, in dilute solutions, independent of the nature of the particles of the solute, depending merely upon the number of particles of solute per given weight of solvent.

This effect of solute particles on the solvent provides an excellent method for studying nonvolatile solute particles. We can determine experimentally how much the equilibrium vapor pressure, or the boiling point, or the freezing point of a given weight of solvent is changed when we add a given weight of solute. From the change we can calculate the

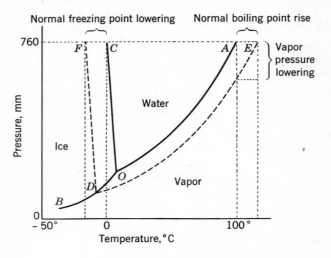

Fig. 59.   Effect of solute on solvent.

number of moles of solute particles that are present in solution. Knowing the weight of solute, we can then compute the weight of one mole of the particles. This is very valuable information because it allows us to come to certain conclusions as to how the atoms constituting the solute are combined in the solute particles. We will see how this is possible by considering freezing-point measurements.

163.   DETERMINATION OF MOLAR WEIGHTS OF SOLUTE PARTICLES BY MOLAL LOWERING OF THE FREEZING POINT

One mole (6.02×10^{23}) of any solute particles in 1,000 g of a solvent constitutes a $1m$ solution of these particles. One mole of solute particles per 1,000 g of solvent lowers the freezing point of the solvent by an amount that is constant and characteristic of the solvent, regardless of what the solute particles are. This amount of lowering for a molal solution is called the *molal freezing-point constant of the solvent*. Its value for the solvents water, benzene, and napthalene is 1.86°, 5.12°, and 6.85°, respectively. All aqueous solutions containing one mole of any solute particles per 1,000 g of water will start to freeze at −1.86°. With change in molal concentration of solute particles, the lowering of the freezing point changes in direct proportion. All aqueous solutions 0.5m with respect to solute particles will start to freeze at $-0.93°$. Figure 60 shows the direct proportionality of lowering of the freezing point with molal concentration for water, benzene, and napthalene. Remember that this holds only for dilute solutions where the attractive forces between the solute particles are negligible.

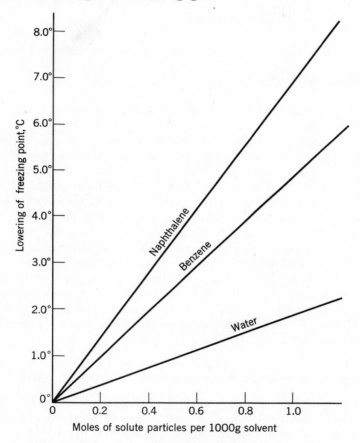

Fig. 60. Lowering of freezing point of solvent due to solute particles.

Let us see what we can learn about sugar in solution in water from freezing-point data. When 34.2 g of sugar is dissolved in 500 g of water, the resulting solution begins to freeze at $-0.372°$. First we calculate the number of grams of sugar there would have to be per 1,000 g of water in order to give the same concentration as the solution used. We get this by dividing the number of grams of solute used by the number of grams of solvent used and multiplying by 1,000.

$$\frac{34.2 \text{ g of sugar}}{500 \text{ g of water}} \times 1{,}000 \text{ g of water} = 68.4 \text{ g of sugar per } 1{,}000 \text{ g of water}$$

A solution of 68.4 g of sugar in 1,000 g of water lowers the freezing point of water 0.372°.

$$\frac{\text{The molality of}}{\text{this solution}} = \frac{\text{the observed lowering of the freezing point}}{\text{lowering of the freezing point expected for } 1m \text{ solution}}$$
$$= \frac{0.372°}{1.86°} = 0.200m$$

This means that 68.4 g of sugar gives 0.200 moles of particles. Therefore,

$$\text{One mole of sugar particles} = \frac{68.4 \text{ g}}{0.200 \text{ mole}} = 342 \text{ g of sugar}$$

and 342 g of sugar gives the Avogadro Number of solute particles when dissolved in water.

When the solute is a molecular substance and its molecules persist unchanged in solution, the weight of one mole of the solute particles will be equal to the gram-molecular weight of the solute. Such is the case when sugar is dissolved in water. The gram-molecular weight of sugar in water therefore is 342 g. This is consistent with the belief that the particles of sugar in water solution are molecules having the formula $C_{12}H_{22}O_{11}$. These are the same molecules that go to build up crystals of sugar. When sugar dissolves in water, the molecules merely separate from the crystal and diffuse in random fashion through the water.

This method for determining molecular weights is particularly useful for substances such as sugar which, when they are heated, decompose before they vaporize, because when these circumstances prevail it is impossible to ascertain their molecular weights by determining the weight of 22.4 liters of the gas STP.

164. DISTRIBUTION OF A SOLUTE BETWEEN TWO IMMISCIBLE SOLVENTS

So far we have considered what happens when a solute is brought in contact with a single solvent. Another case of considerable importance to the chemist is the system involving a solute in contact with two solvents, *A* and *B*, which are insoluble in each other. Under given conditions, the solute will have a definite solubility in *A* and a different solubility in *B*. If the system is thoroughly mixed, so that both solvents have ample contact with the solute, an equilbrium will be established. The solute then will be found to be distributed between the two solvents in such a fashion that the ratio of its concentrations in the two is the same as the ratio of its solubilities in the two.

$$\frac{\text{Concentration in } A}{\text{Concentration in } B} = \frac{\text{solubility in } A}{\text{solubility in } B}$$

If the solubility in A is 10 g per liter and the solubility in B is 20 g per liter, at equilibrium of the solute with A and B, the concentration in A will be one-half the concentration B.   If equal volumes of the two solvents are present, of the total amount of solute taken into solution, one-third will be in A and two-thirds will be in B.

The problem becomes more complicated when the volumes of the two solvents used are not the same.   Suppose that we have a solution containing 0.0177 g of iodine in 200 g of water, and 300 g of chloroform is added to it.   What will be the weight of iodine in the water layer when equilibrium is established, if the solubility of iodine is 0.0270 g per 100 g of water and 2.176 g per 100 g of chloroform?

Let

Grams of iodine left in the 200 g of water $= x$

Then,

Grams of iodine taken up by
the 300 g of chloroform $= 0.0177 - x$

Grams of iodine in 200 g of chloroform $= \frac{2}{3}(0.0177 - x)$

But

$$\frac{\text{Grams of iodine in 200 g of water}}{\text{Grams of iodine in 200 g of chloroform}} = \frac{\text{solubility of iodine in water}}{\text{solubility of iodine in chloroform}}$$

Therefore,

$$\frac{x}{\frac{2}{3}(0.0177 - x)} = \frac{0.0270}{2.176}$$

$x = 0.00014$ g of iodine left in the water layer

We see then that simply by shaking the aqueous solution of iodine with the chloroform we can remove all but 0.00014 g of the 0.0177 g of iodine originally in solution in the water.

The relationship governing the distribution of a solute between two immiscible solvents is useful in the extraction of solutes from solution. Suppose a given substance is somewhat soluble in water and you wish to remove it from the water without evaporation or distillation.   A second liquid, which is not soluble in water and in which the solute is more soluble than it is in water, can be added and will form a second liquid layer.   When the mixture is shaken, the solute will distribute itself between the water and the second solvent according to the law.   Since the solute is more soluble in the second solvent, most of the solute will be removed from the water.   The two liquid phases can then be separated. By repeatedly treating the water with fresh quantities of the second liquid, practically all the solute can be extracted from the water, although the extraction can never be absolutely complete.   Such an operation is known as *liquid-liquid extraction;* it is often used in the laboratory and in industry.

165. SOLVATION. HYDRATION

In ideal solutions we assume that there is no chemical reaction between the solute and solvent particles, and, up to this point in our discussion, we have not considered such a possibility. Actually, very frequently there is chemical activity between solvent and solute with the formation of new substances, and this activity complicates the situation. One case of chemical reaction in solution that is of considerable interest is the direct combination of solute and solvent particles to give a new complex substance in which the molecules of solvent are combined but retain their configuration. Such a complex substance is called a *solvate*. The process of *solvation* is always exothermic. (It should be noted, however, that this exothermic effect may be masked by the endothermic energy change involved in the breakdown of the crystal lattice of a solid solute.) Solvates are usually not very stable, and the reverse change, desolvation, usually takes place readily.

$$\text{Solute} + \text{solvent} \underset{\text{desolvation}}{\overset{\text{solvation}}{\rightleftharpoons}} \text{solvate} + \text{heat}$$

The Principle of Le Châtelier tells us that raising the temperature will favor the dissociation of the solvate into the solute and the solvent.

The most common case of solvation is *hydration*, in which water molecules combine with the solute particles to form *hydrates*.

$$\text{Solute} + \text{H}_2\text{O} \underset{\text{dehydration}}{\overset{\text{hydration}}{\rightleftharpoons}} \text{hydrate} + \text{heat}$$

For example, when water is added in limited amount to colorless copper sulfate, $CuSO_4$, the copper sulfate turns to a brilliant blue color and forms crystals which can be shown to have the composition $CuSO_4 \cdot 5H_2O$.

$$CuSO_{4(s)} + 5H_2O = \underset{\substack{\text{copper sulfate} \\ \text{pentahydrate}}}{CuSO_4 \cdot 5H_2O_{(s)}} + \text{heat}$$

In formulating solvates, we put down the formula for the solute and then write the formula for the solvent molecule, connecting it to the formula of the solute with a dot. This formulation indicates that chemical combination has occurred but that the solvent molecule is not broken up. If the hydrate is crystalline, the water of hydration is called *water of crystallization* because, when dehydration occurs, the crystals are destroyed. The water molecules play an important role in building up the crystal lattice of a hydrate.

166. STABILITY OF HYDRATES. EFFLORESCENCE

Because hydration is a reversible process, at a given temperature equilibrium will tend to be established between the hydrate and the water vapor in contact with it. At a given temperature the hydrate will have a certain equilibrium aqueous vapor pressure. Since the process of dehydration is endothermic, the equilibrium aqueous vapor pressure of a hydrate will increase with increase in temperature. The tendency of the hydrate to lose water will become greater as the temperature is raised. All hydrates will decompose if they are heated sufficiently.

When a crystalline hydrate at room temperature has an equilibrium aqueous vapor pressure that is higher than the prevailing partial pressure of water in the atmosphere, it will lose a part or all of its water of crystallization when exposed to the air. Since the molecules of water are important units in determining the crystal structure of the hydrate, when water is lost the crystal will crumble. It is said to *effloresce*, and *efflorescence* is said to have occurred. Some hydrates, such as $Na_2SO_4 \cdot 10H_2O$, effloresce rapidly when exposed to air; others, such as borax, $Na_2B_4O_7 \cdot 10H_2O$, are stable. Because the partial aqueous vapor pressure of the air changes considerably, some hydrates are stable when the humidity is high but decompose when the air is dry. $CuSO_4 \cdot 5H_2O$ behaves in this fashion.

167. HYGROSCOPIC SUBSTANCES. DELIQUESCENCE

When crystals of calcium chloride or phosphoric oxide are exposed to the air, they rapidly gain in weight. This increase in weight can be shown to be due to the addition of water from the air. A substance that has the ability to remove moisture from the atmosphere is said to be *hygroscopic*. Such materials may be of practical use as *drying agents*, or *desiccants*, for removing water from systems. For instance, calcium chloride is sometimes used for drying basements that are unduly moist. A *desiccator* is a tightly closed vessel in which samples of materials may be dried by means of a desiccant. Anhydrous copper sulfate, a white powder, is an interesting desiccating agent; when it hydrates, it becomes blue, and this color change enables us to follow the drying process. Concentrated sulfuric acid, a liquid, is a very powerful drying agent. Gases can be dried by bubbling them through sulfuric acid if they do not react with it.

Some hygroscopic solids pick up so much water from the air that they completely dissolve in this water, and a solution is formed. Such substances are termed *deliquescent*, and the phenomenon is known as *deliquescence*. Calcium chloride deliquesces when exposed to the atmosphere, and because of this, powdered calcium chloride may be scattered over dry soil to keep down the dust.

The process of deliquescence may be accounted for by applying what we have learned about solutions. A film of moisture tends to condense on all surfaces that are exposed to the air, owing to bombardment by water molecules. If the solid is soluble, it will dissolve in the water film and form a solution. For a very soluble material, the saturated concentrated solution formed will have an equilibrium aqueous vapor pressure less than the prevailing aqueous vapor pressure of the air.   There will then be a tendency for the system to approach equilibrium by the condensation of water from the atmosphere.   As water condenses and dilutes the surface film of the solution, more of the solid is taken into solution. This process continues until the solid is completely dissolved.   Then more water will dilute the solution until it is at equilibrium with the air, that is, until the equilibrium aqueous vapor pressure of the solution just becomes equal to the prevailing partial pressure of water in the air.   Since the latter varies considerably, some substances may deliquesce on a very humid day but will not do so when the air is very dry.   Sea salt becomes very sticky on humid days but dries out when the air has low moisture content.

EXERCISES

1. Solutions and pure substances are spoken of as homogeneous systems. How may these kinds of systems be distinguished from each other?

2. What is the nature of the particles that become dispersed in the solvent water when each of the following solutes is dissolved, assuming that there is no reaction with water: a) iodine? b) sodium chloride? c) carbon dioxide? d) oxygen? e) cane sugar?

3. How many moles of iodine are there in 500 cc of a $0.05M$ solution of iodine? (The molecular formula of iodine is I_2.)

4. How many sodium ions are there in 10 ml of a $2M$ solution of NaCl?

5. How much water must be added to 1 liter of a $2M$ solution of sugar to change the molarity to 0.5?

6. Making use of Figure 57, calculate the approximate molarity of an aqueous solution of KCl that is saturated at 40°.

7. a) According to Figure 57, at about what temperature are the solubilities of KNO_3, KCl, and NaCl practically the same when given in terms of grams per 1,000 g of water?
  b) How do their solubilities at this temperature compare when expressed in terms of molarity?   (Assume that the volume of the solution is approximately that of the water that is present.)

8. a) How many grams of nitric acid, HNO_3, must be present in 1 liter of solution in order that the solution be: 1) $2M$? 2) $0.2N$?
  b) How many milliliters of the $2M$ solution will be equivalent to 200 ml of the $0.2N$ solution?
  c) How many milliliters of the $0.2N$ solution of nitric acid will be needed to just neutralize 100 ml of a $0.1N$ solution of calcium hydroxide, $Ca(OH)_2$?

9. If 31.73 g of iodine is dissolved in 460.7 g of ethyl alcohol, C_2H_5OH, calculate the molality of this solution and the mole fractions of iodine and alcohol that are present.

10. If the solubility of carbon dioxide in water is 335 mg per 100 g of water at 0° when the partial pressure of carbon dioxide is 760 mm, how many milligrams of carbon dioxide will be dissolved in 100 g of water saturated at 0° when the partial pressure of carbon dioxide is 5 atm?

11. What, in general, are the effects of change of pressure and change of temperature on the solubility of a) gases in gases? b) gases in liquids? c) solids in liquids? d) liquids in liquids?

12. a) Why do bottles of carbonated beverages effervesce when uncapped?
b) Which will effervesce more vigorously, a warm or a cold bottle of soda water? Why?

13. From the solubility curves given in Figure 57, deduce for each solute whether the process of solution is endothermic or exothermic.

14. a) Why does powdering a solid solute increase the rate of its solution?
b) Will the solubility increase?

15. Is a given solution unsaturated, saturated, or supersaturated with respect to a certain solid solute if, when a crystal of that solute is added, the crystal: a) grows in size? b) decreases in size? c) remains the same size?

16. Explain how dynamic equilibrium is involved in a system where crystals of a solute are in contact with a saturated solution of this solute.

17. You have a solid completely in solution in a liquid solvent and wish to obtain some crystals of the solid. Describe two different procedures you could use which would be likely to accomplish this.

18. An aqueous solution containing 2.12 g of a molecular solute in 100 g of water freezes at −0.186°. What is the molecular weight of the solute?

19. The freezing point of a solution of 1.05 g of a solute in 200 g of benzene is 4.78°. The normal freezing point of benzene is 5.48°. What is the molecular weight of the solute?

20. What will be the freezing point of a solution which has 0.1 mole of solute particles present in 250 g of naphthalene? The normal freezing point of naphthalene is 80.2°.

21. The solubility of camphor is 0.105 g per 100 ml of water and 200 g per 100 ml of carbon disulfide. Water and carbon disulfide are immiscible liquids. If 500 ml of water saturated with camphor is shaken with 100 ml of carbon disulfide, what percentage of the camphor will be taken up by the carbon disulfide?

22. Distinguish between efflorescence and deliquescence.

23. The solubility of $NaNO_3$ is 73 g in 100 g of water at 0° and 180 g in 100 g of water at 100°.
a) If 300 g of $NaNO_3$ is added to 150 g of water and heated at 100° until the solution is saturated, then filtered at 100°, how much solid $NaNO_3$ will be left as solid on the filter paper?
b) How much solid $NaNO_3$ will separate if the filtrate is cooled to 0° and a small crystal of $NaNO_3$ is added?

24. What is the significance of the terms *solvation* and *hydration?*

Chapter 13

▶ Colloidal Systems

168. COLLOIDAL DISPERSION

When sugar dissolves in water, the crystals separate into single molecules, each of which diffuses through the liquid, and the molecules of sugar soon become dispersed uniformly among the molecules of water. With molecular substances such as sugar, the molecules are of about the same order of magnitude as the particles of the solvent, and the solute particles will stay in suspension indefinitely and cannot be separated from the solvent by filtration. We refer to such mixtures as *true solutions*, and consider them to be homogeneous one-phase systems. Similarly, when substances that are composed of discrete ions dissolve, the individual ions become uniformly dispersed among the solvent particles, and a homogeneous true solution is formed. In such solutions the solutes have become dispersed into the smallest particles that can be obtained without destroying the substance by chemical change.

When coarsely powdered sulfur, which is not appreciably soluble in water, is shaken with water, the coarse pieces of sulfur momentarily become distributed in the water. But when the system is allowed to come to rest, the chunks of sulfur rapidly settle out, separating from the water. Such a system obviously consists of two distinctly separate phases. Similarly, coarsely crystalline barium sulfate does not dissolve appreciably in water, and the large grains settle rapidly from suspension and can be observed as a separate phase. The coarse sulfur and barium sulfate do not remain permanently dispersed in the liquid. It is easy to separate them from the water by decantation or filtration.

If, however, the sulfur or barium sulfate is present as very small particles in suspension, these will not separate so rapidly from water. Indeed, if the particles are small enough, they stay dispersed in water for considerable periods of time. When such a suspension is poured on a filter paper, the very fine particles of sulfur or barium sulfate may pass right through the paper with the water. The particles still consist of thousands of molecules or ions, and the particles are still relatively quite large compared to the water molecules. Such suspensions are examples of *colloidal dispersion*, and the system is an example of a *colloidal system*. Colloidal systems are intermediate between homogeneous solutions and mixtures of massive separate phases where the boundaries are readily apparent and there is relatively very little dispersion of one phase in another. Colloidal systems have one phase dispersed in a rather uniform fashion in a second phase, but the degree of dispersion is relatively much less than that of solutions of small molecules or ions.

169. BROWNIAN MOVEMENT OF COLLOIDAL PARTICLES

The dispersed particles colloidally suspended in a liquid or gaseous phase are so small that they cannot be seen by a microscope. However, when the suspension is studied with an ultramicroscope, the dispersed particles can be detected by means of the light they scatter and are found to be in a constant state of motion. This is an example of Brownian movement, which has already been mentioned in Chapter 9. The colloidal particles are bombarded unequally from different directions at a given instant by the surrounding molecules of the gas or liquid and are kicked around the system in a random fashion. This prevents them from settling. The smaller the particles are, the greater will be the chances that they can be kept permanently dispersed by such Brownian movement. Large massive particles will settle out rapidly.

170. SIZES OF COLLOIDAL PARTICLES

It is possible roughly to compare true solutions, colloidal suspensions, and massive two-phase systems in terms of particle size. The discrete small molecules and ions with which we deal in ordinary solutions have diameters of from 1×10^{-8} cm up to 20×10^{-8} cm. Colloidal particles consisting of aggregations of molecules or ions usually vary in diameter from about 20×10^{-8} up to about 5×10^{-5} cm. Particles larger than the last value can be seen by the ordinary microscope and usually do not remain colloidally dispersed. Highly polymeric substances, however, may have molecules with dimensions in the colloidal range. By means of the electron microscope it is possible to get such high magnification that pictures of particles of colloidal size can be obtained. In some colloidal systems, instead of globular particles, the dispersed phase may be in the form of filaments, thin plates, or thin films in which at least *one dimension is very small.*

171. KINDS OF COLLOIDAL SYSTEMS

Many colloidal systems consist of discrete particles of the *dispersed phase* suspended in another phase which is *continuous*. Because of the different states that are possible for each of these phases, a number of different kinds of colloidal systems are known. Table 26 lists these and gives examples.

In another type of colloidal system, called *gels,* the two phases are both continuous, but they interlace, producing a very large amount of interface between the two phases. One of the phases forms a rigid or semi-rigid network that is porous, so that a gas or liquid phase can interpenetrate. Gelatinous precipitates and jellies are gels that have much liquid associated with a solid network. Silica gel and active alumina consist of very porous and extensive rigid frameworks of the oxides which are penetrated by a maze of tiny intercommunicating cells or

Table 26.   Kinds of Colloidal Systems

Dispersed Phase	Continuous Phase	Example
Gas	Liquid	*Foams;* bubbles of air in soap solution
Gas	Solid	Pumice has gas bubbles dispersed in mineral material
Liquid	Gas	*Clouds, fogs;* droplets of water suspended in air
Liquid	Liquid	*Emulsions;* droplets of oil suspended in water as in milk and mayonnaise
Liquid	Solid	Some minerals have droplets of liquid trapped in them
Solid	Gas	*Smokes;* solid particles dispersed in air
Solid	Liquid	*Sols;* sulfur particles in colloidal suspension in water
Solid	Solid	Black diamonds have particles of graphite dispersed in the diamond

channels open to gases. Wood charcoal is a porous network of carbon.

Many of the materials which are important in everyday life and in industry are colloidal systems. In soils and minerals, colloidal phenomena are often observed, and in biology, colloidal dispersions are particularly common. Many foods and body fluids are highly colloidal in nature.

172. SURFACES IN COLLOIDAL SYSTEMS

In colloidal systems the dispersed phases have a very great amount of surface, which has been estimated to be as high as 1 acre per g in some cases. This means that there will be high percentage of the total amount of the phase exposed at the surfaces. Because the valence forces and intermolecular forces are not completely satisfied at such surfaces, a colloidally dispersed material can be expected to have a higher apparent reactivity than a massive compact phase. The surface behavior of colloidal systems is especially interesting and important.

173. ADSORPTION

The surfaces of colloidally dispersed phases may exert considerable forces of attraction toward other substances, and such substances may concentrate on and adhere to the surfaces. This concentration on a surface is called *adsorption*. Adsorption is highly specific; a given surface will adsorb one substance very strongly, another very weakly. Active forms of wood charcoal adsorb certain poison gases much more strongly than they do air and are therefore used in gas masks to purify air. Silica gel and active alumina adsorb water vapor very strongly and are good drying agents. Silica gel adsorbs many organic solvents strongly and can be used to recover the vapors of these solvents. Since the tendency for adsorption decreases with rise in temperature, adsorbed substances can be driven off by heating.

Some colloidal particles adsorb certain ions strongly from solution. If cations are adsorbed, the particles become positively charged, and *positive sols* are formed. If anions are adsorbed, *negative sols* result. Ferric hydroxide sols are positive, whereas arsenious sulfide sols are negative.

Most solid surfaces have some tendency to adsorb a film of air. If a liquid comes in contact with the surface and is adsorbed more strongly than the air, it will displace the air film and will *wet* the surface. If it wets the surface, it will tend to spread on the surface and remain in contact with it. Such wetting is specific, depending upon the liquid and the nature of the surface. Water wets glass and silicates but will not wet a piece of paraffin or an oily surface. In order to be a good lubricant for a machine bearing, an oil must be adsorbed strongly to the metal surface so it will remain between the bearing surfaces and reduce the friction.

174. FORMATION OF COLLOIDAL SYSTEMS

Colloidal systems can be obtained by *dispersion methods*. Large massive portions of one phase are broken up and dispersed in a second phase. Liquids can be atomized in air to produce fogs. Emulsions are often produced by vigorously shaking or stirring two immiscible liquids together. Milk is homogenized by running it through a machine in which the liquid fats are reduced to such small droplets that they stay dispersed in the water and show little tendency to agglomerate and float to the surface as a layer of cream. Meringue is formed as a foam when air is beaten into egg whites. Air and water do not by themselves yield a stable foam, but when a small amount of soap is added, foams are readily obtained. *Foaming agents*, such as soap, enter into the surface films of the liquid phase and stabilize the dispersion. Soap is also frequently used as an *emulsifying agent* to stabilize emulsions.

Sols consisting of solid particles dispersed in a continuous liquid phase may often be prepared by grinding the solid in the liquid.   The addition of a small amount of a *peptizing agent* is usually of considerable help in securing colloidal dispersion.   The peptizing agent is a substance that will be adsorbed on the surface of the colloidal particles and will keep them from coalescing.   By selecting a proper peptizing agent, very stable sols can be prepared.   Substances, such as gelatin and soap, which themselves readily form colloidal systems, are generally excellent peptizing agents.

Colloidal systems are sometimes established by *condensation methods.* Single molecules or ions unit or condense until particles of colloidal size are built up.   Clouds and fog form when individual molecules of water condense to give very tiny droplets, which are dispersed in the air.   The molecules of gases produced in chemical reactions may accumulate to form bubbles in a foam.   Smokes frequently result when the solid products of combustion build up particles that become suspended in the air. When ions in solution associate to form substances of low solubility, these may build up colloidal particles to give sols.   Sulfides formed rapidly in solution are very apt to be colloidal.   A slow rate of formation favors the building up of larger crystals, which do not remain dispersed.   Adsorption of peptizing agents or of ions by the colloidal particles when they form will prevent them from growing too much and will stabilize the dispersions.   Colloidal particles, which have the same kind of net charge, owing to the adsorption of the same kind of ions, will repel each other and will not agglomerate.

Gels are built up by condensation methods.   When a warm aqueous solution of gelatin cools, the gelatin forms a continuous three-dimensional porous network which contains the water to give a semirigid jelly.   A similar jelly is formed when a solution of sodium silicate is mixed with dilute hydrochloric acid; the setting of this gel involves the building up of a rigid silica network that holds very considerable amounts of water. This water may be removed and air can take its place to produce the silica *aerogel*, which is so useful as an adsorbent.   Gelatinous precipitates are often obtained when an insoluble substance is formed from solution.

175. BREAKDOWN OF COLLOIDAL SYSTEMS

Colloidal systems are essentially unstable with respect to the separate massive phases, and the colloidally dispersed phases have a tendency to agglomerate.   Frequently, it is a great nuisance to have colloidal dispersions form, and steps must be taken to break down these systems into the separate massive phases.

Foams can often be broken up by the addition of some substance that will lower the stability of the surface film, thereby counteracting any foaming agents that may be present.   Lubricating oils foam badly when they are pumped and run into containers.   The addition of very small amounts of liquid silicones is very effective for breaking down such foams. The use of *antifoaming agents* to break down foams quickly after they have been used in ore flotation processes is important.

We often wish to break down emulsions so that we can separate the liquids which are involved. The colloidal particles of fats in milk are caused to coalesce somewhat by the centrifugal forces set up in a cream separator. Churning cream gives the fat particles still further opportunity to agglomerate to form chunks of butter. The use of proper addition agents frequently aids in breaking down emulsions. Freezing has proved an effective way to break an emulsion.

The term *flocculation* refers to the agglomeration of solid particles colloidally dispersed in a liquid, so that large flocs or visible crystals separate. This may sometimes be accomplished by holding the sol at elevated temperatures, so that the growth of crystals is favored. Removal of a peptizing agent, which protects the colloidal particles, renders the suspension unstable. A positive sol whose particles are stabilized because of the repulsion of their charges can be flocculated by bringing it together with a negative sol, so that the charges neutralize each other.

Gelatinous precipitates and jellies can be broken down by shaking them vigorously to destroy the rigid framework that holds the liquid phase. Heating also tends to destroy the structure. Some jellies separate into two distinct phases merely upon standing. This is known as *syneresis*.

176. DETERGENTS

Substances, such as soaps, that are used for cleansing are called *detergents*. The action of detergents depends to a considerable extent upon their ability to act as wetting and peptizing agents. The detergent is adsorbed on the surfaces of the dirt particles so that they can be wetted by the water and go into colloidal dispersion, forming emulsions or sols. This is of great importance in laundry practice. In recent years many new kinds of wetting agents have been discovered and are being marketed widely as substitutes for soap. Because they do not form the objectionable gummy curds produced when ordinary soaps are put in hard water, these new detergents have some advantages.

EXERCISES

1. Distinguish between colloidal dispersions and molecular dispersions.

2. How do Brownian movement and particle size determine the existence of a sol?

3. Mention 10 different examples of colloidal systems that you have observed in everyday life. What phases and structure are involved in each case?

4. Why are surface effects so important in colloidal systems?

5. a) What is adsorption?
b) How is adsorption important in the formation of colloidal systems?

6. Distinguish between condensation and dispersion methods for the formation of colloidal systems, describing three examples of each.

7. a) What procedures are effective for breaking down foams and emulsions?
b) How can sols be treated to cause their flocculation?
c) What is likely to happen to jellies when they are allowed to stand?

8. Why are detergents effective in cleansing operations?

9. Why is the behavior of colloidal systems of interest in: a) metallurgy? b) plant nutrition? c) the petroleum industry? d) medicine? e) meterology? f) the food industry?

Chapter 14

▶ More about Bonding and the Shapes

of Molecules and Complex Ions

177. NEED FOR EXTENSION OF BONDING THEORIES

We have seen that the ionic and covalent bonding theories serve quite well to account qualitatively for the chemical activity of the atoms of the elements. Furthermore, these theories can be used with considerable success to explain and predict qualitatively the combining capacity of atoms and the properties of the compounds which are formed. They are effective as a basis for organizing and understanding a great many chemical facts.

However, not all of the facts of chemical combination are consistent with the simple theories already considered. Many cases of chemical combination that are known to occur are not adequately accounted for. We have already seen that the oxygen molecule does not obey the rules. The bonding in the ozone molecule has not yet been considered, but, as we shall see, the ordinary covalent bonding theory is not satisfactory in this case. In Chapter 12, solvation and hydration were mentioned. These involve chemical combination between solute particles and neutral solvent molecules in which the atoms apparently have their valence requirements satisfied. How can this be explained?

It is evident that the theories of chemical bonding must be extended to cover such cases of chemical combination. We will consider briefly several ideas that have been suggested.

178. DONOR-ACCEPTOR OR COORDINATE COVALENT BONDING

The covalent bond has been described as being established by each of two atoms furnishing one electron to set up a pair of electrons, which are then shared between the two atoms. A shared pair of electrons set up in this fashion has been called a *normal covalent bond*.

N. V. Sidgwick suggested a second way in which a shared pair of electrons may be established. Both of the electrons may be *donated* by one atom and *accepted* by a second atom as indicated in the equation

$$
\begin{array}{cccccccc}
\text{H} & & :\!\overset{\cdot\cdot}{\text{F}}\!: & & \text{H} & & :\!\overset{\cdot\cdot}{\text{F}}\!: & \\
\text{H}:\!\text{N}:\! & + & \overset{\cdot\cdot}{\text{B}}:\!\overset{\cdot\cdot}{\text{F}}\!: & = & \text{H}:\!\text{N} & : & \text{B}:\!\overset{\cdot\cdot}{\text{F}}\!: & \\
\text{H} & & :\!\overset{\cdot\cdot}{\text{F}}\!: & & \text{H} & & :\!\overset{\cdot\cdot}{\text{F}}\!: & \\
\end{array}
$$

In the NH_3 molecule, the nitrogen atom has one pair of unshared electrons in its outermost shell. Boron, in the BF_3 molecule, is associated in its valence shell with only six electrons which are involved in the three normal covalent bonds that boron has formed to fluorine. Boron still lacks two electrons of having the stable electronic configuration of neon. Therefore, when a molecule of ammonia collides with a molecule of boron trifluoride, the unshared pair of electrons is believed to be donated by the nitrogen, and a share in them is accepted by the boron. The pair of electrons, which thus beomes shared by the nitrogen and boron atoms, constitutes a chemical bond linking the original molecules into a new complex substance, which is usually referred to as a *molecular addition compound*. A covalent bond set up in this fashion is referred to as a *coordinate covalent bond*, or by the more descriptive term *donor-acceptor bond*.

Once the pair of electrons is shared, it acts like other pairs of bonding electrons and contributes to the valence shells of both atoms. Formation of a donor-acceptor bond builds up the valence shell of the acceptor atom, but there is no decrease in the number of electrons associated with the donor atom. Such a bonding mechanism provides a means for setting up chemical combination between two molecules whose ordinary valences are already satisfied. The formation of donor-acceptor bonds is possible only when there is available a donor atom (one with an unshared pair of electrons in its valence shell) and an acceptor atom (one that is short a pair of electrons).

If this theory of bonding is a good one, we should be able to use it to predict the formation of molecular addition compounds. For instance, aluminum has only three valence electrons and therefore tends to build molecules by forming three normal covalent bonds. This is the case in $AlCl_3$, in which the aluminum atom is still short two electrons of an inert-gas configuration. If this molecule is brought together with the $N(CH_3)_3$ molecules, in which the nitrogen atom has an unshared pair of electrons, donor-acceptor bonding should be possible. This does take place to form the molecular addition compound, $(CH_3)_3N:AlCl_3$. This

$$
\begin{array}{cccccccc}
\overset{\text{H}_3}{\text{C}} & & :\!\overset{\cdot\cdot}{\text{Cl}}\!: & & \overset{\text{H}_3}{\text{C}} & & :\!\overset{\cdot\cdot}{\text{Cl}}\!: & \\
| & & | & & | & & | & \\
\text{H}_3\text{C}\!-\!\text{N}:\! & + & \text{Al}\!-\!\overset{\cdot\cdot}{\text{Cl}}\!: & = & \text{H}_3\text{C}\!-\!\text{N}\!-\!\!-\!\text{Al}\!-\!\overset{\cdot\cdot}{\text{Cl}}\!: & \\
| & & | & & | & & | & \\
\overset{\text{C}}{\text{H}_3} & & :\!\overset{\cdot\cdot}{\text{Cl}}\!: & & \overset{\text{C}}{\text{H}_3} & & :\!\overset{\cdot\cdot}{\text{Cl}}\!: & \\
\end{array}
$$

kind of chemical activity for $AlCl_3$ is believed to be the reason why it is an excellent catalyst for many reactions; it complexes with one of the reactants to form an intermediate which is very reactive. One of the reasons for learning to write correct electronic formulas is now apparent; they make it easy to decide whether molecules can be expected to form more bonds by donor-acceptor action.

179. THE THEORY OF RESONANCE HYBRID BONDING

Some molecules and complex ions are known, for which it is impossible to write electronic formulas of the ordinary type that still are in accord with the properties of the substances.

For instance, the gas sulfur dioxide is known to consist of bent-chain SO_2 molecules. It is reasonable to expect that each of the oxygen atoms will be covalently bonded to the sulfur atom because the difference in electronegativities is not large. This would lead us to write the electronic formula I,

$$:\overset{..}{\underset{..}{O}}\quad \overset{..}{S}.\quad .\overset{.}{\underset{..}{O}}:\qquad\qquad I$$

in which oxygen atom 1 is doubly bonded to the sulfur atom, which, in turn, is singly bonded to oxygen atom 2. This makes proper use of the available valence electrons and gives each atom eight electrons in its valence shell. But according to this formula, the two oxygen atoms are not structurally equivalent; the bond distance of oxygen 1 to sulfur should be less than that of oxygen 2 to sulfur. Experiments prove that in the actual SO_2 molecule both atoms of oxygen are equidistant from the sulfur atom. The electronic distribution must be the same for both oxygen atoms.

The *Theory of Resonance* suggests a modification in the theory of bonding to account for such cases. The electronic formula II

$$:\overset{..}{\underset{..}{O}}.\quad \overset{..}{S}..\quad .\overset{..}{\underset{..}{O}}:\qquad\qquad II$$

indicates an alternate distribution of electrons to that of formula I, which is just as reasonable as I. The two formulas vary in the position of the double and single bonds. The theory of resonance assumes that when two or more orthodox electronic formulas can reasonably be written for a substance, then the actual electronic structure may be a *resonance hybrid structure*, intermediate between those written. If the actual structure of the sulfur dioxide molecule is intermediate between structures I and II, then each of the sulfur-to-oxygen bonds must be something between a single and a double bond, and the two bonds are equivalent.

No one has been able to devise a way of writing a single formula to describe such a resonance hybrid structure; we can only write the electronic formulas for all the contributing structures and say that the actual structure is intermediate.   The choice of the term *resonance* was unfortunate because it implies an oscillation back and forth between the contributing structures.   It is important to understand that the theory *does not* assume such oscillation.

Apparently, the ozone molecule has a resonance hybrid structure like that for SO_2.   We write the two contributing structures

shifting the position of the double bond, and say that the ozone molecule has a resonance hybrid structure intermediate between I and II.   This amounts to saying that the electronic configurations of the two end oxygen atoms are identical; this is consistent with the experimental fact that the ①—② bond distance is equal to the ②—③ bond distance.   In some way, the six electrons involved in the bonding are spread out in an equivalent fashion between the three atoms.

The carbonate ion, CO_3^{2-}, is also believed to have a resonance hybrid structure.   Experiments indicate that in this ion the three oxygen atoms are at the corners of an equilateral triangle, the carbon atom being at the center and coplanar with the oxygen atoms.   Electronic formula I can be written using normal covalent bonding.   This makes use of the

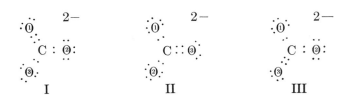

available valence electrons, gives each atom an inert gas structure, and accounts for the charge of the ion.   But this formula indicates that the ①—C bond is a double bond whereas the other oxygen-carbon bonds are single bonds.   These should be longer than the double bond, and such an ion should not have an equilateral shape.   But in fact, the ion is equilateral.   This can be accounted for by writing formulas II and III (moving the double bond to each oxygen in turn) and then saying that the actual structure of the carbonate ion is a resonance hybrid intermediate between I, II, and III.   In other words, all three carbon-oxygen bonds are the same, being intermediate between single and double bonding.

The theory of resonance hybrid bonding is qualitative and vague. Much more elaborate discussions of the nature of the bonding in SO_2, O_3, and $CO_3{}^{2-}$ have been and are being made. However, they are too complicated and still too controversial to introduce here. The imperfect, but nevertheless useful, resonance hybrid bonding picture will serve as a simple way of classifying these cases of intermediate chemical bonding.

180. HYDROGEN BONDING

The formation of chemical compounds by hydrogen is accounted for quite satisfactorily by assuming that the hydrogen atom either forms a covalent bond to one neighboring atom, or it forms the hydride ion H^-, which appears in ionic hydrides. However, in some cases hydrogen atoms that already have formed a covalent bond apparently can link weakly to a second atom. For instance, when water molecules are cooled, the molecules appear to associate. This seems to come about by a hydrogen atom in one molecule bonding weakly to the oxygen atom in a second molecule, as shown in Figure 61.

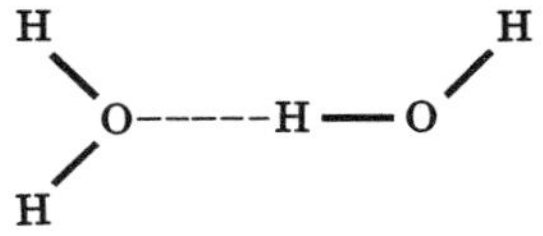

The two molecules of water are held together by one of the hydrogen atoms being shared between two oxygen atoms; this is known as *hydrogen bonding*. It is favored when the two atoms linked by hydrogen are highly electronegative atoms such as oxygen or fluorine, and it becomes noticeable in liquids at low temperatures and in solids. Because of this weak association, water molecules at low temperatures are somewhat restrained, and liquid water is less volatile than would be expected for the simple H_2O molecule. The association of water molecules by hydrogen

Fig. 61. Hydrogen bonding between water molecules.

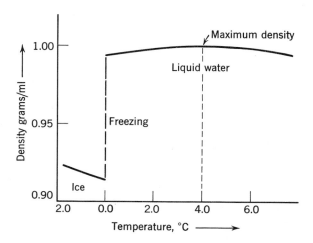

Fig. 62. Change of density of water with change of temperature.

bonding sets up a more open, less densely packed structure.   This accounts for the fact that, while water becomes more dense when cooled from high temperatures (like most liquids), below 4° it decreases in density, as shown in Figure 62, due to hydrogen bonding.   When water at 0° freezes, much more extensive hydrogen bonding is set up, and a very open framework is established in the crystals.   These, therefore, are less dense than liquid water at 0°, and the ice floats on the water.   This has far-reaching effects on our climate.

Just how the electrons may be involved in hydrogen bonding is not yet well explained.

181. BONDING IN COMPLEX IONS

Complex ions are built up of two or more atoms, the type of bonding between the atoms being determined by the nature of the atoms.   If these atoms are not very different in electronegativity, they will share pairs of electrons, and the bonding will be covalent.   In the sulfate ion, SO_4^{2-}, the four oxygen atoms share pairs of electrons with a central sulfur atom, all four oxygen atoms being equivalent.

If there is a large difference in the electronegativities of the atoms in a complex ion, the bonding will be ionic.   In the fluo-aluminate ion, AlF_6^{3-}, six fluoride ions, F^-, surround a central aluminum ion, Al^{3+}, the bonding being so strong that the complex is sufficiently stable to persist through many changes.

Some complex ions are formed by the union of molecules with simple ions.   Thus, the cupric ion combines with four molecules of ammonia to give the complex ion $[Cu(NH_3)_4]^{2+}$.   The nitrogen atom in each ammonia molecule is believed to donate its unshared pair of electrons to be shared by the Cu^{2+} ion.

It is possible that small highly polar molecules will be strongly attracted to simple ions by electrostatic forces, owing to the difference in charge of the ion and one end of the polar molecule. The polar water molecule forms many hydrated complex ions in which this ion-dipole bonding effect may be important.

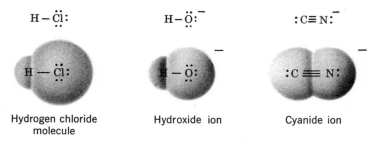

It should be noted that in this case donor-acceptor bonding is also a possibility, since the oxygen atoms in the molecules of water have unshared pairs of electrons.

182. COORDINATION NUMBERS AND THE SHAPES OF MOLECULES AND COMPLEX IONS

In a molecule or complex ion, each atom is associated closely with one or more near neighboring atoms or groups, and we say that it has a corresponding coordination number. The coordination numbers most commonly observed are 1, 2, 3, 4, and 6. Certain spatial configurations are characteristic for molecules or complex ions of a given coordination number.

Hydrogen chloride molecule   Hydroxide ion   Cyanide ion

Fig. 63. Shapes of molecules and ions when the coordination is 1.

When the coordination number is 1, the configuration must be that of a *dumbbell*, as we have already seen to be the case for the H_2 and F_2 molecules (Figure 18, page 83). HCl, OH⁻, and CN⁻ are shown in Figure 63 to have such a shape.

When the coordination number is 2, a *linear* or a *bent-chain* configuration is possible, as shown in Figure 64.   In mercuric chloride, $HgCl_2$, mercury has a coordination of 2 and the molecule is linear, the chain atoms taking up positions as far from each other as possible.

We have seen that the water molecule, in which oxygen has a coordination number of 2, is a bent chain.   The same is true for H_2S.   In this case, the two pairs of unshared electrons on the sulfur presumably repel the two pairs that sulfur shares with the hydrogen atoms, to give a non-linear configuration.   In the complex $Ag(CN)_2^-$, ion, note that the silver atom and the two carbon atoms, each having a coordination number of 2

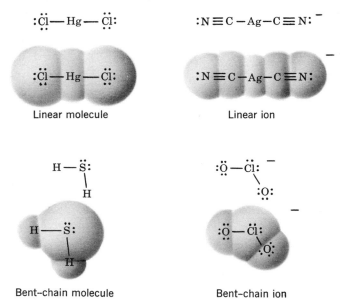

Linear molecule   Linear ion

Bent-chain molecule   Bent-chain ion

Fig. 64.   Shapes of molecules and ions when the coordination is 2.

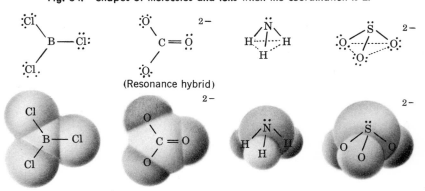

(Resonance hybrid)

Triangular coplanar molecule and ion   Trigonal pyramidal molecule and ion

Fig. 65.   Shapes of molecules and ions when central atom has coordination of 3.

and no unshared pairs of electrons, build a linear arrangement. On the other hand, the ClO_2^- ion has a bent-chain structure, associated with the presence of unshared electron pairs in the valence shell of chlorine. Unshared pairs of electrons in the valence shell of an atom always have a repelling influence on the direction of the covalent bonds formed by that atom.

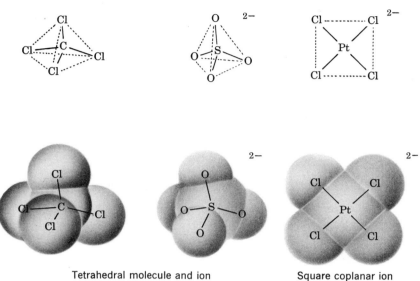

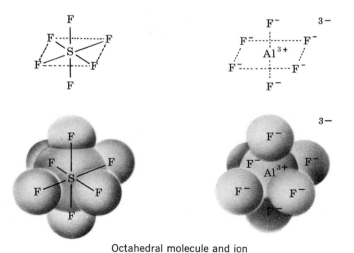

Tetrahedral molecule and ion   Square coplanar ion

Fig. 66. Shapes of molecules and ions when central atom has coordination of 4.

Octahedral molecule and ion

Fig. 67. Shapes of molecules and ions when coordination of central atom is 6.

When the coordination number is 3, a *triangular coplanar* or a *trigonal pyramidal* configuration is observed.   The BCl_3 molecule and the $CO_3{}^{2-}$ ion are coplanar, having no unshared pairs of electrons on the central atoms.   (Figure 65.)   The NH_3 molecule and the $SO_3{}^{2-}$ ion have an unshared pair of electrons on the central atom and are trigonal pyramidal, the bonds being pushed out of a plane.

Tetrahedral or *square coplanar* grouping is obtained about a central atom when its coordination number is 4, as shown in Figure 66.   In CCl_4 and $SO_4{}^{2-}$ the central atom is surrounded by four atoms at the corners of a regular tetrahedron.   The tetrahedral configuration is very common in molecules and complex ions.   But in some of the complex ions of some of the metals, such as $PtCl_4{}^{2-}$, four groups are arranged at the corners of a square, coplanar with the central atom of the metal.

When the coordination number is 6, the configuration is *octahedral*. Figure 67 shows how this is true for SF_6 and $AlF_6{}^{3-}$.

183.   THE IMPORTANCE OF KNOWLEDGE ABOUT SPATIAL CONFIGURATIONS

You may be wondering at this point why so much attention is being paid to the sizes and spatial configurations of molecules and ions.   This has been emphasized from the start because atoms and molecules and ions are so small that it is difficult to believe that they are real.   A large portion of matter, as we ordinarily see it, appears to be so continuous in nature that its particle structure is not easily recognized.   By thinking about the architecture of molecules and ions in detail, one gradually gains an appreciation of their reality and one learns to think in three dimensions.   This is basic if we wish to understand matter and its changes.

The characteristic behavior of matter is not simply a function of *what* elements are present; it also is very much a function of *how* they are present.   The fact that water is composed of hydrogen and oxygen in an atomic ratio of $2:1$ does not take us very far in appreciating why water behaves as it does.   Recognition of the big difference in electronegativity of hydrogen and oxygen helps.   But to understand fully many of the properties of water, it is essential to know that its molecules have a bent-chain shape and therefore are highly polar.   If the water molecule were linear, H—O—H, its properties, such as its behavior as a solvent, would be quite different.

The way ions and molecules pack together in crystals is very much a function of their sizes and shapes, and the properties of the crystals therefore go back to the spatial configurations of the ions and molecules.   The availability for chemical reaction of an atom in an ion or a molecule must depend largely upon its position with respect to the other atoms.   The more we know about the geometry of complex particles, the better chance we will have of understanding why matter behaves as it does.

EXERCISES

1. What features of electronic structure must the molecules of two substances have if they are to be able to unite by donor-acceptor bonding?

2. a) Making use of the discussion in Section 182, indicate the spatial configurations of the NH_3 and BF_3 molecules.
   b) When these two molecules unite by donor-acceptor bonding, what happens to the coordination number of the nitrogen and boron atoms?
   c) Predict what the spatial configuration of the molecular addition complex will be.

3. a) How does the resonance hybrid theory of bonding account satisfactorily for the equivalence of the two oxygen atoms in SO_2?
   b) What is there about the hybrid structure for this molecule that would lead you to suggest that the molecule should have a bent-chain structure?

4. The nitrate ion NO_3^- is isoelectronic with CO_3^{2-} and also is triangular coplanar. Suggest how the theory of resonance hybrid bonding can account for the structure of the nitrate ion.

5. a) Why does water expand so much when it freezes?
   b) According to Figure 62, does ice expand or contract in volume when it is cooled below 0°?

6. Summarize how the shapes of molecules and complex ions are found to change with change in coordination number.

7. Why is it important that we know the shape of the water molecule?

8. SF_6 is shown in Figure 67 as having covalent bonding, whereas the AlF_6^{3-} ion is drawn as an aggregate of Al^{3+} and F^- ions. How is this consistent, with the relative electronegativities of the atoms that are involved?

Chapter 15

▶ Reaction Rates and

Chemical Equilibrium

We have seen that when a chemical change takes place it is possible to determine experimentally the kinds and amounts of reactants and products. This information is summarized quantitatively in the form of a chemical equation. We can supplement this by finding out whether the reaction is exo- or endothermic, and we can measure the amount of energy absorbed or emitted per mole of reactant undergoing change. But in addition to all this, it is also important to inquire about the speed with which the reaction takes place. How long will it take for given quantities of the reactants to be used up and produce the equivalent amounts of products? Does the reaction go with explosive violence, is it of moderate speed so that it can be carried out conveniently, or does it proceed so slowly that it is impractical to use it to produce desired amounts of products? Is the speed of a specific reaction always the same, or can we vary it by changing conditions? Do all chemical changes proceed at the same velocity under comparable conditions? Let us see what answers have been found for these questions.

184. CONDITIONS NECESSARY FOR CHEMICAL CHANGE

On the basis of what we already know about substances and chemical change, we can readily lay down the general conditions that must prevail if chemical change is to take place. The units taking part in the change will be the atoms, molecules, or ions of the reactants. If these reacting particles are all in a homogeneous system, such as a gas or solution phase, the change is a *homogeneous reaction*. The combination of hydrogen with oxygen when a mixture of the gases is being heated is such a change; the neutralization of an acid by a base in solution is another example. If the system consists of more than one phase and the change is taking place at the boundary between two phases, we say a *heterogeneous reaction* is occurring. For example, when a piece of iron rusts in the air, the reaction occurs at the surface of the solid iron where it is in contact with the gas phase.

The simplest homogeneous reaction possible is one in which a complex particle by itself breaks up (decomposes) or rearranges to give other particles. For instance, as indicated in the equation

$$N_2O_4 \rightarrow 2NO_2$$

one molecule of N_2O_4 breaks up to give two molecules of NO_2. Such a change can be expected if the complex N_2O_4 molecule acquires enough energy to activate it so that bonds are ruptured and the new particles can form.

A more complicated kind of homogeneous reaction is one where two or more particles in the same phase must come in contact by collision in order to react with each other. There must be collision between oxygen and hydrogen molecules if these gases are to react to form water. In addition to collision, if reaction is to occur, the particles must also possess enough energy so that the bonding forces in the reacting particles are overcome and rearrangement can take place.

In a heterogeneous reaction where a gas reacts with a solid, the molecules of the gas must collide with the solid surface, and again the reactants must have sufficient energy so that chemical change is possible.

Having established the basic conditions that must prevail if any chemical change is to occur in a system, we go on to consider what then determines the rate of the reaction.

185. RATE OF CHEMICAL CHANGE. FACTORS DETERMINING REACTION RATES

The term *reaction rate* refers to the speed at which the reacting substances are being used up. This rate can be determined experimentally by measuring the change in concentration of the reactants per unit of time. Then we can state that certain quantities of the reactants per unit volume of the system are reacting per unit of time; for example, the rate may be given in moles per liter per second of reactant being used up. This is similar to giving the speed of a train as so many miles per hour. Such an investigation of the rate of a reaction sounds very simple but, unfortunately, the experiments are usually very difficult to carry out quantitatively. Nevertheless, enough experimental data have been collected on a variety of reactions so that certain generalizations have been established and theories have been suggested to account for these generalizations.

Simple qualitative observation of a wide variety of chemical changes shows that reaction rates depend, in general, upon a number of factors.

a. **Nature of the reactants.** Phosphorus oxidizes much more rapidly in air at a given temperature than does iron. Zinc reacts at only a moderate rate with dilute hydrochloric acid, whereas sodium and this acid react with explosive violence under the same conditions. We find that *the rate of reaction is specific for each different chemical change under a particular set of conditions.* It is a function of the kinds of atoms and the bonding in the particular reactant particles and of the ease with which the component atoms rearrange to form new substances. Each specific chemical reaction has a characteristic *energy of activation,* which is a measure of the difficulty of getting the particular reagents to react. (See Section 84.)

b. Temperature. The rate of reaction of hydrogen with oxygen to form water is so slow at room temperature that no observable change occurs. But with increase in temperature of the mixture when we heat it, the rate of reaction increases very rapidly and eventually becomes so fast that it goes explosively. Cold iron oxidizes only very slowly in oxygen at 20°, whereas red-hot iron burns vigorously when thrust into oxygen. *In general, raising the temperature is found to increase the rate of a reaction.* A rough idea of the magnitude of this effect may be gained from the fact that, for many chemical changes, the rate doubles or triples for about every 10° rise in temperature.

We can understand the change of reaction rate with change in temperature by applying what we have already learned. As described in Section 134, at a given temperature the kinetic energy of individual particles of a substance varies, although the average is fixed. In a chemical system at a given temperature, only a certain percentage of the particles may have high enough energy to take part in a reaction that has a given activation energy. With increase in temperature, the average kinetic energy of the particles increases, and the percentage of particles which have sufficient energy for reaction increases. Accordingly, the rate of reaction should increase with rise of temperature.

It becomes clear why we so frequently heat systems to induce chemical change and why we cool them to reduce the violence of a reaction. All chemists and chemical engineers are very much interested in *heat exchange* as a method for controlling chemical processes.

c. Concentration. Phosphorus burns rather quietly in air, but in pure oxygen the combustion proceeds with considerable violence. This difference in rate of reaction is correlated with the difference in the concentration of one of the reactants, the oxygen. The number of molecules per unit volume of pure oxygen is about five times the number of oxygen molecules per unit volume of air. Hence, when pure oxygen is used rather than air, more molecules of oxygen collide with a unit surface area of phosphorus per unit time, and the chances for reaction are correspondingly greater. Qualitatively, we can say that *the velocity of a given chemical change increases with the effective concentration of the particles reacting.* Here we must be careful to specify that it is the concentration of the reacting particles directly available that counts. This will be the total quantity per unit volume of gases and of reactant particles in solutions. In these cases the reactant particles are mobile, and, by diffusion, all can come in contact.

Only the particles at the surfaces of solids can react with other reagents. Thus, in the oxidation of iron, the concentration per unit volume of gaseous oxygen molecules will be important, whereas only the number of atoms of iron at the surface will be effective in determining the reaction rate. The more we subdivide solids by grinding, the greater will be their specific surface (area per unit mass) and the greater will be the percentage of the total number of particles which will be at the surface where they can react. Very finely divided iron, produced by reducing iron oxide powder with hydrogen, oxidizes in air so rapidly that it may become red hot and sometimes bursts into flame. A large piece of iron, such as a file, oxidizes only very slowly at room temperature.

d. Catalysis. We have already observed the effect of the catalyst manganese dioxide in changing the rate of decomposition of potassium chlorate to give oxygen. By proper use of catalysts, reaction rates may be increased. It is useful to distinguish between two kinds of catalysis; in *homogeneous catalysis* the catalytic particles are in the same phase as the particles of the reactants, while in *heterogeneous catalysis* the catalyst is present as an additional phase. We will consider examples of each of these kinds of catalysis and see what suggestions have been made to account for the reaction of the catalysts.

Boron trifluoride is sometimes added in small amounts to a mixture of reactants in a gas or liquid phase to speed up the reaction by homogeneous catalysis. Suppose we are interested in the reaction of molecules of A with molecules of B to form C. We write the equation

$$\text{(Uncatalyzed)} \quad A + B \xrightarrow{\text{slow}} C \tag{1}$$

This goes only slowly under certain particular conditions because the energy of activation is high. The addition of a very small amount of BF_3 is found to increase the rate of disappearance of A and B and the formation of C. This is understandable if we assume the following steps. A molecule of A combines with a molecule of BF_3 to form the complex $A \cdot BF_3$ rapidly because the energy of activation is low.

$$A + \underset{\text{catalyst}}{BF_3} \xrightarrow{\text{fast}} \underset{\text{complex}}{A \cdot BF_3} \tag{2}$$

In turn, $A \cdot BF_3$ reacts rapidly with B because of low activation energy.

$$\underset{\text{complex}}{A \cdot BF_3} + B \xrightarrow{\text{fast}} C + \underset{\text{catalyst released}}{BF_3} \tag{3}$$

The net effect of (2) plus (3) is the same as that of the uncatalyzed change. A and B are used up, C is formed, and the catalyst BF_3 is released so that it may be used over and over. The production of C is speeded up by the catalyst because both (2) and (3) have lower activation energies than (1) and therefore are faster.

The theory that homogeneous catalysis involves the rapid reaction of catalyst particles with reactant particles to form an active intermediate complex, which, in turn, reacts readily to free the catalyst for continual use, agrees well with experiment.   In many cases the intermediate complex has been isolated.

A solid catalyst is usually employed in heterogeneous catalysis.   For example, the reaction between hydrogen and oxygen to form water takes place so slowly at room temperature that it is inappreciable, but when finely divided platinum supported on asbestos fibers is brought in contact with the gas mixture, the reaction proceeds rapidly.   This effect is accounted for by assuming that reactant particles are *adsorbed on the platium;* they are attracted and held to the surface of the platinum. This adsorption is believed to render the reactant particles more susceptible to reaction, and the reaction therefore proceeds more rapidly at the surface of the catalyst than in the gas phase.   This theory is supported by the fact that the effectiveness of a given weight of platinum catalyst is directly proportional to the amount of its surface. The active adsorbed layer of reactant on the catalyst, in cases of heterogeneous catalysis, thus plays a role similar to that of the active intermediate complex particle in homogeneous catalysis; both serve to lower the activation energy below that of the uncatalyzed reaction.

Catalysts are exploited widely, in both research and industry.   Very often, several different reactions may be possible in a given system, but, by choosing a catalyst that will speed up one of these changes and not the others, we can cause that reaction to predominate which will give us the product we desire.   The production of vast quantities of high-grade gasoline that we need to run our automobiles and aeroplanes is possible because of the development of very efficient catalysts for the refining of petroleum.   The manufacture of sulfuric acid, ammonia, nitric acid, and most of our other important chemicals depends upon catalysis.   Catalysts in the form of enzymes are effective in many of the chemical changes taking place in biological systems.

186.   QUANTITATIVE RELATION OF CONCENTRATION AND REACTION RATE

The effect of the concentration of the reacting substances on the reaction rate is so important that we shall discuss it quantitatively and see what exact law can be set up to describe it.   In order to define this relationship precisely, it is necessary to refer accurately to the concentrations of the reacting particles.   We must specify the number of particles of each substance per unit volume.   This is conveniently stated in terms of the *number of moles of each reactant per liter,* and this value is commonly symbolized by enclosing the formula for the particle in brackets or parentheses.   Thus, the concentration of reactant A is given as

$$[A] = \text{number of moles of } A \text{ per liter}$$

If we have **18.016 g** of water vapor per liter, $[H_2O] = 1$; when there is

36.032 g of water vapor per liter, $[H_2O] = 2$. The reaction rate will be measured by the change in concentration per unit time, that is, by the number of moles per liter of the substance reacting per unit time. This is the change in $[A]$ per unit time.

a. Reaction of single particle. Let us first consider the simplest kind of chemical reaction that is possible—one taking place in a single phase where a complex particle of substance A decomposes by itself without interacting with other particles to give certain products.

$$A \rightarrow products$$

The relation of rate of decomposition of A to the concentration of the particles of A can be studied by setting up a series of experiments. In each experiment a given concentration of A is used, the temperature is kept constant, and the rate of disappearance of A is measured. Different concentrations of A are used in the different experiments. It is found that the rate of reaction (the number of moles of A decomposing per liter per unit of time) is directly proportional to the molar concentration of A. This we can summarize by the expression

$$\text{Rate of reaction} = k_t \times [A]$$

where $[A]$ is the concentration of A in moles per liter. The rate of the reaction is said to be *first-order with respect to A* because $[A]$ comes into the rate equation to the first power. The term k_t is the proportionality constant, more specifically referred to as the *rate constant*, for the given reaction at the temperature t. This constant is a number that tells us what fraction of each mole of the particles of A will decompose per unit of time. This will depend upon the nature of the particular complex particle A; the greater the activation energy of A, the less will be the chance that a given particle will decompose in a given period of time and the smaller will be the numerical value of k. Multiplying the actual number of moles per liter of A used in a particular experiment by the fraction per mole that decomposes per unit of time will give the number of moles per liter which are disappearing per unit of time. Doubling $[A]$ doubles the rate; halving $[A]$ will halve the rate.

Some specific numbers will make this clearer. Suppose the particles of A have such a tendency to decompose at $20°$ that in a period of 1 hr one of every 10 particles decompose. Then for every mole (6.02×10^{23} particles) of A per liter $\frac{1}{10}$ of a mole will decompose per hour. The rate constant at $20°$, $k_{20°}$, therefore is 0.1 mole per liter per hour. Therefore

Rate of decomposition of A
in moles per liter per hour $= 0.1 \times [A]$
at $20°$

Now suppose in a given experiment we have two moles per liter of A.

Then $[A]$ is 2 and

Rate of decomposition at $20° = 0.1 \times 2 = 0.2$ moles per liter per hour

Suppose in another experiment the concentration is made twice as great, four moles per liter.   Then

Rate of decomposition at $20° = 0.1 \times 4 = 0.4$ moles per liter per hour

Doubling the molar concentration of A doubles the rate of decomposition at $20°$.   Knowing the rate constant for $20°$, we can calculate the rate of decomposition for any particular molar concentration.

When experiments are run on the decomposition of A at different temperatures, the value of k_t is found to increase with increase in temperature.   This is reasonable because the higher the average kinetic energy of the particles, the higher will be the number per liter that have enough kinetic energy to decompose, and the greater will be the probability that decomposition will take place per unit of time.   There will be a different value of the rate constant for each temperature, each k_t being characteristic of the particular kind of molecule that is decomposing.

b. Reaction of two unlike particles upon collision.   The reaction

$$A + B \rightarrow \text{products}$$

is a more complicated change, where one particle of A must collide with one particle of B in order for the reaction to occur.

Experiments show that the proportionality of rate of change to the concentrations of A and B may be represented by the expression

$$\text{Reaction rate} = k_t \times [A] \times [B]$$

where $[A]$ and $[B]$ are the molar concentrations and k_t is the rate constant at the temperature t.   The reaction rate is *first-order with respect to A* and also *first-order with respect to B*, because the molar concentration of each enters the rate expression to the first power.   It is reasonable that the reaction rate should be proportional to the *product* of the concentrations of A and B; doubling the concentration of either A or B will double the total number of collisions between A and B per unit time, and doubling the concentration of both A and B quadruples the number of collisions between A and B.

Suppose we see how this works out for the reaction

$$H_2 + I_2 \rightarrow 2HI$$

The rate of this reaction is found experimentally to conform to the expression

$$\text{Reaction rate} = k_t \times [H_2] \times [I_2]$$

It is first-order with respect to both hydrogen and iodine.   This is consistent with the conclusion that, for this reaction to take place, a molecule of hydrogen must collide with a molecule of iodine, two molecules of hydrogen iodide being formed, as shown in Figure 68.   If in a given flask there are present one mole per liter of hydrogen and two moles per liter of iodine at 350°, then,

$$\text{Reaction rate of hydrogen with iodine at } 350° = k_{350°} \times 1 \times 2$$

whereas, if there are 10 moles per liter of hydrogen and five moles per liter of iodine at 350°,

$$\text{Reaction rate of hydrogen with iodine at } 350° = k_{350°} \times 10 \times 5$$

The proportionality constant k_t is constant for this reaction as long as the temperature is fixed, and the rate of reaction is a function of the activities of the reacting molecules and of the probability of their colli-

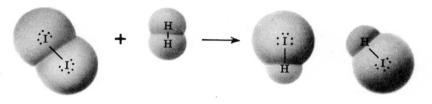

Fig. 68.   Reaction of hydrogen and iodine to form hydrogen iodide.

sion.   If the temperature is raised, a higher percentage of the colliding molecules have enough energy to react, the rate of reaction becomes greater, and the value of k_t increases markedly.   This constant k_t will be equal to the rate of the reaction when the concentrations are unity.

c. Reaction of two identical particles upon collision.   The reaction

$$2A \rightarrow \text{products}$$

in which two identical particles collide and react may also be written as

$$A + A \rightarrow \text{products}$$

In this change $[A]$ can be expected to come into the rate expression twice because two particles of A must collide for reaction to take place.

$$\text{Rate of reaction} = k_t \times [A] \times [A]$$
$$= k_t \times [A]^2$$

The reaction therefore is said to be *second-order with respect to A* because the rate is proportional to the second power of $[A]$.

d. Reactions requiring collision of more than two particles.   We can conceive of still more complicated reactions where more than two particles are involved per collision, as in

$$A + 2B \rightarrow \text{products}$$

If the actual change does involve the simultaneous collision of one particle of A with two of B, then it follows that

$$\text{Rate of reaction} = k_t \times [A] \times [B]^2$$

The reaction is *first-order* with respect to A and *second-order* with respect to B.

187. THE LAW OF MASS ACTION. STEP REACTIONS

The foregoing equations for the rate of reaction are mathematical expressions of the *Law of Mass Action: The rate of a chemical reaction that goes in one step is proportional to the product of the molar concentrations of the reacting particles, the molar concentration of each reactant being taken to a power equal to the number of its particles which must interact simultaneously in order that the change occur.* The importance of this law can readily be appreciated. By increasing the concentration of a reactant, we can make a chemical change go faster; by decreasing the concentration, we can slow down the change.

It should be emphasized that the foregoing treatment of the relation of reaction rate to concentration of the reactants holds only provided the reaction goes in one step, no intermediate products being formed. Actually, most reactions occur in two or more steps, with the formation of intermediates, which then react. *The expression for the rate of reaction must be used for each separate step.* The actual rate for the total change in the system will be determined by the rate of the slowest step. Since the equations for the chemical changes in systems usually represent only the original substances and the end products, it is not safe to derive the reaction-rate expressions from such equations unless it has been proved experimentally that the reaction involves only one step.

For example, N_2O decomposes when heated in contact with gold, and nitrogen and oxygen are the final products. This would normally be represented by the equation

$$2N_2O = 2N_2 + O_2$$

However, experiment indicates that the rate at which N_2O disappears is not proportional to the square of the concentration of N_2O but only to the first power. This is consistent with the idea that the reaction really occurs in two consecutive steps.

a) $$N_2O = N_2 + O \quad \text{(slow)}$$
b) $$O + O = O_2 \quad \text{(fast)}$$

If step a) is slower than step b), then step a) will determine the rate for the over-all reaction, and the rate will be proportional to the first power of the concentration of N_2O.

Most of the reactions that have been studied appear to go in several steps.   Usually, in each step either a complex particle decomposes or a two-particle collision takes place.   Only a few changes involving three-particle collisions have been well established, and no cases are known which go by four-particle collisions.   This is understandable because the probability of three particles colliding simultaneously is small, and four-particle collisions will be extremely improbable.

188.   REVERSIBLE CHEMICAL CHANGE AND CHEMICAL EQUILIBRIUM

So far we have considered chemical change in only one direction. Suppose the *chemical change is reversible*, the products of the reaction in one direction tending to change back to the original substances.   A general example of such a change can be represented by the equation,

$$mA + nB \rightleftharpoons pC + qD$$

opposing arrows being used to indicate reversibility.   This is a *net equation*, written so as to specify the *net reaction* that occurs, regardless of

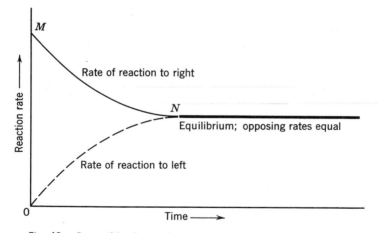

Fig. 69.   Reversible chemical reaction and chemical equilibrium.

whether or not intermediate steps are involved.   The terms A, B, C, and D stand for the different species of particles that initially enter and finally result from the net changes.   This net equation says that the over-all effect of the reaction of m moles of A with n moles of B is to give p moles of C and q moles of D, and that the reverse change also is going on.   What will be the net effect of these two opposed changes on the quantities of the substances in the system?

The reversible change can be studied by bringing together known amounts of A and B in a container where the temperature may be maintained at some value t.   The reaction to the right will begin to take place at a certain rate, as shown by point M in Figure 69.   As time goes on, the concentrations of A and B will decrease, and therefore the rate of reaction to the right will decrease.   The C and D formed will immediately set up the reverse change to the left, re-forming A and B.   At first the rate of reaction to the right will be much faster than that to the left, and the concentrations of A and B will decrease while the concentrations of C and D will build up.   The decrease in the concentrations of A and B with time will lower the rate to the right, while the increase in concentration of C and D will increase the rate to the left.   As the curves show, eventually the two opposing rates will become equal at N, and a state of *dynamic equilibrium* will be established in the system.   Both of the changes continue, but, because the opposing rates are equal, the concentrations of A, B, C, and D will remain constant.

189.   THE LAW OF CHEMICAL EQUILIBRIUM.   EQUILIBRIUM CONSTANTS

When the equilibrium concentrations of A, B, C, and D are determined experimentally for each of a series of experiments, using different starting concentrations of A and B, it is found that they always give the same value for $k_{t(eq)}$ in the equation

$$\frac{[C]^p \times [D]^q}{[A]^m \times [B]^n} = K_{t(eq)}$$

This is a mathematical expression of the *Law of Chemical Equilibrium:* *At equilibrium, the product of the molar concentrations (to the proper powers) of the particles to the right of the equation, divided by the product of the molar concentrations (to the proper powers) of the particles to the left, is a constant for a given temperature.*   The powers are determined by the number of moles of each particle indicated by the net equation.   The constant $K_{t(eq)}$ is called the *equilibrium constant* for the reversible change.   It has a fixed value for a given temperature when equilibrium prevails, irrespective of the absolute values of the molar concentrations.   The presence of a *catalyst does not affect the value of the equilibrium constant;* it only affects the length of time necessary for the system to attain equilibrium because it catalyzes both of the opposing changes.

The expression for the equilibrium constant can always be derived directly from the net equation for the reversible reaction, regardless of whether the opposing changes go in one step or several steps.   At equilibrium the over-all rates in the two directions are equal.   When the several steps which contribute to a net change are added up, the intermediate particles cancel out, and the only concentrations that appear in the equilibrium expression are those of the initial and final particles.   By convention, the concentrations of the particles on the right-hand side of the equation as written are always placed in the numerator, and the concentrations of the particles on the left-hand side of the equation are placed in the denominator. Of course the equation for the reversible reaction can just as well be turned around and written as

$$pC + qD \rightleftharpoons mA + nB$$

This will invert the expression for the equilibrium constant and give a value which will be just the reciprocal of that for the other direction. Therefore it is necessary, when giving the numerical value for an equilibrium constant, also to indicate the chemical equation for which it holds.

In order to make clear how the expression for the equilibrium constant can be derived if the net equation for the reversible change is known, let us consider a number of specific systems. We will write the properly balanced equation first, and then the expression for the equilibrium constant.

$$H_{2(g)} + I_{2(g)} \rightleftharpoons 2HI_{(g)} \qquad K_{t(eq)} = \frac{[HI]^2}{[H_2] \times [I_2]}$$

$$2H_{2(g)} + O_{2(g)} \rightleftharpoons 2H_2O_{(g)} \qquad K_{t(eq)} = \frac{[H_2O]^2}{[H_2]^2 \times [O_2]}$$

$$N_{2(g)} + 3H_{2(g)} \rightleftharpoons 2NH_{3(g)} \qquad K_{t(eq)} = \frac{[NH_3]^2}{[N_2] \times [H_2]^3}$$

The above examples are for homogeneous reversible reactions when the equilibrium is for a heterogeneous reversible reaction, the equilibrium expression can be written omitting pure solid or liquid phases. Because the concentrations per unit volume (density) of solid and liquid phases vary only slightly with change of conditions, their molar concentrations can be treated as constants in a system at equilibrium. Therefore, these molar concentrations are not written as separate terms in the equilibrium expression but are included in the equilibrium constant. The equation for the reversible decomposition of calcium carbonate is

$$CaCO_{3(s)} \rightleftharpoons CaCO_{(s)} + CO_{2(g)}$$

For this system at equilibrium

$$K_{t(eq)} = [CO_2]$$

As long as some solid $CaCO_3$ and some solid CaO are present at a given temperature, the equilibrium partial pressure of CO_2 must always be the same. The total quantities of the solid phases which are present do not affect the equilibrium constant.

190. DETERMINATION OF EQUILIBRIUM CONSTANTS

The equilibrium constant for a given reversible chemical change at a given temperature may be determined by allowing the system to come to equilibrium and then measuring the molar concentrations of each substance that is present.   Take the case of the reversible reaction

$$H_2 + I_2 \rightleftharpoons 2HI$$

This has been studied at 440°.   When equilibrium was established for a given mixture, the molar concentrations of H_2, I_2, and HI were determined by analysis.   For one particular experiment the values found were

$$[H_2] = 3.17 \times 10^{-3} \text{ moles/liter}$$
$$[I_2] = 8.06 \times 10^{-3} \text{ moles/liter}$$
$$[HI] = 34.7 \times 10^{-3} \text{ moles/liter}$$

Substituting these values in the expression for the equilibrium constant for this system as given above, we find

$$K_{440°(eq)} = \frac{(34.7 \times 10^{-3})^2}{(3.17 \times 10^{-3}) \times (8.06 \times 10^{-3})} = 47.2$$

This value for the equilibrium constant will hold at 440°, irrespective of the total number of atoms of hydrogen and iodine per liter in the system. The expression defines precisely how these atoms will be distributed among the molecular species H_2, I_2, and HI at equilibrium.

If we start with just HI, or with any mixture of H_2 and I_2, or with any mixture of H_2, I_2, and HI and hold the system at 440° until equilibrium is established, the molar concentrations of the three substances then present will be such that the value 47.2 for $K_{(eq)}$ is met.

EXAMPLE: What will be the molar concentration of iodine at equilibrium at 440° in a 1-liter flask with 2.016 g of hydrogen and 255.8 g of hydrogen iodide?

$$\frac{2.016 \text{ g of } H_2}{2.016 \text{ g of } H_2 \text{ per mole}} = \frac{1.000 \text{ mole of } H_2 \text{ per liter}}{\text{at equilibrium}}$$

$$\frac{255.8 \text{ g of HI}}{127.9 \text{ g of HI per mole}} = \frac{2.000 \text{ moles of HI per liter}}{\text{at equilibrium}}$$

At equilibrium at 440°

$$\frac{[HI]^2}{[H_2] \times [I_2]} = 47.2$$

Substituting the equilibrium molar concentrations of H_2 and HI

$$\frac{(2.000)^2}{1.000 \times [I_2]} = 47.2$$

$$[I_2] = \frac{(2.000)^2}{1.000 \times 47.2} = \frac{0.0848 \text{ mole of } I_2 \text{ per liter}}{\text{at equilibrium}}$$

Once $K_{(eq)}$, the equilibrium constant, is known for a given reversible change at a given temperature, it is possible to calculate just what will happen to any mixture of the substances involved when the system is allowed to attain equilibrium.

EXAMPLE: Suppose we put 20.0 moles of HI in a 5-liter container and hold it at 440°. Decomposition to H_2 and I_2 will proceed, and, as soon as these are formed, the reverse reaction will also take place. Eventually, equilibrium will be set up. What will be the molar concentration of each substance present?

$$\text{The initial [HI]} = \frac{20.0}{5.00} = 4.00 \text{ moles/liter}$$

Let

$$\begin{array}{c}\text{The decrease in [HI] when reaction}\\ \text{has reached equilibrium}\end{array} = x \text{ moles/liter}$$

For every mole of HI decomposing, one-half mole of H_2 and one-half mole of I_2 are formed. Therefore, at equilibrium at 440°

$$[H_2] = \frac{x}{2} \text{ moles/liter}$$

$$[I_2] = \frac{x}{2} \text{ moles/liter}$$

$$[HI] = 4.00 - x \text{ moles/liter}$$

$$K_{440°(eq)} = 47.2 = \frac{(4.00 - x)^2}{\frac{x}{2} \times \frac{x}{2}} = \frac{(4.00 - x)^2}{\left(\frac{x}{2}\right)^2}$$

$$x = 0.902 \text{ mole/liter decrease of [HI]}$$

$$[HI] \text{ at equilibrium} = 4.00 - 0.902 = 3.10 \text{ moles/liter}$$

$$[H_2] \text{ at equilibrium} = \frac{x}{2} = 0.450 \text{ mole/liter}$$

$$[I_2] \text{ at equilibrium} = \frac{x}{2} = 0.450 \text{ mole/liter}$$

191. APPLICATION OF LE CHÂTELIER'S PRINCIPLE TO REVERSIBLE CHEMICAL CHANGES

Since chemical equilibrium is a case of dynamic equilibrium, the Principle of Le Châtelier may be applied. If a system in which a reversible chemical change is occurring is subjected to any stress so that chemical equilibrium does not prevail, changes which will tend to remove the stress and establish equilibrium will be favored. The stresses which may operate on such reversible chemical changes may be changes in concentration, temperature, or pressure. By manipulating such stresses, we can cause that chemical change to predominate which will throw the net reaction in the direction we desire. In order to see how this works out, we will consider the way changes of concentration, temperature, or pressure affect the reversible reaction

$$mA + nB \rightleftharpoons pC + qD$$

where

$$K_{(eq)} = \frac{[C]^p \times [D]^q}{[A]^m \times [B]^n}$$

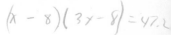

a. Effect of change of concentration.   Suppose that the above system is at equilibrium and that more of one of the substances, say A, is added. The molar concentration of A then exceeds the equilibrium value, and the ratio of the products of the molar concentrations is now less than $K_{(eq)}$.   Owing to the increase in the molar concentration of A, the reaction rate to the right is increased, and the change which tends to use up A and thus remove the stress will be favored. A and B will be used up faster than they are formed, and the molar concentration of C and D will increase.   However, as the concentrations of C and D increase, the rate of their reaction to form A and B will also increase.   Eventually, the opposing changes will attain equal rates and equilibrium will be re-established.   The stress put on the system, when the concentration of A was increased, will have been removed by changes in the molar concentrations of all of the substances such that $K_{(eq)}$ is met.   Note that when A is added, the net changes which take place in the system are such that the concentration of B is lowered while the concentrations of C and D are increased.   In other words, we can cause B to be used up more completely and C and D to be formed more completely by increasing the concentration of A.   If we are interested in converting a given amount of expensive iodine as completely as possible to hydrogen iodide, we can accomplish this by increasing the concentration of cheap hydrogen at a high value.

We can also put a stress on a reversible system by withdrawing one of the substances, say A, from the scene of the reaction.   That change will be favored which forms A and thus restores equilibrium.   If we are able to remove hydrogen iodide from the system in which it has been at equilibrium with hydrogen and iodine, we favor the net change involving formation of more hydrogen iodide.

Thus, by using high concentrations of hydrogen and removing hydrogen iodide from the reaction zone, we can convert a given amount of iodine rather completely to hydrogen iodide.   Because of the reversibility of the reaction, the conversion can never go to absolute completion.

b. Effect of change of pressure.   This is really a special case of change in concentration, because as the pressure increases, substances undergo compression and their concentration per unit volume increases. Change of pressure is not very important for liquids or solids because of their very low compressibility, but it is very important for gases because the concentration of molecules in a gas is proportional to the pressure. Le Châtelier's Principle indicates that, if we put a stress on a reversible system by increasing the pressure, that chemical change will be favored which will tend to lower the pressure.   For a gaseous system, the increase in pressure is accomplished by increasing the total number of molecules per unit volume that are present.   This procedure will favor the net chemical change that will reduce the total number of molecules per unit volume.

Consider the reversible chemical reaction

$$N_2 + 3H_2 \rightleftharpoons 2NH_3$$

A total of four molecules of nitrogen and hydrogen give only two molecules of ammonia. The formation of ammonia will therefore decrease the total number of molecules in the system, and the total gaseous pressure will therefore be reduced. Increasing the total pressure on the system will favor the conversion of nitrogen and hydrogen to ammonia, whereas lowering the total pressure will increase the dissociation of ammonia to the elements. In the industrial production of ammonia, the use of very high pressures aids in obtaining high yields.

Consider the reversible chemical reaction

$$H_2 + I_2 \rightleftharpoons 2HI$$

There is no change in the total number of molecules in the system during the reaction, and therefore there is no change in pressure when either change occurs. Compressing or expanding the gas mixture has no effect on the equilibrium. Changes in pressure affect equilibria measurably only when gaseous substances are involved, and in such cases only when the chemical change involves a change in the total number of molecules in the system.

In the "burning" of limestone to obtain calcium oxide, represented by the equation

$$CaCO_{3(s)} \rightleftharpoons CaO_{(s)} + CO_{2(g)}$$

increasing the pressure does not change the concentration of solid $CaCO_3$ or CaO appreciably but does increase the concentration of the gas CO_2 markedly. Therefore, an increase in pressure will favor the change using up CO_2 and will decrease the proportion of CaO present at equilibrium. Decreasing the pressure of CO_2 will favor the decomposition of limestone.

c. Effect of change of temperature. All chemical changes are accompanied by energy changes, exothermic or endothermic. If we have a reversible system at equilibrium and add heat, the state of equilibrium will be upset, and the chemical change which will absorb heat will be favored. This is correlated with the change in the equilibrium constant for the system when the temperature is changed. Increase of temperature increases both rates of reaction for the reversible system, but the rate of the endothermic change will increase more rapidly than that of the exothermic change. The net effect of the change of temperature will be to exchange the equilibrium constant.

Consider the reverisible change

$$2H_{2(g)} + O_{2(g)} \rightleftharpoons 2H_2O_{(g)} + 115{,}240 \text{ cal}$$

At temperatures around 800° the reaction to the right goes practically to completion. If the temperature is raised sufficiently, the decomposition of water to the elements takes place, and at 2000°, this decomposition is realized to a considerable extent; equilibrium is set up. Lowering the temperature of this system favors the formation of water, $K_{(eq)}$ increasing as the temperature is lowered; increasing the temperature favors the decomposition of water.

EXERCISES

1. What factors determine the rate of a given reaction?

2. The reaction
$$NO + O_3 \rightarrow NO_2 + O_2$$
has been shown to be first-order with respect to both NO and O_3. Write the expression for the rate of this reaction.

3. The reaction
$$2NO + Cl_2 \rightarrow 2NOCl$$
proceeds in one step. Write the expression for the rate of this change.

4. Write the expression for the equilibrium constant for the reversible reaction
$$2SO_{2(g)} + O_{2(g)} \rightleftharpoons 2SO_{3(g)}$$
What will happen to the total weight of SO_2 in this system if it is at equilibrium, and
   a) More oxygen is added, the volume and temperature remaining constant?
   b) A catalyst is added?
   c) The volume is decreased, the temperature remaining constant?
   d) SO_3 is removed, the volume and temperature remaining constant?

5. The equilibrium constant for the reversible reaction
$$O_{2(g)} + 2CO_{(g)} \rightleftharpoons 2CO_{2(g)} + \text{heat}$$
is 3,000 at temperature t.
   a) If the pressure of the system were doubled, would you get more or less CO_2? Would the value of $K_{t(eq)}$ change?
   b) If the temperature of the system is raised above t will $K_{(eq)}$ become larger or smaller? Explain.

6. Suppose the reversible system represented by the equation
$$\text{Heat} + BaCO_{3(s)} \rightleftharpoons BaO_{(s)} + CO_{2(g)}$$
is at equilibrium at temperature t. What will be the effect on the equilibrium partial pressure of CO_2 in this system of: a) decreasing the volume? b) raising the temperature? c) adding more $BaCO_3$? d) removing part of the BaO?

7. Consider equilibrium to exist in each of the following cases of reversible chemical change
   a) $N_{2(g)} + 3H_{2(g)} \rightleftharpoons 2NH_{3(g)} + \text{heat}$
   b) $C_{(s)} + CO_{2(g)} + \text{heat} \rightleftharpoons 2CO_{(g)}$

Predict what will happen in each of these systems when: 1) the total pressure is increased; 2) the temperature is lowered; 3) a catalyst is added; 4) more of the first reagent is added; 5) some of the inert gas, helium, is added.

8. a) Calculate the equilibrium constant for the reversible reaction

$$2A_{(g)} + B_{(g)} \rightleftharpoons A_2B_{(g)}$$

if at equilibrium at 20° the moles per liter of A, B, and A_2B are 2.00, 4.00, and 16.00, respectively.

b) Suppose that chemical equilibrium involving this reaction at 20° is established in a container and $[A]$ is found to be 0.500 and $[A_2B]$ is 0.250. What will be the concentration of B in the equilibrium mixture?

Chapter 16

▶ Electrolytic Dissociation
and Ionic Equilibrium

192. CONDUCTION OF ELECTRICITY

Having learned something of the electrical nature of atoms, we are now in a position to consider the conduction of electricity by matter. The electric current consists of a movement or transfer of electrical charges. In the ordinary electrical circuit made up of metallic wire, the electric current is a stream of moving electrons. A generator or a battery acts as an electron pump, forcing electrons into the circuit at one point

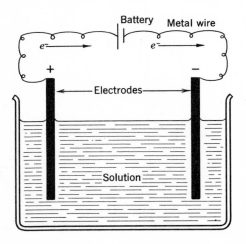

Battery   Metal wire

e^- e^-

+   —

←————Electrodes————→

Solution

Fig. 70.   An electrolytic cell.

and removing them at another point. Metals such as copper permit the flow of electrons through a massive piece without any obvious chemical changes. The wire merely heats up somewhat. No appreciable transportation of atomic systems takes place; the metal is not used up and the wire may be employed indefinitely for conducting the current. Such conduction of electricity is known as *metallic conduction*.

Another kind of conduction is called *electrolytic conduction*. Certain compounds form solutions which conduct the electric current when they are placed in an electrolytic cell of proper design. Figure 70 shows the essential parts of such a cell.

A battery or generator pumps electrons through the metallic wire. The wire is connected to two *electrodes* that are good conductors. These electrodes dip down into a vessel containing the solution which conducts the current. When the circuit is completed, electrons flow through the wire to one electrode and enter the solution. Electrons are conducted away from the solution by the other electrode. We say that the cell conducts the electric current. In this type of conduction, however, chemical changes are observed. Gases and other new substances may form at the electrodes, or the electrodes themselves may react. When dilute sulfuric acid is placed in such a cell, the solution conducts the electric current. Oxygen is formed at one electrode and hydrogen is evolved at the other, water being used up as the cell operates.

It can be shown that, during the operation of an electrolytic cell, *ions migrate* in an ordered fashion through the liquids *toward each electrode*. Such conduction of the electric current is known as *electrolytic conduction*. This is always associated with the migration of charged atoms or groups of atoms toward the electrodes, chemical changes always taking place at the electrodes.

193. ELECTROLYTES AND NONELECTROLYTES

The term *electrolyte* is used for a substance that will yield a solution which conducts the electric current. Solutes that give nonconducting solutions are called *nonelectrolytes*. It is a simple matter to determine to which of these classes a given substance belongs. We set up the electrolytic cell diagramed in Figure 70, placing in the circuit some device, such as an ammeter or an electric lamp, which will indicate by movement of a pointer or by the emission of light when the electric current is flowing. The solution to be tested is placed in the cell between the electrodes. If the substance is an electrolyte, the circuit will be completed, and electricity will flow. If the substance is a nonelectrolyte, the circuit is not completed between the electrodes, and no current flows.

When we test various aqueous solutions, we find that acids such as HCl, HNO_3, and H_2SO_4, bases such as $NaOH$ and $Ca(OH)_2$, and salts such as $NaCl$, $MgCl_2$, and Na_2SO_4 are electrolytes. On the other hand aqueous solutions of cane sugar or alcohol will not conduct the electric current. Sugar and alcohol are not electrolytes.

How can the operation of an electrolytic cell be accounted for? What is the reason for the difference in the behavior of electrolytes and nonelectrolytes?

194. THEORY OF ELECTROLYTIC DISSOCIATION

In 1887 Arrhenius proposed a theory to explain the difference between electrolytes and nonelectrolytes. This theory has been modified considerably, in the light of our present knowledge of atomic structure and chemical bonding, by A. A. Noyes, P. Debye, and others.

According to the *theory of electrolytic dissociation,* when an electrolyte is dissolved in a suitable solvent, the electrolyte dissociates into *independent* electrically charged positive and negative *ions.*   The charge on each ion is equal to the valence of the atom, or radical, and the total number of positive charges on the ions in a solution is just equal to the total number of negative charges on the ions.   These charged ions diffuse in random fashion in the solution.   During electrolysis, they migrate toward the electrode of opposite charge and are responsible for conduction in the solution.   (The term *ion* refers to this characteristic migration toward the electrodes.)   The *passage of an electric current is not necessary to cause dissociation.*   This occurs when solution takes place.   Nonelectrolytes do not dissociate when their solutions are formed, and these solutions therefore do not contain ions.   Nonelectrolytes are present in solution as neutral molecules.   The characteristic behavior of electrolytes is determined by their dissociation into relatively independent ions.

195.   DISSOCIATION EQUATIONS

The dissociation of an electrolyte into independent ions is a form of chemical change, and the change is reversible.   The dissociation equations that follow show the typical way in which the three important classes of electrolytes, acids, bases, and salts dissociate.

Acids, as we have already seen, yield hydrogen ions easily when they dissociate.

$$HCl = H^+ + Cl^-$$
$$HNO_3 = H^+ + NO_3^-$$

Bases dissociate to give independent hydroxide ions.

$$NaOH_{(s)} = Na^+ + OH^-$$
$$Ca(OH)_{2(s)} = Ca^{2+} + 2OH^-$$

Amphoteric hydroxides dissociate either as acids or bases.

$$\begin{cases} Al(OH)_{3(s)} = H^+ + H_2O + AlO_2^- \\ Al(OH)_{3(s)} = Al(OH)_2^+ + OH^- \end{cases}$$

Salts that are soluble in water dissociate to give the positive ions of a metal or radical and negative ions of an acid.

$$NaCl_{(s)} = Na^+ + Cl^-$$
$$MgCl_2 = Mg^{2+} + 2Cl^-$$
$$Na_2SO_{4(s)} = 2Na^+ + SO_4^{2-}$$
$$NH_4Cl = NH_4^+ + Cl^-$$

It should be noted that when electrolytic dissociation occurs, the number of negative ions formed is not necessarily equal to the number of positive ions, but the total number of positive charges on the ions produced must be just equal to the total number of negative charges.

196. PROPERTIES OF IONS

As we have already seen, ions are quite different in electronic structure from neutral atoms, radicals, or molecules. Ions have either more or fewer planetary electrons than the neutral units, and therefore ions must have quite different properties.

A molecule of iodine, I_2, is colored and has a powerful oxidizing effect, whereas the iodide ion, I^-, is colorless and is a reducing agent. Sodium metal is very reactive toward water and is a very active reducing agent, while the sodium ion is colorless, stable toward water, and has no reducing ability. The properties of a solution of ions will be determined by the properties of the ions that are present and by the properties of the solvent particles.

197. LOWERING OF THE FREEZING POINT OF A SOLVENT BY NONELECTROLYTES AND ELECTROLYTES

The soundness of the theory of electrolytic dissociation is confirmed when we study the effect of nonelectrolytes and electrolytes on the behavior of solvent molecules. Sections 162 and 163 have already described the general relationship between molal concentration of solute particles and the behavior of solvents.

The difference between nonelectrolytes and electrolytes is clearly shown in Table 27, which lists the lowering of the freezing point of water observed for each of various molal concentrations of a number of solutes.

The solutes, sugar and ethyl alcohol, which we have listed as nonelectrolytes because their aqueous solutions do not conduct electricity, give quite different lowering than do equimolar amounts of the solutes that we have classified as electrolytes because they give conducting solutions.

For the nonelectrolytes, 0.100 mole of the solute per 1,000 g of water lowers the freezing point about 0.186°. Notice that 0.200 mole of a nonelectrolyte has about twice the lowering effect of 0.100 mole, and 0.300 mole has about three times the effect of 0.100 mole. These data indicate that when nonelectrolytes dissolve in water, their neutral molecules separate, and the 0.100 mole, 0.200 mole, and 0.300 mole of nonelectrolytes give 0.100 mole, 0.200 mole, and 0.300 mole of solute particles, respectively. Nonelectrolytes are molecular substances whose molecules do not dissociate into ions when put into solution. In dilute solution the molecules of nonelectrolytes, regardless of kind, all have an equivalent effect on the solvent particles.

The lowering of the freezing point of water by 0.100 mole of electrolytes is seen in Table 27 to be very much larger than for nonelectrolytes. The equations for the electrolytic dissociation of these electrolytes suggest why this is so.   When 0.100 mole of HCl dissociates to ions according to the equation

$$HCl = H^+ + Cl^-$$

there is formed 0.100 mole of H^+ and 0.100 mole of Cl^-, or a total of 0.200 mole of solute particles.   Accordingly, the lowering effect should be proportional to 0.200 mole of particles.   When Na_2SO_4 dissociates to ions according to the equation

$$Na_2SO_4 = 2Na^+ + SO_4{}^{2-}$$

a total of 0.300 mole of ionic solute particles will be formed for every 0.100 mole of Na_2SO_4 used.

Table 27.   Lowering of the Freezing Point of Water by Various Solutes

Solute	Moles of Solute per 1,000 g of water	Freezing Point Lowering, ° C	
Nonelectrolytes			
	0.100	0.186	0.186
Cane sugar	0.200	0.372	0.372
	0.300	0.558	0.558
	0.100	0.183	0.183
Ethyl alcohol	0.200	0.365	0.366
	0.300	0.546	0.549
Electrolytes			
HCl	0.100	0.352	0.372
HNO₃	0.100	0.351	0.372
NaOH	0.100	0.342	0.372
NaCl	0.100	0.348	0.372
MgCl₂	0.100	0.494	0.558
Na₂SO₄	0.100	0.434	0.588

on the assumption that 0.100 moles lowers freezing point 0.186 °C

If each independent ion particle has the same effect on the solvent as one molecule of sugar, then one mole of an electrolyte will produce greater lowering of the freezing point than one mole of nonelectrolyte. The actual amount of lowering observed may be somewhat less than would be calculated for complete dissociation of the electrolyte if the dissociation is not complete or if the ions in solution are not completely independent.   This will be discussed further in Section 200.   The same solutes whose solutions conduct the electric current produce greater molal lowering of the freezing point than do the nonelectrolytes.   Acids, bases, and salts usually behave as electrolytes when they go into solution in polar solvents such as water.

198. MECHANISM OF ELECTROLYTIC DISSOCIATION OF IONIC SUBSTANCES

Crystals of most bases and salts, such as NaOH, NaCl, and Na₂SO₄, are ionic; the solids are composed of positive and negative ions packed closely together.   These ions are strongly *associated* with each other and are firmly anchored in the crystal lattice because of the large electrostatic forces of attraction.   They cannot readily move from their lattice positions and are not independent of the surrounding ions of opposite charge.   Such a solid substance is *100 per cent ionic,* but the ions in it are *100 per cent associated.*   Hence, crystals of NaOH, NaCl, and Na₂SO₄ do not conduct the electric current because their ions are not free to migrate.   When the ionic solid melts, the ions become mobile and can travel about, changing neighbors.   Molten sodium chloride, like all ionic liquids, conducts the electric current when placed in an electrolytic cell. This action reflects the ability of the ions to migrate and produce a transference of electric charges.

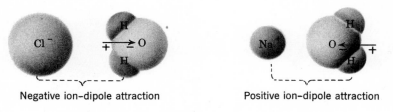

Negative ion–dipole attraction   Positive ion–dipole attraction

Fig. 71.   Attraction of polar water molecules to ions.

You will remember that the water molecule, as a whole, is highly polar (Section 70).   When an ionic solid such as NaCl is placed in the polar solvent water, the positive hydrogen end of the water molecule has a strong attraction for the negative chloride ions, and the negative oxygen end of the water molecule has a strong attraction for the positive sodium ions, as seen in Figure 71.   These forces of attraction between the water molecules and the ions tend to overcome the interionic forces holding the soldium and chloride ions together in the crystal, and the ions leave the crystal and become separated, as indicated in Fig. 72.   As the ions leave the crystal, they are believed to become surrounded by water molecules oriented because of the polarity of the water molecule and the charge of the ions.   The association of water molecules in this fashion is especially strong for the smaller positive ions, and the shell of water molecules tends to accompany the ion as it diffuses about in the solution.   We say that *the ions are hydrated* in the solution, although it is very difficult to measure the exact amount of this hydration.

The importance of having polar solvent molecules available, in order that ionic solids may dissolve by undergoing electrolytic dissociation, cannot be overemphasized.   *Ionic substances* usually *dissolve only in polar solvents,* and the process of solution is made possible by the strong ability of the polar solvent molecules to attract the ions and to separate them so they can act in relatively independent fashion in solution.   Ionic substances usually are not appreciably soluble in nonpolar solvents, such as benzene, because no strong forces of attraction are possible between **ions and nonpolar molecules.**

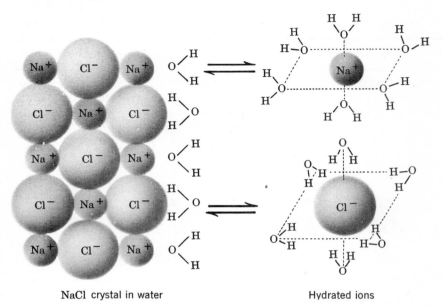

NaCl crystal in water   Hydrated ions

Fig. 72.   Dissociation of NaCl in water.

199. MECHANISM OF ELECTROLYTIC DISSOCIATION OF MOLECULAR SUBSTANCES

Hydrogen chloride is molecular in the gaseous, liquid, and solid states, with covalent bonding between the hydrogen and chlorine atoms.   The electron pair

$$H : \overset{..}{\underset{..}{Cl}} :$$

$$\xrightarrow{}$$

$$+ -$$

is not equally shared, because the chlorine atom has a much greater affinity for electrons than has the hydrogen atom.   The HCl molecule therefore has considerable polar character.   Dry HCl in the liquid state does not conduct the electric current, and accordingly, there must not be any ions present.   But when HCl dissolves in water, the solution that is formed conducts electricity and has acidic properties.   We conclude that electrolytic dissociation has occurred and that the hydrogen chloride molecules have been broken up to give relatively independent ions. Since this dissociation does not take place until the hydrogen chloride molecules come in contact with water, the polar water molecules must play an important part in bringing about the electrolytic dissociation.

The mechanism that is believed to be involved in summarized in Figure 73. The water molecule removes a proton from the molecule of hydrogen chloride, the oxygen atom in water sharing one of its pairs of electrons with the proton to form H_3O^+, the *hydronium ion*. When the proton splits away from the chlorine, the pair of electrons that bonded the two atoms together in the HCl molecules remains with the chlorine, and

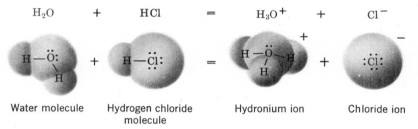

$$H_2O \quad + \quad HCl \quad = \quad H_3O^+ \quad + \quad Cl^-$$

| Water molecule | Hydrogen chloride molecule | Hydronium ion | Chloride ion |

Fig. 73.   Reaction when hydrogen chloride molecules dissolve in water.

this becomes the chloride ion. This chloride ion probably also is somewhat loosely hydrated. The hydronium ions and the chloride ions diffuse about in the solution and are relatively independent of each other in dilute solution. The proton is believed to pass quite readily from one water molecule to another in the solution, and in chemical reactions the proton separates from the hydronium ion, leaving a water molecule. When we are working with aqueous solutions it is customary, for convenience, to omit the water molecule from both sides of the dissociation equation and write it as

$$HCl = H^+ + Cl^-$$

In a similar fashion we do not usually indicate that other ions, such as Na^+ and Cl^-, actually are hydrated in aqueous solutions.

All acids are polar molecular substances and dissociate electrolytically like hydrochloric acid when they are placed in aqueous solution. The hydronium ions formed are responsible for all the properties which are characteristic of acids in aqueous solution.

Molecular substances dissociate electrolytically only when they are somewhat polar, and only when they are placed in a solvent that has molecules polar enough to cause ionization. *Electrolytic dissociation of a molecular substance involves the breaking of the covalent bond and the formation of ions that can act relatively independently in solution.* The more equally the electron pairs that constitute the bonds are shared, the less will be the tendency of molecular substances to act as electrolytes.

200. DEGREE OF DISSOCIATION OF ELECTROLYTES

Careful inspection of Table 27 reveals that 0.100 mole of an electrolyte does not lower the freezing point of 1,000 g of water quite as much as would be expected if all of the solute in solution were in the form of ions acting completely independently of each other, as do neutral molecules. For instance, 0.100 mole of NaCl lowers the freezing point 0.348°, whereas if there were present in its solution 0.100 mole of Na⁺ and 0.100 mole of Cl⁻ completely independent of each other, the lowering should be 0.372°. NaCl behaves as if it is not 100 per cent dissociated.   The term *apparent degree of dissociation* refers to *the per cent* of the electrolyte that *seems to be dissociated* in a solution.

We can readily calculate the apparent degree of dissociation of NaCl in 0.100*m* solution from the data in Table 27.   If there were no dissociation and NaCl behaved like a molecular nonelectrolyte, 0.100 mole should lower the freezing point 0.186°.   If the 0.100 mole of NaCl behaved as if it were 100 per cent dissociated, the lowering expected would be 0.372°. The lowering would be increased 0.372° − 0.186°, or 0.186°, because of dissociation.   But Table 27 says that the lowering actually is only 0.348°, an increase of only 0.348° − 0.186°, or 0.162°.   The percentage to which the NaCl in 0.100*m* solution has realized complete dissociation of its ions is therefore equal to 0.162°/0.186° × 100, or 87 per cent.

For any electrolyte in solution

$$\text{The apparent degree of dissociation} = \frac{\substack{\text{actual increase in lowering over that}\\ \text{calculated if there were no dissociation}}}{\substack{\text{increase in lowering calculated}\\ \text{for complete dissociation}}} \times 100$$

This is shown graphically in Figure 74 for 0.100*m* solutions of electrolytes where complete dissociation should give 0.200 mole of ions.   It is seen that with increase of the lowering beyond 0.186 there is a proportional increase in the apparent degree of dissociation of an electrolyte.

Suppose we calculate the apparent degree of dissociation of MgCl₂ in 0.100*m* solution.   The lowering of the freezing point listed in the table is 0.494°.   If the 0.100 mole of MgCl₂ behaved as a molecular nonelectrolyte, the lowering should be 0.186°.   If the MgCl₂ were 100 per cent dissociated, the lowering would be 0.558°.   One hundred per cent dissociation would increase the lowering 0.558° − 0.186°, or 0.372° over the lowering if MgCl₂ behaved like a molecular nonelectrolyte.   The actual increase observed is 0.49° − 0.186° = 0.308°.

$$\text{The apparent degree of dissociation of MgCl}_2 \text{ in 0.100} m \text{ solution} = \frac{0.308°}{0.372°} \times 100 = 83\%$$

MgCl₂ in 0.100*m* solution behaves as if its ions are only 83 per cent independent as measured by their effect on the freezing point of water.

The apparent degree of dissociation of electrolytes can also be **cal-culated** from the electrical conductivity of their solutions. Without going into detail, this involves calculating what per cent the observed conductivity is of that expected for complete dissociation into independent ions.

Why should the apparent degree of dissociation of ionic electrolytes such as NaCl or $MgCl_2$ be less than 100 per cent? We have already seen that these substances are 100 per cent ionic in their crystals. When these crystals dissolve, the material going into solution must all be in the

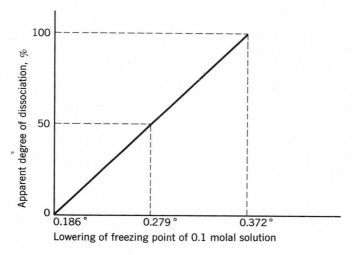

Fig. 74. Relation between lowering of freezing point and apparent degree of dissociation in 0.100 molal solution where complete dissociation should give 0.200 mole of ions.

form of individual hydrated ions relatively free to move about the solution. But because of their charges, they still are restrained by attractive forces to ions of opposite charge upon close approach and actually, therefore, cannot be expected to be completely independent like neutral molecules. They are believed to be less active in their effect on the freezing point or in producing electrical conductivity because of the attractive forces between the ions of opposite charge. *Ionic solutes in solution are believed to be 100 per cent ionic but may show less than 100 per cent apparent dissociation.*

It is believed that molecular solutes actually enter solution as molecules, a certain percentage of which may react with the polar solvents to form ions. Such a molecular electrolyte then may be present partially as molecules and partially dissociated into ions. Its apparent degree of dissociation may be less than 100 per cent because some of it is not ionized.

201.   FACTORS AFFECTING THE DEGREE OF DISSOCIATION

Table 28 gives the apparent degree of dissociation calculated for a variety of electrolytes in given concentrations in water. (The concentrations are given in terms of molarity for convenience in calculations we shall make later.   For dilute aqueous solutions the difference between molarity and molality is negligible.)

Table 28.   Apparent Degree of Dissociation in Water, 25°

Concentration	0.100M	0.010M	0.001M
NaCl	84.4	93.7	97.9
KCl	86.1	94.3	98.1
HCl	91.8	96.7	98.9
KNO$_3$	83.1	91.6	97.8
NaOH	89.1	95.6	98.8
HC$_2$H$_3$O$_2$	1.35	4.1	12.4
NH$_4$OH (NH$_{3(aq)}$)	1.4	4.0	11.7

Such experimental data indicate that the apparent degree of dissociation of an electrolyte depends upon the following:

a. Nature of the solute.   There is great variation in the degree of dissociation of different solutes in a given solvent such as water at a given temperature.   Substances, such as NaCl, KOH, and HCl, that are highly dissociated into ions are called *strong electrolytes*.   Substances, such as HC$_2$H$_3$O$_2$, that have only a small tendency to dissociate are called *weak electrolytes*.   Weak electrolytes are always molecular substances, but molecular substances may be strong electrolytes.

Most *salts* are ionic solids and therefore act as strong electrolytes when they are dissolved in water and other highly polar solvents.   They are 100 per cent ionized, but, owing to the electrostatic forces of attraction between the ions of opposite charge, the movements of their ions in solution may be somewhat restricted by the neighboring ions.   They may not be able to act completely independently, especially in concentrated solutions.   They behave as if they are partly associated in solution, and the apparent degree of dissociation may not be 100 per cent, even if they are 100 per cent ionic.

Bases vary considerably in their electrolytic behavior.   The hydroxides of the very active metals, such as NaOH and KOH, are ionic solids. They are very soluble in water, 100 per cent ionized, and are strongly dissociated.   The hydroxides of less active metals, such as Al(OH)$_3$ and Fe(OH)$_3$, are only slightly soluble in water.   An aqueous solution of ammonia contains small concentrations of NH$_4^+$ and OH$^-$.   This led chemists to assume the formation of NH$_4$OH molecules which by dissociation would behave as a weak electrolyte.   Section 283 discusses an alternate explanation.   For convenience we will continue to use the term *ammonium hydroxide* as synonomous with *aqueous ammonia*.

Acids are covalent molecular systems with varying polarity.   They differ widely in strength as electrolytes.   HCl, HClO$_4$, H$_2$SO$_4$, and HNO$_3$ are *strong acids;* their molecules are ionized to a great degree in dilute solution by water.   H$_3$PO$_4$ is only a *moderately strong acid.*   HC$_2$H$_3$O$_2$, H$_2$S, and HCN are *weak acids;* they are present in aqueous solution largely as undissociated molecules.

b. Dilution.   As we add more solvent to a solution and decrease the concentration of the solute, the degree of dissociation increases, as can be seen in Table 28.   The Principle of Le Châtelier predicts this.   Dilution decreases the concentration of solute particles and favors the change that will increase the number of particles; the degree of dissociation increases.   This increase in dissociation with dilution is consistent with the fact that, with increased average distance between ions of opposite charge, the average attractive forces fall off rapidly and the ions become increasingly independent of each other.   If a solution is diluted sufficiently, the degree of dissociation of an electrolyte will approach 100 per cent.

c. Temperature.   The process of electrolytic dissociation is always accompanied by energy changes.   Therefore, with change in temperature for the system, the degree of dissociation will change.

d. Nature of the solvent.   From the account we have given of the mechanisms involved in the process of dissociation, the importance of the polarity of the solvent molecules will be recognized.   Hydrogen chloride is highly dissociated in water but shows no appreciable dissociation in nonpolar liquids, such as benzene.

202.   IONIC EQUILIBRIUM AND IONIZATION CONSTANTS FOR WEAK ELECTROLYTES

Electrolytic dissociation is a reversible change.   The ions, which are acting independently in solution, will tend to associate when they collide and the strong electrostatic forces due to their opposite charges come into play.   As is the case for all reversible changes, equilibrium between the ions and the undissociated electrolyte will be set up if the system is allowed to stand.   If the electrolyte is an ionic substance, the equilibrium will be between the ions in solution and crystals of the solid.   If the electrolyte is a molecular material, equilibrium will be established between its molecules and its ions in solution.   Equilibrium involving ions is usually attained very rapidly because ionic reactions are generally very fast.

To get the equilibrium constants for ionic changes for weak molecular electrolytes, we can apply the same expression that we used for molecular equilibria.   The equation for the reversible electrolytic dissociation of acetic acid is

$$HC_2H_3O_2 \rightleftharpoons H^+ + C_2H_3O_2^-$$

Therefore,

$$K_{t(eq)} = \frac{[H^+] \times [C_2H_3O_2^-]}{[HC_2H_3O_2]}$$

in which the concentration is expressed in moles per liter. The equilibrium constant in this case is called the *ionization constant* because it deals with the formation of ions from the molecules of the weak electrolyte. It is constant for a given solute in a given solvent at a given temperature. Ionization constants for weak electrolytes can be determined experimentally, as illustrated for acetic acid.

By conductivity experiments it can be shown that in a $0.10000M$ solution of $HC_2H_3O_2$ at $25°$ the acetic acid is 1.35 per cent dissociated, as noted in Table 28. The concentrations of H^+ and $C_2H_3O_2^-$ therefore are each $0.00135M$. The concentration of undissociated $HC_2H_3O_2$ is $0.10000 - 0.00135$ or $0.09865M$, since each molecule of acetic acid that dissociates produces one H^+ and one $C_2H_3O_2^-$.

Therefore,

$$K_{(i),\ \text{acetic acid}} = \frac{0.00135 \times 0.00135}{0.09865} = 1.85 \times 10^{-5}$$

This ionization constant for acetic acid will hold for all solutions of acetic acid at $25°$, provided that they are not too concentrated. The constant for a solution of acetic acid of one concentration having been determined, this constant then can be used to calculate the concentration of H^+ and $C_2H_3O_2^-$ that will be present for solutions of the acid of other molarities at the same temperature. Table 29 lists the ionization constants for some of the common weak electrolytes.

Table 29. Ionization Constants, 25°

Compound		$K_{(i)}$
Acetic acid	$HC_2H_3O_2 \rightleftharpoons H^+ + C_2H_3O_2^-$	1.85×10^{-5}
Boric acid	$H_3BO_3 \rightleftharpoons H^+ + H_2BO_3^-$	6.0×10^{-10}
Carbonic acid	$H_2CO_3 \rightleftharpoons H^+ + HCO_3^-$	4.2×10^{-7}
Hydrogen cyanide	$HCN \rightleftharpoons H^+ + CN^-$	4×10^{-10}
Hydrogen sulfide	$H_2S \rightleftharpoons H^+ + HS^-$	1.0×10^{-7}
Phosphoric acid	$H_3PO_4 \rightleftharpoons H^+ + H_2PO_4^-$	7.5×10^{-3}
Sulfurous acid	$H_2SO_3 \rightleftharpoons H^+ + HSO_3^-$	1.2×10^{-2}
Ammonium hydroxide	$NH_4OH \rightleftharpoons NH_4^+ + OH^-$	1.8×10^{-5}

Since the ionization constant is a measure of the tendency of a weak electrolyte to dissociate in a given solvent, comparison of the constants for the different electrolytes allows us to compare their strength as electrolytes. The data in Table 29 tell us that acetic acid is a weaker acid than phosphoric acid, and that boric acid, hydrogen cyanide, and hydrogen sulfide are all very weak acids.

The Principle of Le Châtelier can be applied to ionic equilibria, since these involve reversible changes. If an ionic system is at equilibrium and a stress is applied so that the equilibrium no longer prevails, that change will tend to occur which will relieve the stress and restore equilibrium. Keeping this in mind, we can predict the effect of changing conditions, such as concentrations on a given ionic system.

203. DISSOCIATION OF POLYPROTIC ACIDS

A *monoprotic acid* is one that dissociates to give only one hydrogen ion per molecule; HCl, HBr, $HC_2H_3O_2$, and HCN are monoprotic. (The term *monobasic* has been widely used for such acids. The term *monoprotic* now is preferred by many because it is self-descriptive, referring to the separation of a proton from the molecule of acid.) Such acids with only one ionizable hydrogen dissociate in one step.

$$HBr \rightleftharpoons H^+ + Br^-$$

There can be only one salt of such an acid with a given positive ion of unit charge. Na^+ and Br^- can associate to form only NaBr.

A *polyprotic acid* is one that can dissociate to give more than one hydrogen ion per molecule. H_2SO_4 and $H_2C_2O_4$ are *diprotic* acids; H_3PO_4 and H_3AsO_4 are *triprotic* acids. The molecules of the polyprotic acids undergo stepwise dissociation. Sulfuric acid dissociates in two steps.

$$H_2SO_4 \rightleftharpoons H^+ + \underset{\text{hydrogen sulfate ion}}{HSO_4^-}$$

$$HSO_4^- \rightleftharpoons H^+ + \underset{\text{sulfate ion}}{SO_4^{2-}}$$

Since there are two different negative ions derived from sulfuric acid, there will be two series of salts of this acid. $NaHSO_4$ is called *sodium hydrogen sulfate*. This is an example of an *acid salt*, so called because it has some hydrogen present which may dissociate in solution to give an acid reaction. Na_2SO_4 is *sodium sulfate*. It is an example of a *normal salt*, a salt that has no hydrogen which will dissociate.

Phosphoric acid dissociates in three steps:

$$H_3PO_4 \rightleftharpoons H^+ + \underset{\substack{\text{dihydrogen} \\ \text{phosphate ion}}}{H_2PO_4^-}$$

$$H_2PO_4^- \rightleftharpoons H^+ + \underset{\substack{\text{monohydrogen} \\ \text{phosphate ion}}}{HPO_4^{2-}}$$

$$HPO_4^{2-} \rightleftharpoons H^+ + \underset{\text{phosohate ion}}{PO_4^{3-}}$$

The sodium ion associates with these different phosphate ions to give NaH_2PO_4 (*monosodium dihydrogen phosphate*), Na_2HPO_4 (*disodium monohydrogen phosphate*), and Na_3PO_4 (*trisodium phosphate*). NaH_2PO_4 and Na_2HPO_4 are acid salts; Na_3PO_4 is a normal salt.

Although acetic acid, $HC_2H_3O_2$, has more than one hydrogen atom, it is only a monoprotic acid.   Its molecule has the structural formula

$$H—O—\overset{\overset{\displaystyle H}{|}}{\underset{\underset{\displaystyle O}{\|}}{C}}—\overset{\overset{\displaystyle H}{|}}{\underset{\underset{\displaystyle H}{|}}{C}}—H$$

Only the hydrogen atom which is bonded to oxygen ionizes when this acid is added to water.

When dissociation proceeds in two or more steps, there will be as many ionic equilibria involved simultaneously in the system as there are steps. In an aqueous solution of phosphoric acid, the three equilibria indicated by the three reversible dissociation equations will be set up.   In the dissociation of a polybasic acid, the degree of dissociation is always much less for each successive step, the ionization constants for the successive equilibria becoming smaller and smaller.   Table 30 gives the ionization constants for the various dissociation steps for dilute solutions of sulfuric and phosphoric acids.

Table 30.   Ionization Constants for Sulfuric and Phosphoric Acids

	$K_{25°(i)}$
$H_2SO_4 \rightleftharpoons H^+ + HSO_4^-$	Very large
$HSO_4^- \rightleftharpoons H^+ + SO_4^{2-}$	1×10^{-2}
$H_3PO_4 \rightleftharpoons H^+ + H_2PO_4^-$	7.5×10^{-3}
$H_2PO_4^- \rightleftharpoons H^+ + HPO_4^{2-}$	6.2×10^{-8}
$HPO_4^{2-} \rightleftharpoons H^+ + PO_4^{3-}$	1.0×10^{-12}

On the basis of such data, H_2SO_4 is a very strong acid, HSO_4^- is weaker, H_3PO_4 is a moderately strong acid, $H_2PO_4^-$ is quite weak, and HPO_4^{2-} is very weak.

We have seen that acid salts have hydrogen present, which may dissociate in solution to give hydrogen ions.   *Basic salts*, such as $Bi(OH)_2Cl$, have hydroxyl groups present.   Basic salts frequently lose molecules of water and form oxysalts, such as $BiOCl$.

$$Bi(OH)_2Cl = BiOCl + H_2O$$

204.   ELECTROLYTIC DISSOCIATION OF WATER

When pure water is placed in an electrolytic cell, it does not conduct current noticeably.   However, it can be shown that water does have some slight conductivity and is very slightly dissociated. We summarize this dissociation in the equation

$$2H_2O \rightleftharpoons H_3O^+ + OH^-$$

or, by omitting the water of hydration of the hydrogen ion,

$$H_2O \rightleftharpoons H^+ + OH^-$$

There are, therefore, always hydrogen and hydroxide ions in low concentrations in water, and it behaves as a very weak electrolyte. The concentration of hydrogen ions in pure water at room temperature is 1×10^{-7} mole per liter. Since there are 6.02×10^{23} ions in one mole, there will be $1 \times 10^{-7} \times 6.02 \times 10^{23} = 6.02 \times 10^{16}$ hydrogen ions per liter of pure water. This is, of course, a very large total number of ions. But 1 liter of water consists of about $1,000 \text{ g} \div 18.016 \text{ g} = 55.5$ moles. This is equivalent to a total of $55.5 \times 6.02 \times 10^{23}$ molecules of water per liter. To provide each hydrogen ion, one molecule of water must dissociate; and to provide 6.02×10^{16} hydrogen ions, 6.02×10^{16} molecules of the total amount of water in a liter must be dissociated. Therefore,

$$\frac{\text{Molecules dissociated}}{\text{Total molecules per liter}} = \frac{6.02 \times 10^{16}}{55.5 \times 6.02 \times 10^{23}} = \frac{1}{55.5 \times 10^7}$$
$$= \frac{1}{555,000,000}$$

Only one water molecule in 555 million is dissociated at room temperature.

For every hydrogen ion produced by the dissociation of water, there will be one hydroxide ion formed. Pure water contains equal numbers of hydrogen and hydroxide ions, the concentration of each being 1×10^{-7} mole per liter. Whenever hydrogen and hydroxide ions collide, they tend to associate to form water. Conversely, water is a potential source of hydrogen and hydroxide ions. For the reversible change

$$H_2O \rightleftharpoons H^+ + OH^-$$

the expression for the ionization constant is

$$K_{(i)} = \frac{[H^+] \times [OH^-]}{[H_2O]}$$

But, with such very small concentrations of ions, the concentration of water will be essentially constant, and we can include this in the equilibrium constant for the dissociation, the expression becoming

$$K_{H_2O} = [H^+] = [OH^-]$$

K_{H_2O} is sometimes written as K_W. Putting in the values for the **molar** concentrations of the ions in pure water,

$$K_{H_2O} = (1 \times 10^{-7}) \times (1 \times 10^{-7}) = 1 \times 10^{-14}$$

In an aqueous system at equilibrium at room temperature, the product $[H^+] \times [OH^-]$ must always be 1×10^{-14}. For example, if the hydrogen-ion concentration in an aqueous solution is 1×10^{-3} moles per liter, then substitution in the expression for K_{H_2O} gives

$$1 \times 10^{-3} \times [OH^-] = 1 \times 10^{-14}$$

Therefore

$$[OH^-] = \frac{1 \times 10^{-14}}{1 \times 10^{-3}} = 1 \times 10^{-11}$$

EXERCISES

1. What is the difference between metallic and electrolytic conduction of electricity?

2. Write dissociation equations for each of the following electrolytes: a) $MgCl_2$; b) K_2SO_4; c) HI; d) $LiOH$; e) $Ca(NO_3)_2$; f) HNO_3.

3. How many moles of ions will be formed by the complete electrolytic dissociation of 0.50 mole of each of the electrolytes listed in Exercise 2?

4. What is the essential difference between the mechanisms of the electrolytic dissociation of ionic electrolytes and molecular electrolytes?

5. Calculate the apparent degree of dissociation of Na_2SO_4 in a 0.100 molal solution from the data given in Table 27.

6. If the electrolyte AY dissociates according to the equation $AY = A^+ + Y^-$ and a 0.100 m aqueous solution of it freezes at $-0.279°$, what will be the apparent degree of dissociation in this solution?

7. What will be the lowering of the freezing point of a solution which is $0.100M$ with respect to KCl? (Make use of Table 28.)

8. The monoprotic weak acid HX is 0.50 per cent dissociated in a $0.010M$ solution at 25°. What is the ionization constant for this acid? Is it a weaker or stronger acid than HCN?

9. How many hydrogen ions will there be in 10.0 ml of $0.100M$ acetic acid at 25° if its degree of dissociation is 1.35 per cent?

10. Making use of the electronegativity values given in Figure 15, page 74, predict which will be the better dissociating solvent for ionic solids; H_2O or H_2S. H_2S has a molecular configuration very much like water.

11. Applying the Principle of Le Châtelier, account for the fact that the degree of dissociation of an electrolyte increases with dilution.

12. If the dissociation of a certain weak electrolyte is an endothermic change, will its ionization constant increase or decrease with increase in temperature? Explain.

13. H_2CO_3 is a diprotic acid.

a) Write equations showing the stepwise electrolytic dissociation of the substance.

b) Which step will have the higher ionization constant?

c) Write the formulas for two different potassium salts of this acid and name them.

d) Which of these salts is a normal salt, and which is an acid salt?

14. A drop of water has a volume of about 0.02 ml. Calculate the number of hydroxide ions in one drop of pure water.

15. What is the hydrogen-ion concentration in an aqueous solution if the concentration of hydroxide ions is 1×10^{-8} mole per liter?

16. What is the hydrogen-ion concentration in an aqueous solution if 500 ml contains 0.000085 g of hydroxide ion?

Chapter 17

▶ Ionic Reactions

205. ION ASSOCIATION IN SOLUTION

When ions are in solution, they are able to react by association with ions of opposite charge or with molecules. Such association results in the formation of neutral molecules, the precipitation of ionic solids, or the building up of complex ions. These ionic reactions usually proceed at very rapid rates and approach completion when:

a. Weak electrolytes are formed. Weak electrolytes are molecular substances that have very small ionization constants, so that when the ions are brought together in solution they tend to combine. Equilibrium will be set up rapidly between the ions and the undissociated molecules, and the concentration of the ions will be reduced to the values demanded by the ionization constant. The association of hydrogen ions and hydroxide ions to form water is perhaps the most important ionic reaction we deal with.

$$H^+ + OH^- \rightleftharpoons H_2O$$

Whenever hydrogen ions and hydroxide ions are brought together in aqueous solution, they tend to associate and come to equilibrium with undissociated water. At equilibrium the product of the molar concentrations of hydrogen ions and hydroxide ions must be equal to 1×10^{-14}. Regardless of the original amounts of the ions, when they are mixed the reaction will involve changes in their concentrations until their ion product reaches this value. Since this value is very low and water is such a very weak electrolyte, the ionic reaction between hydrogen ions and hydrogen ions can be said to go practically to completion.

We have seen that acetic acid also is a rather weak electrolyte. Hydrogen ions and acetate ions will therefore have a strong tendency to associate and come to equilibrium with molecules of acetic acid, as indicated in the equation

$$H^+ + C_2H_3O_2^- \rightleftharpoons HC_2H_3O_2$$

By adding acetate ions to a solution containing a high concentration of hydrogen ions, we can reduce the concentration of hydrogen ions to a very low value. This value of the [H⁺] is governed by the expression

$$K_{(i)} = \frac{[H^+] \times [C_2H_3O_2^-]}{[HC_2H_3O_2]}$$

b. Substances low in solubility are formed.   When certain combinations of ions are brought together in sufficiently high concentrations, they form solids that are of very low solubility (insoluble), and the association of the ions will proceed very nearly to completion.   The ionic substance will precipitate out as a solid, which finally will come to equilibrium with its saturated solution.   Suppose we mix a $0.1M$ solution of barium ions, Ba^{2+}, with a $0.1M$ solution of sulfate ions, SO_4^{2-}.   A precipitate of tiny colorless crystals of $BaSO_4$ immediately appears, and in a short time the solid is at equilibrium with the ions in the solution.

$$Ba^{2+} + SO_4^{2-} \rightleftharpoons BaSO_{4(s)}$$

Since this final condition for the system involves equilibrium, we can write an expression for the equilibrium constant, using the equilibrium concentrations.   It can be shown that for the saturated solution of barium sulfate,

$$K = [Ba^{2+}] \times [SO_4^{2-}]$$

The ion product (product of the molar concentrations of the ions in solution, taken to the power indicated by the number of ions involved in the equation for the saturated solution) has a fixed value at a given temperature.   The absolute concentration of each ion in solution may vary, as long as the ion product remains constant.   The ion product of a saturated solution of a slightly soluble strong electrolyte is known as the *solubility product*, a special kind of equilibrium constant which we may label $K_{s.p.}$.   For barium sulfate

$$K_{s.p.} = [Ba^{2+}] \times [SO_4^{2-}]$$

The concentration of the undissociated barium sulfate does not appear in this expression.   This substance is a strong electrolyte, and the very small amount of it that is present in the saturated solution can be assumed to be completely dissociated.   The solid barium sulfate that is at equilibrium with the ions has a fixed concentration at a given temperature and is assumed to have unit active concentration.

We can determine the solubility product at a given temperature for barium sulfate by measuring the solubility of this salt.   At 20° this solubility is found to be 1×10^{-5} mole per liter.   Since all of the salt in solution is dissociated, the saturated solution will contain 1×10^{-5} mole per liter of Ba^{2+} and 1×10^{-5} mole per liter of SO_4^{2-}.   Therefore,

$$K_{s.p.} \text{ for } BaSO_4 \text{ at } 20° = (1 \times 10^{-5}) \times (1 \times 10^{-5}) = 1 \times 10^{-10}$$

When barium sulfate dissolves in pure water, the molar concentrations of Ba^{2+} and SO_4^{2-} in the saturated solution will be equal.   If solid $BaCl_2$ is then dissolved in the solution, the equilibrium concentration of Ba^{2+} may be stepped up, but the SO_4^{2-} concentration must decrease accordingly. If $[Ba^{2+}]$ is 1×10^{-3}, $[SO_4{}^{2-}]$ must be 1×10^{-7}; if $[SO_4{}^{2-}]$ is increased to 1, $[Ba^{2+}]$ will be reduced to 1×10^{-10}. The concentration of the two ions in solution at equilibrium with solid $BaSO_4$ may vary, provided that the ion product is equal to the solubility product 1×10^{-10}.

Knowing the solubility product for barium sulfate at 20°, we can calculate whether or not any precipitation will occur when barium and sulfate ions are brought together in given concentrations at this temperature. If the product of the molar concentrations of the ions exceeds the solubility product, precipitation will take place. The precipitate will accumulate until equilibrium is established, and the concentrations of barium and sulfate ions will be reduced until the ion product just equals the solubility product. If barium and sulfate ions are mixed in concentrations such that the solubility product is not exceeded, no precipitate will form.

EXAMPLE: Suppose that we add 100 ml of a 0.025M solution of $Ba(NO_3)_2$ to 400 ml of a 0.0005M solution of Na_2SO_4. Will any $BaSO_4$ be precipitated?

Both $Ba(NO_3)_2$ and Na_2SO_4 are strong ionic electrolytes and in very dilute solution will be essentially 100 per cent dissociated. Therefore, the original solution of $Ba(NO_3)_2$ is 0.025M with respect to Ba^{2+}, and the original solution of Na_2SO_4 is 0.0005M with respect to $SO_4{}^{2-}$. When the solutions are mixed, the combined volume is 500 ml, and the concentrations of the two ions become accordingly smaller.

$$\begin{array}{l}[Ba^{2+}] \text{ in the} \\ \text{combined solutions}\end{array} = \text{original molarity} \times \frac{\text{original volume}}{\text{combined volume}}$$

$$= 0.025M \times \frac{100 \text{ ml}}{500 \text{ ml}} = 0.005M$$

$$\begin{array}{l}[SO_4{}^{2-}] \text{ in the} \\ \text{combined solutions}\end{array} = 0.0005M \times \frac{400 \text{ ml}}{500 \text{ ml}} = 0.0004M$$

Therefore, in the combined solutions the initial ion product,

$$[Ba^{2+}] \times [SO_4{}^{2-}] = 0.005 \times 0.0004$$
$$= 0.000002 = 2 \times 10^{-6}$$

But

$$K_{s.p.(BaSO_4)} = 1 \times 10^{-10}$$

Therefore, the initial ion product when the two solutions are mixed exceeds the solubility product, and $BaSO_4$ will precipitate very rapidly until equilibrium is established.

Notice that for every $SO_4{}^{2-}$ removed from solution during precipitation one Ba^{2+} ion also is removed. When $BaSO_4$ dissolves, one $SO_4{}^{2-}$ is added for every Ba^{2+}.

It is important to remember that the expression for the solubility product is accurate only when we are dealing with strong electrolytes that have low solubilities. In these cases it is safe to assume that the small amounts of the solutes in the saturated solution are completely dissociated, and it is proper to calculate the solubility product from the solubility data.   Table 31 gives expressions for the solubility products and the numerical values for a number of common substances at room temperature.   The magnitude of $K_{s.p.}$ in each case describes quantitatively the tendency of the ion association to approach completion and defines the solubility of the substance.

Table 31.   Solubility Products, 25°

Substance	Expression for Solubility Product	$K_{s.p.}$
$BaSO_4$	$[Ba^{2+}] \times [SO_4{}^{2-}]$	1×10^{-10}
$Mg(OH)_2$	$[Mg^{2+}] \times [OH^-]^2$	8.9×10^{-12}
$AgCl$	$[Ag^+] \times [Cl^-]$	2.8×10^{-10}
CuS	$[Cu^{2+}] \times [S^{2-}]$	4×10^{-36}
ZnS	$[Zn^{2+}] \times [S^{2-}]$	4.5×10^{-24}
Ag_2S	$[Ag^+]^2 \times [S^{2-}]$	1.0×10^{-50}

c. Stable complex ions are formed.   The formation of complex ions, as described in Section 182, involves the association of a single ion with other ions or molecules.   Thus,

$$Ag^+ + 2NH_3 \rightleftharpoons Ag(NH_3)_2{}^+$$
$$Ag^+ + 2S_2O_3{}^{2-} \rightleftharpoons Ag(S_2O_3)_2{}^{3-}$$
$$Ag^+ + 2CN^- \rightleftharpoons Ag(CN)_2{}^-$$

When the complex ion is very stable, the association will proceed very strongly, and the simple ion will react rather completely.   The dissociation constants for stable complex ions are low.   For the silver cyanide complex,

$$K_{(i)} = \frac{[aq^+] \times [CN^-]^2}{[Ag(CN)_2{}^-]} = 1.8 \times 10^{-19}$$

d. A volatile substance is formed.   When ions associate to form molecules, they may have high volatility and escape from the solution to the vapor phase.   For example, the hydrogen ion tends to associate with the chloride ion to form molecules of HCl in solution, an equilibrium being set up.   But HCl is a very strong electrolyte, and the formation of HCl molecules in solution alone does not cause the association of the ions to progress very far.   However, the HCl molecules are highly volatile and tend to escape from the solution, especially if the temperature is raised and the partial pressure of HCl in the vapor phase is kept low.   As HCl escapes from the solution, the association of the ions is favored.

$$H^+ + Cl^- \rightleftharpoons HCl_{(aq)} \rightleftharpoons HCl_{(g)}$$

206. THE DRIVING FORCE IN IONIC REACTIONS

Consideration of the association of ions in solution allows us to generalize about the possibilities for the occurrence of ionic reactions. When ions are involved in chemical change and there is competition between various units to associate with the ion, that change will occur which will use up the ion most completely.

If we have silver ions in solution and add a mixture of chloride ions, thiosulfate ions, and ammonia, what will happen? It can be shown that the formation of silver thiosulfate complex ions will be favored, rather than the precipitation of silver chloride or the formation of the complex silver ammonia ion. The thiosulfate ion has by far the greatest tendency of the three units to associate with silver ions.

207. SOLUTION OF SOLIDS

The possibility of causing a solid to go into solution by manipulating the concentration of ions in the solution is interesting. If we place in a given volume of water a solid electrolyte that is only slightly soluble, the amount taken into solution will reach a maximum when the ion product equals the solubility product, and very little of the solid dissolves. Obviously, if we can in some way keep the concentration of one of the ions in the solution so low that the ion product is not as large as the solubility product, the solid will continue to dissolve. Consider the case of silver chloride. When solid AgCl is in contact with water, it comes to equilibrium with silver and chloride ions according to the reversible equation

$$AgCl_{(s)} \rightleftharpoons Ag^+ + Cl^-$$

The solubility product for silver chloride is very low, so that very little of the solid dissolves in water. But if we add ammonia to the solution, these molecules will associate with the silver ions, according to the equation

$$Ag^+ + 2NH_3 \rightleftharpoons Ag(NH_3)_2{}^+$$

to form the very stable silver ammonia ions that remain in solution. This reaction uses up the silver ions and favors the solution of the silver chloride. By adding enough ammonia we are able to dissolve the silver chloride completely.

208. ACID-BASE NEUTRALIZATION

The equilibrium of water with hydrogen and hydroxide ions is of fundamental importance in the neutralization of acids by bases. By definition, any acid dissociates to give hydrogen ions, and any base dissociates to give hydroxide ions. When aqueous solutions of acids and bases are mixed, the hydrogen and hydroxide ions will tend to associate to form the very weak electrolyte, water. *The acid solution is neutralized* because the hydrogen ions, which are responsible for the acidic behavior, are removed. *The basic solution is neutralized* because the hydroxide ions, which are responsible for the basic properties, are used up.

In describing acid-base neutralization, such as the reaction between hydrochloric acid and sodium hydroxide, *stoichiometric equations* are frequently used.

$$HCl + NaOH = NaCl + H_2O$$

Here the empirical formulas for the substances are given. This equation does describe the over-all reaction, provided that we start with gaseous HCl and solid NaOH, allow these to react, and separate the water and sodium chloride that are produced. But, since the neutralization of hydrochloric acid by sodium hydroxide is usually carried out in water solution, and since the substances concerned, with the exception of water, are strong electrolytes, the above equation does not describe the actual ionic reactions that occur, especially in dilute solution.

When HCl is dissolved in water, there is set up the dissociation

$$HCl = H^+ + Cl^-$$

If the solution is dilute, the acid will be practically completely dissociated to the ions. When sodium hydroxide is dissolved in water, the ions separate

$$NaOH_{(s)} = Na^+ + OH^-$$

When the two dilute solutions are mixed, all four ions are present, and their association is possible. As the equation

$$H^+ + Cl^- + Na^+ + OH^- \rightleftharpoons H_2O + Na^+ + Cl^-$$

shows, the only effective reaction that occurs in dilute solution is the union of the hydrogen and hydroxide ions to form the weak electrolyte, water. The other possible products of ion association, NaCl, NaOH, and HCl, are such strong electrolytes that their formation in dilute solution is not realized to any appreciable extent.

The only change that takes place when a dilute solution of a strong acid is mixed with a dilute solution of a strong base is the association of the H^+ and OH^- to form water. The equation

$$H^+ + OH^- = H_2O$$

represents the *net reaction* that occurs in solution and is called the *net equation*. (See Sections 189 and 215.) That this is the only change which occurs can be demonstrated by a study of the energy change. Acid-base neutralization reactions are always exothermic, and we can measure the *molar heat of neutralization* in each case. This is the heat liberated per mole of water formed when the neutralization takes place in dilute solutions. We find that the molar heat of neutralization is always the same, namely, 13,800 cal, whenever any strong acid is neutralized by any strong base, provided that dilute solutions are used. This can mean only that in every such case the effective chemical change is the same, the formation of water from the ions,

$$H^+ + OH^- = H_2O + 13,800 \text{ cal}$$

The story is different, however, when weak acids or weak bases take part in neutralization. Acetic acid dissociates according to the equation

$$HC_2H_3O_2 \rightleftharpoons H^+ + C_2H_3O_2^-$$

Acetic acid, however, is a weak acid and at equilibrium only a small fraction of the acetic acid is dissociated, even in dilute solution. When a dilute solution of acetic acid is mixed with a dilute solution of sodium hydroxide, which is completely dissociated, acid-base neutralization occurs. The association

$$H^+ + OH^- = H_2O$$

proceeds effectively. As H^+ is used up in this association, the equilibrium between undissociated acetic acid and its ions is upset, and more acetic acid dissociates to provide more H^+. In this fashion the dissociation of the acetic acid progresses as neutralization occurs, until practically all of the acetic acid has been used up. The Na^+ and $C_2H_3O_2^-$ accumulate in solution because there is little tendency for them to form the soluble strong electrolyte, $NaC_2H_3O_2$. Two chemical changes are thus involved in the neutralization of a dilute solution of acetic acid by a dilute solution of sodium hydroxide; hydrogen ions and hydroxide ions unite to form water molecules, and acetic acid molecules dissociate progressively to provide hydrogen ions and acetate ions. The *net reaction* therefore is

$$HC_2H_3O_2 + OH^- = H_2O + C_2H_3O_2^-$$

The weak base NH_4OH in dilute solution dissociates only to a small extent.

$$NH_4OH \rightleftharpoons NH_4^+ + OH^-$$

HCl dissociates very strongly. When a dilute solution of HCl is mixed with dilute NH_4OH, the association of H^+ and OH^- takes place very strongly, and, as OH^- is used up, the dissociation of NH_4OH proceeds until it is all used up. The ammonium and chloride ions remain unassociated in solution because NH_4Cl is a soluble strong electrolyte. In the neutralization in dilute solution of the weak base NH_4OH by the strong acid HCl, *two changes* occur. As water is formed, ammonium hydroxide dissociates, and the net reaction can be written as

$$NH_4OH + H^+ = NH_4^+ + H_2O$$

Neutralization of weak acids or weak bases involves the progressive dissociation of the weak electrolytes as well as the formation of water from its ions. With weak acids and bases the *heat of neutralization* involves not only the heat of formation of water from its ions, but also the heat of dissociation of the weak electrolytes. In such cases the heat of neutralization never is found to be equal to 13,800 cal. For example,

$$NH_4OH + H^+ = NH_4^+ + H_2O + 12,300\ cal$$

For the neutralization of a weak acid, such as $HC_2H_3O_2$, by a weak base, say NH_4OH, the net reaction will be

$$NH_4OH + HC_2H_3O_2 = H_2O + NH_4^+ + C_2H_3O_2^-$$

209. INDICATORS

Chemical indicators are substances that are used to follow the progress of a chemical reaction. They make possible the determination of the point at which equivalent amounts of reacting substances are present, *the end point of the reaction.* Litmus, phenolphthalein, and methyl orange are examples of acid-base indicators that are useful because, by color changes, they indicate changes in the concentrations of H^+ and OH^- in solution. Remember that the product of the molar concentrations of these two ions in equilibrium with water must always be equal to 1×10^{-14}. As the concentration of H^+ decreases, the concentration of OH^- must increase, as is shown in Table 32.

When the concentrations of both OH^- and H^+ are 1×10^{-7}, the solu-

Table 32. Equilibrium Concentrations of H^+ and OH^-

[H⁺]	[OH⁻]	pH	Color		
			Litmus	Phenolphthalein	Methyl Orange
1	1×10^{-14}	0	Red	Colorless	Pink
1×10^{-1}	1×10^{-13}	1	Red	Colorless	Pink
1×10^{-2}	1×10^{-12}	2	Red	Colorless	Pink
1×10^{-3}	1×10^{-11}	3	Red	Colorless	Pink
1×10^{-4}	1×10^{-10}	4	Red	Colorless	Yellow
1×10^{-5}	1×10^{-9}	5	Red	Colorless	Yellow
1×10^{-6}	1×10^{-8}	6	Red	Colorless	Yellow
1×10^{-7}	1×10^{-7}	7	Violet	Colorless	Yellow
1×10^{-8}	1×10^{-6}	8	Blue	Colorless	Yellow
1×10^{-9}	1×10^{-5}	9	Blue	Pink	Yellow
1×10^{-10}	1×10^{-4}	10	Blue	Pink	Yellow
1×10^{-11}	1×10^{-3}	11	Blue	Pink	Yellow
1×10^{-12}	1×10^{-2}	12	Blue	Pink	Yellow
1×10^{-13}	1×10^{-1}	13	Blue	Pink	Yellow
1×10^{-14}	1	14	Blue	Pink	Yellow

tion is neutral.   When the concentration of H^+ is greater than 1×10^{-7} and the concentration of OH^- is less than 1×10^{-7}, as in the upper half of the table, the solutions will be acid.   For the equilibrium concentrations in the lower half of the table the solutions will be basic.   The table also gives the characteristic colors of the three indicators in solutions of different concentrations of H^+ and OH^-.   Litmus has a red color in acid solution and a blue color in basic solution.   If we have a dilute solution of hydrochloric acid and add litmus, we observe a red color.   If we then add a dilute solution of sodium hydroxide dropwise, the concentration of H^+ will decrease and the concentration of OH^- will increase.   The red color of litmus will persist until the H^+ concentration reaches 1×10^{-7}. At that point the litmus has a violet color.   When more OH^- is added, the litmus changes to a blue color, which persists as the OH^- concentration mounts.   By observing the color of the system, we can tell when we have added enough sodium hydroxide to *neutralize* the hydrochloric acid.

You will notice in the table that the color change for phenolphthalein does not come at the true neutral point for the solution, but occurs when there is some excess of hydroxide ion, that is, when the solution is slightly basic.   Methyl orange shows a color change when the solution still is somewhat acid.   There is a large number of substances that show color changes when the hydrogen-ion concentration of a solution is varied; these are potential acid-base indicators.   For each such indicator there is a specific hydrogen-ion concentration at which it changes color.

210.   HYDROGEN-ION CONCENTRATION AND pH

For many purposes it is convenient to use the pH system for expressing hydrogen-ion concentration.   The pH *of a solution* is the logarithm of the reciprocal of the hydrogen-ion concentration

$$pH = \log \frac{1}{[H^+]}$$

Accordingly, when the $[H^+]$ of a solution is 1×10^{-1} the pH is 1, and when $[H^+]$ is 1×10^{-8} the pH is 8.   The third column in Table 32 gives the pH corresponding to the various hydrogen-ion concentrations.   The pH is also an index of the hydroxide-ion concentration because, when an aqueous solution is at equilibrium there is an $[OH^-]$ corresponding to every value for $[H^+]$.   Solutions having a pH of 7 have equal concentrations of hydrogen and hydroxide ions and therefore are neutral.   Solutions whose pH values lie between 0 and 7 are acidic; those having a pH greater than 7 are basic.

The pH of a solution may be determined by testing with a variety of indicators.   For example, suppose that separate portions of a given solution are tested with the three indicators listed in Table 32, and that the color with litmus is blue, the phenolphthalein gives no color, and the color with methyl orange is yellow.   According to Table 32, this combination could only be true for a solution whose pH is about 8, that is, a solution in which the $[H^+]$ is about 1×10^{-8} and the $[OH^-]$ is about 1×10^{-6}. In this solution the hydroxide-ion concentration is higher than the hydrogen-ion concentration, and the solution is basic.   (By using a greater variety of indicators which have sharp color changes at different pH values, it is possible to determine the pH of a solution with considerable accuracy.)

211. TITRATION OF ACIDS AND BASES

Titration is the process by which we determine the volume of a solution of a given reactant that is just chemically equivalent to a given volume of a solution of another reactant.   We titrate a solution of an acid by putting a given volume of the solution in a container, adding an acid-base indicator, and then adding a solution of a base dropwise.   The solutions are mixed thoroughly, and we measure the volume of the solution of the base that we must add to make the indicator change color. By proper choice of indicator, depending upon the particular acid and base that we use, we can thus determine exactly what volumes of the two solutions contain equivalent amounts of the acid and base.

212. OTHER SYSTEMS OF ACIDS AND BASES

We have, so far in our discussion, used the terms *acid* and *base* in the original sense in which they were introduced and later interpreted by Arrhenius.   An acid furnishes hydrogen ions; a base furnishes hydroxide ions.   In an effort to broaden the classification, other sets of definitions have been developed and have come into use.

According to the *proton donor-acceptor theory*, an acid is a proton donor and a base is a proton acceptor.   This involves no essential change from the Arrhenius concept of acids, except that it emphasizes the acidic character of ions, such as NH_4^+ and H_3O^+.   The concept of what shall be called a base does differ very much from the traditional definition. Practically all negative ions become bases according to this definition, since they accept (associate readily with) protons. Cl^-, SO_4^{2-}, and $C_2H_3O_2^-$ are bases.   Molecules such as NH_3 and H_2O, which combine with H^+ to form NH_4^+ and H_3O^+, are bases. OH^- is a base, but the substance NaOH is not a base; it contains the base OH^-. $H_2PO_4^{2-}$ is both an acid and a base.

Another acid-base theory that has been proposed *defines an acid as an electron-pair acceptor and a base as an electron-pair donor.*   As we have already seen in Section 179, BF_3 has a strong tendency to accept a share in a pair of electrons and therefore is classed as an acid in this scheme, whereas NH_3 is a strong electron donor system and qualifies as a base.

These newer theories of acids, and bases do have the advantage that, by their use, the acid-base classification can be extended to nonaqueous systems, and the similarity of behavior of solutes in different solvents can be emphasized. Their introduction, however, has led to considerable confusion, since the ways in which the terms *acid* and *base* are used differ with the various theories. The older hydrogen-ion and hydroxide-ion terminology is still the one in most common use, and this so-called *water system of acids and bases* is quite adequate for aqueous chemistry. We will, therefore, in this book continue to use the terms *acid* and *base* in this traditional sense, but you should be prepared to encounter the other specialized terminology in other courses in chemistry.

213. HYDROLYSIS

Hydrolysis, in the literal sense, refers to the decomposition of a substance by reaction with water. One important kind of hydrolysis is that which salts suffer when they are placed in solution in water. Because salts are usually very strong electrolytes, such salt hydrolysis must involve ionic change, ions of the salt reacting with water. Suppose that we consider a number of different cases where ionic hydrolysis is favored.

a. A weak acid is formed. When sodium acetate is added to water and phenolphthalein is added to the solution, a pink color is observed. Looking back at Table 32, we see that this pink color indicates that the addition of sodium acetate to water has caused the concentration of OH^- to become greater than the concentration of H^+. How can we account for this? Any change in the concentration of H^+ and OH^- for the system must involve some change in the equilibrium between them and water, and water molecules must take part in this change. Sodium acetate is a strong electrolyte, and when it dissolves, it dissociates quite completely, according to the equation

$$NaC_2H_3O_{2(s)} = Na^+ + C_2H_3O_2^-$$

There will then be possible reactions between each of the ions and water molecules. The reaction of Na^+ with H_2O to give $NaOH_{(s)}$ and H^+ will not go appreciably, because water is a very weak electrolyte and sodium hydroxide is a very soluble strong electrolyte. But we may expect the reaction

$$C_2H_3O_2^- + H_2O \rightleftharpoons HC_2H_3O_2 + OH^-$$

to proceed to some extent because acetic acid is a weak acid. So an equilibrium will be set up between the acetate ions, water, acetic acid, and hydroxide ions. The OH^- concentration in solution will increase, and the H^+ equilibrium concentration must decrease accordingly. The solution will be basic and turn phenolphthalein pink. The net chemical change, which takes place when sodium acetate is placed in water, is the hydrolysis of the acetate ion.

Whenever the negative ion of a salt is such that a weak acid will be formed by hydrolysis, such hydrolysis will proceed to an extent determined by the dissociation constant of the acid and by the concentration. The Principle of Le Châtelier allows us to predict that, as we dilute the solution of a salt, hydrolysis will become more pronounced.

b. A weak base is formed. Ammonium chloride is a strong electrolyte and dissociates strongly when dissolved.

$$NH_4Cl_{(s)} = NH_4^+ + Cl^-$$

The solution gives a red color with litmus, indicating that hydrolysis has occurred to give an acidic solution. The chloride ions will have little tendency to hydrolyze, since hydrochloric acid is such a strong electrolyte. But the ammonium ions will hydrolyze considerably, according to the equation

$$NH_4^+ + H_2O \rightleftharpoons NH_4OH + H^+$$

This will proceed to some extent because NH_4OH is a weak base. The net reaction will therefore be the hydrolysis of the ammonium ions, and the concentration of H^+ will become greater than the concentration of OH^- for the system. Whenever a salt contains the positive ion of a weak base, hydrolysis of the ion will occur in aqueous solution.

c. A weak acid and a weak base are formed. From our discussion, it can readily be seen that both ions present in a solution of a salt of a weak acid and a weak base will hydrolyze considerably. When ammonium acetate is added to water, both ions react, the net equation being

$$NH_4^+ + C_2H_3O_2^- + H_2O \rightleftharpoons NH_4OH + HC_2H_3O_2$$

The equilibrium concentrations of NH_4OH and $HC_2H_3O_2$ are considerable. Notice that in the case where the net reaction involves the formation of both a weak acid and a weak base, the solution does not necessarily become decidedly richer in either H^+ or OH^-. The hydrolysis of the positive ion may be matched by an equivalent amount of hydrolysis of the negative ion.

d. A stable complex ion is formed. When aluminum sulfate, $Al_2(SO_4)_3$, is added to water, the solution gives a very strong acid reaction with litmus. This can only be due to the hydrolysis of the aluminum ion. This ion, like many other polyvalent ions of the metals, shows a considerable tendency to form rather stable complex ions in which OH groups are involved. We may indicate the nature of the hydrolysis of Al^{3+} by the equation

$$Al^{3+} + H_2O \rightleftharpoons Al(OH)^{2+} + H^+$$

The aluminum ions and the complex hydroxyaluminum ion probably are strongly hydrated. There is reason to believe that aluminum probably tends to associate with six groups, such as OH^- or H_2O, and in the above reaction we may be dealing with $Al(H_2O)_6{}^{3+}$ instead of simply Al^{3+}, and the hydrolysis product probably is something like $Al(OH)(H_2O)_5{}^{2+}$. Unfortunately, we do not have a satisfactory experimental method to determine just what the constitutions of such ions actually are in solution. In such cases we shall not attempt to indicate the water of hydration but, as we have done for the hydronium ion, write just the non-aqueous part of the formula. As indicated in the equation above, the aluminum ion hydrolyzes extensively to produce complex hydroxy ions, and hydrogen ions accumulate in the solution to give an acid reaction.

When we add sodium carbonate, Na_2CO_3, to water, a basic solution results. Here we believe that hydrolysis of the $CO_3{}^{2-}$ to $HCO_3{}^-$ occurs, according to the net equation

$$CO_3{}^{2-} + H_2O \rightleftharpoons HCO_3{}^- + OH^-$$

and OH^- accumulates.

e. An insoluble substance is formed. Under proper conditions, as when associated with the ion of a weak acid, aluminum ions may hydrolyze to such an extent that solid $Al(OH)_3$ may be formed.

$$Al^{3+} + 3H_2O \rightleftharpoons Al(OH)_{3(s)} + 3H^+$$

Since $Al(OH)_3$ is only slightly soluble, it precipitates, and the reaction goes strongly to the right.

f. A volatile substance is formed. A solution of sodium sulfide, Na_2S, is quite basic toward litmus and smells strongly of H_2S. The sulfide ion hydrolyzes strongly for two reasons. H_2S is a very weak diprotic acid and so the reactions

$$S^{2-} + H_2O \rightleftharpoons OH^- + HS^-$$
$$HS^- + H_2O \rightleftharpoons OH^- + H_2S$$

will take place. In addition, the H_2S is highly volatile and tends to escape as a gas from the solution, further hydrolysis thus being favored.

$$H_2S_{(solution)} \rightleftharpoons H_2S_{(g)}$$

The hydrolysis of chlorides may be quite serious, especially when the solutions are boiled, because of the escape of HCl.

214. THE COMMON-ION EFFECT

We have seen that we can write the expression for the ionization constant of a weak electrolyte such as acetic acid.

$$K_{(i)} = \frac{[H^+] \times [C_2H_3O_2{}^-]}{[HC_2H_3O_2]}$$

This describes the system when it is at equilibrium. Suppose the system is placed under stress by the addition of more of one of the ions, say by the addition of some solid $NaC_2H_3O_2$. This is a strong electrolyte and will provide an ample supply of $C_2H_3O_2^-$. The concentration of acetate ions will then be above the equilibrium value, and the ion product divided by the concentration of the undissociated acid will be greater than $K_{(i)}$. The change tending to relieve this stress by using up acetate ions will be favored; H^+ and $C_2H_3O_2^-$ will combine to step up the concentration of $HC_2H_3O_2$ until equilibrium finally is re-established. The hydrogen-ion concentration will have been lowered. *The addition of a substance providing an ion in common with a solute represses the dissociation of the solute.* This is called the *common-ion effect,* and it constitutes a valuable means of adjusting the concentration of ions in solution.

215. NET REACTIONS AND EQUATIONS

In Sections 189 and 208 the term *net equation* was introduced to describe the *net reaction* that predominates in a chemical system. Because net equations are the equations that must be used for the derivation of equilibrium constants and for the application of Le Châtelier's Principle, it will be useful to summarize how they are written. In the net reaction certain substances or ions are used up and are produced. The net equation includes only the formulas for these substances or ions that are being used up or formed. Other units that may be present but do not undergo appreciable changes in amounts are omitted. Intermediates that form and then are used up again also are omitted from the net equation.

In writing the equations for the net reactions in dissociating solvents, weak electrolytes and solids low in solubility are formulated as being undissociated, whereas the ions of soluble strong electrolytes are indicated. Thus, when a solution of Na_2CO_3 reacts with a solution of $CaCl_2$, we write the equation for the net reaction as

$$Ca^{2+} + CO_3^{2-} = CaCO_{3(s)}$$

Both sodium carbonate and calcium chloride are soluble strong electrolytes, and the solubility of calcium carbonate is very low. The units that have entered the reaction are calcium ions and carbonate ions, and the product of the reaction is calcium carbonate.

EXERCISES

1. If the concentration of OH^- in a solution is $0.02M$, what will be the equilibrium H^+ concentration?

2. To what value must the molarity of acetate ions be raised if the equilib-

rium hydrogen-ion concentration in a solution is to be reduced to $1 \times 10^{-3}M$? The solution is originally $1M$ with respect to acetic acid.

3. The solubility of $PbCO_3$ in water is 4×10^{-7} mole per liter at room temperature. What is the solubility product of this substance?

4. Calculate the solubility in grams per liter of ZnS, using data given in Table 31.

5. If the concentration of Zn^{2+} in equilibrium with solid ZnS is $1 \times 10^{-6}M$, what is the molarity of S^{2-} in the solution?

6. Will there be any precipitation:
a) When 200 ml of a $0.10M$ solution of Ag^+ is added to 400 ml of a solution $0.001M$ with respect to Cl^-?
b) When 10 ml of a solution $0.002M$ with respect to Mg^{2+} is mixed with 10 ml of a solution $0.00002M$ with respect to OH^- ions?

7. If the concentration of Mg^{2+} in a solution at equilibrium with solid $Mg(OH)_2$ is $1.5 \times 10^{-3}M$, what will be the concentration of OH^-?

8. If a solution contains equimolar amounts of Zn^{2+} and Cu^{2+} and a certain amount of S^{2-} is added, which will be the more completely precipitated?

9. Calculate the $[SO_4^{2-}]$ for a saturated solution of $BaSO_4$ when the $[Ba^{2+}]$ is:
a) 1×10^{-2}; b) 1×10^{-8}.

10. You wish to reduce the concentration of Ba^{2+} in a given solution to as low a value as possible. Explain why the addition of solid Na_2SO_4 could be used effectively for this purpose.

11. Which will be more effective for lowering the concentration of silver ions in solution, the addition of Cl^- or the addition of I^-? $K_{s.p.(AgCl)} = 2.8 \times 10^{-10}$, $K_{s.p.(AgI)} = 8.5 \times 10^{-17}$.

12. How can you account for the fact that the addition of NH_3 increases the amount of AgCl which is taken into solution?

13. a) If the pH of an aqueous solution is 9, what is the $[H^+]$ and the $[OH^-]$?
b) Is the solution acidic or basic?
c) What will be the color in this solution of: 1) litmus, 2) phenolphthalein, and 3) methyl orange?

14. The addition of methyl orange to a solution gives a yellow color.
a) What range of pH values could this solution have?
b) Is it acidic or basic?

15. a) Write the net equation for the neutralization of a dilute solution of HNO_3 by a dilute solution of KOH. HNO_3, KOH, and KNO_3 are all strong and very soluble electrolytes.
b) Will the reaction be endo- or exothermic?
c) What will be the number of calories of energy change involved when 0.25 mole of HNO_3 is neutralized in this reaction?

16. Write the net equation for the neutralization of dilute HCN by dilute NaOH (see Table 29).

17. Write the net equation for the hydrolysis of NaCN.

18. a) Using the data in Table 30, what conclusions can you draw concerning the relative tendencies of Na_2SO_4 and Na_3PO_4 to hydrolyze?

b) Write equations for the net reactions which are involved.

Chapter 18

▶ **Oxidation-Reduction Half Reactions**

▶ **Galvanic Cells**

216. OXIDATION AND REDUCTION IN IONIC SYSTEMS

Oxidation and reduction have been discussed in a general way. We found that the term *oxidation* is used in the broad sense to refer to a change of an atomic system to a more electropositive condition, to a higher oxidation state. *Reduction* in the broad sense refers to a change of an atomic system to a more electronegative condition, to a lower oxidation state.

An atomic system can go to a higher oxidation state by becoming less associated with electrons. For ionic systems this is accomplished by the complete loss of one or more electrons, as indicated by the following:

$$Na \rightarrow e^- + Na^+$$
$$Cu \rightarrow 2e^- + Cu^{2+}$$
$$Fe \rightarrow 2e^- + Fe^{2+}$$
$$Fe^{2+} \rightarrow e^- + Fe^{3+}$$
$$2Cl^- \rightarrow 2e^- + Cl_2$$

In the first three cases, neutral atoms lose one or more electrons and form positive ions. In the fourth case, a positive ion loses another electron to form a more highly charged positive ion. In the last case, negative ions lose electrons to form a neutral molecule. In each of these changes, the atomic system goes to a higher oxidation state and is oxidized. The equations in which electrons appear, as written, are known as *oxidation half reactions*.

An atomic system can go to a lower oxidation state by becoming more associated with electrons. For ionic systems this is accomplished by the complete gain of one or more electrons, as indicated by the following:

$$Cl_2 + 2e^- \rightarrow 2Cl^-$$
$$S + 2e^- \rightarrow S^{2-}$$
$$Fe^{3+} + e^- \rightarrow Fe^{2+}$$
$$Fe^{2+} + 2e^- \rightarrow Fe$$

In the first two instances, neutral elements gain electrons and form negative ions, thus going to lower oxidation states. In the third example,

282

a highly charged positive ion gains one electron and changes to a less highly charged positive ion. In the last case, a positive ion gains electrons and forms a neutral atom. In each of these changes, the atomic system goes to a lower oxidation state and is reduced. The equations that are written above describe the *reduction half reactions*.

217. OXIDATION-REDUCTION AND IONIC HALF REACTIONS

Oxidation must always be accompanied by an equivalent amount of reduction. The electrons lost in oxidation must be accepted by a system that undergoes reduction. Oxidation-reduction reactions involving ionic change, therefore, can be represented by a combination of an oxidation half reaction with a reduction half reaction. Consider the reaction between sodium and chlorine, which we can represent by the net equation

$$2Na_{(s)} + Cl_{2(g)} \rightarrow 2NaCl_{(s)}$$

This can be broken down into the two half reactions

$$2Na_{(s)} \rightarrow 2Na^+ + 2e^-$$

and

$$Cl_{2(g)} + 2e^- \rightarrow 2Cl^-$$

the sum being

$$2Na_{(s)} + Cl_{2(g)} \rightarrow 2NaCl_{(s)}$$

where the sodium and chloride ions that are formed are associated in the solid crystal. The total number of electrons lost by sodium must be equal to the total number of electrons gained by chlorine. *For every oxidation there must be an equivalent amount of reduction, the two occurring simultaneously.* When ions are involved, we can always split such a net change up into the two half reactions and so analyze what is happening in the system. Working through the two half reactions also may aid materially in balancing the net oxidation-reduction reaction.

218. RELATIVE STRENGTHS OF OXIDIZING AND REDUCING AGENTS

The relative strengths of oxidizing and reducing agents can be studied by examining a number of ionic-displacement reactions in which two metals compete for electrons. In each of the following, a metal is added to a solution of the positive ions of another metal: the first metal goes into solution, losing electrons and forming its ions; the ions of the second metal gain electrons and are reduced and the metal precipitates out.

a) $\qquad Zn + Fe^{2+} \rightarrow Fe + Zn^{2+}$
b) $\qquad Fe + Pb^{2+} \rightarrow Pb + Fe^{2+}$
c) $\qquad Pb + Cu^{2+} \rightarrow Cu + Pb^{2+}$
d) $\qquad Cu + 2Ag^+ \rightarrow 2Ag + Cu^{2+}$

In this series of displacements, the metal that displaces the ion from solution is acting as a reducing agent, while the ion that gains electrons in the change is the oxidizing agent.   It is obvious that zinc is a stronger reducing agent than iron because Zn reduces Fe^{2+} and Fe is formed; and Fe^{2+} must be a stronger oxidizing agent than Zn^{2+}.   No reaction occurs when iron is added to a solution of zinc ions.

In turn, reaction (b) shows that Fe is a stronger reducing agent than Pb, and Pb^{2+} is a stronger oxidizing agent than Fe^{2+}.   Reactions (c) and (d) may be interpreted in a similar fashion, and we are thus able to list the metals in order of decreasing strength as reducing agents.   Their ions can be listed in order of increasing strengths as oxidizing agents.

$$Zn > Fe > Pb > Cu$$
Strength as reducing agent

$$Zn^{2+} < Fe^{2+} < Pb^{2+} < Cu^{2+}$$
Strength as oxidizing agent

In an analogous fashion, we can study displacement reactions for the nonmetals, which form negative ions.

$$Br_2 + 2I^- \rightarrow 2Br^- + I_2$$
$$Cl_2 + 2Br^- \rightarrow 2Cl^- + Br_2$$

I^- is a stronger reducing agent than Br^-, and Br^- is a stronger reducing agent than Cl^-. I_2 is a weaker oxidizing agent than Br_2, and Br_2 is a weaker oxidizing agent than Cl_2.

Each of the above ionic-replacement reactions can be broken up into two half reactions, one representing the oxidation, the other representing the reduction.

$$Zn + Fe^{2+} \rightarrow Zn^{2+} + Fe$$

can be resolved into

$$Zn \rightarrow 2e^- + Zn^{2+}$$
oxidation half reaction

and

$$Fe^{2+} + 2e^- \rightarrow Fe$$
reduction half reaction

By tabulating the oxidation half reactions in order of their tendency to proceed, we can summarize all of the above information about the relative strength of oxidizing and reducing agents.   In Table 33 several additional half reactions, which we will make use of, are included.   Notice that the reverse of any reduction half reaction is an oxidation half reaction; we indicate the combination by using the double arrow.

If H^+ or OH^- enters into the half reaction, their concentrations will influence the tendency of the reaction to go.   Table 33 is given for $1M$ H^+ concentration.   Appendix IV gives a more extensive listing of the more common oxidation-reduction half reactions.

So far in this discussion we have spoken only qualitatively of the relative strengths of oxidizing and reducing agents. It is possible, however, to measure accurately the relative tendency of oxidizing and reducing agents to lose or gain electrons in solution. Let us see how this is done.

Table 33. Oxidation-Reduction Half Reactions, Acid Solution

	Reducing Agents (Furnish Electrons)		Oxidizing Agents (Take Up Electrons)		Standard Oxidation-Reduction Potential, Volts
Increase in strength as reducing agents	Zn	$\rightleftharpoons 2e^- +$	Zn^{2+}	Incease in strength as oxidizing agents	$+0.762$
	Fe	$\rightleftharpoons 2e^- +$	Fe^{2+}		$+0.440$
	Pb	$\rightleftharpoons 2e^- +$	Pb^{2+}		$+0.126$
	H_2	$\rightleftharpoons 2e^- +$	$2H^+$		$+0.0000$
	Cu	$\rightleftharpoons 2e^- +$	Cu^{2+}		-0.345
	$2I^-$	$\rightleftharpoons 2e^- +$	I_2		-0.535
	Ag	$\rightleftharpoons e^- +$	Ag^+		-0.799
	$2Br^-$	$\rightleftharpoons 2e^- +$	Br_2		-1.065
	$I_2 + 6H_2O$	$\rightleftharpoons 10e^- + 12H^+ +$	$2IO_3^-$		-1.20
	$2Cl^-$	$\rightleftharpoons 2e^- +$	Cl_2		-1.358
	$2Cr^{3+} + 7H_2O$	$\rightleftharpoons 6e^- + 14H^+ +$	$Cr_2O_7^{2-}$		-1.36
	$Mn^{2+} + 4H_2O$	$\rightleftharpoons 5e^- + 8H^+ +$	MnO_4^-		-1.52
	$2F^-$	$\rightleftharpoons 2e^- +$	F_2		-2.85

219. HALF REACTIONS AND SINGLE ELECTRODES

When a strip of zinc is placed in an aqueous solution of zinc ions, as shown in Figure 75, the reversible half reaction

$$Zn \rightleftharpoons 2e^- + Zn^{2+}$$

is set up. Equilibrium will be established rapidly between the two opposing changes.

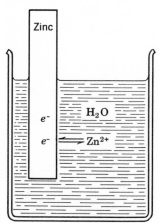

Fig. 75. The zinc | Zn^{2+} single electrode.

In the reaction to the right, zinc atoms ionize and enter the solution. The electrons liberated in the process accumulate on the strip of zinc, where they are shared in general by all of the atoms. This change tends to build up negative charge on the zinc and positive charge in the solution, producing a difference in electrical potential (voltage) between the zinc strip and the solution of zinc ions. In the reverse reaction to the left, positive zinc ions from solution gain electrons and join the other zinc atoms on the strip, thereby reducing the difference in potential between the zinc and the solution. The two opposing reactions have opposite effects on the potential difference.

At equilibrium there will be a definite difference in electrical potential between the zinc and the solution. The specific value of this potential, usually expressed in volts, will be a function of the strength of zinc as a reducing agent, the strength of the zinc ion as an oxidizing agent, and of the equilibrium concentration of zinc ions in solution. The combination of zinc $|$ $Zn^{2+}_{(aq)}$ constitutes what is known as a *single electrode.*

Other oxidation-reduction half reactions involving ions in solution can also be set up as single electrodes. If a gas is involved, the electrode can be established by bubbling the gas over an inert metallic conductor. This will conduct the electrons but will not react itself. For example, the half reaction

$$H_2 \rightleftharpoons 2e^- + 2H^+$$

can be arranged as the hydrogen electrode, $H_2 | H^+$, indicated in Figure 76. A piece of platinum foil is covered with very finely divided platinum, immersed in water, and hydrogen gas is bubbled over it. The hydrogen tends to ionize at the surface of the platinum, which takes up the electrons. The hydrogen ions accumulate in the solution. The

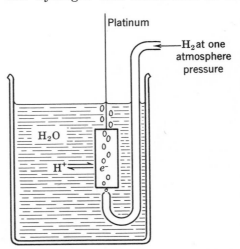

Fig. 76.   The hydrogen $|$ **H$^+$ single electrode.**

change is reversible, and equilibrium is established rapidly. An electrode potential characteristic of the tendency for hydrogen to be oxidized is developed.

The magnitude of the electrode potential built up by a given half reaction varies with the concentration of the reactants. According to the Principle of Le Châtelier, if we add zinc ions to the zinc electrode, the equilibrium will be forced to the left, and the electrode potential will decrease. Since zinc is a solid, its concentration is fixed. In the hydrogen and other gas electrodes, the potential will increase slightly with increase in the partial pressure of the gas but will decrease if the concentration of the ions in solution is increased. Electrode potentials should be compared when they are set up under comparable conditions of concentration. *Standard electrode potentials* are measured when the solutions are 1M with respect to the active ions in solution and when the pressure of any gas involved is 1 atm.

There is no way to measure the difference in potential of a single electrode by itself. We must combine two electrodes to give a cell whose voltage we can measure. Figure 77 shows a zinc electrode combined with a hydrogen electrode to produce such a cell. The two electrodes are connected by a glass tube filled with a solution of an electrolyte such as KCl. This solution *salt bridge* establishes an electrical connection between the two electrodes. The electrolyte used in the bridge is so chosen that its ions will not react. When the zinc and hydrogen electrodes are connected externally by a copper wire through a voltmeter,

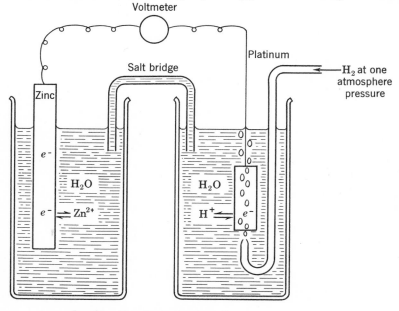

Fig. 77. The zinc-hydrogen cell.

the net difference in potential for the cell can be measured in volts.   The cell composed of a standard zinc electrode and a standard hydrogen electrode gives 0.762 volt.   This cell voltage is equal to the algebraic difference between the two single electrode potentials.   We cannot break this cell voltage down into the absolute values for each single electrode potential because there is no way to determine either.   But suppose that we arbitrarily assign the value zero to the potential for the standard hydrogen electrode.   Then, compared with it, the zinc electrode potential is 0.762 volt.

$$\text{Voltage of standard} \atop \text{zinc-hydrogen cell} = \text{voltage of standard zinc electrode} \atop -\text{ voltage of standard hydrogen electrode}$$

$$0.762 \text{ volt} = \text{voltage of standard zinc electrode} - 0$$

$$\text{Voltage of standard} \atop \text{zinc electrode} = 0.762 \text{ volt}$$

Other oxidation-reduction half reactions can in turn be set up in cells as standard single electrodes opposed to the standard hydrogen electrode. The voltage developed by the cell in each case will be the relative standard electrode potential for the half reaction employed.   For example, a standard chlorine electrode can be arranged by bubbling chlorine at a pressure of 1 atm over an inert conductor, such as graphite immersed in a $1M$ solution of Cl^-.   This involves the half reaction $Cl_2 + 2e^- \rightleftharpoons 2Cl^-$. When this standard chlorine electrode is combined with the standard hydrogen electrode, the cell voltage is 1.358.   Since the chloride ion is found to have less of a tendency to liberate electrons than H_2, the standard chlorine electrode is assigned the negative value -1.358 volts compared to the standard hydrogen electrode as 0.

220.   STANDARD OXIDATION-REDUCTION POTENTIALS

Since the magnitude of each standard electrode potential is a measure of the tendency for a given oxidation-reduction half reaction to proceed to the right, these potentials are also referred to as *standard oxidation-reduction potentials*.   In the last column in Table 33 the standard oxidation-reduction potentials are listed for each half reaction.   The more positive the value listed, the greater is the tendency for the half reaction to proceed to the right, releasing electrons.   Half reactions that have less tendency to proceed to the right than the hydrogen half reaction are assigned negative values.   A more complete list of standard oxidation-reduction potentials is given in Appendix IV.

221.   THE DRIVING FORCE IN OXIDATION-REDUCTION REACTIONS

As in any reversible reaction, equilibrium will tend to be established in oxidation-reduction reactions.   However, when the standard potentials of the two half reactions differ to any extent, the equilibrium will be far to the right, and the oxidation-reduction will proceed very nearly to completion. The driving force in such reactions is the tendency for electron transfer to occur in such a fashion that the system as a whole goes to a lower energy state and becomes more stable.

Tables of oxidation-reduction half reactions and their standard potentials can be used very effectively to predict whether a given reducing agent will react with a particular oxidizing agent. Any reducing agent (to the left in Table 33) will react with any oxidizing agent (to the right in Table 33) if the latter is below it in the table, but not if the latter is above it. Lead will reduce silver ions

$$\text{Pb} + 2\text{Ag}^+ = \text{Pb}^{2+} + 2\text{Ag}$$

Copper reduces chlorine

$$\text{Cu} + \text{Cl}_2 = \text{Cu}^{2+} + 2\text{Cl}^-$$

But copper will not reduce zinc ion

$$\text{Cu} + \text{Zn}^{2+} = \text{no reaction}$$

Chloride ion will not reduce iodine

$$2\text{Cl}^- + \text{I}_2 = \text{no reaction}$$

If we wish to select an oxidizing agent that will oxidize a given reducing agent, a table of half reactions and their oxidation-reduction potentials will provide a list of candidates from which we may choose the one that will be most suitable.

It is very important to remember that the order given in Table 33 is that obtained when the half reactions involve standard $1M$ solutions. The tendency for the half reactions to proceed to the right will be affected by changes in the concentration of the solutions; by lowering the concentration of the oxidizing agent formed, we increase the effective strength of a reducing agent. If we use concentrations other than $1M$, we may find the order somewhat changed from that given in Table 33.

222. GALVANIC CELLS

The zinc-hydrogen and hydrogen-chlorine cells already described are examples of *galvanic cells*. In these cells, an oxidation-reduction reaction is carried out in such a fashion that chemical energy is converted to electrical energy. The two half reactions are set up so that electrons are not transferred directly from the reducing agent to the oxidizing agent. These are not allowed to come in contact, but the electron transfer takes place through an external metallic circuit. The flow of electrons through the external circuit constitutes an electric current and makes available the energy of the exothermic oxidation-reduction reaction.

The Daniell gravity cell has been much used.   This is a combination of the Zn | Zn²⁺ and the Cu | Cu²⁺ electrodes, as shown in Figure 78.

Crystals of $CuSO_4 \cdot 5H_2O$ and a copper grid are placed in the bottom of the cell and it is half filled with a saturated solution of $CuSO_4$.   A zinc grid is supported at the top of the cell and a dilute solution of $ZnSO_4$ is carefully added, so that it does not mix with the solution of $CuSO_4$. The crystals of copper sulfate keep the solution at the bottom saturated, and gravity prevents this dense solution from mixing with the solution of zinc sulfate.   The copper ions do not come in contact with the zinc grid.

When the two electrodes are connected externally by copper wire, electrons flow from the zinc, a region of high electron density, to the copper, a region of low electron density.   Continuous removal of elec-

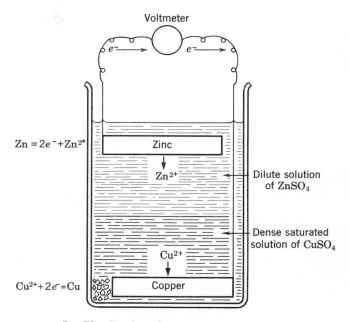

Fig. 78.   The Daniell gravity galvanic cell.

trons from the zinc favors continuous oxidation of the zinc, and the grid corrodes, zinc ions accumulating in the solution and migrating toward the copper grid.   Addition of electrons to the copper grid favors the continued discharge of copper ions and copper plates out on the grid.

The net oxidation-reduction action for the Daniell cell is the sum of the two half reactions.

$$Zn = 2e^- + Zn^{2+} \quad \text{(oxidation half reaction)}$$
$$\underline{Cu^{2+} + 2e^- = Cu} \quad \text{(reduction half reaction)}$$
$$Zn + Cu^{2+} = Zn^{2+} + Cu \quad \text{(net oxidation-reduction reaction)}$$

The voltage developed by such a galvanic cell is equal to the algebraic difference of the two electrode potentials. If the concentrations of Zn^{2+} and Cu^{2+} in contact with the grids is $1M$, the Daniell cell voltage should be equal to $0.762 - (-0.345) = 1.107$ volts. But if the concentrations of the ions are not $1M$, the voltage developed should be some other value. The higher the concentration of Cu^{2+}, the more negative will be the single potential of the copper electrode; by keeping the concentration of Zn^{2+} low, the potential of the zinc electrode can be raised. In this fashion the voltage developed by the cell may be increased.

Any combination of an oxidation half reaction with a reduction half reaction can be used to build a galvanic cell, provided that it is possible to arrange the half reactions as electrodes. Unfortunately, very few of these combinations have been found to be practical for economical and convenient operation. *Dry cells* are built by using moist pastes rather than solutions, as described later in Chapter 31. The construction and operation of the common lead storage cell is discussed in Chapter 35. The Edison storage cell is summarized in Chapter 32. *Electric batteries* are manufactured by combining a number of cells, so that the combined voltage or amperage developed can be made as large as desired.

EXERCISES

1. Write equations for the following half reactions: a) the oxidation of Ca; b) the reduction of Br_2; c) the reduction of Al^{3+}; d) the oxidation of S^{2-}.

2. By combining two of the above half reactions, derive an oxidation-reduction reaction such that: a) aluminum will be produced; b) bromide ion will be formed.

3. In the oxidation-reduction equations written for Exercise 2, which are the oxidizing agents and which are the reducing agents? What changes in oxidation states are involved?

4. Break down each of the following oxidation-reduction reactions into the two contributing half reactions:
a) $2Mg + O_2 = 2MgO$
b) $2K + Cl_2 = 2KCl$
c) $Ba + Br_2 = BaBr_2$
d) $2Al + 3F_2 = 2AlF_3$

5. You have pieces of tin and copper and solutions of Sn^{2+} and Cu^{2+} available. Outline a laboratory experiment which would allow you to decide the relative strengths of tin and copper as reducing agents. Write equations for the oxidation and reduction half reactions which would occur in your experiment.

6. How would you go about setting up the oxidation-reduction half reaction

$$Fe \rightleftharpoons 2e^- + Fe^{2+}$$

as a standard single electrode in the laboratory?

7. Making use of Table 33, predict whether or not oxidation-reduction takes place when the following are mixed, writing equations when reactions occur: a) $Fe + Ag^+$; b) $Ag + Cu^{2+}$; c) $Pb + I_2$; d) $H^+ + Fe$.

8. Which has the greater tendency to release electrons when placed in contact with water: a) Cu or Pb? b) I_2 or F^-? c) Cl^- or Fe?

9. a) Devise three different galvanic cells by combination of half reactions given in Table 33.

b) Write the net equation for each of the cells.

c) What changes in oxidation states are involved in the operation of each cell?

d) Calculate the voltage that should be developed by each cell, assuming standard electrodes are used.

10. Which $Pb \mid Pb^{2+}$ electrode will have the higher potential, one in which the Pb^{2+} concentration is $0.1M$ or one where it is $0.5M$?

11. Which of the following Daniell cells will deliver the higher voltage:

a) One in which Zn^{2+} is $0.1M$ and Cu^{2+} is $2M$ or one in which Zn^{2+} is $0.1M$ and Cu^{2+} is $1M$?

b) One in which Zn^{2+} is $0.1M$ and Cu^{2+} is $2M$ or one in which Zn^{2+} is $0.5M$ and Cu^{2+} is $2M$?

Chapter 19

▶ Electrolysis

223. THE GENERAL MECHANISM OF ELECTROLYSIS

The theory of electrolytic dissociation can be used very successfully to account for the facts of electrolysis. We shall discuss first the nature of electrolysis in general and then consider a number of examples that will illustrate the various factors that are important.

The general parts and operation of an electrolytic cell were discussed in Section 192. Suppose that we set up the electrolytic cell diagramed in Figure 79. The battery or generator pumps electrons away from the electrode on the left, and it, as a whole, becomes deficient in electrons and positively charged. We call such a positive electrode in an electrolytic cell the *anode*. Electrons are forced toward the other electrode, the *cathode*, which as a whole then has an excess of electrons and is negatively charged, relative to the anode. If a fused ionic substance or a solution of an electrolyte is placed in the cell, there will be present positive and negative ions that are able to move relatively independently. *The dissociation of the electrolyte takes place when the ionic substance is fused or when the electrolyte goes into solution in a dissociating solvent.* Weak electrolytes involved in the chemical changes will continue to dissociate as electrolysis proceeds.

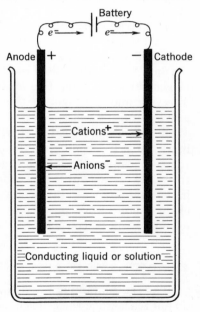

Fig. 79.   An electrolytic cell.

When the current is turned on and the electrodes become charged, they attract the ions of opposite charge, and these ions start to migrate. The positive ions move toward the cathode and are called *cations*. The negative ions move toward the anode and are called *anions*. The rate at which a given ion migrates will depend upon the nature of the particular ion and other factors. By studying the migration of ions, chemists have been able to gain considerable information about the probable composition and structure of ions. It must be remembered that besides the directed migration toward the electrode of opposite charge, ions also undergo random diffusion owing to their kinetic energy. The net effect of both kinds of movement will be a net migration toward the electrode of opposite charge.

In the operation of the cell, chemical changes are observed to take place at each electrode. These electrode reactions always involve the transfer of electrons. Electrons enter the solution at the cathode and leave the solution at the anode. Since electrons are being pumped away from the anode, the changes that are favored there will be those which provide electrons readily. *An oxidation half reaction will occur at the anode.* The cathode has an excess of electrons, and this will favor changes that use up electrons. *A reduction half reaction will occur at the cathode.* If there are several half reactions possible at a given electrode, the changes will be favored that will produce electrons most easily at the anode and use up electrons most easily at the cathode. The operation of an electrolytic cell involves a combination of an oxidation half reaction and a reduction half reaction, and, in the cell as a whole, oxidation-reduction occurs. The net reaction for the cell is equal to the sum of the anode and cathode half reactions. By pumping electrons, the battery or generator is forcing this oxidation-reduction to proceed in the desired direction and is providing the necessary energy. The net reaction for any electrolytic cell is endothermic, the system gaining chemical energy at the expense of electrical energy. The actual changes which take place in a given cell depend upon the nature of the conducting electrolytic bath, the composition of the electrodes, and the conditions under which electrolysis is carried out. The concentration of the cell solution is important in determining what the reactions at the electrodes will be because of the change in electrode potential with concentration. A number of typical examples will be considered.

224. ELECTROLYSIS OF FUSED NaCl, USING INERT ELECTRODES

The cell containing fused NaCl and electrodes made of materials that do not react when the cell is in operation is as simple as any we can select. The only units in the bath which can react are Na^+ and Cl^-. The cell is set up with graphite electrodes and is heated so that there is liquid sodium chloride between the electrodes. When the sodium chloride melts, the Na^+ and Cl^- dissociate and become free to move. The chloride anions migrate toward the anode and there react, according to the equation

$$2Cl^- = 2e^- + Cl_{2(g)}$$

The chlorine molecules collect as chlorine gas, which can be stored and marketed. This *anode half reaction*, like all anode reactions, involves oxidation. No other chemical change is possible at the anode in this cell. The sodium cations migrate toward the cathode and there react, according to the reduction half reaction

$$Na^+ + e^- = Na_{(l)}$$

The sodium metal collects as a liquid at the temperature prevailing (about 600° in industrial practice where some Na_2CO_3 is added to lower the melting point of NaCl). The *net reaction for the cell* is

$$2Na^+ + 2Cl^- = 2Na_{(l)} + Cl_{2(g)}$$

225. ELECTROLYSIS OF AQUEOUS NaCl, USING INERT ELECTRODES

This system is more complicated than the preceding one because water molecules have been added, and we must consider the possibility of the water reacting at the electrodes. When solid sodium chloride dissolves in water, its ions dissociate and become relatively independent,

$$NaCl_{(s)} = Na^+ + Cl^-$$

There are then present in the aqueous solution Na^+, Cl^-, and water molecules, the latter only slightly dissociated. The concentrations of H^+ and OH^- are very small compared to the concentrations of the other units in the solution, and therefore we will assume that they do not contribute appreciably to the net reaction for the cell. When the circuit is closed, the sodium ions start migrating to the cathode, and the chloride ions migrate to the anode. If the difference in potential between the two electrodes is sufficiently high and the solution is fairly concentrated, hydrogen is produced at the cathode and chlorine is formed at the anode. In order to account for these products, we must consider all the possible anode and cathode net half reactions for the cell and see which ones take place more readily.

Possible anode oxidation half reactions

$$2Cl^- = 2e^- + Cl_2$$
$$2H_2O = 4e^- + O_2 + 4H^+$$

Electrons are furnished more easily by the first reaction when the $[Cl^-]$ is high, and it should predominate when only moderate amounts of current flow. If the flow of current through the cell is very great, and if the chloride-ion concentration is small, the second half reaction may also take place to some extent, and some oxygen may be mixed with the chlorine formed at the anode. With very dilute solutions practically no chlorine is obtained.

Possible cathode reduction half reactions

$$Na^+ + e^- = Na$$
$$2H_2O + 2e^- = H_2 + 2OH^-$$

Reduction of the water molecules takes place much more readily than the reduction of sodium ion, the second cathode reaction occurs, and hydrogen gas bubbles off at the cathode. The hydroxide ions which form in the neighborhood of the cathode begin to migrate toward the anode. They are not discharged and tend to accumulate in solution. The sodium ions also remain in solution. When the solution is evaporated, NaOH crystallizes out.

It should be pointed out that the anode and cathode equations, describing the half reactions above, are *net equations*. They indicate which of the units present in the cell at the start are used up and what the final products are. They do not necessarily indicate the actual mechanism of the changes at the electrodes; these are not very well understood. It used to be commonly stated that in this cell the sodium ions were discharged at the cathode to form sodium metal, and that this metal then reacted with water to form hydrogen and sodium hydroxide. It seems very unlikely that this is so to any appreciable extent. Water molecules should be reduced much more easily than sodium ions. It is possible that the reaction of water molecules at the electrodes may first involve the dissociation of the water and then the reaction of the H^+ or OH^- at the electrodes. But the net effects would still be those indicated by the net half reactions.

The *net reaction for the cell* will be the sum of the two net half reactions.

$$2H_2O + 2Cl^- = Cl_2 + H_2 + 2OH^-$$

Three valuable products, chlorine, hydrogen, and sodium hydroxide, are produced when an aqueous solution of NaCl is electrolyzed, and this process is a basic one in chemical industry. The over-all or stoichiometric equation for the whole process, going back to the starting materials, is

$$2NaCl + 2H_2O = Cl_2 + H_2 + 2NaOH$$

226. ELECTROLYSIS OF AQUEOUS HCl, USING INERT ELECTRODES

When HCl is dissolved in water it dissociates very strongly.

$$HCl = H^+ + Cl^-$$

Water molecules, H^+, and Cl^- are present in high concentrations in this electrolytic bath. When the cell is in operation, the hydrogen ions migrate to the cathode, and the chloride ions migrate toward the anode. If a moderate amount of current is flowing and there is a sufficiently high concentration of chloride ion, chlorine is observed to form at the anode and hydrogen is liberated at the cathode.

Possible anode half reactions

$$2Cl^- = 2e^- + Cl_2$$
$$2H_2O = 4e^- + O_2 + 4H^+$$

The anode situation is exactly like that described for the electrolysis of aqueous NaCl, and the formation of chlorine takes place.

Possible cathode half reactions

$$2H^+ + 2e^- = H_2$$
$$2H_2O + 2e^- = H_2 + 2OH^-$$

Hydrogen ions are more easily reduced than water molecules, and, as long as plenty of hydrogen ions are available at the cathode, it is reasonable to assume that the first half reaction takes place.

The *net reaction for the cell* is

$$2H^+ + 2Cl^- = H_2 + Cl_2$$

The supply of acid in the cell is depleted during its operation.

227. ELECTROLYSIS OF AQUEOUS H_2SO_4, USING INERT ELECTRODES

In dilute solution, sulfuric acid is strongly dissociated according to the net equation

$$H_2SO_4 = 2H^+ + SO_4{}^{2-}$$

When this cell is in normal operation, oxygen is formed at the anode and hydrogen is liberated at the cathode.

Possible anode half reactions.

$$2SO_4{}^{2-} = 2e^- + S_2O_8{}^{2-}$$
$$2H_2O = 4e^- + O_2 + 4H^+$$

The second reaction proceeds, because in dilute solution water is oxidized more easily than the sulfate ion. The hydrogen ions formed around the anode join those from the sulfuric acid in migrating toward the cathode.

Possible cathode half reactions

$$2H^+ + 2e^- = H_2$$
$$2H_2O + 2e^- = H_2 + 2OH^-$$

The cathode possibilities are like those discussed for **hydrochloric acid**, and the first reaction is favored.

The *net reaction for the cell* is

$$2H_2O = 2H_2 + O_2$$

Although many of the hydrogen ions discharged at the cathode may have originally come from the sulfuric acid, in the normal operation of the cell, water is used up and hydrogen and oxygen are formed. The hydrogen-ion and sulfate-ion concentrations in the bath increase as the water is used up. Their migration in solution is responsible for the electrical conduction of the bath. The sulfate ion tends to pile up about the anode when the cell is run. The operation of the apparatus used for making oxygen and hydrogen by the electrolysis of water is thus accounted for.

228. ELECTROLYSIS OF AQUEOUS Na_2SO_4, USING INERT ELECTRODES

Sodium sulfate is a strong electrolyte and dissociates practically completely in water.

$$Na_2SO_{4(s)} = 2Na^+ + SO_4^{2-}$$

Its aqueous solution has Na^+, SO_4^{2-}, and water molecules present in considerable concentrations. When a dilute solution is electrolyzed with inert electrodes and with a moderate amount of current flowing, oxygen is formed at the anode and hydrogen is liberated at the cathode.

Possible anode half reactions

$$2SO_4^{2-} = 2e^- + S_2O_8^{2-}$$
$$2H_2O = 4e^- + O_2 + 4H^+$$

The second takes place more readily.

Possible cathode half reactions

$$Na^+ + e^- = Na$$
$$2H_2O + 2e^- = H_2 + 2OH^-$$

The second of these takes place.

The *net reaction for the cell* is

$$2H_2O = 2H_2 + O_2$$

This is the same as for the sulfuric acid cell, the function of the Na^+ and SO_4^{2-} ions being merely to conduct the current through the solution. Since H^+ is produced at the anode, its concentration about the anode will exceed that of OH^-, and the solution around that electrode will become somethat acid. Likewise, the OH^- produced by the net reaction at the cathode will be responsible for the solution around that electrode becoming basic.

We can, therefore, substitute sodium sulfate for sulfuric acid in cells where we wish to electrolyze water to produce oxygen and hydrogen. It would not do to substitute NaCl.

229. PARTICIPATION OF ELECTRODES IN ELECTROLYSIS

In the examples of electrolysis that we have discussed so far, we have specified that the electrodes be of conducting material which will not undergo reaction. Graphite or very inactive metals such as platinum are used commonly for such inert electrodes. If we construct the electrodes of materials that may undergo oxidation or reduction under the conditions prevailing in the cell, then we must also consider their possible half reactions at the electrodes. For instance, if we electrolyze aqueous sulfuric acid using copper electrodes, the copper may be involved in the electrode reactions.

Possible anode half reactions

$$2SO_4{}^{2-} = 2e^- + S_2O_8{}^{2-}$$
$$2H_2O = 4e^- + O_2 + 4H^+$$
$$Cu = 2e^- + Cu^{2+}$$

The oxidation of copper takes place most readily, and the copper anode is corroded and used up. Cupric ions accumulate in solution and migrate toward the cathode, where they may react.

Possible cathode half reactions

$$2H^+ + 2e^- = H_2$$
$$2H_2O + 2e^- = H_2 + 2OH^-$$
$$Cu^{2+} + 2e^- = Cu$$

The reduction of cupric ions occurs, and copper plates out on the cathode. This makes possible the purification of copper by electrorefining, as will be described in Chapter 33.

In case the cathode is constructed so that it has present something like Cl_2 which can be reduced easily, this half reaction will be in competition with the other possible reduction half reactions at the cathode.

230. THE NATURE OF ELECTROLYTIC CONDUCTION

Having considered the operation of several kinds of electrolytic cells, we are now in a good position to summarize the general mechanism of electrolytic conduction. At the anode an oxidation half reaction occurs that provides electrons to be pumped through the external metallic circuit, and the solution either loses electrons from its ions or molecules or gains positive ions from the anode. The electrons pumped onto the cathode are used up by combination with ions or molecules in the solution, or by forming negative ions of the cathode material. Electric charges traverse the solution because of the net ordered migration of all of the anions and cations that are present. Thus, there is an effective transfer of electric current through the cell. Free electrons do not traverse the solution.

231. FARADAY'S LAW OF ELECTROLYSIS

It is important to be able to relate the *amounts of material undergoing chemical change* at each electrode with the *amount of electricity* passing through an electrolytic cell. Faraday studied this relationship quantitatively and in 1833 was able to summarize it: *The amount of material undergoing chemical change at an electrode is proportional to the quantity of electricity flowing through the cell and to the gram-equivalent weight of the substance.*

Having considered electrode reactions in detail and being familiar with the electron transfers which are involved, we can see how Faraday's Law arises. Table 34 lists several electrode half reactions together with the electron transfers which occur.

Table 34. Electron Transfers in Electrode Half Reactions

Half Reactions	Electrons Transferred		
	Per Atom	Per Gram Atom (6.02×10^{23} Atoms)	Per Equivalent Weight
$2Cl^- = 2e^- + Cl_2$	1	6.02×10^{23}	6.02×10^{23}
$2H^+ + 2e^- = H_2$	1	6.02×10^{23}	6.02×10^{23}
$Cu^{2+} + 2e^- = Cu$	2	$2 \times 6.02 \times 10^{23}$	6.02×10^{23}
$2H_2O = 4e^- + O_2 + 4H^+$	1 (for H)	6.02×10^{23}	6.02×10^{23}
	2 (for O)	$2 \times 6.02 \times 10^{23}$	6.02×10^{23}

For each gram-equivalent weight of material undergoing change at each electrode, 6.02×10^{23} electrons must flow through the circuit. The term *faraday* is used to refer to that quantity of electricity which will cause a gram equivalent of change at each electrode.

> 1 faraday = 6.02×10^{23} electrons
>
> 1 coulomb = amount of electricity flowing when a current of 1 amp is maintained for 1 sec
>
> 1 faraday = 96,500 coulombs

It is possible to calculate how much matter will undergo change at an electrode when a given quantity of electricity flows, or how much electricity must flow to produce a given amount of change.

EXAMPLE: How much electricity must traverse a cell for the production of 46 g of sodium, when fused sodium chloride is electrolyzed?

$$\frac{\text{Number of gram-equivalent}}{\text{weights of sodium desired}} = \frac{46 \text{ g}}{23 \text{ g}} = 2$$

One faraday of electricity is needed to produce 1 gram-equivalent weight. Therefore,

2 faradays will be needed to produce 46 g of sodium

2 faradays $= 2 \times 6.02 \times 10^{23}$ electrons, which must be transferred from the cathode to Na^+ to produce 46 g of sodium

2 faradays $= 2 \times 96{,}500$ coulombs of electricity, needed to produce 46 g of sodium

When 2 amp of current is maintained through the cell for 96,500 sec, 46 g of sodium will be formed; or if 200 amp of current is maintained for 965 sec, 46 g of sodium will be formed.

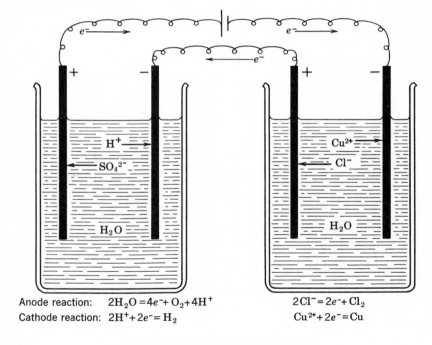

Anode reaction: $2H_2O = 4e^- + O_2 + 4H^+$ $2Cl^- = 2e^- + Cl_2$
Cathode reaction: $2H^+ + 2e^- = H_2$ $Cu^{2+} + 2e^- = Cu$

Fig. 80.   Electrolysis in cells in series.

If two or more cells are connected in series and electrolysis is carried out, the same quantity of electron transfer must take place in all of the cells, and the number of gram-equivalent weights of material undergoing oxidation or reduction must be the same.

EXAMPLE: Suppose the two cells shown in Figure 80 are operated in series. The first contains an aqueous dilute solution of H_2SO_4, the second a rather concentrated solution of $CuCl_2$, and both have inert electrodes. The equations are those for the half reactions favored at each electrode.

If 8 faradays of electricity is used in the circuit, how many grams of oxygen, hydrogen, chlorine, and copper will be produced?

8 faradays will produce 8 × the gram-equivalent weight of each product

$$\frac{\text{The gram-equivalent weight}}{\text{of each product}} = \frac{\text{gram-formula weight}}{\text{number of electrons transferred}}$$
$$\text{per formula}$$

Therefore, when 8 faradays of electricity is used

$$\text{The weight of oxygen produced} \quad = 8 \times \frac{32.00 \text{ g}}{4} = 64.00 \text{ g}$$

$$\text{The weight of hydrogen produced} = 8 \times \frac{2.016 \text{ g}}{2} = 8.064 \text{ g}$$

$$\text{The weight of copper produced} \quad = 8 \times \frac{63.54 \text{ g}}{2} = 254.2 \text{ g}$$

$$\text{The weight of chlorine produced} \quad = 8 \times \frac{70.92 \text{ g}}{2} = 283.7 \text{ g}$$

It is clear that Faraday's Law will also hold for the operation of galvanic cells. The number of faradays, or coulombs, or electrons, that will flow through the external circuit when a given amount of material reacts at an electrode in a galvanic cell can easily be calculated from the equation for the half reaction taking place at the electrode.

EXERCISES

1. Draw a labeled sketch showing the essential parts of an electrolytic cell, indicating the direction of flow of electrons in the external circuit. Explain how the contents of the cell enters into the electrical conduction of the circuit.

2. How is the oxidation-reduction involved in the operation of an electrolytic cell?

3. a) List all the kinds of particles that are present in considerable concentration in a dilute aqueous solution of NaCl.
   b) What happens to each of the particles when this solution is electrolyzed, using inert electrodes?

4. Account for the fact that when we electrolyze a dilute aqueous solution of Na_2SO_4 with litmus present, the solution does not have the same color around the anode as it does around the cathode.

5. How does the electrolysis of a dilute solution of sulfuric acid using a copper anode compare with that when a platinum anode is employed?

6. a) In the electrolysis of dilute sulfuric acid between inert electrodes, how many faradays of electricity will be needed to produce 10 moles of oxygen gas?
   b) How many moles of hydrogen will be produced at the same time?
   c) How long would it be necessary to run the cell to accomplish this if a current of 2 amp is maintained through the cell?

7. How many electrons must flow through the wires connecting the electrodes of an electrolytic cell to a generator in order to produce 0.355 g of chlorine by the electrolysis of fused sodium chloride?

8. a) Assuming that the electrolysis of fused KCl with inert electrodes is analogous to that of fused NaCl, write equations for the reactions that will occur at the electrodes when fused KCl is electrolyzed.

b) What is the net equation for the cell?

c) How many faradays of electricity would be needed to electrolyze 1 ton of KCl?

d) How many gram moles of each of the products will be formed?

9. a) Account for the fact that if we wish to decompose water by electrolysis to produce hydrogen and oxygen, we must add a solute, such as H_2SO_4 or Na_2SO_4.

b) Why is NaCl not so satisfactory for this purpose?

c) Why does NaCl become less satisfactory as its concentration increases?

10. Suppose that a rather concentrated aqueous solution of an equimolar mixture of NaCl and NaI is electrolyzed. Making use of Table 33, predict what the reaction at the anode will be.

11. a) Calculate what will be the loss in weight of the zinc grid in a Daniell cell when the cell is used for 1 hr to maintain a current of 0.1 amp through a circuit.

b) What change in weight will occur to the copper grid?

Chapter 20

▶ The Halogens

232. THE HALOGEN FAMILY

We have covered enough of the fundamental physical and chemical principles so that we are now in position to discuss the behavior of the more common and important elements in detail. We shall take up these elements by groups or subgroups, developing and exploiting the group relationships of the periodic table.

The elements known as the *halogens* (salt formers) have already been mentioned several times. The halogens are the nonmetallic elements occurring just before the inert gases at the ends of the periods. Table 35, listing the halogens in order of increasing atomic numbers, shows the distribution of the electrons in the shells and summarizes their properties. Astatine, element 85, is not included, since it is so rare.

Table 35. The Halogens

	Fluorine	Chlorine	Bromine	Iodine
Symbol	F	Cl	Br	I
Atomic number	9	17	35	53
Atomic weight	19.00	35.457	79.916	126.92
Electronic structure	2, 7	2, 8, 7	2, 8, 18, 7	2, 8, 18, 18, 7
Radius of X⁻, Å	1.36	1.81	1.95	2.16
Covalent bond radius, Å	0.64	0.99	1.14	1.33
Molecular formula	F_2	Cl_2	Br_2	I_2
Molecular weight	38.00	70.914	159.83	253.84
Standard state	Gas	Gas	Liquid	Solid
Melting point, ° C	−223	−101.6	−7.2	113.5
Boiling point, ° C	−187	−34.6	58.78	184.35
Relative density as gas (air = 1)	1.31	2.49	5.53	8.75
Color	Pale yellow	Greenish yellow	Reddish brown	(s) Black (g) Violet
Relative sizes of atoms, comparable conditions	Increasing →			
Electronegativity	Decreasing →			
Strength as oxidizing agent	Decreasing →			

The halogens illustrate very well what we may expect of a family of elements. With increasing atomic number, the number of shells of electrons increases. All of the halogen atoms have seven valence electrons, one short of the inert-gas structures. We may therefore expect that their properties, especially the way in which they form chemical bonds, will be quite similar. On the other hand, with increasing atomic number the properties should vary in a regular fashion. The increase in the number of the shells of electrons is accompanied by an increase in the relative sizes of the atoms under comparable conditions. Table 35 lists the crystal radii of the halide ions, X^- (X is commonly used to stand for any halogen atom), and you will note the great increase in size. The single covalent bond radius given in the table indicates the effective contribution of each halogen to the distance between the centers of two atoms that share a pair of electrons. Here again, the effect on the size of the atoms of increasing the number of shells of electrons is apparent. With increasing size, the electronegativity and strength as an oxidizing agent decrease. The other properties also vary in a regular fashion. If we know the trends of the variations of properties with increasing atomic number, and if we also know the characteristic behavior of the most common element of the group, chlorine, we can estimate what the characteristics of the other halogens will be.

233. OXIDATION STATES

The oxidation states for fluorine are **−1** and **0**. The rest of the halogens are known to have the oxidation states of **−1, 0, +1, +3, +5,** and **+7,** except that bromine apparently does not attain the **+7** state. These reflect the number of valence electrons that each element has and the ways in which the atoms can use these electrons to form chemical

Table 36.   Oxidation States of Chlorine

Oxidation State	Typical Molecules and Ions for Chlorine
−1	HCl, Cl^-
0	Cl_2
+1	HClO, ClO^-
+3	$HClO_2$, ClO_2^-
+4	ClO_2
+5	$HClO_3$, ClO_3^-
+7	$HClO_4$, ClO_4^-

bonds. Fluorine is unique in this respect. Because it has the highest electronegativity of all the elements, when it forms chemical bonds, it always is more associated with the electrons involved than the atom to which it is bonded. It therefore can show no positive oxidation states.

The large number of oxidation states that the rest of the halogens can assume makes possible the formation of many different series of compounds. The behavior of chlorine is typical of all the halogens except fluorine. The molecules or ions that are most characteristic of the different oxidation states of chlorine are listed in Table 36, the most common oxidation state being indicated by heavy italic type. Chlorine achieves the negative oxidation state of 1 when it is combined with less electronegative elements; that is true for all its compounds except those it forms with fluorine or oxygen. Chlorine realizes positive oxidation states only when it is combined with fluorine or oxygen.

234. OCCURRENCE

Chlorine is the most abundant of the halogens. Fluorine, bromine, and iodine are less common but are reasonably available. Element 85, astatine, has not been found in nature. Apparently the nuclei of possible isotopes of this element are very unstable and undergo rapid radioactive change (see Chapter 36), so that they cannot persist in any appreciable quantity. They have been obtained in very small amounts in the laboratory and have been identified, but it is unlikely that we shall ever have this element available on the ordinary scale.

Table 37.   Occurrences of the Halogens

Fluorine CaF_2, the mineral fluorspar
Na_3AlF_6, cryolite
In enamel of teeth

Chlorine Cl^- in solution in oceans (2.07%) and salt lakes, usually accompanied by Na^+
NaCl in salt beds widely distributed
KCl, $MgCl_2$, $CaCl_2$ also in salt beds
An essential element in the body, especially as HCl in the gastric juice

Bromine   **Br**$^-$ in solution in oceans (0.008%) and in salt brines
NaBr and other bromides in salt beds

Iodine I^- in solution in oceans (0.000004%) and in **salt brines**
NaIO₃ in Chilean sodium nitrate deposits
In the body, combined in the essential hormone thyroxin

Because of the ease with which these elements gain electrons to form negative halide ions having stable inert-gas structures, the halogens almost invariably are found in nature as these ions. The halide ions occur in *sea water* and salt lakes in considerable concentrations, and are present in vast *salt beds* which have been formed by the evaporation of salt water. In these salt beds the ions are in ionic crystals, associated with the cations of the more common active metals.   Table 37 lists the principal occurrences of each of the halogens, heavy type indicating those which are important sources of the element for industry.

235.   PREPARATION OF THE ELEMENTARY HALOGENS

For both the laboratory and industrial preparations of the halogens, the halide ions constitute the best sources.   These ions must be oxidized to the zero oxidation state, the general oxidation half reaction being

$$2X^- \rightleftharpoons 2e^- + X_2$$

The half reactions for the oxidation of the different halide ions, given in order of increasing difficulty, as shown by their standard oxidation-reduction potentials in volts, are

$$
\begin{array}{ll}
2I^- \rightleftharpoons 2e^- + I_2 & -0.535 \\
2Br^- \rightleftharpoons 2e^- + Br_2 & -1.065 \\
2Cl^- = 2e^- + Cl_2 & -1.358 \\
2F^- \rightleftharpoons 2e^- + F_2 & -2.85
\end{array}
$$

It is relatively easy to oxidize the iodide ions to free iodine, but it is very difficult to oxidize the fluoride ion to fluorine.   The strength of the oxidizing effect necessary to oxidize the ions is greatest for F^-, least for I^-.

The *production of fluorine* is very difficult to accomplish.   Because fluorine is the most electronegative element, its affinity for the extra electron in its ion is so strong that no chemical oxidizing agent is powerful enough to oxidize the fluoride ion.   Electrolytic oxidation offers the only means of accomplishing this.   Fused KHF_2 can be electrolyzed in cells constructed of graphite, copper, magnesium, or nickel.   Recently, fluorine gas under pressure in steel tanks has been offered for sale.   Very special precautions must be observed in handling it to prevent serious accidents.

The *preparation of chlorine* is more easily carried out.   The chloride ion may be oxidized, either electrolytically or by very powerful chemical oxidizing agents.   The industrial method of production utilizes the electrolysis of fused chlorides or of aqueous solutions of chlorides (see Sections 224 and 225).   The chlorine gas is liquefied and stored in steel cylinders and tank cars.   Tremendous amounts of chlorine are manufactured for use by chemical industry.   In the laboratory, we use chemical oxidizing agents to obtain chlorine.   Sodium chloride is treated with $3M$ sulfuric acid and manganese dioxide, potassium permanganate, or sodium dichromate to give the following net reactions, in which the changes in oxidation states are indicated:

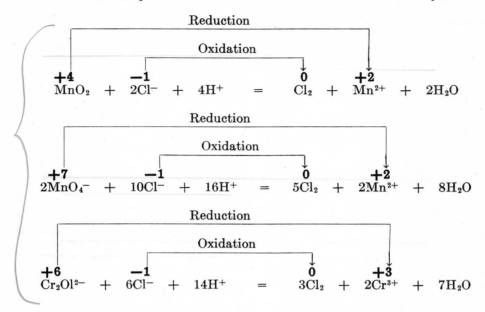

$$\overset{+4}{MnO_2} + 2\overset{-1}{Cl^-} + 4H^+ = \overset{0}{Cl_2} + \overset{+2}{Mn^{2+}} + 2H_2O$$

$$2\overset{+7}{MnO_4^-} + 10\overset{-1}{Cl^-} + 16H^+ = 5\overset{0}{Cl_2} + 2\overset{+2}{Mn^{2+}} + 8H_2O$$

$$\overset{+6}{Cr_2Ol^{2-}} + 6\overset{-1}{Cl^-} + 14H^+ = 3\overset{0}{Cl_2} + 2\overset{+3}{Cr^{3+}} + 7H_2O$$

The choice of the oxidizing agents used in these reactions with chloride ions in acid solution is in line with the position of their half reactions in the list of oxidation half reactions given in Table 33, page 285.

Less powerful oxidizing agents are needed to produce bromine. The methods listed above for chlorine can be used, and, in addition, any other oxidizing agents below bromine in Table 33 can be employed. One very convenient way to oxidize the bromide ion is to use chlorine.

$$2Br^- + Cl_2 = Br_2 + 2Cl^-$$

Bromine is now being extracted from sea water by adding chlorine to it and then recovering the bromine that is liberated.

The iodide ion may be oxidized by a wide variety of oxidizing agents. Chlorine works very effectively, and an iodide solution is even attacked slowly by atmospheric oxygen to give elementary iodine. The iodate ions in sodium iodate are strong oxidizing agents and react with suitable reducing agents, such as sulfurous acid, to give free iodine, when iodate is in excess.

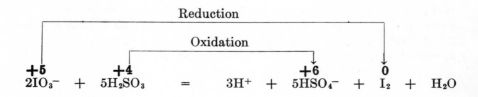

$$2\overset{+5}{IO_3^-} + 5\overset{+4}{H_2SO_3} = 3H^+ + 5\overset{+6}{HSO_4^-} + \overset{0}{I_2} + H_2O$$

236. PROPERTIES

All the halogens form diatomic molecules with one covalent bond linking the two atoms.

$$: \overset{..}{\underset{..}{X}} - \overset{..}{\underset{..}{X}} :$$

The physical properties of these elements vary in a regular fashion with increase in atomic number and atomic weight, as shown in Table 35. The attractive forces between their molecules are small, and they have relatively low melting points and boiling points, these increasing as the molecular weight increases. The color increases in intensity with increase in atomic number.

The chemical activity of the halogens decreases with increase in atomic number, this activity usually being due to the ability of the halogen to act as an oxidizing agent. We may summarize the activity of the halogens toward various classes of other substances.

a. Action toward metals. The halogens tend to oxidize the metals to cations, being reduced to anions in the process. Most metals will burn vigorously in fluorine at somewhat elevated temperatures to form solid *ionic fluorides*, in very exothermic reactions.

$$Mg + F_2 = MgF_{2(s)} + heat$$

Many fluorides of the metals are insoluble in water and are inert materials. Films of these fluorides on the surface of a metal may give protection against continued reaction. Hence, *dry* fluorine can be stored in steel cylinders, and nickel, copper, and magnesium can be used in the construction of cells for the electrolytic production of fluorine.

Chlorine attacks metals rapidly in the presence of moisture to form *chlorides*. Very dry chlorine does not attack steel at room temperature, so steel cylinders can be used for storing the gas. At high temperatures, many metals undergo active combustion in chlorine gas to give ionic salts, which are solids with relatively high melting points and low volatility.

$$Cu + Cl_2 = CuCl_{2(s)}$$
$$Zn + Cl_2 = ZnCl_{2(s)}$$

Bromine and iodine are less active than chlorine toward the metals but tend to form *bromides* and *iodides* under the proper conditions.

b. Action toward hydrogen. All the halogens react with hydrogen under proper conditions to form molecular compounds of the type HX, the *hydrogen halides*.

$$H_2 + X_2 = 2HX$$

The violence of the reaction is greatest for fluorine and least for iodine. In all cases, the hydrogen is oxidized and the halogens are reduced. The tendency for the more active halogens to combine with hydrogen is so great that they may be able to remove it from other compounds. Turpentine bursts into flame when it is dropped into chlorine gas, a black cloud of finely divided carbon is formed, and the fumes of hydrogen chloride can be observed.

$$C_{10}H_{16} + 8Cl_2 = 10C + 16HCl$$

c. Action toward nonmetals. Many of the nonmetallic elements combine directly with the halogens by establishing covalent bonds and forming molecular compounds. Phosphorus combines directly with a limited amount of chlorine to form PCl_3.

$$2P + 3Cl_2 = 2PCl_3$$

If there is an excess of chlorine, PCl_5 may be produced.

$$2P + 5Cl_2 = 2PCl_5$$

These molecular compounds of the nonmetallic elements with the halogens are usually quite volatile compounds, with low melting points.

d. Action toward water. Fluorine reacts strongly with water to give hydrofluoric acid and the evolution of oxygen. Some OF_2 may also be formed.

$$2F_2 + 2H_2O = 4HF + O_2$$
$$2F_2 + H_2O = 2HF + OF_2$$

The other halogens also react to some extent with the water. Thus, *chlorine water*, formed by dissolving chlorine, is acidic, and the solution contains chloride ions and is believed to have molecules of hypochlorous acid present.

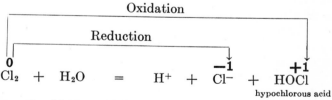

This is a case of oxidation-reduction, in which one of the chlorine atoms in the molecule is reduced to the chloride ion, while the other is oxidized to hypochlorous acid. Such self-oxidation-reduction, where a given substance acts as its own oxidizing and reducing agent, is known as *auto-oxidation-reduction*. This is rather common for systems in which a given element is in an intermediate oxidation state and can be both oxidized and reduced. The very strong bleaching and antiseptic action of chlorine water is believed to be due to the presence of hypochlorous acid.

Bromine and iodine react in an analogous, but much less extensive, fashion with water.

e. Action toward other common materials. Fluorine is so reactive
that it is very difficult to handle. Wood and many other materials burst
into flame when thrust into a stream of the gas. It corrodes glass rapidly
when any traces of moisture are present. Rubber is attacked by fluorine, and explosions may result when it is bubbled into many organic
liquids. Only certain metals such as steel or copper and some new synthetic plastics that have a high percentage of fluorine can be used safely
in contact with fluorine. The other less reactive halogens do not corrode glass appreciably, even in the presence of moisture, but rubber
deteriorates rapidly when in contact with them.

237. PHYSIOLOGICAL ACTION

The halogens have pungent characteristic odors and are dangerous to
breathe. *Fluorine* is especially dangerous, even in small quantities. It
is very corrosive, and the fluoride ion is highly toxic. Very serious burns
result from contact of fluorine with the skin. Children who drink water
containing an excessive amount of fluoride ion are likely later to have
mottled teeth. However, some fluoride ion is necessary for the proper
development of teeth. When water is deficient in fluorine, NaF is sometimes added, or children's teeth may be treated directly with NaF.

Chlorine is very irritating to the mucous lining of the respiratory tract,
and breathing the gas soon produces all the symptoms of a painful bron-
chial cold. Concentrations above 7 parts per 1,000 by volume in air
are sufficient to cause the mucous membranes to inflame and the lungs to
become flooded, so that the death soon occurs. This effect is the reason
why chlorine was introduced in the World War I as a *poison war gas.*

Bromine is very corrosive to the skin, liquid bromine causing exceedingly painful burns which are slow to heal. First-aid treatment is ren-
dered by flushing the bromine off with much water and then applying
glycerin or a solution of sodium thiosulfate. Bromides are much used
in medicine as sedatives.

Iodine has an irritating odor, but it is much safer to handle than the
other halogens. The solutions in alcohol or aqueous potassium iodide
have a strong antiseptic action. Iodine is essential in small amounts in
our diet for the proper functioning of the thyroid gland. This gland
manufactures thyroxin, a complex compound containing iodine, which
plays an important role in regulating the functioning of the body. Defi-
ciency or excess of iodine in the diet leads to the disease called goiter.

238. USES OF THE HALOGENS

Up to the present, fluorine has not been used much, because it is so
difficult to produce and store, and because of the hazards involved in
working with it. There has been much research done with it in the last
decade, and we may expect it to be exploited more in the future.

Chlorine is used in very large amounts in chemical industry for the production of other chemicals. Most of its uses depend upon its powerful oxidizing action. Drinking water is treated with chlorine gas to kill bacteria. Bleaching operations make use of this element.

Bromine is important in the synthesis of many compounds. A large fraction of the total amount of bromine produced is used in the manufacture of tetraethyl lead, employed as an antiknock agent in gasoline. The use of iodine as an antiseptic is well known.

239. COMPOUNDS OF THE HALOGENS IN THE OXIDATION STATE OF —1

The halogens undergo reduction relatively easily to achieve the oxidation state of **—1**. In this state, they may be bonded covalently to somewhat less electronegative atoms to give covalent molecular compounds, such as HCl or CCl_4. Or if they are combined with atoms of very low electronegativity, such as the metals, they are present as halide ions, X^-, the compounds being ionic. The common compounds of the halogens in this oxidation state are the hydrogen halides, HX, composed of hydrogen and the different halogens, and their derivatives, the halide salts. The hydrogen halides, HF, HCl, HBr, and HI, are very corrosive in the presence of water and are too reactive to accumulate in nature. Vast quantities of the chlorides of the common metals are found as minerals, and these chlorides are often accompanied by small amounts of the other halides.

240. FORMATION AND PRODUCTION OF THE HYDROGEN HALIDES

The hydrogen halides are formed in a number of different ways.

a. By direct union of the elements. The combination of hydrogen with the halogens has already been mentioned, the general reaction being

$$H_2 + X_2 = 2HX + heat$$

The tendency for this reaction to go to the right decreases with increasing atomic number and size of the halogen, the H—X bond becoming progressively weaker. When hydrogen is mixed with fluorine, a violent explosion occurs, and hydrogen fluoride is formed, even at low temperatures in the dark. The reaction is highly exothermic and dangerous.

$$H_{2(g)} + F_{2(g)} = 2HF_{(g)} + 128,000 \text{ cal}$$

No reaction occurs when hydrogen is mixed with chlorine at room temperature in the absence of sunlight. But when this mixture is activated by heating or by the ultraviolet radiation present in sunlight, it explodes, producing hydrogen chloride.

$$H_{2(g)} + Cl_{2(g)} = 2HCl_{(g)} + 44,000 \text{ cal}$$

The large quantities of hydrogen and chlorine produced as by-products in industrial electrolytic operations are frequently burned to produce hydrochloric acid.

Hydrogen will unite with bromine and with iodine only when heated in the presence of a catalyst, such as finely divided platinum.

$$H_{2(g)} + Br_{2(g)} = 2HBr_{(g)} + 24,950 \text{ cal}$$
$$H_{2(g)} + I_{2(g)} = 2HI_{(g)} + 3,400 \text{ cal}$$

The decrease in the tendency of the respective halogens to combine with hydrogen is indicated clearly by the decrease in the exothermic character of the reactions. This also reflects the decrease in strengths of the bond between hydrogen and the halogen atom. The H—F bond is very strong, and this molecule does not dissociate into the elements, even at very high temperatures. The H—I bond is quite weak, and, even at ordinary temperatures, the HI molecules undergo some appreciable dissociation.

b. Formation of hydrogen halides by the action of a concentrated nonvolatile acid on the halides. When a concentrated, stable and relatively nonvolatile acid, such as sulfuric or phosphoric acid, is heated with a given halide, the volatile hydrogen halide is formed and distills off, the reaction therefore being driven to completion. This method is convenient for preparing the compounds in the laboratory and also is effective for large-scale production.

When powdered fluorspar is moistened with concentrated sulfuric acid, hydrogen fluoride comes off as a gas, even at room temperature.

$$CaF_{2(s)} + H_2SO_4 = 2HF_{(g)} + CaSO_{4(s)}$$

In this net equation the sulfuric acid has been written in the molecular form, because, in the highly concentrated acid, it is very little dissociated into its ions.

Concentrated sulfuric acid is also commonly employed to make hydrogen chloride from sodium chloride. Both of these reagents are inexpensive, so that this method affords a cheap process for the industrial production of hydrochloric acid. Because sulfuric acid is diprotic, the reaction actually proceeds in two steps.

$$NaCl_{(s)} + H_2SO_4 = HCl_{(g)} + NaHSO_{4(s)}$$

The first step will take place readily if the mixture is heated moderately. When the temperature is increased, if sufficient NaCl is present, a second reaction occurs

$$NaCl_{(s)} + NaHSO_{4(s)} = HCl_{(g)} + Na_2SO_{4(s)}$$

and all of the capacity of sulfuric acid to furnish hydrogen is used.

When this reaction is carried out with NaBr or NaI, the changes do not stop with the formation of hydrogen bromide or hydrogen iodide. Concentrated sulfuric acid is a potential oxidizing agent. It is not powerful enough to oxidize the very stable HF or HCl molecules, but it does attack HBr and HI to form bromine or iodine, the sulfur being reduced.

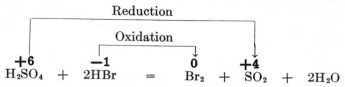

$$\overset{+6}{H_2SO_4} + \overset{-1}{2HBr} = \overset{0}{Br_2} + \overset{+4}{SO_2} + 2H_2O$$

Thus, the hydrogen bromide or hydrogen iodide, produced by heating concentrated sulfuric acid with bromides or iodides, will be contaminated with sulfur dioxide and bromine or iodine. Phosphoric acid, H_3PO_4, may be heated with the salts to make hydrogen bromide or hydrogen iodide because phosphoric acid is nonvolatile, and it is not a strong enough oxidizing agent to oxidize HBr or HI.

c. Formation of hydrogen halides by the hydrolysis of phosphorus trihalides. Many of the halides of the nonmetals react readily with water to form hydrogen halides. Phosphorus combines readily with the halogens to form phosphorus trihalides.

$$2P + 3Br_2 = 2PBr_3$$

These halides react with water, and the hydrogen halides are obtained.

$$PBr_3 + 3H_2O = 3HBr_{(g)} + H_3PO_3$$

With a very limited amount of water, the volatile HBr distills off and can be concentrated. H_3PO_3 is not volatile and is not capable of oxidizing the HBr. This method is also suitable for preparing HI.

241. PROPERTIES OF THE ANHYDROUS HYDROGEN HALIDES

HCl, HBr, and HI have colorless diatomic molecules in which the hydrogen and halogen atoms are linked together with a pair of shared electrons.

$$H\!-\!\overset{..}{\underset{..}{X}}:$$

The covalent bond is highly polar in HCl, but the polarity decreases with decreasing electronegativity of the halogen atom. The very highly polar hydrogen fluoride molecules have a strong tendency to *polymerize; the simple molecules combine to form more complicated molecules having the same percentage composition.* There is evidence that hydrogen fluoride at ordinary temperatures consists of a mixture of HF and its *polymers*, H_2F_2, H_3F_3, H_4F_4, H_5F_5, and H_6F_6. The average molecular weight is about that of H_3F_3. We usually use the simplest formula for the substance, or $(HF)_n$, indicating some polymerization. This polymerization is caused by the formation of hydrogen bonds between two fluorine atoms to link the HF molecules together, as shown in Figure 81.   The very high electronegativity of fluorine favors this, as we saw in Section 181.

The polymerization of hydrogen fluoride decreases its volatility and changes its properties considerably from those which we would predict for the simple molecule HF.   As seen in Table 38, the properties of HF

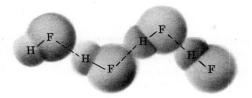

Fig. 81.   Polymerization of HF by hydrogen bonding.

do not fall in line with the properties of the rest of the hydrogen halides, which show no appreciable tendency to polymerize because they are not sufficiently electronegative to form hydrogen bonds of any strength.   All the hydrogen halides are colorless at room temperature, and they have sharp and very irritating odors.

Table 38.   Properties of the Hydrogen Halides

	$(HF)_n$	HCl	HBr	HI
Molecular weight	$66_{(av)}$	36.465	80.924	127.92
Melting point, °C	−83	−111	−86	−50.8
Boiling point, °C	19.4	−85	−67	−35.5
Solubility in water, g/100 g H_2O	98(−10°)	93.3(−15°)	239(−15°)	41.5(−10°)
$K_{(i)}$	6.9×10^{-4}	Very large	Very large	Very large
Polarity	Decreasing ⟶			
H—X bond length	Increasing ⟶			
Thermal stability	Decreasing ⟶			

note

The very dry hydrogen halides are rather inert chemically and do not corrode dry metals at room temperature.   Anhydrous hydrogen fluoride is a very powerful catalyst for certain reactions and has been used in the manufacture of aviation-grade gasoline.

242. AQUEOUS HYDROGEN HALIDES.   HYDROHALIC ACIDS

The hydrogen halides fume in moist air because their molecules act as condensation centers, and the water molecules condense to give tiny droplets of solutions of the halides.   As noted in Table 38, the hydrogen halides are highly soluble in water.   With the exception of HF these compounds are *strong electrolytes*, dissociating in water to give acidic solutions, which are commonly referred to as the acids. The aqueous solutions have the characteristic properties to be expected for high concentions of hydrogen ions. They neutralize basic systems and oxidize the more active metals to their cations, hydrogen being liberated.

$$Zn + 2H^+ = Zn^{2+} + H_2$$

The aqueous acids are therefore very corrosive toward the more active metals.

The concentrated solutions of the hydrohalic acids attack organic tissue, producing painful burns. Considerable caution should be used in handling them. When the concentrated acid is spilled on the skin, it should be flushed with great quantities of water and then the adhering acid should be neutralized by applying a *dilute* basic solution, such as sodium bicarbonate or borax. *Never use concentrated ammonia or strong bases for this purpose.* The heat of reaction will only aggravate the burn.

The ordinary *concentrated hydrochloric acid* that is marketed is about an 11*M* solution, which fumes strongly, owing to the escape of HCl molecules from solution. The term *muriatic acid* has long been used to refer to this solution. Hydrochloric acid is present to about 0.5 per cent in the gastric juices of the human stomach where it is important in the digestive process. Some animals, such as the dog, may have as high as 5 per cent hydrochloric acid in their digestive tracts, and they can therefore digest bones.

Hydrofluoric acid is not as strong an acid as the other hydrogen halides. However, it has the unique property of attacking compounds containing silicon. Thus sand, silicon dioxide, is corroded rapidly by aqueous HF.

$$SiO_{2(s)} + 4HF = SiF_{4(g)} + 2H_2O$$

Silicon tetrafluoride is a volatile molecular substance which escapes to the vapor phase, and the reaction to the right is favored. Silicates such as Na_2SiO_3 and $CaSiO_3$ are also corroded rapidly.

$$CaSiO_{3(s)} + 6HF = CaF_{2(s)} + SiF_{4(g)} + 3H_2O$$

Glass and porcelain are complex mixtures of compounds of silicon, and they are "etched" (surface eaten away) by hydrofluoric acid. Glass bottles and most metallic containers cannot be used for storing this aqueous solution. Certain waxes and plastic materials are not attacked and are used to make vessels for holding the acid. Lead forms a surface coating of insoluble PbF_2, which protects the underlying metal from further corrosion, so that lead-lined tanks can be used for hydrofluoric acid baths.

243. HALIDES OF THE METALS

The formation of halides of the metals by direct union has been considered in Section 236. Such halides can also usually be prepared by passing the dry hydrohalogen gas over the heated metal.

$$Zn_{(s)} + 2HCl_{(g)} = ZnCl_{2(s)} + H_{2(g)}$$

Halide ions in solution with cations of the metals may associate to form solid salts. The halides that are soluble may be obtained by crystallization when the solutions are evaporated.

$$Na^+ + Cl^- = NaCl_{(s)}$$

Many of the fluorides of the metals and a few of the chlorides, bromides, and iodides are only slightly soluble, and these precipitate rather completely when the appropriate ions are brought together in solution.

$$Mg^{2+} + 2F^- = MgF_{2(s)}$$
$$Ca^{2+} + 2F^- = CaF_{2(s)}$$
$$Ag^+ + Cl^- = AgCl_{(s)}$$

The very insoluble MgF_2 can be deposited in thin films on glass by sublimation in high vacuum. Such a film on a glass lens reduces the reflection and increases the transmission of light, making the lens "faster" when it is used in a camera.

Halides of metals in high oxidation states, such as **+5** or **+6**, are molecular and rather volatile. Uranium forms UF_6, which is the only compound of uranium volatile enough to be used in the gaseous state for the separation of isotopes of uranium. This is important in the production of the atomic bomb and power for peaceful use.

244. FLUO- AND CHLORO- COMPLEX IONS

The smaller halide ions, F^- and Cl^-, tend to associate strongly with polyvalent metals to form stable complex ions. $[AlF_6]^{3-}$ has already been mentioned in Sections 182 and 183. $[PtCl_6]^{2-}$ and $[AuCl_4]^-$ are important complex ions of platinum and gold.

245. POSITIVE OXIDATION STATES FOR THE HALOGENS

The halogens go to positive oxidation states when they combine with more electronegative elements. This is impossible in the case of fluorine, but it becomes more and more possible as the atomic number in the group increases. Oxygen is more electronegative than chlorine, bromine, and iodine, and the oxycompounds of these halogens are the best examples of substances in which the halogens are in their higher oxidation states. Those for chlorine are most common and are typical. We shall discuss these chlorine oxycompounds in some detail, and it can be remembered that usually the corresponding compounds of bromine and of iodine will resemble those of chlorine.   We shall be interested to learn how the large number of positive oxidation states that are known for chlorine are possible.   How are the seven valence electrons of the chlorine atoms involved in bonding in each of these oxidation states?   This is best seen if we consider the oxyacids of chlorine and their salts.

Table 39.   Oxyacids, Oxyanions, and Oxysalts of Chlorine

Oxidation State	Oxyacid	Oxyanion	Sodium salt
+1	$HClO$ hypo-chlor-ous	ClO^- hypo-chlor-ite	$NaClO$ hypochlorite
+3	$HClO_2$ chlor-ous	ClO_2^- chlor-ite	$NaClO_2$ chlorite
+5	$HClO_3$ chlor-ic	ClO_3^- chlor-ate	$NaClO_3$ chlorate
+7	$HClO_4$ per-chlor-ic	ClO_4^- per-chlor-ate	$NaClO_4$ perchlorate

As shown in Table 39, for each positive oxidation state there is an oxyacid, a corresponding oxyanion, and a corresponding sodium salt. The system used to name the acids, their ions, and their salts is that commonly employed for the oxyacids of all elements that form several oxyacids.   The root of the name of the element is combined with various prefixes and endings, depending upon the amount of oxygen present. The ending *-ic* is used for the oxyacid that is most common or whose salts are most common.   The acid having more oxygen than the *-ic* acid, retains the ending *-ic* and has the prefix *per-*.   The oxyacid with one less oxygen atom than the *-ic* acid has the ending *-ous*, and the oxyacid with still less oxygen has the prefix *hypo-* and the ending *-ous*.   In naming the oxyanions and salts, the prefixes of the acids are retained, the ending *-ic* is changed to *-ate*, and the ending *-ous* is changed to *-ite*.

Figure 82 shows how the atoms are believed to be bonded together in the oxyacids and the oxyanions of chlorine.   Since the difference in electronegativity between the oxygen and chlorine atoms is not great, the chlorine-oxygen bonds are covalent, consisting of shared pairs of electrons as shown.   The hydrogen atoms are bonded to an oxygen atom covalently to give a hydroxyl group, as is common for all oxyacids.   The acids are molecular, although the H—O bond is highly polar.   In hypochlorous acid, only one pair of the eight electrons in the valence shell of the chlorine atom is shared with oxygen.   Three pairs are unshared. Only one of the valence electrons of the chlorine is involved in the bonding, and the valence and oxidation state of chlorine in hypochlorous acid is therefore 1. It is **+1** because the oxygen is more electronegative than the chlorine.

The chlorine atom can share one of the three remaining pairs of electrons in its valence shell with a second oxygen atom to produce the chlorous acid molecule. And in turn, a third and a fourth oxygen can

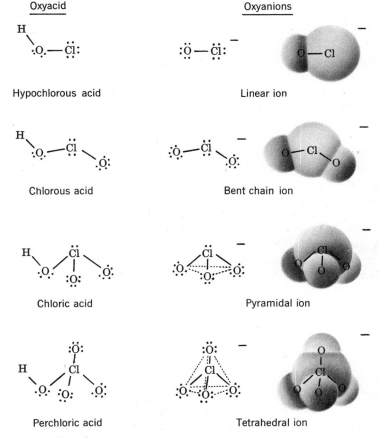

Fig. 82. Configurations of the oxyacids and oxyanions of chlorine.

likewise be bonded to the chlorine to give the chloric and perchloric acids. In chlorous acid, three of the electrons used in bonding have been furnished by the chlorine, and it therefore is in the oxidation state of **+3**. And in chloric acid and perchloric acid, five and seven of the valence electrons of chlorine are employed, respectively, and the oxidation states of chlorine are **+5** and **+7**. We now can account for the fact that the positive oxidation states of chlorine (and bromine and iodine) vary by jumps of two units in the oxyacids. In order to bond additional oxygen atoms to the chlorine, pairs of the valence electrons of chlorine must be used.

When the molecules of the oxyacids of chlorine are in solution in a dissociation polar solvent, such as water, the protons tend to split off to form hydronium ions, and the acids tend to dissociate to give the oxy-anions. In this dissociation the pair of electrons that were shared by the hydrogen and the oxygen atom remain with the oxygen, and this accounts for the negative charge of the oxyanion. In each ion the total number of electrons is one more than the total number of positive charges on the nuclei.

Figure 82 also indicates the arrangement in space of the atoms with respect to each other, as determined by X-ray study of ionic crystals of salts of these oxyanions. In the hypochlorite anion there is, of course, a linear configuration. The chlorite ion consists of a bent chain and is spatially unsymmetrical. In the chlorate ion the three oxygen atoms are at the corners of an equilaterial triangle, equidistant from the chlorine atom. The chlorine atom lies above the center of the plane of the three oxygen atoms, the whole structure being trigonal pyramidal. The perchlorate ion is tetrahedral, the four oxygen atoms lying at the corners of a regular tetrahedron and the chlorine being at the center of the tetrahedron, equidistant from all four oxygen atoms.

Knowledge of the structures of the oxyacids of the halogens enables us to understand better the properties of these acids and their ions. The oxyacids of chlorine are observed to increase in acid strength as the number of oxygen atoms per molecule increases, as shown in Table 40.

Table 40.   Dissociation of the Oxyacids of Chlorine

	$K_{(i), 25°}$
$HClO \rightleftharpoons H^+ + ClO^-$	5.6×10^{-8}
$HClO_2 \rightleftharpoons H^+ + ClO_2^-$	1×10^{-2}
$HClO_3 \rightleftharpoons H^+ + ClO_3^-$	Large
$HClO_4 \rightleftharpoons H^+ + ClO_4^-$	Very large

$HClO$ is a very weak acid and $HClO_4$ is one of the strongest acids. This is to be expected. Oxygen atoms have high electron affinity, tending to pull electrons toward them. As more and more oxygen atoms become attached to the central chlorine atom, the bonding electrons will be pulled more and more away from the hydrogen atom in the molecule. With decreasing share in the pair of bonding electrons, the forces holding the hydrogen atom in the molecule decrease, and the tendency for the molecule to dissociate to yield hydrogen ions increases.

The *thermal stability* of the oxyacids of chlorine and of their ions increases with increase in the number of oxygen atoms. This may reasonably be correlated with the fact that more and more the electrons in the valence shell of the chlorine atom become shared. The thermal stability of the oxyacids of chlorine is not great in any case; even $HClO_4$ is not very stable. The molecules tend to break down when attempts are made to separate them from aqueous solution, and even in solution they are rather unstable, especially the lower oxyacids.

The acids and their ions are powerful oxidizing agents, the chlorine being reduced to Cl_2 or Cl^-. As the number of oxygen atoms increases, the total *oxidizing capacity increases.*

246. HYPOCHLOROUS ACID AND HYPOCHLORITES

Hypochlorous acid is produced when chlorine reacts with water.

$$Cl_2 + H_2O = H^+ + Cl^- + HClO$$

The HClO molecules decompose in solution, and the acid is a very powerful oxidizing agent.

Solutions of hypochlorites are obtained by bubbling chlorine into cold dilute basic solution.

$$2OH^- + Cl_2 = Cl^- + ClO^- + H_2O$$

Here auto-oxidation-reduction occurs, half of the chlorine atoms being reduced to chloride ions, the others being oxidized to hypochlorite. Solutions of sodium hypochlorite made in this fashion are widely used for laundry bleaching.

Bleaching powder, chloride of lime, is made by passing chlorine over slaked lime, the equation being usually written as

$$Ca(OH)_2 + Cl_2 = CaCl(ClO)_{(s)} + H_2O$$

There is good reason to believe that bleaching powder actually is a mixture of equivalent amounts of $Ca(ClO)_2$ and hydrated $CaCl_2$, the mixture having an over-all analysis of about that of the empirical formula given in the equation.

Hypochlorites hydrolyze considerably when placed in water because hypochlorous acid is such a weak electrolyte.

$$ClO^- + H_2O = OH^- + HClO$$

In acid solution, hypochlorites are largely converted to HClO.

$$H^+ + ClO^- = HClO$$

HClO is a more rapid oxidizing agent than ClO^-, and the bleaching action of hypochlorites is speeded up in laundry practice by acidifying the solution.

247. CHLOROUS ACID AND CHLORITES

Chlorous acid and chlorites are not very stable and are difficult to make. $NaClO_2$ is now produced industrially and is marketed as an oxidizing agent that is very useful for bleaching. Chlorites have a greater total oxidizing capacity than hypochlorites.

248. CHLORATES AND CHLORIC ACID

Chlorate ions are obtained by the auto-oxidation-reduction of hypochlorite ions, which progresses rapidly in hot concentrated solutions.

$$3ClO^- = 2Cl^- + ClO_3^-$$

This action occurs when chlorine is run into hot, concentrated sodium or potassium hydroxide solutions. Notice, however, that a very large amount of the total chlorine used is converted to chloride ion. Chlorate ions may also be made by electrolysis of hot concentrated solutions of potassium chloride which are stirred vigorously. $KClO_3$ precipitates out because it is not very soluble. Chlorates decompose when heated sufficiently to give chloride and oxygen.

$$2KClO_3 = 2KCl + 3O_2$$

$KClO_3$ is a powerful oxidizing agent and forms a highly explosive mixture with substances that are easily oxidized, such as sugar, sulfur, or charcoal. Considerable amounts of $KClO_3$ are used for preparing fireworks and in the manufacture of matches. Great caution should always be used in handling powerful oxidizing agents like $KClO_3$. *Never grind or heat them in contact with combustible substances.*

A solution of *chloric acid* is formed when sulfuric acid is added to barium chlorate. The $HClO_3$ molecule is unstable in concentrated sulfuric acid and decomposes rapidly to chlorine dioxide.

$$4HClO_3 = 4ClO_2 + 2H_2O + O_2$$

The chlorine dioxide is a very unstable substance and explodes spontaneously and with tremendous violence.

$$2ClO_2 = Cl_2 + 2O_2$$

It is *very dangerous* to add concentrated sulfuric acid to a solid chlorate.

249. PERCHLORATES AND PERCHLORIC ACID

Potassium perchlorate may be made by gently heating potassium chlorate, auto-oxidation-reduction again occurring.

$$4KClO_3 = KCl + 3KClO_4$$

Perchlorates are powerful oxidizing agents. $Mg(ClO_4)_2$ is a very efficient desiccant which is frequently used in the laboratory. One should never use it for drying substances that are easily oxidized; some very bad accidents have resulted when such mixtures have exploded.

Perchloric acid can be prepared by treating perchlorates with sulfuric acid. An aqueous solution of the acid can be concentrated by distillation under reduced pressure. Such solutions are quite stable thermally up to concentrations of something over 60 per cent, and these solutions are marketed. In higher concentrations the acid is unstable and unsafe to store. Perchloric acid solutions are useful in analytical chemistry. The acid should be employed only with great caution. When it is mixed with substances that are easily oxidized, violent explosions may result.

Perbromic acid and perbromate ions are not known, the oxidation state of $+7$ apparently being very unstable for bromine. Two periodic acids, HIO_4 and H_5IO_6, with the corresponding ions, are known. The existence of H_5IO_6 is due to the fact that the iodine atom is so large that it can have a maximum coordination number of 6 toward oxygen. The smaller chlorine atom can coordinate to only four oxygen atoms.

250. OXIDES OF THE HALOGENS

The oxides of the halogens are not easy to prepare and, in general, they are quite unstable and difficult to work with. The compounds listed below are known and are of interest in showing the variety of molecules that can be formed. (Since fluorine is more electronegative than oxygen, OF_2 should be called oxygen difluoride.)

OF_2	Cl_2O	No oxides	
O_2F_2	Cl_2O_3	of bromine	
	ClO_2	have been	I_2O_4
	Cl_2O_7	isolated	I_2O_5

EXERCISES

1. What is characteristic of the atomic structures of the halogens?

2. Describe qualitatively for the halogens how each of the following vary with increasing atomic number: a) number of shells of electrons; b) number of valence electrons; c) atomic size; d) radius for X^-; e) covalent bond radius; f) strength as oxidizing agent; g) electronegativity; h) molecular weight; i) standard state; j) melting point; k) boiling point; l) density as a gas; m) color.

3. Astatine has the atomic number 85 and belongs in the halogen family. On the basis of the data given in Table 35 for the other halogens, predict: a) its standard state; b) its approximate melting point; c) its relative strength as an oxidizing agent.

4. a) What are the characteristic oxidation states of the halogens?

b) How can these be accounted for on the basis of the electronic structures of the halogens?

c) Why does fluorine have so few oxidation states?

5. What is the oxidation state of the halogen atom in: a) HBr? b) Cl_2O? c) IO_4^-? d) $NaIO_3$? e) OF_2? f) Br_2? g) Cl_2O_7?

6. a) In what oxidation state are the halogens ordinarily found in nature?

b) What electronic rearrangement must be carried out to prepare the free elements?

c) Write balanced equations for four different reactions which could be used to prepare bromine, indicating all changes in oxidation states which occur.

7. Break down the oxidation-reduction reactions given in Section 245 for the preparation of chlorine and bromine into the oxidation half reactions and the reduction half reactions.

8. Write a balanced equation to show the reaction of bromine with: a) magnesium; b) hydrogen; c) phosphorus; d) water.

9. a) Compare the tendencies of the halogens to combine with hydrogen.

b) How is this correlated with the oxidation-reduction potentials of the halogens?

10. Write balanced equations that describe what happens when each of the sodium halides is heated with concentrated sulfuric acid. Account for any differences in the reactions.

11. In what respects does hydrogen fluoride differ from the other hydrogen halides? Account for this.

12. Compare the oxyacid anions formed by chlorine with respect to: a) electronic structures; b) oxidation state of chlorine; c) spatial configurations.

13. How can the fact that $HClO_4$ is a stronger acid than $HClO_2$ be accounted for on the bases of structure and bonding?

14. a) To what does the term auto-oxidation-reduction refer?

b) Write two balanced equations dealing with the chemistry of chlorine that illustrate such a process.

15. Which will have the greatest tendency for hydrolysis, KCl, $KClO_2$, or $KClO_3$? Account for your answer.

16. Six moles of sodium chloride react completely with MnO_2 in dilute sulfuric acid.

a) How many grams of chlorine are formed and what volume would this chlorine occupy at 10 atm pressure and 20°?

b) What is the gram-equivalent weight of MnO_2 in this reaction?

Chapter 21

▶ The Sulfur Family

251. THE SULFUR FAMILY

Sulfur, selenium, tellurium, and polonium are in the second places preceding the inert gases in their respective periods, immediately before

Table 41. Elements of the Sulfur Family

	Oxygen	Sulfur	Selenium	Tellurium	Polonium
Symbol	O	S	Se	Te	Po
Atomic number	8	16	34	52	84
Atomic weight	16.000	32.066	78.96	127.61	210
Electronic structure	2, 6	2, 8, 6	2, 8, 18, 6	2, 8, 18, 18, 6	2, 8, 18, 32, 18, 6
Radius anion^{2-}, Å	1.40	1.84	1.98	2.21	
Covalent bond radius Å	0.66	1.04	1.17	1.37	
Common oxidation states	−2, −1, 0	−2, 0, +2, +4, +6	−2, 0, +4, +6	−2, 0, +4, +6	
Molecular formula	O_2	S_8	Endless chain	Endless chain	
Molecular weight	32	256.53			
Standard state	Gas	Solid	Solid	Solid	Solid
Melting point, ° C	−218.8	112.8	220	450	
Boiling point, ° C	−183	444.6	680	1390	
Color	Colorless	Yellow	Gray	Gray	
Relative sizes of atoms under comparable conditions	Increasing ⟶				
Electronegativity	Decreasing ⟶				
Strength as oxidizing agent	Decreasing ⟶				

the halogens. Oxygen nominally falls in this category, but it is so different in many respects from the remaining elements of the family that it is usually treated separately. The remaining elements of the family show close physical and chemical analogies and are conveniently considered together. In Table 41, oxygen is also included for purposes of comparison.   The properties listed are those of the allotropic form stable under ordinary conditions.

With increase in atomic number, the number of shells of electrons and the sizes of the atoms in comparable states increase.   Each has six valence electrons.   Oxygen is more electronegative than any other element except fluorine, and oxygen therefore usually goes to the oxidation state of **—2** when it combines with other elements; in peroxy compounds oxygen is in the **—1** oxidation state.   Sulfur and the remaining elements are increasingly less electronegative and can achieve both negative and positive oxidation states.

We have already considered oxygen.   Sulfur is also a common and important element, and we will discuss it and its compounds in detail. Selenium and tellurium are much less abundant and have very few uses. We shall consider them only very briefly, pointing out their family resemblances.   Polonium is obtained only as a product of radioactive change, and very little is known about its chemistry.

252.   OXIDATION STATES FOR SULFUR

Sulfur with its six valence electrons can achieve a number of different oxidation states, depending upon the number of electrons of the valence

Table 42.   Oxidation States of Sulfur

Oxidation State	Typical Molecules and Ions	Achieved When:
—2 **—1**	H_2S, S^{2-} H_2S_2, S_2^{2-}	Sulfur is combined with less electronegative elements, such as hydrogen and the metals
0	S_8	Sulfur atoms are bonded together in molecules of the free element
+2	SCl_2	Sulfur atoms are bonded to more electronegative elements, such as oxygen, nitrogen, bromine, chlorine, and fluorine. This oxidation state is not very stable and is not important
+4	SO_2, SO_3^{2-}, SCl_4, $SOCl_2$	Sulfur atoms are bonded to more electronegative elements, and oxidizing conditions are only moderate
+6	SO_3, H_2SO_4, SO_4^{2-}, SO_2Cl_2	Sulfur atoms are bonded to more negative elements, and oxidizing conditions are stronger than for **+4**

shell that are involved.   These electrons are commonly used in pairs in the formation of bonds, and the oxidation states differ by jumps of two units.   Table 42 summarizes the way in which sulfur can achieve the different oxidation states.

253. OCCURRENCE OF SULFUR

Sulfur is not nearly as abundant as oxygen, there being only 0.048 per cent of sulfur in the crust of the earth, but it is quite readily available in a variety of materials.   Table 43 summarizes the way sulfur is found in nature.

Table 43.   Occurrence of Sulfur

Elementary sulfur	*Beds of very pure sulfur*, buried under several hundred feet of soil; Texas, Louisiana, offshore under Gulf of Mexico, Mexico, S. America
	Limited amounts of impure sulfur in volcanic regions; Sicily, Mexico, Japan
Combined sulfur	*As S^{2-} in sulfides of metals*, such as Cu_2S, PbS, As_2S_3, Sb_2S_3, Bi_2S_3
	As H_2S in spring water and as a product of decay of plant and animal matter
	As S_2^{2-} in FeS_2
	As SO_4^{2-} in sulfates of metals, such as $CaSO_4$, $SrSO_4$, $BaSO_4$
	In organic compounds in plant and animal material; eggs, mustard, onions, garlic, cabbage, and horseradish contain combined sulfur, the sulfur compounds usually being responsible for the strong odors and tastes
	In petroleum

254. PRODUCTION OF SULFUR

The various deposits of elementary sulfur are exploited.   The volcanic sulfur is collected and purified by melting and recrystallization or distillation.   The sulfur deposits in Texas and Louisiana are worked by the *Frasch process*, using the scheme illustrated in Figure 83.   The concentric pipes shown are sunk through the overlying material into the sulfur beds.   Steam and hot water are pumped down, and the sulfur is melted. Compressed air is also pumped into the deposit to form a froth having a density so low that it can easily be forced to the surface.   The sulfur is allowed to solidify in large storage bins and then is broken up and marketed.   It is so pure that it can be used directly in chemical industry. Unfortunately, the deposits of pure sulfur are being depleted so rapidly that other sources of the element must be developed for supplying the large amounts needed in chemical industry.

In the refining of petroleum, considerable amounts of sulfur are encountered.   A large potential supply of *by-product sulfur* is thus available, and this is being developed.

Sulfur is available on the market in the finely divided form as *flour*, or *flowers of sulfur*, and in the massive form as chunks or cast into *rolls*.

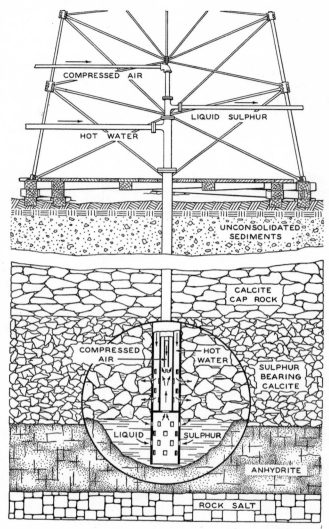

Fig. 83.   The Frasch process for mining sulfur.   (Courtesy Texas Gulf Sulfur Co.)

255.   PROPERTIES OF SULFUR

Table 41 lists the common properties of sulfur.   The study of the behavior of the element is rather complicated because of its great ability to assume various *allotropic forms*.   Two crystalline allotropic forms of sulfur are commonly encountered, and several others have been reported.

Rhombic sulfur is the crystalline form that is stable under ordinary conditions.   Any sample of the element that has existed for some time under such conditions will be in this crystalline form. Flowers of sulfur and roll sulfur are made up of rhombic crystals. Well-formed diamond-shaped crystals of rhombic sulfur can be obtained by crystallization from a solution of sulfur in carbon disulfide. This form of sulfur is lemon yellow in color and is tasteless and odorless. It is very brittle and a poor conductor of electricity. It is insoluble in water but is quite soluble in carbon disulfide.

Monoclinic sulfur consists of long needlelike crystals which are obtained by rapidly cooling molten sulfur. This crystalline form is stable above 95.5°, but, below this temperature, it undergoes a *transition* to the rhombic form, which is stable below 95.5°. The transition is reversible, and at 95.5°, *the transition point*, both forms can coexist in equilibrium.

$$\text{Rhombic sulfur} \underset{\text{below 95.5°}}{\overset{\text{above 95.5°}}{\rightleftharpoons}} \text{monoclinic sulfur}$$
$$\text{m.p. 112.8°} \qquad\qquad \text{m.p. 119°}$$

Sulfur behaves in a very curious fashion when it is heated. When rhombic sulfur is heated rapidly, inversion to the monoclinic form at 95.5° is not complete, and the sample melts at about 114°. A pale-yellow, mobile liquid is formed. As the temperature is raised, the liquid gradually becomes darker in color and less mobile. Around 160°, it is a dark reddish-brown liquid which is about as viscous as cold molasses. With further increase in temperature, the dark color persists, but the liquid becomes more and more fluid and its vapor tension becomes appreciable. It boils at 444.6° at 1 atm pressure to give yellow sulfur vapor. When the very hot liquid is rapidly chilled by dropping it into water, a light-brown rubbery material, known as *plastic sulfur*, is obtained. Plastic sulfur is noncrystalline, or *amorphous* (without crystalline form), in structure. It is undercooled liquid sulfur. At room temperature, this plastic sulfur is in a very unstable condition, and it rapidly changes to the stable crystalline rhombic sulfur, becoming yellow and brittle.

The polymorphism of sulfur must be due to the fact that sulfur atoms can be combined and packed together in many different ways. The stable rhombic crystals of sulfur have been studied by X-ray methods. These crystals are built up of S_8 molecules packed together in a regular pattern. The S_8 molecules, as shown in Figure 84, consist of puckered rings, or "crowns," of eight sulfur atoms. Each sulfur atom is covalently bonded to two neighboring sulfur atoms by shared pairs of electrons, each sulfur thus building up its valence shell to eight electrons. The eight atoms are not all in the same plane; four are in one plane, the other four are in a second plane parallel to the first.

These S_8 molecules may be present in the other allotropic forms of sulfur, although we know very little about the structure of the forms that are not stable at room temperature. When rhombic sulfur melts, the S_8 rings may persist and be present in the liquid phase and perhaps

even in sulfur vapor to some extent.   Several ring molecules may open
up and join together when heated to give long-chain molecules, and the
formation of such chains of sulfur atoms has been suggested to account
for the curious behavior of sulfur in the liquid state.

Note that the sulfur atom forms single covalent bonds to each of two
neighboring sulfur atoms to give a large molecule, whereas the common
oxygen molecule is diatomic.   This is in line with the general observation
that the coordination number increases with increase in the sizes of atoms.

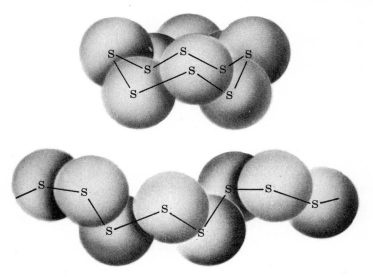

Fig. 84.   The S_8 molecule and a random puckered sulfur chain.

Sulfur is not active chemically at ordinary temperatures, but, when
heated, it will oxidize the metals, being reduced to the oxidation state
of **−2.**

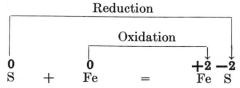

Sulfur is a much weaker oxidizing agent than oxygen.   At high temperatures sulfur combines readily with the more electronegative elements,
fluorine, chlorine, and oxygen, being oxidized to positive oxidation states.

256.   USES OF SULFUR

The importance of sulfur as a basic chemical cannot be overemphasized.   Very large amounts of it are used to prepare sulfuric acid, our

most important acid. Sulfur is essential in the compounding and vulcanization of rubber, its presence in rubber modifying the properties of
crude rubber in a remarkable fashion. Sulfur is used in making lime-
sulfur sprays, which are widely employed for controlling plant diseases.
It enters into the composition of many organic compounds, such as the
sulfa drugs.

257. HYDROGEN SULFIDE

Sulfur is reduced to the oxidation state of **−2** when it is combined
with hydrogen to form hydrogen sulfide. This compound can be formed
in a number of ways.

a. Formation by direct union.

$$H_2 + S \rightleftharpoons H_2S$$

When we recall how violently hydrogen and oxygen combine, we might
expect that sulfur would also unite readily with hydrogen. The reaction
does proceed above 200°, but the H_2S molecule is not very stable at
these temperatures, and it decomposes rapidly to the elements. The
equilibrium set up is not favorable for the production of hydrogen sulfide.
This situation reflects the fact that sulfur is a much weaker oxidizing
agent than oxygen.

b. Formation by the action of H^+ on sulfides of metals. The sulfides
of the active metals give hydrogen sulfide readily when they are treated
with dilute acids. Hydrochloric acid reacts rapidly with ferrous sulfide
at room temperature.

$$FeS_{(s)} + 2H^+ = H_2S_{(g)} + Fe^{2+}$$

The generation of hydrogen sulfide proceeds readily because it is both
a weak electrolyte and a gas of limited solubility in acidic solutions.

Hydrogen sulfide is sold as the liquid under pressure in steel cylinders.

Table 44 gives the common physical properties of hydrogen sulfide
and also those of water, hydrogen selenide, and hydrogen telluride.
Notice that the properties of water are out of line with those of the other
compounds of this series. This, as in the similar case for HF discussed
in Section 241, is attributed to association of the water molecules due to
hydrogen bonding (see Section 181). H_2S, H_2Se, and H_2Te have no
appreciable tendency to form hydrogen bonds.

Hydrogen sulfide has a bent-chain structure like that of water (see Fig-

$$H \overset{\nwarrow}{\underset{92°}{}} \overset{S}{\underset{\diagdown}{}}$$
$$H$$

ure 64). Since sulfur is much less electronegative than oxygen, the sulfur-
hydrogen bonds are much less polar than the oxygen-hydrogen bonds,

and hydrogen sulfide is therefore much less polar than water.   Hydrogen sulfide is a colorless gas which is easily liquefied.   It has a unique and very disagreeable odor which makes its presence, even in minute amounts, readily apparent.   Hydrogen sulfide is *very poisonous* and is dangerous to breathe.   One part of hydrogen sulfide in 200 parts of air may be fatal if inhaled for some time.   *Always work with hydrogen sulfide in an efficient ventilating hood.*

Table 44.   **Properties of the Hydrides of the Sulfur Family**

	$(H_2O)_n$	H_2S	H_2Se	H_2Te
Molecular weight	18.0 (vapor)	34.08	80.98	129.63
Melting point, ° C	0.0	−85.5	−64	−48
Boiling point, ° C	100.0	−59.6	−42	−1.8
Color	Colorless	Colorless	Colorless	Colorless
Relative density (air = 1) of gas, STP		1.18	2.84	4.49
Thermal stability	Decreasing $\longrightarrow$			
Polarity	Decreasing $\longrightarrow$			

Dry hydrogen sulfide decomposes noticeably, when heated to about 300°, to hydrogen and sulfur.   It is combustible in air or oxygen, the products formed depending upon the amount of oxygen available.

$$2H_2S + O_2 = 2H_2O + 2S$$
$$2H_2S + 3O_2 = 2H_2O + 2SO_2$$

The dry gas is a powerful reducing agent at advanced temperatures.

Hydrogen sulfide dissolves sparingly in water and dissociates as a *very weak diprotic acid.*

$$H_2S \rightleftharpoons H^+ + \underset{\text{hydrosulfide ion}}{HS^-} \quad \dfrac{K_{(i)}}{1.0 \times 10^{-7}}$$

$$HS^- \rightleftharpoons H^+ + \underset{\text{sulfide ion}}{S^{2-}} \quad 1.3 \times 10^{-13}$$

It is such a weak acid that it is not important as an acid for providing hydrogens ions.   However, the sulfide ions that it makes available in aqueous solution are important in the precipitation of cations of many of the metals that form sulfides of very low solubility.   This is important in analytical chemistry when one wishes to find out what cations are present in a given sample.

Since in H_2S, in HS^-, and as the S^{2-}, sulfur is in its lowest oxidation state, a *solution of hydrogen sulfide will have a strong reducing action.* When H_2S is bubbled into a solution of iodine, the brown color disappears because the iodine is reduced to I^-, and sulfur precipitates out.

$$H_2S + I_2 = 2H^+ + 2I^- + S_{(s)}$$

Likewise, ferric ions are reduced by hydrogen sulfide to ferrous ions.

$$H_2S + 2Fe^{3+} = 2H^+ + 2Fe^{2+} + S_{(s)}$$

258. SULFIDES. PRECIPITATION BY HYDROGEN SULFIDE

Two series of sulfides are formed from this diprotic acid: hydrosulfides, such as NaHS, and normal sulfides, such as Na_2S.   The normal sulfides are of greater importance.   They can be formed by heating a metal with sulfur.   Films of the colored sulfides form on the surfaces of many metals when they are exposed to compounds of sulfur.   The tarnishing of silver in air and the very rapid blackening of silver in contact with eggs is due to the sulfur compounds which are present.

In the laboratory, we are very much concerned with the *precipitation of sulfides by the use of hydrogen sulfide*.   Here is a good opportunity to apply what we know about *solubility products*.   In a saturated solution of hydrogen sulfide in water at room temperature, the concentration of S^{2-} ions is very low, about 1.3×10^{-13} mole per liter.   If cations of a metal are present and the solubility product of its sulfide is exceeded, the sulfide will precipitate.   It will be useful to examine the possibilities of precipitating a number of different common cations by the use of hydrogen sulfide.

When hydrogen sulfide is bubbled into a $0.1M$ solution of barium chloride until the solution becomes saturated, no precipitation is observed.

$$Ba^{2+} + S^{2-} = \text{no precipitation}$$

This is because BaS is quite soluble and its solubility product

$$K_{s.p.} = [Ba^{2+}] \times [S^{2-}]$$

is very large.   The maximum concentration of S^{2-} made available by saturating the solution with H_2S is only 1.3×10^{-13}.   Hence, no matter how high the Ba^{2+} concentration in solution, the S^{2-} concentration is so low that the actual ion product of the solution never exceeds the solubility product of BaS, and *we cannot precipitate Ba^{2+} by the use of hydrogen sulfide*.   In fact, if we make solid barium sulfide by some other method and add it to water, it goes into solution and hydrolyzes to give H_2S.

When hydrogen sulfide is bubbled into a $0.1M$ solution of $CuCl_2$, a black precipitate of CuS is immediately formed, and the blue color due to the presence of hydrated cupric ions in the solution disappears.

$$Cu^{2+} + S^{2-} \rightleftharpoons CuS_{(s)}$$

$$K_{s.p.(CuS)} = [Cu^{2+}] \times [S^{2-}] = 4 \times 10^{-36}$$

The solubility product for CuS is so very low that, when cupric ions are present even at very low concentration and the solution is saturated with H_2S, the ion product will exceed the solubility product. Precipitation will occur, removing practically all of the Cu^{2+} from solution. The concentration of Cu^{2+} need only be greater than about 3×10^{-23} mole $(6 \times 10^{23} \times 3 \times 10^{-23} = 18 \ Cu^{2+})$ per liter, in order that precipitation take place. As the sulfide ions are used up by the precipitation, more H_2S dissociates to maintain the dissociation equilibria for the saturated solution. The hydrogen ions accumulate in the solution, and it becomes more and more acid as precipitation proceeds; the equilibrium concentration of sulfide ions therefore decreases. But it still remains high enough so that the solubility product of CuS is exceeded if there is an appreciable concentration of Cu^{2+}. One can even add hydrochloric acid to the solution to produce a very high H^+ concentration and repress the dissociation of H_2S, thus lowering the concentration of S^{2-}, without causing an appreciable amount of CuS to dissolve. *Cu^{2+} can be precipitated practically quantitatively by the use of H_2S, even in acid solution.*

When hydrogen sulfide is bubbled into a $0.1M$ solution of $ZnCl_2$, a white precipitate of ZnS is formed.

$$Zn^{2+} + S^{2-} \rightleftharpoons ZnS_{(s)}$$
$$K_{s.p.(ZnS)} = [Zn^{2+}] \times [S^{2-}] = 4.5 \times 10^{-24}$$

Since, by saturating the solution with H_2S, we can provide 1.3×10^{-13} mole per liter of S^{2-}, if the initial concentration of Zn^{2+} is above 3.5×10^{-11}, a precipitate will form. As precipitation proceeds, the hydrogen-ion concentration increases, and the concentrations of Zn^{2+} and S^{2-} decrease. Finally, the ion product in solution is reduced to the solubility product for ZnS, and no more precipitation occurs. A considerable amount of zinc ions still remains in solution. When hydrochloric acid is added to the suspension of ZnS precipitated by H_2S, the ZnS dissolves. The addition of H^+ reduces the dissociation of the H_2S, and the concentration of sulfide ion falls so low that the ion product in solution is much less than the solubility product for ZnS. Therefore, the ZnS goes into solution to provide S^{2-}. *Zinc ions are not precipitated very completely by H_2S and not at all if the solution is acidified to the proper degree.* Reducing the H^+ concentration by adding hydroxide ion gives more complete precipitation of zinc by hydrogen sulfide.

Thus, by adjusting the hydrogen-ion concentration, it is possible to control the precipitation of cations of the metals by the use of hydrogen sulfide. We can, in this manner, separate a mixture of certain cations and determine their amounts quantitatively.

Polysulfides (persulfides) are formed when a solution of a soluble sulfide is treated with sulfur. The sulfide ion combines with sulfur to produce the complex polysulfide ion.

$$S^{2-} + nS = (S_{n+1})^{2-}$$

Here n varies from one to four or five. Polysulfide ions are composed of puckered chains of sulfur atoms bonded by shared pairs of electrons.

$$\left[:\overset{\cdot\cdot}{\underset{\cdot\cdot}{S}}-\overset{\cdot\cdot}{\underset{\cdot\cdot}{S}}: \right]^{2-} \qquad\qquad \left[\begin{array}{c} \overset{\cdot\cdot}{S}\cdot \quad\; \cdot\overset{\cdot\cdot}{S}\cdot \\ \diagup\;\diagdown\;\diagup\;\diagdown \\ :\overset{}{\underset{\cdot\cdot}{S}}\cdot \quad\; \cdot\overset{}{\underset{\cdot\cdot}{S}}\cdot \end{array} \right]^{2-}$$

They are analogous to peroxide ions, but sulfur shows a greater tendency to form long chains than does oxygen. The polysulfide ions are not very stable and tend to decompose to give sulfide ions and sulfur. *Lime-sulfur spray* is made by boiling a suspension of slaked lime, $Ca(OH)_2$, with sulfur. Polysulfide ions are formed in the solution, and the spray is very effective as a fungicide for agricultural purposes.

259. POSITIVE OXIDATION STATES FOR SULFUR

As indicated in Section 252, sulfur usually achieves its positive oxidation states by combining with oxygen to form oxides, oxyacids, or oxyanions. The oxidation states of **+4** and **+6** are particularly important. Table 45 summarizes the oxyacids, oxyanions, and oxysalts of sulfur for these two oxidation states. The electronic formulas are given in Figure 85 for the acids and their ions, and the spatial configurations of the sulfite and sulfate ions are indicated.

Table 45.   Oxyacids, Oxyanions, and Oxysalts of Sulfur

Oxidation State	Oxyacids	Oxyanions	Sodium Salts
+4	H_2SO_3 sulfur-ous	HSO_3^- hydrogen sulf-ite	$NaHSO_3$ sodium hydrogen sulfite
		SO_3^{2-} sulf-ite	Na_2SO_3 sodium sulfite
+6	H_2SO_4 sulfur-ic	HSO_4^- hydrogen sulf-ate	$NaHSO_4$ sodium hydrogen sulfate
		SO_4^{2-} sulf-ate	Na_2SO_4 sodium sulfate

In sulfurous acid and the sulfite ions, four of the valence electrons of sulfur are involved in bonds to the more negative oxygen atoms, and the oxidation state of **+4** is thus achieved. By sharing the fourth pair of electrons in its valence shell, sulfur can combine with a fourth atom of oxygen and form sulfuric acid and the sulfate ions, in which sulfur is in the oxidation state of **+6**. These oxysystems of sulfur are much like the oxysystems for chlorine, except that the number of hydrogen atoms in the sulfur acids and the number of charges on the sulfur ions are greater.

Sulfur is two electrons short of the inert-gas structure, whereas chlorine is only one electron short.

The spatial configuration of the sulfite ion is like that of the chlorate ion, and the shape of the sulfate ion duplicates that of the perchlorate ion.

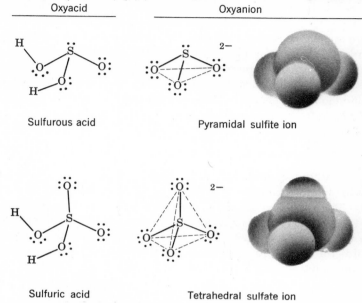

Oxyacid	Oxyanion

Sulfurous acid　　　　　　Pyramidal sulfite ion

Sulfuric acid　　　　　　Tetrahedral sulfate ion

Fig. 85. Configurations of oxyacids and oxyanions having one atom of sulfur.

Sulfuric acid is a much stronger acid than sulfurous acid. Sulfuric acid and the sulfate ions are much more stable in the air than sulfurous acid and the sulfite ions. As in the case of the oxyacids of chlorine, the increase in acid strength and thermal stability that occurs in going to the higher oxidation state may be correlated with the increased sharing of the electrons of the central atom.

260. SULFUR DIOXIDE

Sulfur dioxide may be *prepared* in a number of ways.

a. Combustion of sulfur in air. Sulfur burns quietly in air when it is ignited, and sulfur dioxide is formed. In this reaction sulfur is oxidized from the zero oxidation state to **+4.**

$$S + O_2 = SO_2$$

b. Oxidation of sulfides. Natural sulfides of the metals are "roasted" by heating them in air. Oxides of the metals are formed, and sulfur dioxide comes off as a gas.

$$2ZnS_{(s)} + 3O_{2(g)} = 2ZnO_{(s)} + 2SO_{2(g)}$$

The roasting of sulfides is carried out on a large scale in the industrial smelting of ores to produce the metals, and sulfur dioxide is produced in vast quantities as a by-product.   Formerly, and still to some extent, this was allowed to escape into the air, and it not only was wasted, but it also constituted a serious public nuisance, killing vegetation and corroding metals.   Much of this by-product sulfur dioxide is now converted to sulfuric acid.

c. Action of strong acids on sulfides.   A convenient method for making sulfur dioxide in the laboratory involves adding hydrochloric acid to a solution of a sulfite, such as Na_2SO_3.

$$2H^+ + SO_3^{2-} = H_2O + SO_{2(g)}$$

The sulfur dioxide is evolved readily at room temperature.   No change in the oxidation state of sulfur takes place.

d. Reduction of sulfuric acid.   Many reducing agents react with sulfuric acid, especially when it is concentrated and hot, to produce sulfur dioxide.

$$2H_2SO_4 + Cu = SO_2 + Cu^{2+} + SO_4^{2-} + 2H_2O$$

The *properties of sulfur dioxide* are summarized in Table 46.

Table 46.   Properties of Oxides of Sulfur

Properties	Sulfur Dioxide	Sulfur Trioxide
Molecular formula	SO_2	SO_3, $(SO_3)_n$
Molecular weight	64.07	80.07
Melting point, ° C	−75.5	16.83
Boiling point, ° C	−10.0	44.6
Color	Colorless	Colorless
Relative density (air = 1)	2.26	2.82

The sulfur dioxide molecule has a bent-chain configuration and is believed to have a resonance hybrid structure as already described in Section 180. Sulfur dioxide has a very sharp odor and a choking effect when it is breathed.   It is easily liquefied and has long been used in mechanical refrigerating systems, but because of its strong corrosive action, it is now used less commonly as a refrigerant.   The sulfur dioxide molecule is quite polar because of the difference in electronegativity of sulfur and oxygen and the bent-chain shape of the molecule.   Accordingly, in the liquid state it acts as a good dissociating solvent for electrolytes.   Since, in sulfur dioxide, sulfur is in an intermediate oxidation state, the oxide can act either as an oxidizing agent or as a reducing agent.

261.   SULFUROUS ACID AND SULFITES

Sulfur dioxide dissolves in water to give an acidic solution.   It is generally assumed that this is due to the tendency of SO_2 to combine with water to give *sulfurous acid*.

$$H_2O + SO_2 \rightleftharpoons H_2SO_3$$

Sulfurous acid then will dissociate stepwise as a diprotic acid.

	$K_{(i)}$
$H_2SO_3 \rightleftharpoons H^+ + HSO_3^-$	1.25×10^{-2}
$HSO_3^- \rightleftharpoons H^+ + SO_3^{2-}$	5.6×10^{-8}

Hydrogen sulfite ions and sulfite ions will be present in the solution. H_2SO_3 has never been isolated, because when the solution is evaporated sulfur dioxide is driven off.

Two series of salts of sulfurous acid, containing respectively the hydrogen sulfite ion and the sulfite ion, are formed. $NaHSO_3$ and Na_2SO_3 are quite soluble and are commonly used to provide sulfite ions.   Sulfites hydrolyze considerably, because of the weak acidic character of H_2SO_3, the low stability of this acid, and the limited solubility of SO_2, as the odor of SO_2 above their solutions indicates.

Aqueous solutions of sulfur dioxide and the sulfites are *strong reducing agents*, being oxidized readily, even by air, up to the more stable sulfates. The solutions are used extensively for bleaching and for killing microorganisms.   Sulfites are used extensively in the manufacture of paper and for preserving fruit.

Sulfur dioxide solutions have an oxidizing effect toward strong reducing agents such as H_2S.   When H_2S is bubbled into a solution of SO_2, sulfur is formed, the sulfur in SO_2 being reduced and that in H_2S being oxidized.   We may write the equation

$$2H_2S + SO_2 = 3S + 2H_2O$$

but the reaction is actually much more complicated, with other products also being formed.

262. SULFUR TRIOXIDE

Sulfur trioxide is obtained by the reaction

$$2SO_2 + O_2 = 2SO_3$$

This reaction is very slow, but suitable catalysts can be used to give good yields at reasonable temperatures.   Finely divided platinum serves as an excellent catalyst for this oxidation.

Sulfur trioxide is a colorless liquid which rapidly polymerizes upon standing to long silky crystals whose structure is not well understood. This oxide is important chiefly because it is the acid anhydride of sulfuric acid, probably our most important acid. SO_3 fumes strongly in moist air and, when it is dropped in water, there is a violent exothermic action as it goes into solution. With limited water, the undissociated acid is formed.

$$SO_3 + H_2O = H_2SO_4 + heat$$

263. SULFURIC ACID

Two methods are commonly employed for the production of sulfuric acid.

a. The contact process for sulfuric acid. Usually in the contact process pure sulfur is burned to give pure sulfur dioxide. The sulfur dioxide is oxidized to sulfur trioxide by passing it together with oxygen over a suitable catalyst at about 400°. The fumes of sulfur trioxide are absorbed in concentrated sulfuric acid to produce "fuming sulfuric acid," which has been shown to contain some pyrosulfuric acid, $H_2S_2O_7$. Water is added to the fuming acid to give the concentrated sulfuric acid that is marketed.

$$S + O_2 = SO_2$$
$$2SO_2 + O_2 = 2SO_3$$
$$SO_3 + H_2SO_4 = H_2S_2O_7$$
$$H_2S_2O_7 + H_2O = 2H_2SO_4$$

This process is excellent for producing pure concentrated acid. Very pure sulfur dioxide must be used in the second reaction, otherwise the catalyst may be "poisoned" and will not be effective. Platinum gauze or other finely divided forms of platinum are commonly used as the catalyst.

b. The lead-chamber process for sulfuric acid. In the lead-chamber process impure sulfur dioxide, from the roasting of sulfide ores, is mixed with oxygen and steam in the presence of oxides of nitrogen. The oxides of nitrogen have a catalytic effect. The reaction is carried out in lead-lined chambers. The over-all reaction may be summarized as

$$2H_2O + 2SO_2 + O_2 = 2H_2SO_4$$

The oxides of nitrogen probably enter into the reaction to form intermediates, which react further to give the acid and to regenerate the oxides of nitrogen, which are used over and over again. Impure and only moderately concentrated sulfuric acid is produced very cheaply by this method. Recently, methods have been perfected for purifying SO_2 that are so effective that the contact process for making sulfuric acid is superseding the lead-chamber process in smelters.

Concentrated sulfuric acid is a colorless, heavy, sirupy liquid. The concentrated C.P. acid which is marketed is about 93 to 95 per cent (approximately $18M$). The 100 per cent acid is low in volatility, boiling at 340°. It decomposes when heated strongly to give fumes of SO_3. Sulfuric acid is ordinarily used in aqueous solution.

Sulfuric acid is a very strong diprotic acid. It dissociates strongly to give HSO_4^- and SO_4^{2-} ions and high concentrations of hydrogen ions (see Section 203). It is our most common and cheapest strong acid, used in innumerable cases where strong acidic behavior is desired.

Sulfuric acid is an oxidizing agent. H_2SO_4, HSO_4^-, and SO_4^{2-} act as oxidizing agents, undergoing reduction to SO_2, HSO_3^-, SO_3^{2-}, S, H_2S, or S^{2-}. The course of the reduction of sulfuric acid depends upon the concentration of the acid, the nature of the reducing agent it reacts with, and other factors such as temperature and catalysis. The oxidizing action is particularly characteristic of the hot concentrated acid when it is in contact with metals such as copper. Copper is oxidized to cupric ions and sulfur dioxide is formed, as described in Section 260.

$$2H_2SO_4 + Cu = Cu^{2+} + SO_4^{2-} + 2H_2O + SO_2$$

Concentrated sulfuric acid acts as a powerful dehydrating agent. It absorbs water readily from moist gases which are bubbled through it. It will even remove oxygen and hydrogen from other compounds in the proportions to form water, charring such organic materials as sugar and wood. These materials turn black because, in the decomposition, carbon is formed. Thus, for sugar, the decomposition indicated in the equation

$$C_{12}H_{22}O_{11} = 11H_2O + 12C$$

takes place in contact with sulfuric acid.

When concentrated sulfuric acid is diluted with water *the heat of dilution is very large*, and this operation should always be carried out with considerable caution to avoid violent spattering of the acid. *Very serious burns* are produced when concentrated sulfuric acid comes in contact with the skin because of the combined action of the substance as an acid, oxidizing agent, and dehydrating agent.

Sulfuric acid *is indispensable in chemical industry and in the laboratory.* Tremendous amounts of the acid are used in the production of other chemicals, in metallurgical operations, and in the manufacture of phosphate fertilizers.

264. SULFATES

Two series of salts of sulfuric acid are possible, formed by the association of hydrogen sulfate ions or normal sulfate ions with cations. Sodium hydrogen sulfate and sodium sulfate are typical examples. The former is an acid salt and is used industrially as a source of hydrogen ions. The sulfates of most of the metals are quite soluble in water, the notable exceptions being the sulfates of lead, calcium, strontium, and barium. The solubility product of barium sulfate is exceptionally low. The presence of sulfate ions in solution can be detected, and the amount determined quantitatively by the addition of barium ion, usually as a solution of barium chloride.   Sulfate ions show very little tendency to hydrolyze but are believed to be fairly strongly hydrated in solution.

265. OTHER OXYACIDS OF SULFUR

A large number of other oxyacids of sulfur and their salts can be prepared.   The formation of *pyrosulfuric acid*, $H_2S_2O_7$, by the addition of SO_3 to concentrated sulfuric acid, is important in the contact process for making sulfuric acid.   Pyrosulfuric acid fumes in air due to the liberation of SO_3.   The pyrosulfate (or disulfate) ion, $S_2O_7{}^{2-}$, has the electronic and spatial configuration shown in Figure 86, in which one oxygen is bonded to both atoms of sulfur.

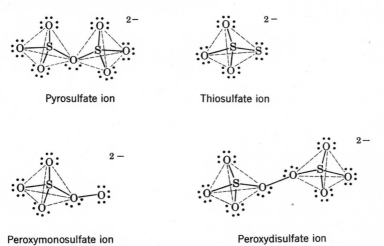

Fig. 86.   **Oxyanions of sulfur having two atoms of sulfur or having peroxy groups.**

Peroxymonosulfuric acid, H_2SO_5, and *peroxydisulfuric acid*, $H_2S_2O_8$, and their ions have some peroxy bonding, as shown by the structure of their ions.

Thiosulfuric acid, $H_2S_2O_3$, has a sulfur atom substituted for one of the oxygen atoms in H_2SO_4.   (The prefix *thio* indicates the substitution of sulfur for oxygen.)   The thiosulfate ion is made by boiling a solution of sulfite with sulfur.

$$SO_3{}^{2-} + S = S_2O_3{}^{2-}$$

The structure of the thiosulfate ion resembles that of $SO_4{}^{2-}$.   In all the *-ic* acids of sulfur, the central sulfur atom has a coordination number of 4. Sodium thiosulfate, $Na_2S_2O_3$, is obtained by crystallization from a solution of sodium ions and thiosulfate ions.   As the miscalled "hypo" (sodium hyposulfate), it is very useful in the "fixing" of photographic plates (see Chapter 33).

266. SELENIUM AND TELLURIUM

Selenium and tellurium resemble sulfur fairly closely, and small amounts of selenium and tellurium are present in many minerals containing sulfur, especially the sulfides. Selenium and tellurium are much less electronegative than sulfur and have properties that are somewhat metallic. They are on the border line between metallic and nonmetallic nature. One form of selenium shows the curious property of being a poor electrical conductor in the dark, but a rather good conductor in the light. Because of this, selenium is made part of the electrical circuits in exposure meters and other light-actuated instruments.

The resemblance to the chemical behavior of sulfur is evident in the list of compounds given below and in the properties for H_2Se and H_2Te given in Table 44.

H_2Se	H_2Te	H_2SeO_3
SeO_2	TeO_2	H_2SeO_4
SeO_3	TeO_3	$CuSeO_4$

EXERCISES

1. a) Where do the elements of the sulfur family occur in the periodic table?
b) What is characteristic of the structures of their atoms?

2. a) Which is larger, O^{2-} or S^{2-}?
b) Which has the lower melting point, sulfur or tellurium?
c) Which is more electronegative, sulfur or chlorine?
d) Which is the stronger oxidizing agent, oxygen or sulfur?

3. What is the oxidation state of sulfur in: a) HS^-; b) SO_3; c) $S_2O_7^{2-}$; d) HSO_3^-; e) H_2S_2; f) ZnS?

4. Compare the allotropy of oxygen and sulfur.

5. What properties does sulfur have which are favorable for getting it from its deposits by the Frasch process?

6. Why are all of the compounds in which sulfur is in positive oxidation states those in which it is bonded either to halogen, oxygen, or nitrogen atoms?

7. What is the electronic structure and the spatial configuration of: a) S_8; b) H_2S; c) SO_3^{2-}; d) SO_2; e) $S_2O_3^{2-}$?

8. a) Why does the addition of hydrochloric acid prevent the precipitation of Zn^{2+} by H_2S?
b) Why does it have no appreciable effect on the precipitation of Cu^{2+} by H_2S?

9. Write balanced equations and indicate any changes in oxidation states that are involved for: a) the preparation of H_2S from FeS; b) the formation of

SO_2 by the reduction of sulfuric acid; c) for the preparation of the thiosulfate ion from the sulfite ion; d) the electrolytic dissociation of H_2SO_3.

10. Name each of the following: a) $NaHSO_3$; b) $Na_2S_2O_3$; c) TeO_2; d) Na_2S; e) $K_2S_2O_8$.

11. Compare the contact and the lead-chamber processes for making sulfuric acid by: a) writing balanced equations for the chemical reactions involved; b) contrasting the quality of the products.

12. a) How many tons of sulfur would be needed to prepare 100 tons of sulfuric acid by the contact process?
b) What weight of oxygen would be needed for the reaction?
c) What volume STP would this oxygen have?

13. a) What will be the volume of 68 g of H_2S at 20° and 740 mm pressure?
b) What volume of SO_2 at the same conditions of temperature and pressure will be formed when H_2S in (a) is burned in an excess of oxygen?

14. Write equations which account for the fact that when Na_2SO_3 is dissolved in water the solution has a noticeable odor.

15. What are the anhydrides of H_2SO_3 and H_2SO_4?

16. Give the electronic and spatial configurations of two different oxyanions each of which has two atoms of sulfur present.

Chapter 22

▶ Nitrogen

Nitrogen is three places before the inert gas, neon, in Period II, being three electrons short of the neon structure. It is the first element in Group V and, like other "first" elements, it differs in many ways from the remaining elements of the family. For this reason we shall discuss nitrogen by itself. Its characteristics are summarized in Table 47.

Table 47. Structure and Properties of Nitrogen

Symbol	N	Melting point, ° C	-209.86
Atomic number	7	Boiling point, ° C	-195.8
Atomic weight	14.008	Relative density as gas	
Electronic structure	2, 5	(air = 1)	0.969
Covalent bond radius, Å	0.70	Color	Colorless
Molecular formula	N_2	Odor	None
Molecular weight	28.016	Solubility in water, ml/liter,	
Standard state	Gas	18°, 760 mm	16.0

268. OXIDATION STATES

With five valence electrons, nitrogen shows great versatility in achieving different oxidation states. These are listed in Table 48, with exam-

Table 48. Oxidation States of Nitrogen

Oxidation States	Typical Molecules and Ions
—3	NH_3, NH_4^+, N^{3-}
—2	N_2H_4, $N_2H_5^+$, $N_2H_6^{2+}$
—1	NH_2OH, NH_3OH^+
0	N_2
+1	N_2O
+2	NO
+3	N_2O_3, HNO_2, NO_2^-
+4	NO_2, N_2O_4
+5	N_2O_5, HNO_3, NO_3^-

ples of molecules or ions representing each state. The more common oxidation states are **−3, 0, +3,** and **+5,** and we will be principally concerned with the behavior of nitrogen in these states. The negative oxidation states are achieved when less electronegative elements, usually hydrogen or the metals, are combined with nitrogen. The positive oxidation states are best known in the oxides, oxyacids, and oxyanion systems.

269. OCCURRENCE OF NITROGEN

The total amount of nitrogen is not very large compared with oxygen, but it is readily available, since most of it is present in the air or in organic materials on the surface of the earth. About four-fifths of the air by volume is elementary nitrogen. There is a large deposit of sodium nitrate in the desert regions of Chile (Chile saltpeter), and nitrate ions and nitrogen-containing substances are present in soil. All plant and animal material contains considerable nitrogen, usually combined with carbon, oxygen, and hydrogen in the form of *proteins*. Coal contains some combined nitrogen.

270. PREPARATION AND PRODUCTION

Supplies of elementary nitrogen can be obtained either by extracting it from the atmosphere or by the decomposition of compounds of nitrogen. The former is, of course, especially attractive.

a. Extraction of elementary nitrogen from the air. The extraction of elementary nitrogen from the air can be accomplished in a number of ways. All involve separating the nitrogen from oxygen, the other principal constituent of air. This separation can be done chemically by causing the oxygen to combine with various substances. Phosphorus, copper, and hydrogen do not combine under most conditions with nitrogen, but all unite readily with oxygen to form oxides, which can easily be separated from the gaseous nitrogen. We have already discussed in Section 137 the liquefaction and fractional distillation of air as a means of obtaining oxygen. In this fractional distillation, the first fractions are rich in nitrogen, and large quantities of nitrogen are produced industrially in this fashion. The nitrogen obtained from air by separating it from oxygen is usually contaminated with small amounts of the inert gases, but these do not ordinarily interfere with its use.

b. By decomposition of compounds of nitrogen. Very pure nitrogen may be obtained by releasing it from its compounds. When ammonium nitrite is heated mildly, it decomposes to give nitrogen.

$$\overset{-3}{}\overset{+3}{}\qquad\overset{0}{}$$
$$NH_4NO_2 = N_2 + 2H_2O$$

The oxidation-reduction changes in this reaction are particularly interesting. The nitrogen atom in the ammonium ion is in the oxidation state of **−3,** whereas the nitrogen atom in the NO_2^- is in the oxidation state of **+3.** When heated, oxidation-reduction occurs, and both atoms of nitrogen are converted to the zero oxidation state. The ammonium ion is the reducing agent and the nitrite ion is the oxidizing agent. Any compound that contains such a combination of oxidizing and reducing agents will not be very stable and is likely to decompose readily, even explosively.

Ammonia may be oxidized by hot cupric oxide to give nitrogen.

$$2NH_3 + 3CuO = 3Cu + N_2 + 3H_2O$$

271. PROPERTIES AND USES OF NITROGEN

Table 47 lists the common properties of this element. Its atoms are small and are less electronegative than oxygen but about as electronegative as chlorine. Its diatomic molecule has the electronic formula

$$: N \equiv N :$$

in which three pairs of electrons are shared by the two nitrogen atoms to form a very stable molecule. The molecules of nitrogen are light and nonpolar, and the attractive forces between these molecules are very small. The element is a colorless gas that is quite difficult to liquefy and freeze. It is odorless and tasteless. Its stable molecules are relatively inert at room temperature, and it is not readily oxidized or reduced. At higher temperatures, nitrogen becomes more active, and it then combines with certain metals and with hydrogen and oxygen. For instance, when nitrogen is passed over very hot magnesium, magnesium nitride is formed.

$$3Mg + N_2 = Mg_3N_{2(s)}$$

Nitrogen frequently is used when an inert gas is needed in electric light bulbs, thermometers, and other systems. Large quantities of it enter into the manufacture of ammonia and other compounds of nitrogen. Liquid nitrogen is a good refrigerating agent to use instead of liquid air when the powerful oxidizing capacity of the latter is undesirable.

272. AMMONIA

Ammonia, NH_3, is the most important compound of nitrogen when it is in the oxidation state of **−3.** It is formed in nature by the decomposition of other compounds of nitrogen, but it does not persist because it is oxidized by the air. Ammonia can be prepared by a variety of methods.

a. Formation of ammonia by synthesis. The combination of hydrogen and nitrogen is carried out on a large scale by the Haber process. The reaction is exothermic.

$$N_2 + 3H_2 \rightleftharpoons 2NH_3 + 22,000 \text{ cal}$$

It does not occur appreciably at room temperature, but at higher temperatures a reversible change is set up and the hydrogen and nitrogen come to equilibrium with ammonia. By applying the principles governing chemical equilibria, Haber was able to specify the conditions that are favorable for the production of a good yield of ammonia. Increased pressure will force the equilibrium to the right. Since the formation of ammonia is exothermic, increasing the temperature will shift the equilibrium to the left and, for this reason, will be unfavorable. On the other hand, at low temperature the rate of reaction is exceedingly slow. By raising the temperature somewhat, the rate of attainment of equilibrium is increased. A compromise has to be struck, and a temperature of 500° is about the optimum. By using a suitable catalyst, such as platinum, active iron, or vanadium pentoxide, the attainment of equilibrium can be facilitated. The Haber process for synthesizing ammonia is commonly run at about 500° and at very high pressures in the presence of an active catalyst. Only a small fraction of the nitrogen and hydrogen are converted to ammonia in the reactor, but this ammonia can be separated from the uncombined elements, and these can be recirculated through the reactor. The process is continuous, the elements being fed in and ammonia being taken out.

b. Formation of ammonia in the destructive distillation of coal. Coal has compounds of nitrogen present. When coal is heated in the absence of air to produce coke or coal gas, ammonia is formed as a by-product in reasonably large quantities.

c. Formation of ammonia by the action of a strong base on an ammonium salt. A strong base, such as sodium hydroxide, is mixed with an ammonium salt and heated. Ammonia comes off as a gas.

$$NaOH_{(s)} + NH_4Cl_{(s)} = NaCl_{(s)} + H_2O + NH_{3(g)}$$

This method is also effective with solutions and is very convenient for the production of small quantities of pure ammonia.

d. Formation of ammonia by the hydrolysis of calcium cyanamide.

$$CaCN_2 + 3H_2O = CaCO_3 + 2NH_3$$

This action proceeds slowly at room temperature but more rapidly when steam is used. The method is not commercially important at present in the United States.

e. Formation of ammonia by the hydrolysis of nitrides of metals. This reaction is characteristic of many nitrides but it is not used primarily as a source of ammonia, because the production of the nitrides is too costly.

$$Mg_3N_{2(s)} + 6H_2O = 3Mg(OH)_{2(s)} + 2NH_{3(g)}$$

Table 49.   Properties of Ammonia

Formula	NH_3
Molecular weight	17.03
Melting point, ° C	−77.7
Boiling point, ° C	−33.4
Relative density (air = 1)	0.5971
Color	Colorless
Odor	Pungent
Solubility in water, 20°, 760 mm, ml/ml H_2O	690

The ammonia molecule has the three hydrogen atoms covalently bonded to the nitrogen in a pyramidal configuration.

Fig. 87.   Polarity of the ammonia molecule.

The nitrogen-hydrogen bond has considerable polarity, and the ammonia molecule is quite polar. The intermolecular attraction is therefore quite large, and, although ammonia has a very small molecular weight, it can be liquefied readily. Liquid ammonia is a good dissociating solvent for salts and is used as a refrigerating agent. The gas has a pungent odor. If breathed in high concentrations, the effect is painful, but the gas is not toxic and small amounts are quite refreshing. "Aromatic spirits of ammonia" is an alcoholic solution of ammonia, ammonium carbonate, and oil of lemon.

Under suitable oxidizing conditions, ammonia may be oxidized to hydroxylamine, NH_2OH, which has an OH group in place of one of the hydrogen atoms. A proton will add to this molecule to give a complex cation, NH_3OH^+.

$$H : \overset{..}{\underset{H}{N}} : \overset{..}{\underset{..}{O}} : H + H^+ = \left[H : \overset{\overset{\textstyle H}{|}}{\underset{H}{N}} : \overset{..}{\underset{..}{O}} : H \right]^+$$

hydroxylamine

Ammonia loses hydrogen when heated with a very active metal, such as sodium, and forms amides.

$$2NH_3 + 2Na = 2NaNH_2 + H_2$$

sodamide

273. AQUEOUS AMMONIA, AMMONIUM HYDROXIDE

Ammonia is very soluble in water.   This high solubility is, to some extent, due to chemical reaction with water, the following equilibria usually being written for the system.

$$NH_3 + H_2O \rightleftharpoons NH_4OH \rightleftharpoons NH_4^+ + OH^-$$

The solution is weakly basic.   Molecular ammonium hydroxide has never been isolated, and there is little proof of its actual existence.   The net reaction for ammonia and water may well be written

$$NH_3 + H_2O \rightleftharpoons NH_4^+ + OH^-$$

Heating the system tends to drive the equilibrium to the left, owing to volatilization of the ammonia.   In fact, the standard way of testing a solution for the presence of ammonium ion is to heat the sample with a base.   If NH_4^+ is present in any quantity, the odor of NH_3 can be detected above the solution, or moistened red litmus paper will turn blue.

The aqueous solution of ammonia, usually called *ammonium hydroxide*, is widely used in the laboratory, in industry, and in the home.   It offers a convenient way of supplying NH_3, OH^-, and NH_4^+, and its uses depend upon the availability of these units.

Aqueous ammonia furnishes NH_3 for ammoniation.   The NH_3 molecules tend to associate with other ions or molecules to form ammoniates.

$$Ag^+ + 2NH_3 \rightleftharpoons Ag(NH_3)_2^+$$

The ammonia molecules retain their configurations in building up the complex, and *ammoniation* is comparable to hydration.   When anhydrous copper sulfate is exposed to dry ammonia gas, the solid turns a dark blue, ammoniation having occurred.

$$CuSO_{4(s)} + 5NH_{3(g)} = CuSO_4 \cdot 5NH_3$$

Aqueous ammonia furnishes OH^- for the precipitation of hydroxides. The solution is useful for the precipitation from solution of cations whose hydroxides have low solubility products, so that a low concentration of OH^- is sufficient. Al^{3+} and Fe^{3+} can thus be precipitated quantitatively from solution by adding aqueous ammonia.

$$Al^{3+} + 3NH_3 + 3H_2O = Al(OH)_{3(s)} + 3NH_4^+$$
$$Fe^{3+} + 3NH_3 + 3H_2O = Fe(OH)_{3(s)} + 3NH_4^+$$

As precipitation proceeds, the ammonia solution continues to dissociate, and ammonium ions accumulate in solution.   The excess of the precipitating agent is easily removed by boiling.

Aqueous ammonia provides NH_4^+ for the formation of ammonium salts.

274.   THE AMMONIUM ION AND AMMONIUM SALTS

The ammonium ion is formed by the addition of a proton to the ammonia molecule, the nitrogen using its unshared pair of electrons to form a bond to the proton.

$$NH_3 + H^+ \rightleftharpoons NH_4^+$$

This reaction is reversible, and hydroxide ions are able to remove the proton from the ammonium ion to regenerate ammonia.   The four hydrogen atoms are covalently bonded to the nitrogen to form a tetrahedral structure.

Fig. 88.   Tetrahedral ammonium ion.

The ammonium ion has the same charge and about the same size as the potassium ion and behaves very much like the potassium ion in forming salts.   *Ammonium salts* are obtained when ammonium ions associate with anions to form crystals, usually by the evaporation of solutions.   Ammonium salts are quite soluble, ammonium chloroplatinate, $(NH_4)_2PtCl_6$, being about the only one which has a solubility low enough so that it is useful in the precipitation of ammonium ions.

Ammonium salts decompose when heated sufficiently.   *Some* ammonium salts, such as the halides where the anion is not an oxidizing agent, *dissociate reversibly* into ammonia and the acid.

$$NH_4Cl \rightleftharpoons NH_3 + HCl$$

Ammonium chloride sublimes at reasonably low temperatures, and in the vapor phase it is completely dissociated.   *Ammonium salts, which have anions capable of acting as oxidizing agents, undergo auto-oxidation-reduction* when heated, the ammonium ion providing a powerful reducing effect.

$$(NH_4)_2Cr_2O_{7(s)} = N_{2(g)} + Cr_2O_{3(s)} + 4H_2O$$
$$NH_4NO_2 = N_2 + 2H_2O$$
$$NH_4NO_3 = N_2O + 2H_2O$$

These reactions are quite exothermic.   They go quietly when small amounts are heated cautiously.   With large amounts of the ammonium salts, however, the heat is not dissipated, and the temperature may rise to the point where the whole mass detonates, exploding violently.   The recent catastrophic explosions of shiploads of ammonium nitrate are examples of what may happen to such systems. Since ammonium nitrate is commonly used in large amounts in fertilizers, proper storage of this material is a matter of concern to the general public.

275. OTHER HYDRONITROGEN COMPOUNDS

Hydrogen can unite with nitrogen to form compounds other than ammonia, depending upon how the atoms are bonded together.

Hydrazine has the formula N_2H_4, and in its molecule there is a covalent bond between the two nitrogen atoms.

$$
\begin{array}{ccc}
\text{H} \quad \text{H} &
\left[\begin{array}{cc} \text{H} \;\; \text{H} \end{array}\right]^{+} &
\left[\begin{array}{cc} \text{H} \;\; \text{H} \end{array}\right]^{2+} \\
\;\; \cdots \;\; \cdots & & \\
: \text{N} : \text{N} : & \text{H} : \text{N} : \text{N} : & \text{H} : \text{N} : \text{N} : \text{H} \\
\;\; \cdots \;\; \cdots & & \\
\text{H} \quad \text{H} & \text{H} \;\; \text{H} & \text{H} \;\; \text{H}
\end{array}
$$

It is a colorless liquid at room temperature. This molecule, like ammonia, can combine with protons to form complex cations, and these cations associate with anions to form salts of hydrazine, such as N_2H_5Cl and $N_2H_6Cl_2$. In hydrazine and its ions, nitrogen is in the oxidation state of **−2** and can act as a powerful reducing agent, usually being oxidized to elementary nitrogen. Mixtures of hydrazine and oxidizing agents are being developed for rocket propulsion.

Hydrogen trinitride, HN_3, is a very unstable substance which is liable to explode violently, even at room temperature. The three nitrogen atoms are bonded together in a chain.

$$
\text{H} : \ddot{\text{N}} : \text{N} :: \text{N} :
$$

The gas dissolves in water and dissociates as a very weak acid to give the N_3^- ion. This ion associates with cations of the metals to form salts, the *trinitrides* or *azides*. $Cu(N_3)_2$, AgN_3, and $Pb(N_3)_2$ explode when struck and can be used as *detonators* to set off explosions of more stable systems, such as TNT.

276. POSITIVE OXIDATION STATES OF NITROGEN

The positive oxidation states of **+3** and **+5** are the most important ones and are to be expected for an element with five valence electrons. Nitrogen achieves these oxidation states usually by combining with oxygen. Table 50 summarizes the formulas and names of the oxyacids, their ions, and their salts, which are the most important examples of nitrogen in these oxidation states. Figure 89 gives the configurations of the nitrite and nitrate ions.

Table 50.   Oxyacids, Oxyanions, and Oxysalts of Nitrogen

Oxidation Salt	Oxyacids	Oxyanions	Sodium Salt
+3	HNO_2 nitr-ous	NO_2^- nitr-ite	$NaNO_2$ sodium nitrite
+5	HNO_3 nitr-ic	NO_3^- nitr-ate	$NaNO_3$ sodium nitrate

In these systems the tendency of the small nitrogen atom to form multiple covalent bonds in building up its valence shell of electrons is apparent.   In the nitrite and nitrate ions all of the oxygen atoms are exactly alike, and their bonds to nitrogen must actually be something

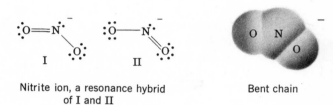

Nitrite ion, a resonance hybrid   Bent chain
of I and II

Nitrate ion, a resonance hybrid of I, II, and III   Planar triangular

Fig. 89.   Configuration of nitrite and nitrate ions.

between single and double covalent bonds.   The nitrite ion is quite similar to the SO_2 molecule, and the nitrate ion resembles the carbonate ion.

Nitrogen forms a long list of oxides having the molecules indicated by the formulas given in Table 51. N_2O_3 and N_2O_5 are the anhydrides of nitrous and nitric acids and are characteristic of the group.   The other oxides of nitrogen are anomalous, and the bonding in their molecules is not well understood.

Table 51.   Properties of the Oxides of Nitrogen

	Nitrous Oxide	Nitric Oxide	Nitrogen Trioxide	Nitrogen Dioxide	Nitrogen Tetroxide	Nitrogen Pentoxide
Molecular formula	N_2O	NO	N_2O_3	NO_2	N_2O_4	N_2O_5
Molecular weight	44.02	30.01	76.02	46.01	92.02	108.02
Melting point, ° C	−90.8	−164	−102			30
Boiling point, ° C	−88.5	−152	3.5			47
Standard state	Gas	Gas	Liquid (0°)	Gas	Gas	Solid
Relative density as gas (air = 1)	1.530	1.036	2.63	1.59	3.18	3.74
Color	Colorless	Colorless	Blue	Redbrown	Yellow	White

277. NITROUS OXIDE

Nitrous oxide is obtained by the thermal decomposition of ammonium nitrate, as already discussed in Section 274.   Nitrous oxide is a colorless gas having a very slight and pleasant odor.   The molecule is not very stable and breaks down when heated mildly.

$$2N_2O = 2N_2 + O_2$$

It *supports combustion.*   Nitrous oxide produces *anesthesia* when it is inhaled and was the first anesthetic to come into use.   It still is employed widely for minor operations.   The popular term "laughing gas" has been applied to it because the patient is apt to laugh hysterically when recovering consciousness.   This oxide does not decompose to provide oxygen at the temperature of the lungs, and therefore it will not support respiration.   Some oxygen must be administered with it.

278. NITRIC OXIDE

Nitric oxide can be *obtained by direct synthesis* from the elements.

$$N_2 + O_2 + 43,000 \text{ cal} \rightleftharpoons 2NO$$

This reaction is highly endothermic and does not proceed unless a very high temperature is maintained.   Increased pressure has no beneficial effect.   This synthesis is carried out industrially by the *arc process.*   Air is passed through an electric arc, which is spread out into a large area to give a *brush discharge.*   In the area, very high temperature prevails and sufficient energy is available so that a small concentration of nitric oxide is built up.   By rapidly cooling the mixture of gases, the nitric oxide can be extracted.   The process is arranged so that it can be operated continuously.   It is quite practical when cheap hydroelectric power is available, but it is not important now in the United States.

Nitric oxide can also be obtained by the reduction of dilute nitric acid, using a proper reducing agent, such as copper.

$$8H^+ + 2NO_3^- + 3Cu = 3Cu^{2+} + 2NO_{(g)} + 4H_2O$$

Other oxides of nitrogen are also formed in this reaction, so the nitric oxide is not pure.

Nitric oxide is a colorless gas that is oxidized readily by molecular oxygen at room temperature, brown NO_2 being formed.

$$2NO + O_2 = 2NO_2$$

It cannot, therefore, persist in the air.   Other oxidizing agents, such as concentrated nitric acid, also convert it to the dioxide.

$$2HNO_3 + NO = 3NO_2 + H_2O$$

279.   NITROGEN TRIOXIDE, NITROUS ACID, AND NITRITES

Nitrogen trioxide can be obtained as a blue unstable liquid by cooling a mixture of nitric oxide and nitrogen dioxide to 0°.   The reaction reverses when the system is warmed.

$$NO + NO_2 \rightleftharpoons N_2O_3$$

The trioxide is the anhydride of nitrous acid.

$$N_2O_3 + H_2O = 2HNO_2$$

Nitrous acid, is a weak acid, dissociating only feebly.

$$HNO_2 = H^+ + NO_2^- \qquad K_{(i)} = 4.5 \times 10^{-4}$$

It is unstable in solution, undergoing auto-oxidation-reduction

$$3HNO_2 = H^+ + NO_3^- + 2NO + H_2O$$

and being rapidly oxidized by air.

The nitrite ion is oxidized very readily to nitrate ion.   Nitrites are quite soluble and cannot be obtained by precipitation reactions.   Nitrites of the very active metals may be obtained by heating the nitrates.

$$2NaNO_3 = 2NaNO_2 + O_2$$

Polluted water usually contains some nitrous acid and nitrite ions owing to the decomposition of nitrogeneous material.   A standard test used to detect contamination of drinking water involves checking for nitrites.

280. NITROGEN DIOXIDE AND NITROGEN TETROXIDE

When NO_2 is cooled, it tends to *polymerize* to N_2O_4, the simple molecules uniting to form a more complex molecule having the same per cent composition.

$$2NO_2 \underset{\text{depolymerization}}{\overset{\text{polymerization}}{\rightleftharpoons}} N_2O_4 + 14{,}600 \text{ cal}$$

brown   light
                                        yellow

This reaction is reversible, heating favoring depolymerization, cooling favoring polymerization. Since the two oxides have different colors, it is possible to follow the reaction by watching the color change. At room temperature we ordinarily have an equilibrium mixture of the two oxides.

These can be obtained as a mixture by a variety of methods. For convenience, we will use only the formula for nitrogen dioxide in the equations. We have already seen in Section 278 that nitric oxide is readily oxidized by air.

$$2NO + O_2 = 2NO_2$$

When concentrated nitric acid is treated with a reducing agent, a mixture of the oxides of nitrogen is obtained, principally NO_2.

$$4HNO_3 + Cu = Cu^{2+} + 2NO_3^- + 2NO_{2(g)} + 2H_2O$$

A product quite free of other oxides of nitrogen is obtained by heating the nitrate of a moderately active metal.

$$2Pb(NO_3)_2 = 2PbO_{(s)} + 4NO_{2(g)} + O_{2(g)}$$

The physical properties of nitrogen dioxide and nitrogen tetroxide are summarized in Table 51. These oxides are quite soluble in water, hydrolyzing to give an acid solution containing nitrate ions, essentially a solution of the strong acid, HNO_3.

$$3NO_2 + H_2O = 2H^+ + 2NO_3^- + NO$$

This is another case of auto-oxidation-reduction. Nitrogen dioxide is not an acid anhydride; a product other than the ions of an oxyacid is also formed when the oxide reacts with water.

281. NITROGEN PENTOXIDE

This oxide is of interest chiefly because it is the anhydride of nitric acid. It can be prepared by the dehydration of concentrated nitric acid. The acid is brought together with a very powerful dehydrating agent such as phosphoric oxide.

$$2HNO_3 = H_2O + N_2O_5$$

N_2O_5 can also be made by the reaction of NO_2 with ozone.

$$2NO_2 + O_3 = N_2O_5 + O_2$$

The crystalline N_2O_5 reacts vigorously with water to form nitric acid.

282. NITRIC ACID

Nitric acid is one of the most important compounds of nitrogen. It is manufactured in large quantities by a number of different methods, the first one described below being the one that is now important in this country.

a. The oxidation of ammonia, the Ostwald process. Ammonia, produced by the Haber process or by other methods, is oxidized by oxygen over a catalyst at about 1000°.

$$4NH_3 + 5O_2 = 4NO + 6H_2O$$

Platinum is an excellent catalyst for this reaction. The NO is then cooled with excess oxygen to give NO_2, and this is reacted with water to give a solution of nitric acid.

$$2NO + O_2 = 2NO_2$$
$$3NO_2 + H_2O = 2H^+ + 2NO_3^- + NO$$

b. Sodium nitrate is heated with sulfuric acid.

$$NaNO_3 + H_2SO_4 = HNO_3 + NaHSO_4$$

Only one of the hydrogen atoms of sulfuric acid is used in the reaction that proceeds when the system is heated moderately. The sodium primary sulfate will react with more sodium nitrate, if heated considerably more, but at the higher temperature nitric acid decomposes. It is not practical to carry this reaction beyond the first stage. The nitric acid, being volatile, distills off and can be collected as the concentrated acid. The sodium hydrogen sulfate, which is formed as a by-product, is useful in other chemical operations because of its acidic properties. This method is the most convenient way for preparing nitric acid in the laboratory, and it is practical industrially if cheap sodium nitrate from deposits, such as Chile saltpeter, is available. It has been superseded in this country by other methods which exploit the supply of nitrogen in the air.

c. The electric arc method. This process makes use of the electric arc method for making nitric oxide from the air. The nitric oxide is then converted to NO_2, which is reacted with water to give a solution of nitric acid.

Pure nitric acid is a colorless liquid. It fumes strongly and decomposes to give oxides of nitrogen, which color it brown.

$$4HNO_3 = 2H_2O + 4NO_2 + O_2$$

The concentrated C.P. nitric acid that is marketed is an aqueous solution containing about 68 per cent by weight of the acid.   It is about $15M$. The chemical behavior of nitric acid is complicated because it not only is a strong acid but it also is a very versatile oxidizing agent.

Nitric acid behaves in the characteristic fashion of all strong acids.   It dissociates very strongly in dilute aqueous solution

$$HNO_3 = H^+ + NO_3^-$$

The hydrogen ions neutralize bases and oxidize metals.   The nitrate ions associate with cations to form nitrates.

Nitric acid is a powerful oxidizing agent.   It is readily reduced, with the possibility that nitrogen may go to any of the lower oxidation states. NO_2, NO_2^-, NO, N_2, or NH_4^+ is usually formed, depending upon the conditions.   The extent of reduction is found to depend upon the strength of the reducing agent, the concentration of the nitric acid, the temperature, and upon catalysis.   The situation is also complicated by the possibility of secondary reactions.   Usually several reduction products are formed simultaneously.   It is very difficult to do more than to determine which reaction probably predominates.   We can study the effect of each factor by varying it while the others are held constant.   It is then possible to generalize about the oxidizing behavior of the acid.

The change in oxidation state of nitrogen increases as the strength of the reducing agent increases.   Thus, when dilute nitric acid is treated with each of the following reducing agents, the nitrogen is reduced predominantly to the molecule or ion noted.   The reducing agents are arranged in order of increasing strength.

Reducing Agent	Reduction Product
Ag, Hg	NO_2
Cu, Fe^{2+}	NO
$SnCl_2$ + HCl	N_2O
Sn	N_2
Zn	NH_4^+
Mg, Na	$NH_4^+ + H_2$

The change in oxidation state of nitrogen increases as the concentration of the acid is decreased.   When copper reacts with concentrated nitric acid, the nitrogen is reduced to NO_2.   When the nitric acid is dilute it is reduced by copper predominantly to NO (see Sections 278 and 280).

No good generalization can be made about the effect of temperature or catalysts on the course of the reduction of nitric acid.   These factors are quite specific for each case.

The powerful oxidizing action of nitric acid is made use of in *aqua regia*. This reagent is a mixture of one part concentrated nitric acid with three parts concentrated hydrochloric acid.   The solution undergoes changes in color upon standing, and the odor of chlorine becomes quite strong.

The changes taking place must be very complicated and are not well understood, but the following equation is believed to describe, in part, what happens.

$$HNO_3 + 3HCl = NOCl + 2H_2O + Cl_2$$

Because gas is liberated in this reaction, aqua regia should never be stored in closed containers. The nitrosyl chloride, NOCl, is rather unstable and is a powerful oxidizing and chlorinating agent. Aqua regia is a very corrosive solution, capable of attacking and taking into solution such metals as gold and platinum. These are not corroded by either concentrated nitric acid or concentrated hydrochloric acid alone. The metals form the stable complex chloro-ions $AuCl_4^-$ and $PtCl_6^{2-}$.

Nitric acid is used widely as a nitrating agent. Nitric acid reacts with organic materials, such as cotton or toluene. High explosives, such as gun cotton or TNT (trinitrotoluene), are formed.

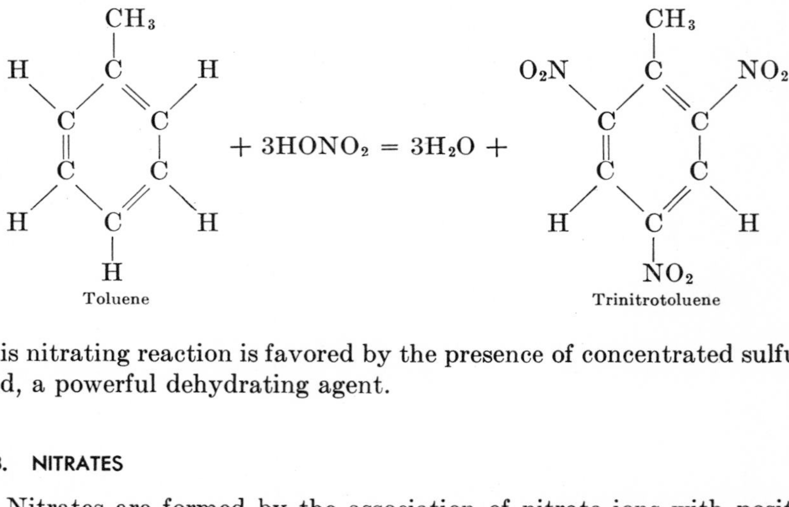

Toluene   Trinitrotoluene

This nitrating reaction is favored by the presence of concentrated sulfuric acid, a powerful dehydrating agent.

283. NITRATES

Nitrates are formed by the association of nitrate ions with positive ions. All nitrates are rather highly soluble and are obtained by crystallization from solution.

The nitrate ion is not very stable thermally, and any nitrate will decompose when it is heated sufficiently. The decomposition products depend upon the cations that are present in the salt. *Nitrates of the very active metals* decompose to nitrites and oxygen.

$$2NaNO_3 = 2NaNO_2 + O_2$$

Nitrates of the less active metals give NO_2.

$$2Cu(NO_3)_2 = 2CuO + 4NO_2 + O_2$$

Nitrates of the metals of intermediate activity, such as calcium **and** barium, give nitrites at low temperatures and NO_2 at higher temperatures. *Ammonium nitrate* forms N_2O.

284. FIXATION OF NITROGEN

Nitrogen is of great importance to living organisms and is essential for both animal and plant life. Most plants and animals cannot, however, utilize free atmospheric nitrogen for food. The very stable inert nitrogen molecules do not react readily enough at ordinary temperatures. The atmospheric nitrogen must first be caused to form compounds that can be used. The term *fixation of nitrogen* includes all processes whereby atmospheric nitrogen combines with other substances to form compounds. This is accomplished as follows:

a. In nature in various ways. The most important process involves *bacterial action*. Leguminous plants (peas, beans, clover, alfalfa, and so on) have nodules on their roots which contain colonies of nitrogen-fixing bacteria. These bacteria are able to convert atmospheric nitrogen to compounds of nitrogen, which accumulate and are available as plant food. Huge amounts of nitrogen are constantly being fixed in this fashion, and the process is of tremendous importance to agriculture. Atmospheric nitrogen is also converted to oxides of nitrogen when electrical discharge (lightning) occurs in the air.

b. In industry. We have already seen how it is possible by the Haber process to transform atmospheric nitrogen to ammonia, and how the electric arc process may be used to form nitric oxide from air. A third industrial method is used for fixing nitrogen on the large scale. Calcium carbide, a cheap material readily made from limestone and coal, is heated with nitrogen gas that has been extracted from air.

$$CaC_{2(s)} + N_{2(g)} = CaCN_{2(s)} + C_{(s)}$$

The calcium cyanamide formed can be used directly on the soil as a fertilizer, or it may be used in the manufacture of many other important compounds of nitrogen.

EXERCISES

1. Give the formula for one substance that illustrates each oxidation state that can be achieved by nitrogen.

2. Write a balanced equation that describes what happens when each of the following systems is heated, indicate the changes in oxidation states involved, and point out which of the reactions are examples of auto-oxidation-reduction: a) NH_4NO_3; b) $Mg + N_2$: c) KNO_3; d) concentrated HNO_3; e) dilute $HNO_3 + Cu$; f) NH_4NO_2; g) $CaC_2 + N_2$.

3. What equilibria exist in a system consisting of NH_3 and its saturated solution in water?   Predict and explain what will happen

a) When the solution is heated.

b) When the partial pressure of NH_3 above the solution is increased.

c) When solid sodium hydroxide is added to the solution.

d) When solid anhydrous cupric sulfate is added to the solution.

4. What is the spatial configuration of: a) NO_3^-? b) NH_4^+? c) NH_3? d) NO_2^-?

5. Compare the strength as acids of nitrous and nitric acids.

a) How can you account for this on the basis of their structures?

b) Which will have the greater tendency for hydrolysis, $NaNO_2$ or $NaNO_3$? Why?

6. Write the equation for the polymerization of NO_2.   Is the polymerization endo- or exothermic?   What two different methods can you suggest for following the progress of the polymerization?

7. What factors determine the extent to which HNO_3 is reduced when it acts as an oxidizing agent?   What are the possible products of the reduction of nitric acid?   Indicate the change in oxidation state of nitrogen involved in each case.

8. Describe two important industrial processes for manufacturing compounds of nitrogen that employ catalysts.   Write equations for the reactions involved, and specify the conditions used.

9. How many liters of oxygen at STP will be required for the oxidation of 10 liters of nitric oxide at STP?

10. Complete and balance the following equations, for the oxidizing action of dilute HNO_3, using the change of oxidation state method:

a) $Ag + H^+ + NO_3^- = Ag^+ + NO_2 + H_2O$

b) $Cu + H^+ + NO_3^- = Cu^{2+} + NO + H_2O$

c) $Sn^{2+} + H^+ + NO_3^- + Cl^- = SnCl_6^{2-} + N_2O + H_2O$

d) $Zn + H^+ + NO_3^- = Zn^{2+} + NH_4^+ + H_2O$

11. What is meant by the term *fixation of nitrogen*, and why is it important to accomplish this?

Chapter 23

▶ Phosphorus, Arsenic, Antimony, and Bismuth

285. THE NITROGEN FAMILY

This family of elements includes nitrogen, phosphorus, arsenic, antimony, and bismuth. These are in Group V of the periodic table, each occurring in the third place preceding the inert gas at the end of its period. The electronic structures are given in Table 52.

Table 52. Elements of the Nitrogen Family

	Nitrogen	Phosphorus	Arsenic	Antimony	Bismuth
Symbol	N	P	As	Sb	Bi
Atomic number	7	15	33	51	83
Atomic weight	14.008	30.98	74.91	121.76	209.00
Electronic structure	2, 5	2, 8, 5	2, 8, 18, 5	2, 8, 18, 18, 5	2, 8, 18, 32, 18, 5
Covalent bond radius, Å	0.70	1.10	1.21	1.41	
Common oxidation states	**−3, 0, +3, +5**	**−3, 0, +3, +5**	**−3, 0, +3, +5**	**−3, 0, +3, +5**	**−3, 0, +3, +5**
Color	Colorless	White	Gray	Shiny gray	Shiny gray
Standard state	Gas	Solid	Solid	Solid	Solid
Melting point, ° C	−209.9	44.1	817	630.5	271
Boiling point, ° C	−195.8	280	sublimes	1440	1420
Relative sizes of atoms	Increasing ⟶				
Electronegativity	Decreasing ⟶				
Metallic nature	Increasing ⟶				

Each of the elements of this family has five electrons in its outermost shell. With increase in atomic number down the family, the number of shells of electrons increases and the atoms increase in size. The electronegativity decreases as the atomic number increases. Nitrogen and phosphorus are definitely nonmetallic, but arsenic is on the border line

361

between the metals and nonmetals. The properties of antimony and bismuth are quite metallic in many respects, and these elements are usually listed as metals. The transition from nonmetallic to metallic behavior is very pronounced in this family.

We have already considered nitrogen in detail, but this element is not very typical of the rest of the family. We will take up the remaining four elements together, centering the discussion around phosphorus.

286. OXIDATION STATES

The characteristic oxidation states for the family are **−3, 0, +3, +5.** These are to be expected for atoms with five valence electrons. The **−3** oxidation state is achieved when the atom becomes associated with three more electrons, either by forming an anion with a charge of $3-$ or by forming three covalent bonds to less electronegative atoms. In the oxidation state of **+3** one pair of the five valence electrons is inert, and only the other three are used for chemical bonding to more electronegative atoms. The **+5** oxidation state involves the use of all five valence electrons to form covalent bonds. Table 53 gives examples of common molecules or ions representative of phosphorus in each oxidation state.

Table 53. Oxidation States of Phosphorus

Oxidation State	Typical Molecules and Ions
−3	PH_3, P^{3-}
0	P_4
+3	P_4O_6, H_3PO_3, $H_2PO_3^-$, PCl_3
+5	P_4O_{10}, H_3PO_4, PO_4^{3-}, PCl_5

The oxidation state of **−3** is assumed by phosphorus when it is combined with hydrogen or with metals such as calcium. With increase in atomic number in the family, this negative oxidation state becomes less stable and is realized less commonly. Again we find that compounds with oxygen are most representative of the positive oxidation states, the oxides, oxyacids, and oxysalts being the most familiar compounds of the family. The halides are also well known. With decrease in electronegativity, there is some tendency for the formation of positive ions, especially for antimony and bismuth.

287. OCCURRENCE AND PREPARATION

Phosphorus is far too active to be found in the elementary state in nature. It usually occurs combined with oxygen in the phosphate ion. This ion is present in many minerals, the chief one being phosphate rock, $Ca_3(PO_4)_2$. Phosphorus is also present in plant and animal material.

Bones, teeth, nerves, and muscle tissue contain combined phosphorus. It has been shown that the phosphorus in animal skeletons is constantly undergoing a rather rapid renewal. To obtain the needed phosphorus for the body we eat such foods as eggs, beans, peas, whole wheat, and milk. Plants must obtain phosphorus from the soil, and, if a soil is deficient in available phosphorus, fertilizers are used to supply it.

Elementary phosphorus is manufactured by heating a mixture of calcium phosphate, sand, and coke to high temperatures. The volatile phosphorus distills off and is protected from oxidation by condensation under water.

$$2Ca_3(PO_4)_2 + 6SiO_2 + 10C = 6CaSiO_{3(s)} + 5CO_{(g)} + P_{4(g)}$$

Cast into sticks, it appears on the market as white phosphorus.

Arsenic, antimony, and bismuth are found as the sulfides and oxides. The sulfides are "roasted" by heating them in the air, and the oxides that are formed are reduced by heating them with carbon.

$$2As_2S_3 + 9O_2 = As_4O_6 + 6SO_2$$
$$As_4O_6 + 6C = 4As + 6CO$$

288. PROPERTIES AND USES OF THE ELEMENTS

The story about the properties of these elements is rather complicated because of the many allotropic forms which they can assume. In Table 52 the properties of the allotropic form commonly encountered are listed. These properties show the variations to be expected with change in atomic number and size.

Phosphorus has a remarkable tendency for allotropy. Two varieties, known as *white* and *red* phosphorus, are common. White phosphorus is obtained by rapid condensation of phosphorus vapor. It is not stable under ordinary conditions and slowly changes to the red variety. This transition goes rapidly when the temperature is raised or when white phosphorus is exposed to light. The properties of these two forms are compared in Table 54.

Table 54. Allotropic Forms of Phosphorus

White Phosphorus	Red Phosphorus
Metastable	Stable under ordinary conditions
Metals at 44.1°	Sublimes; the vapor formed condenses to white phosphorus
Insoluble in water	Insoluble in water
Soluble in CS_2	Insoluble in CS_2
Very active; low kindling point in air; undergoes spontaneous combustion in air; must be stored under water	Less reactive; higher kindling point in air and can be exposed to air without appreciable oxidation
Poisonous	Nonpoisonous

White phosphorus must be handled and stored with proper precautions because of its spontaneous inflammability and its poisonous nature. It was formerly used in the manufacture of match heads by mixing it with a suitable oxidizing agent and using a protective coating to keep it from the air. The poisonous nature of white phosphorus made the manufacture and handling of such matches hazardous. The use of white phosphorus in matches is now outlawed, red phosphorus or P_4S_3 replacing it. White phosphorus was used extensively in incendiaries in World War II. Whenever possible, the use of red phosphorus is preferred.

The structure of the phosphorus molecule, P_4, as it appears in white phosphorus crystals and in the vapor at low temperatures, is now known.

Fig. 90.   Configuration of the P_4 molecule.

The four phosphorus atoms are at the corners of a regular tetrahedron. Each phosphorus atom is bonded to each of the other three atoms by a shared pair of electrons, so that each atom has built up its valence shell of electrons to eight. The molecule is therefore quite symmetrical, and the volatility of the element is high.

Phosphorus will combine readily when heated with many of the metals to form phosphides, such as Ca_3P_2. It also is used in some alloys, phosphor bronze being a good example. Phosphorus combines directly with the halogens to give molecular substances such as PCl_3 and PCl_5.

Arsenic, antimony, and bismuth also have different allotropic forms. The common form of arsenic is more nonmetallic than metallic in character, whereas the stable forms of antimony and bismuth are quite metallic. All three of these elements are used to produce alloys. In the manufacture of lead shot, arsenic is added to lead to harden it. Antimony and bismuth are much used for making low-melting alloys to be used in bearing metals, in type metal, for safety fuses in electrical circuits, and in automatic systems for protection against fire.

289.   HYDRIDES

All the elements of the nitrogen family combine with hydrogen to form compounds like ammonia.

Table 55.   **Hydrides of the Nitrogen Family**

Properties	NH_3	PH_3	AsH_3	SbH_3	BiH_3
Name	Ammonia	Phosphine	Arsine	Stibine	Bismuth hydride
Molecular weight	17.032	34.00	77.93	124.78	212.02
Melting point, ° C	−77.4	−132.5	−113.5	−88	
Boiling point, ° C	−33.4	−85	−55	−17	
Standard state	Gas	Gas	Gas	Gas	Gas
Color	None	None	None	None	None
Odor	Pungent	Garlic-like	Garlic-like	Garlic-like	Garlic-like
Solubility					
Polar character					
Stability		Decreasing			
Tendency to unite with protons					

All of these hydrides can be obtained by hydrolyzing the compounds which the elements of this family form with the active metals.   This reaction proceeds faster in acid solutions.

$$Ca_3P_2 + 6H_2O = 2PH_{3(g)} + 3Ca(OH)_2$$
$$Ca_3As_2 + 6H_2O = 2AsH_{3(g)} + 3Ca(OH)_2$$
$$Mg_3Sb_2 + 6H^+ = 2SbH_{3(g)} + 3Mg^{2+}$$

Phosphine can be made by boiling white phosphorus with an alkaline solution, auto-oxidation-reduction occurring.

$$\overset{0}{P_4} + 3OH^- + 3H_2O = \overset{-3}{PH_3} + 3\overset{+1}{H_2PO_2^-}$$

Some of the phosphorus is reduced to phosphine; the rest is oxidized to the primary hypophosphite ion, in which phosphorus is in the very unstable oxidation state of **+1**.

These hydrides are all colorless gases with very strong odors, the odor becoming increasingly noisome as we go down the group.   The molecular structures are all like that of ammonia, the bonds to the hydrogens being covalent.   With increasing size, the bonding becomes weaker and less polar.   The abnormally high melting and boiling points of ammonia are to be attributed to the fact that this substance is very much more polar than the rest of the hydrides.   Perhaps some hydrogen bonding also is involved.

Arsine decomposes to the elements readily when passed through a hot glass tube.

$$2AsH_{3(g)} = 2As_{(s)} + 3H_{2(g)}$$

This is the basis of the Marsh test used to detect arsenic poisoning. The sample suspected of containing arsenic is added to a generator containing zinc and hydrochloric acid. Assuming that the arsenic is present as the oxide, the following reaction occurs.

$$As_2O_3 + 6Zn + 12H^+ = 2AsH_3 + 6Zn^{2+} + 3H_2O$$

Hydrogen is also formed. When the mixture of gaseous products is passed through a hot glass tube, any arsine that is present will decompose, and a brilliant mirror of arsenic deposits on the walls of the tube. Bismuth hydride decomposes rapidly at room temperature.

The hydrides are combustible. Phosphine inflames spontaneously in the air, due to the presence of some P_2H_4.

$$PH_3 + 2O_2 = H_3PO_4$$

All but ammonia are extremely poisonous.

None of the hydrides of the nitrogen family acts as an acid. Instead, as we found for ammonia, they tend to combine with a proton to form complex positive ions. Phosphine forms the phosphonium ion, but only when a high concentration of H^+ is used.

$$PH_3 + H^+ = PH_4^+$$

However, this tendency to combine with protons fades out rapidly as we go down the family and is not known at all for SbH_3 and BiH_3.

290. POSITIVE OXIDATION STATES

The positive oxidation states of $+3$ and $+5$ are important for all the nitrogen family elements. The oxides, hydroxides, and ions for these oxidation states are listed in Table 56.

Table 56. **Oxides, Oxyacids, and Oxyanions of the Nitrogen Family**

Oxidation state $+3$	Oxides	N_2O_3	P_4O_6	As_4O_6	Sb_2O_3	Bi_2O_3
	-ous acids	HNO_2	H_3PO_3	H_3AsO_3	H_3SbO_3	$Bi(OH)_3$
	-ite ions	NO_2^-	PO_3^{3-}	AsO_3^{3-}	SbO_3^{3-}	
Oxidation state $+5$	Oxides	N_2O_5	P_4O_{10}	As_4O_{10}	Sb_2O_5	
	-ic acids	HNO_3	H_3PO_4	H_3AsO_4	H_7SbO_6	H_7BiO_6
	-ate ions	NO_3^-	PO_4^{3-}	AsO_4^{3-}	$H_6SbO_6^-$	$H_6BiO_6^-$

With increasing atomic number, the oxides become less acidic and more basic, and the hydroxides of antimony and bismuth have considerable basic character, becoming amphoteric.

Phosphorous acid and the phosphites are powerful reducing agents. As_4O_6 and the other compounds of arsenic are very poisonous, and the arsenites and arsenates are useful as insecticides. Remember that the ending *-ous* is used to name the acids and the oxides of these elements in the oxidation state of **+3**.   *The correct spelling for the name of the element is phosphorus.*

Notice that in the oxidation state of **+5,** the number of oxygen atoms combined with the atom of the Group V element increases from three for nitrogen, to four for phosphorus and arsenic, to six for antimony and bismuth.   This is a consequence of the increase in size of the central atom with increase in atomic number.   More oxygen atoms can get close enough to the larger central atoms to form strong bonds.

291. STRUCTURE OF THE OXIDES AND OXYANIONS OF PHOSPHORUS

The bonding typical of the oxycompounds of phosphorus and arsenic is shown in Figure 91.

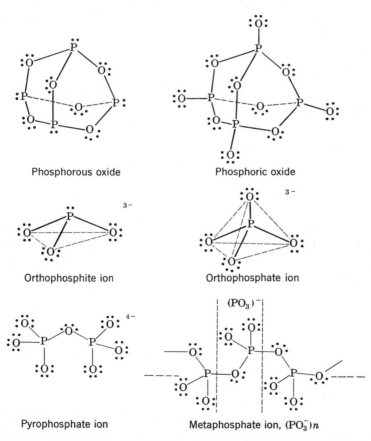

Phosphorous oxide

Phosphoric oxide

Orthophosphite ion

Orthophosphate ion

Pyrophosphate ion

Metaphosphate ion, $(PO_3^-)n$

Fig. 91. Configurations of the common oxides and oxyanions of phosphorus.

In P_4O_6 each phosphorus atom is covalently bonded to three oxygen atoms, each of which is bonded to two phosphorus atoms.   The molecule is a globular one, with the phosphorus atoms in tetrahedral positions with respect to each other.   In the phosphite ion, the phosphorus atom is bonded to three oxygen atoms which have acquired one more electron each from outside, so that the phosphite ion has a triple negative charge. In both phosphorous oxide and the phosphite ion each phosphorus atom has an unshared pair of electrons which it has not used for bonding. When oxidation to phosphoric oxide and the phosphate ion occurs, each phosphorus atom uses this pair of electrons to form a bond to another oxygen atom, and the oxidation state of phosphorus rises to $+5$.

292. PHOSPHORIC OXIDE AND THE PHOSPHORIC ACIDS

Phosphoric oxide is easily prepared by the complete combustion of phosphorus in air.   The simplest formula for this compound is P_2O_5, and it commonly is called phosphorus pentoxide.   In the vapor phase the molecule is P_4O_{10}, but the structure is more extended in the crystals.   It has a tremendous tendency to combine with water.   The reaction is so exothermic that it must be carried out with considerable caution.   The combination with water is believed to occur stepwise to give a series of phosphoric acids, although the exact course, of the reaction is not well understood.

$$2H_2O + P_4O_{10} = \underset{\text{metaphosphoric acid}}{4HPO_3}$$

$$H_2O + 2HPO_3 = \underset{\text{pyrophosphoric acid}}{H_4P_2O_7}$$

$$H_2O + H_4P_2O_7 = \underset{\text{orthophosphoric acid}}{2H_3PO_4}$$

In the meta- and pyroacids, oxygen bridges are formed between adjacent phosphorus atoms to build up extended structures, in which there are always four oxygen atoms bonded to every phosphorus atom. The metaphosphoric acid is believed to be highly polymerized.   In dilute solution, the hydrolysis to the orthophosphoric acid is favored.

293. PHOSPHATE IONS AND PHOSPHATES

The phosphoric acids dissociate stepwise to give a series of phosphate ions (Section 203).   These tend to form several series of salts.   Thus, there are three sodium salts known for orthophosphoric acid.

NaH_2PO_4, monosodium dihydrogen orthophosphate, dissolves in water to give an acidic solution.   This must be due to dissociation of the $H_2PO_4^-$ ion.

$$H_2PO_4^- \rightleftharpoons H^+ + HPO_4^{2-}$$

Because of this acid reaction, the salt is useful in baking powders.

Na₂HPO₄, disodium monohydrogen orthophosphate, gives a slightly alkaline reaction when dissolved in water, the secondary phosphate ion hydrolyzing somewhat to produce OH^-.

$$HPO_4{}^{2-} + H_2O \rightleftharpoons H_2PO_4{}^- + OH^-$$

Na₃PO₄, trisodium orthophosphate, gives a highly basic solution with water because the $PO_4{}^{3-}$ hydrolyzes very strongly.

$$PO_4{}^{3-} + H_2O \rightleftharpoons HPO_4{}^{2-} + OH^-$$

Trisodium phosphate is widely used as a cleansing agent because of its ability to produce an alkaline solution which will attack grease. It also tends to soften the water by precipitating calcium ions.

$$3Ca^{2+} + 2PO_4{}^{3-} = Ca_3(PO_4)_{2(s)}$$

Calcium dihydrogen phosphate is formed in the manufacture of phosphate fertilizers when phosphate rock is treated with concentrated sulfuric acid.

$$Ca_3(PO_4)_2 + 2H_2SO_4 = Ca(H_2PO_4)_2 + 2CaSO_4$$

The mixture of the products of this reaction is marketed as "superphosphate" fertilizer. The calcium dihydrogen phosphate is more soluble than normal calcium phosphate, and phosphate ions can be made more available to plants by use of superphosphate.

The *pyrophosphates* are obtained when monohydrogen orthophosphates are heated.

$$2Na_2HPO_4 = H_2O + Na_4P_2O_7$$

Metaphosphates are formed by heating dihydrogen orthophosphates.

$$NaH_2PO_4 = H_2O + NaPO_3$$

Metaphosphates actually involve highly polymerized phosphate ions, the formula $NaPO_3$ merely indicating the ratio of atoms. $(NaPO_3)_n$ is a remarkable material. It is obtained in several crystalline modifications and also as a glass. Chips of this glass dissolve in water to give solutions in which the metaphosphate ions affect polyvalent cations, such as Ca^{2+} and Al^{3+}, in some obscure manner, so that they cannot be precipitated by soap. The formation of boiler scale is also prevented. Sodium metaphosphate glass, therefore, is important as a water softener and for the treatment of boiler water.

294. SULFIDES

The sulfides of phosphorus are curious compounds in which the combining ratios are rather anomalous. They are highly combustible, and the use of P_4S_3 in matches has already been mentioned.

When arsenic, antimony, and bismuth are in the oxidation state of **+3**, they are precipitated as highly colored sulfides by hydrogen sulfide. As_2S_3 is yellow, Sb_2S_3 is red, and Bi_2S_3 is black. These compounds have been used as pigments down through the ages.

295. HALIDES

All the elements of this family except nitrogen are oxidized readily by the halogens to form tri- and pentahalides.

$$2P + 3Cl_2 = 2PCl_3$$
$$2PCl_3 + 2Cl_2 \rightleftharpoons 2PCl_5$$

The second equation is written as reversible since, at ordinary temperatures, PCl_5 has a considerable tendency to dissociate to PCl_3 and Cl_2. These are volatile covalent systems for phosphorus and arsenic but decrease in volatility for antimony and bismuth. They hydrolyze rather completely, the volatile hydrogen halides being formed and oxyacids and ions accumulating in solution.

$$PCl_3 + 3H_2O = 3H^+ + 3Cl^- + H_3PO_3$$
$$PCl_5 + 4H_2O = 6H^+ + 5Cl^- + H_2PO_4^-$$

Antimony and bismuth chlorides hydrolyze to give insoluble hydroxy- and oxychlorides.

$$BiCl_3 + 2H_2O = Bi(OH)_2Cl_{(s)} + 2H^+ + 2Cl^-$$
$$Bi(OH)_2Cl = BiOCl_{(s)} + H_2O$$

EXERCISES

1. Compare the elements of the nitrogen family with respect to: a) atomic structure; b) covalent bond radii; c) common oxidation states; d) standard states; e) electronegativity; f) nonmetallic nature.

2. a) How does phosphorus occur in nature?
   b) How is the element manufactured?
   c) Compare white and red phosphorus.

3. a) What general method can be used for the preparation of the hydrides of the nitrogen family?
   b) What is the characteristic bonding and configuration of their molecules?
   c) Outline the chemistry that is involved in the Marsh test for arsenic, giving equations.

4. a) What is the bonding and configuration of the P_4O_6 molecule?
   b) Account for the fact that this oxide is readily oxidized to phosphoric oxide.

5. What are the characteristic coordination numbers toward oxygen of each of the elements of the nitrogen family when they are in the oxidation state of **+5?**

6. Account for the fact that there are so many different kinds of phosphate ions.

7. Discuss the hydrolysis of the three different sodium salts of orthophosphoric acid, giving balanced equations for the net reactions.

8. Write balanced equations for the action of water on: a) PCl_3; b) PCl_5; c) $BiCl_3$.

9. How can $NaPO_3$ glass be obtained, and for what is it used?

Chapter 24

▶ Carbon and Its Inorganic Compounds

296. CARBON AND RELATED ELEMENTS

Of the elements of Group IV, carbon, silicon, germanium, tin, and lead have analogous atomic structures. Each is four places before the inert gas in its respective period. As indicated in Table 57, each of these

Table 57. Carbon and Related Elements

	Carbon	Silicon	Germanium	Tin	Lead
Symbol	C	Si	Ge	Sn	Pb
Atomic number	6	14	32	50	82
Atomic weight	12.010	28.06	72.60	118.70	207.21
Electronic structure	2, 4	2, 8, 4	2, 8, 18, 4	2, 8, 18, 18, 4	2, 8, 18, 32, 18, 4
Covalent bond radius, Å	0.771	1.17	1.22	1.40	1.46
Nature	Non-metallic	Non-metallic	Semimetallic	Metallic	Metallic
Relative size of atoms under comparable conditions	Increasing ⟶				

elements has four electrons in its outermost shell, and similarities in valence and chemical behavior are to be expected. However, the increase in the number of shells of electrons with increase in atomic number is accompanied by an increase in atomic size, and this is correlated with a considerable but gradual variation in the nature of the elements. The shift from nonmetallic character to decidedly metallic character is very marked, and the differences between the elements are so great that we shall discuss first carbon and then silicon, as examples of nonmetallic elements, and later come back to tin and lead when the metals are considered. Germanium will not be dealt with any further because it is relatively unavailable and unfamiliar. Its properties are roughly midway between those of silicon and tin.

297. BONDING AND OXIDATION STATES OF CARBON

Carbon is in the center of its period and is of intermediate electro-negativity. It shows little tendency to ionize to form simple carbon anions or cations by complete transfer of electrons. Instead, it usually forms four covalent bonds, becoming associated with eight electrons in its valence shell and thus achieving great stability. When these four bonds are formed to four separate identical neighboring atoms, the bonds are directed toward the corners of a regular tetrahedron, and the four other atoms will be symmetrically grouped about the central carbon atom, as indicated for methane in Figure 92.

Fig. 92. Tetrahedral covalent bonding of carbon to four atoms.

Such *tetrahedral bonding* is particularly characteristic of the carbon atom when it is united to four neighboring atoms. If the four units bonded to a carbon atom are not identical, as in CH_3Cl, the tetrahedron will be somewhat distorted. Carbon atoms frequently bond to other carbon atoms to form carbon frameworks to which atoms of other elements are attached.

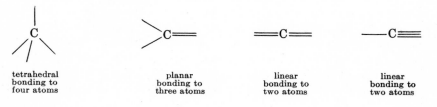

puckered carbon framework

Carbon atoms also form *multiple bonds* to other atoms. When a carbon atom combines with three other atoms by means of one double and two single bonds, the bonds are all in the same plane and a coplanar structure is observed. When the carbon atom is united to only two neighboring atoms by two double bonds or by a combination of a triple bond and a single bond, linear molecules are formed. The various ways by which carbon can form a total of four covalent bonds and the directions of these bonds may be summarized as follows.

tetrahedral bonding to four atoms	planar bonding to three atoms	linear bonding to two atoms	linear bonding to two atoms

Because of the great variety of ways in which carbon is able to form covalent bonds and because of the remarkable ability of carbon atoms to bond to other carbon atoms to form stable extended structures, a vast number of compounds of carbon are known.

The oxidation states of carbon atoms can vary from -4 to $+4$, depending upon whether carbon is combined with less electronegative atoms or with more electronegative atoms. Remember that any carbon–carbon bonds do not count toward the oxidation state. Different carbon atoms in the same molecule are in different oxidation states if they have different numbers of bonds to other carbon atoms. Although the difference in electronegativity between hydrogen and carbon is not great, carbon is more electronegative than hydrogen.

$$\underset{CH_4,}{-4} \quad \underset{CCl_4,}{+4} \quad \underset{CO_2,}{+4} \quad \underset{H_3C-CH_3,}{-3\ -3} \quad \underset{H_2C=CH_2,}{-2\ -2} \quad \underset{H_3C-\underset{H_2}{C}-CH_3}{-3\ -2\ -3}$$

298. OCCURRENCE

Carbon is not one of the most abundant elements but much of the carbon is readily available, and it is one of our very important elements. *Elementary carbon* is found in the earth crystallized as diamond or graphite. Carbon occurs *combined* in a great variety of compounds. It is an essential constituent of *all plant and animal matter*, commonly being combined with oxygen, hydrogen, and nitrogen. Materials derived from plants and animals usually contain carbon. Thus, *coal* deposits have been formed by the degradation of plant matter over long periods of time when it has been held at high pressures and temperatures. The genesis of coal is believed to involve the progressive loss of volatile substances, such as oxides of carbon and methane, and the increase in carbon content of the residual material.

Dry plant material	Dry peat	Lignite	Bituminous or soft coal	Anthracite or hard coal
44%C	50%C	57%C	78%C	81%C

(Dry plant material → Dry peat → Lignite → Bituminous or soft coal → Anthracite or hard coal)

Carbon forms an enormous number of compounds with hydrogen, the *hydrocarbons*, because of the tendency of carbon to form strong covalent bonds with other carbon atoms and thus produce chain, branched chain, and ring structures. Such hydrocarbons make up the *natural gas* and *crude petroleum* mixtures found in nature. The hydrogen in these hydrocarbons may be replaced by atoms of other elements, giving rise to hundreds of thousands of derivative compounds. The study of the hydrocarbons and their derivatives comprises the important field of *organic chemistry*. This division of chemistry was so termed because, in the early days, it was believed that such compounds could be formed only by the action of living organisms. However, chemists have found ways of synthesizing not only the organic compounds found in nature but also many that have not been observed in natural materials.

Carbon dioxide occurs in the air, in spring waters, and in natural-gas wells.   It is constantly being added to the atmosphere as a product of respiration, combustion, and decay, and removed from the atmosphere by plants and in the formation of *carbonates*.   In the earth there is much carbon tied up in carbonate ions, $CO_3{}^{2-}$, which are part of the carbonates of various common metallic elements.   Limestone, $CaCO_3$, is one of our most common minerals and a basic raw material in chemical industry.

299. THE DIAMOND ALLOTROPIC FORM OF CARBON

Carbon can achieve different crystalline forms by varying the way in which the carbon atoms are bonded together.   In the *diamond* crystal each carbon atom in the interior of the crystal is covalently bonded to four other carbon atoms at tetrahedral positions about it.   The distance

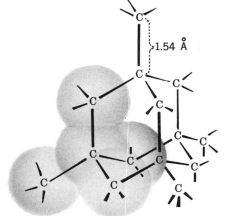

Fig. 93.   Structure of the diamond.

between the centers of any two adjacent carbon atoms is 1.54 Å.   This gives an extended continuous three-dimensional network, producing what may be termed a *giant molecule*, which is as large as the crystal itself. This symmetrical, close-packed, and strongly bonded structure is reflected in the properties of the diamond.   It is by far the hardest substance known and has an extremely high melting point, about 3600°.   Its refractive index, 2.417, is very high compared with that of most other transparent substances.   It is a poor conductor of heat and electricity because its valence electrons are tied up firmly in covalent bonds and are not mobile.   It is very inert chemically.   The use of the diamond in cutting tools, as an abrasive and polishing agent, and in jewelry exploits these unique properties.

The possibility of converting ordinary cheap forms of carbon to precious diamonds has frequently been an attractive objective of research.

Moissan reported the preparation of very small crystals by allowing carbon to crystallize from solution in molten iron at high temperature and tremendous pressure. There has been considerable doubt expressed as to whether these crystals actually were diamonds. It is now known that the diamond form of carbon is metastable under ordinary conditions of pressure and temperature. Recently, research workers at the General Electric Company have been able to obtain very small and imperfect diamonds by heating carbon to high temperatures under enormous pressure in a hydraulic press.

300. GRAPHITE

Carbon is found in a second allotropic form as the mineral, graphite. In a graphite crystal the arrangement of carbon atoms is quite different

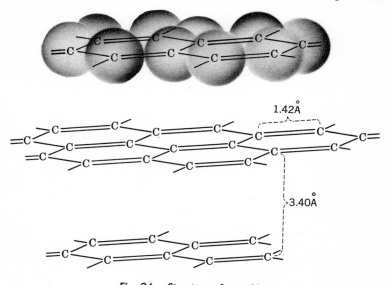

Fig. 94.   Structure of graphite.

from that in the diamond. The atoms are arranged in planar sheets, which extend continuously in two dimensions through the crystal. In the interior of each sheet each carbon atom is tightly bonded to three close neighboring carbon atoms to form an interlocking hexagonal ring, or "chicken-wire" pattern. The bonding between these like atoms is essentially covalent, with each bond being intermediate between single and double bonding. Graphite is considered to have a resonance hybrid structure, that shown in Figure 94 being merely one of a great many contributing structures. The distance between the centers of any two adjacent carbon atoms in a sheet is 1.42 Å, and all three bonds formed by each carbon atom to its three neighbors are alike. Each sheet constitutes a giant molecule.   These molecular sheets are stacked on each other in a regular fashion to produce the massive crystal.   The distance between the centers of the atoms in two adjacent sheets is 3.40 Å, much larger than the distance between the centers of adjacent atoms in a sheet.

The forces holding each carbon atom in its layer molecule in graphite are very strong, and hence the melting point is very high—about 3500°. Graphite crystals cleave easily between the planes of atoms, and the substance is soft and breaks up readily into flakes.   The surface of graphite becomes covered with a film of water molecules and then is *slippery and an excellent lubricant*.   It has recently been shown that when the film of water is not there, the dry graphite does not act as a lubricant.   Powdered graphite may be used as a "dry" lubricant, or it may be suspended in oil or water.   It is an electrical conductor and has a black shiny luster, presumably because the valence electrons are less firmly held than in diamond.   When it is rubbed on paper, fragments break off and adhere to the paper, leaving a mark.   The name *graphite* refers to this characteristic.   Graphite powder is mixed with clay, and rods of this mixture are baked to give the cores used in "lead" pencils.   The hardness of these cores can be controlled by varying the percentage of clay and the temperature and duration of baking.

Massive graphite is inert chemically, since its atoms are anchored so securely in the crystals.   It resists corrosion by most reagents, including even hydrogen fluoride and fluorine.   It burns to the oxides of carbon when heated sufficiently in oxygen or the air and is attacked by other very powerful oxidizing agents.

While some natural graphite is mined, most of the supply for industrial use is produced by the *Acheson process*.   Powdered coke is mixed with pitch or other binders and molded into shape.   The articles are then heated in electric furnaces to very high temperatures, whereupon massive crystals of graphite are formed.   Graphite is used widely in constructing crucibles, high-temperature furnaces, electrodes, and electrical apparatus.   Corrosion-resistant paints contain powdered graphite as a pigment.

301.   CHARCOAL, BONE BLACK, COKE, AND CARBON BLACK

Besides massive graphite, there are several other important materials of commerce that are aggregates of tiny graphitic crystals.

Wood charcoal is prepared by the *destructive distillation* of wood.   This simply means that chunks of wood are heated in the absence of air until the complex compounds of carbon constituting wood are decomposed to give volatile substances and a residue of carbon in the form of charcoal. In the early days, the wood was charred by letting it smolder under a layer of sod, and only the charcoal was saved.   Now the process is carried out in closed retorts, or ovens, and the valuable volatile material is collected and processed to yield wood alcohol, acetic acid, acetone, and other by-products.   If pine wood is used, turpentine is also obtained.

When a piece of wood is converted to charcoal, much of the matter is volatilized, but the residual piece of charcoal has almost the same volume as the original wood.   Charcoal is porous and light, having a honeycomb structure built up of tiny graphitic crystals.   Owing to the very large surface at which the carbon atoms do not have all of their valence forces satisfied, charcoal is more reactive than massive graphite. It burns more readily and is more effective as a reducing agent.

Charcoal has a strong tendency to attract certain substances to its extensive surface and to hold them there.   This concentration of one substance on the surface of another is called *adsorption*.   Wood charcoal is a powerful *adsorbing agent*, especially for certain gases, and it can be *activated* by heating and blowing with steam.   Many special uses have been made of this characteristic adsorption of gases by charcoal.   In gas-mask canisters, suitable layers of charcoal adsorb poison gases but allow oxygen and nitrogen to pass, because the process of adsorption is *selective*.   By impregnating the charcoal with various chemicals, the removal or destruction of the noxious gases can be made much more effective.   At low temperatures, active charcoals adsorb even oxygen and nitrogen very effectively.   With increase in temperature, the forces of adsorption are less able to counteract the tendency of the adsorbed material to break away from the surface, owing to their increased kinetic energy.   By heating an adsorbent charcoal sufficiently, the adsorbed material may be completely removed.

Bone black is produced by the destructive distillation of bones and waste animal material from the meat-packing industry.   Bone black is composed of very small fragments of graphitic carbon mixed with considerable amounts of calcium phosphate, which remains from the bones. Bone black is a very good *adsorbent* for solids from colloidal suspensions. It is used industrially for removing colored impurities from solutions, as in the removal of yellow or brown impurities from sugar solutions in the refining of molasses.

Coke is manufactured by the destructive distillation of bituminous coal.   Formerly, the *beehive-oven* process was used; this is very wasteful because all the valuable volatile by-products are lost.   Now, more commonly, coke is made in *by-product coke ovens* where the volatile substances driven from the soft coal are collected.   Coal gas, ammonia, and coal tar are thus obtained in large amounts, and by this improved technique better conservation of our natural resources is realized.

Like wood charcoal, coke has a microcrystalline graphitic structure and is very porous, so that it has a large specific surface (surface area per gram) and is more reactive than graphite.   Because of its large surface it is frequently used to support thin films of catalysts.   It burns readily as a fuel and is one of our most important industrial reducing agents. Enormous amounts of coke are used in metallurgical operations for reducing the ores of the metals. By special treatment, highly *activated carbon* for use as an adsorbent can be produced from coal. Coke is used widely in the manufacture of graphite, silicon, carbides, the oxides of carbon, and in the synthesis of many other compounds of carbon, such as high-polymer plastics. It is a basic starting material in chemical industry, and the location of chemical manufacturing plants is often determined by the availability of proper supplies of coking coal.

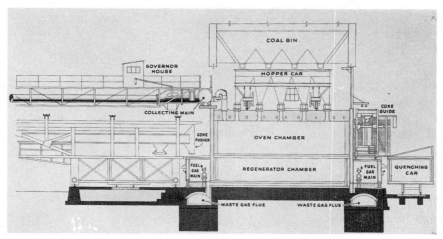

Fig. 95. Cross section of a by-product coke oven.   When coal is decomposed by heat in the oven chamber, the volatile products escape into the collecting main.   The ends of the oven are then removed and the pusher rams the white-hot coke out into the quenching car, where it is immediately quenched with water to prevent it from burning in the air.   (Courtesy Bethlehem Steel Co.)

Carbon black, frequently called *lampblack,* is a very finely divided form of carbon obtained by the incomplete combustion of hydrocarbons, such as natural gas. This cheap raw material is caused to burn in a limited amount of air, and when the sooty flame strikes a cold moving iron surface, carbon black deposits and can be scraped off. It is a volu-

$$CH_4 + O_2 = C + 2H_2O$$

minous powder consisting of exceedingly fine graphitic particles that usually have a rather oily surface film. It is extensively used as a pigment in paints, shoe polish, and printing ink. The addition of a considerable proportion of carbon black in rubber processing imparts desirable characteristics to the product.

302. CARBIDES

Carbon combines with many metals at high temperatures to give solid carbides. Many of these carbides have useful properties, and some of them are produced in large quantities. The possibility of formation of carbides frequently leads to complications in metallurgical operations when carbon is used as a reducing agent to produce the metal.

Calcium carbide, CaC_2, is manufactured on the large scale by heating lime with coke in an electric furnace.

$$CaO + 3C = CaC_2 + CO$$

It is obtained as a gray-colored solid that hydrolyzes rapidly at room temperature to give the gas, acetylene.

$$CaC_2 + 2H_2O = Ca(OH)_2 + C_2H_2$$

This reaction is very important because the acetylene can be used to synthesize a very extended list of valuable organic materials, such as plastics and rubber.

Iron carbide, Fe_3C, is present in steels and is responsible, in part, for the remarkable properties of these materials.

Tungsten carbide, WC, *silicon carbide*, SiC, *boron carbide*, B_4C, and several other carbides are very hard substances that are used as abrasives and in cutting tools.

303. CARBON DIOXIDE

This compound is the most common oxide of carbon. Its importance in nature is understood when one considers that it is either formed or used up in the processes of respiration, combustion, plant nutrition, fermentation, and decay. It can be *prepared or produced* in large amounts in a number of ways.

a. Complete combustion of carbon or compounds of carbon.

$$C_{(s)} + O_{2(g)} = CO_{2(g)} + 94,450 \text{ cal}$$
$$CH_4 + 2O_2 = CO_2 + 2H_2O$$

b. Action of acids on carbonates.

$$CaCO_3 + 2H^+ = Ca^{2+} + CO_2 + H_2O$$

This is a very convenient method, especially for laboratory use. Sulfuric acid should not be used because $CaSO_4$ is low in solubility and precipitates out on the chunks of carbonate, preventing the continued generation of carbon dioxide.

c. Thermal decomposition of carbonates.

$$\underset{\text{limestone}}{CaCO_{3(s)}} + 43,350 \text{ cal} = \underset{\text{lime}}{CaO_{(s)}} + CO_{2(g)}$$

d. Fermentation.

Sugars undergo fermentation in the presence of yeasts, forming alcohol and carbon dioxide.

$$\overset{\text{yeast}}{C_6H_{12}O_6} = 2C_2H_5OH + 2CO_2$$
$$\underset{\text{glucose}}{} \qquad \underset{\text{ethyl alcohol}}{}$$

Vast quantities of carbon dioxide are formed in the fermentation of molasses, fruit juices, and grains in the manufacture of industrial alcohol, distilled liquors, wine, and beer. Much of the carbon dioxide that comes on the market is recovered from such fermentation operations.

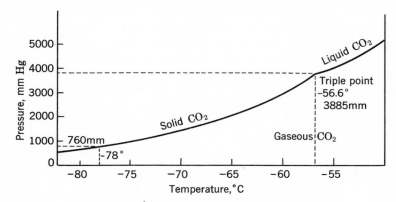

Fig. 96. Equilibrium vapor pressure of CO_2

Carbon dioxide has a simple molecule with the centers of all three atoms in a straight line (Figure 19, page 84). The polar character of the bonds in this molecule, its deviation from the ideal gas laws, and its critical temperature and pressure have already been discussed in Sections 70, 129, and 132.

Figure 96 summarizes the equilibrium vapor pressure–temperature relationship for carbon dioxide in the solid and liquid states. It shows that solid carbon dioxide (dry ice) may be obtained readily by cooling

Table 58.   Properties of the Oxides of Carbon

Properties	CO_2	CO
Molecular weight	44.010	28.010
Melting point, ° C	−56.6 (5.2 atm)	−207
Boiling point, ° C	−78.5 (sublimation)	−192
Relative density (air = 1)	1.52	0.967
Color	Colorless	Colorless
Odor	None	None
Solubility, ml/liter H_2O, 20°, 760 mm	878	23.2

the gas, even at ordinary pressures.   Liquid carbon dioxide exists only at pressures of more than 5.2 atm.   Solid carbon dioxide vaporizes at atmospheric pressure without melting and stays at about $-78°$ during this vaporization.   It is a valuable refrigerating agent and is particularly convenient to use because the gas diffuses into the atmosphere and no messy residue is left behind.   In the laboratory it is frequently employed to cool liquids such as alcohol or acetone for use in low-temperature baths. Rain making has been accomplished by scattering small pellets of dry ice from airplanes into clouds to produce condensation.

Dry carbon dioxide will neither burn nor support the combustion of ordinary materials.   It is reduced by very active metals and by carbon at high temperatures.   Because it is much heavier than air and does not support ordinary combustion, it is useful for *extinguishing fires*.   It "smothers" the fire by excluding oxygen from the burning material, and it also cools the system.   Various types of fire extinguishers that supply carbon dioxide gas, or snow, or foams are now available on the market. Because magnesium burns in carbon dioxide, the latter cannot be used for extinguishing magnesium fires.

Carbon dioxide is quite soluble in water, the solubility increasing with pressure, as shown in Figure 56, page 199.   It is possible to prepare carbonated beverages by bottling them under high partial pressures of carbon dioxide.   When the bottles are opened and the pressure of carbon dioxide over the solution is lowered, effervescence occurs.   There is evidence that there is some tendency for the dissolved carbon dioxide to react with water to set up the following equilibria.

$$CO_2 + H_2O \rightleftharpoons H_2CO_3$$
$$\text{carbonic acid}$$

$$H_2CO_3 \rightleftharpoons H^+ + HCO_3^- \qquad K_{(i)} = 4.2 \times 10^{-7}$$
$$\text{bicarbonate ion}$$

$$HCO_3^- \rightleftharpoons H^+ + CO_3^{2-} \qquad K_{(i)} = 4.8 \times 10^{-11}$$
$$\text{carbonate ion}$$

Presumably, molecules of carbonic acid, H_2CO_3, are formed in solution and exist in equilibrium with carbon dioxide, water, and the ions.   The carbonic acid molecules are very unstable thermally, and when the solution is evaporated, they decompose and cannot be isolated.   We can consider this acid as being diprotic, since both HCO_3^- and CO_3^{2-} ions are known.   The equilibrium concentrations of hydrogen ions are small, and such solutions have only a slight sour taste.   However, basic solutions may be neutralized by bubbling in carbon dioxide, which behaves as an acid anhydride.

$$CO_2 + OH^- = HCO_3^-$$
$$HCO_3^- + OH^- = H_2O + CO_3^{2-}$$

304. CARBONATES AND BICARBONATES

The *carbonate ion* is planar, with the oxygen atoms at the corners of an equilateral triangle and the carbon at the center. All three oxygen atoms are equivalent and each carbon-oxygen bond is intermediate between a single and a double bond, the structure being a resonance hybrid, as has already been discussed in Section 179. The carbonate ion is isoelectronic with and structurally similar to the nitrate ion; the ionic charge is 2− rather than 1− because the carbon nucleus contains one fewer protons than does the nitrogen nucleus. Note, however, that the

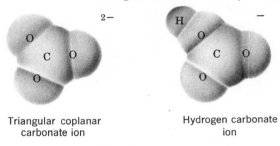

Triangular coplanar carbonate ion

Hydrogen carbonate ion

Fig. 97. Configurations of oxyanions of carbonic acid.

carbonate ion does not resemble the sulfite ion, $SO_3{}^{2-}$, either in the spatial arrangement of the atoms or in the distribution of electrons. The *bicarbonate ion* is formed when a proton becomes attached to one of the oxygen atoms of the carbonate ion. The term *hydrogen carbonate ion* is more consistent with the conventions for naming such acid ions, but the term *bicarbonate ion* is firmly established in popular use.

Solid ionic *carbonates* crystallize from solution when carbonate ions associate with various cations.

$$2Na^+ + CO_3{}^{2-} = Na_2CO_{3(s)}$$
$$Ca^{2+} + CO_3{}^{2-} = CaCO_{3(s)}$$

The carbonates of the alkali metals and ammonia are quite soluble. Carbonates of calcium, strontium, and barium are only slightly soluble, and carbon dioxide can be absorbed very effectively by bubbling it into solutions of the hydroxides of these elements. The presence of even small amounts of carbon dioxide in a gas mixture can be detected by bubbling it through *lime water*, a solution of calcium hydroxide. A white precipitate of finely divided calcium carbonate appears.

$$Ca^{2+} + 2OH^- + CO_2 = CaCO_{3(s)} + H_2O$$

Solid ionic *bicarbonates* are formed when bicarbonate ions associate with cations. The bicarbonates of sodium and potassium are less soluble than the carbonates, but the bicarbonate of calcium is more soluble than the carbonate.

When a soluble carbonate is dissolved in water, the carbonate ions hydrolyze and the solution is basic.   The net reaction is

$$CO_3{}^{2-} + H_2O \rightleftharpoons HCO_3{}^- + OH^-$$

When a soluble bicarbonate is dissolved in water, the following equilibria are important.

$$HCO_3{}^- \rightleftharpoons H^+ + CO_3{}^{2-}$$
$$HCO_3{}^- + H_2O \rightleftharpoons H_2CO_3 + OH^-$$
$$H_2CO_3 \rightleftharpoons H_2O + CO_2$$

The latter two predominate, and the solution is somewhat basic.   Because of their tendency to combine with hydrogen ions to give carbon dioxide and water, carbonates and bicarbonates are frequently used to neutralize acid systems.   Insoluble carbonates can be brought into solution readily by treating them with strong acids, carbon dioxide escaping as a gas when its solubility is exceeded.

$$CaCO_{3(s)} + H^+ = Ca^{2+} + HCO_3{}^-$$
$$HCO_3{}^- + H^+ = H_2O + CO_{2(g)}$$

When bicarbonates are heated sufficiently, carbonates are formed.

$$2NaHCO_{3(s)} \overset{\text{heat}}{=} Na_2CO_{3(s)} + H_2O_{(g)} + CO_{2(g)}$$

Because of this, powdered sodium bicarbonate may be used effectively for extinguishing fires by pouring it on the burning material.

Carbonates of the less active metals break down at high temperatures.

$$MgCO_{3(s)} \overset{\text{heat}}{=} MgO_{(s)} + CO_2$$

305. CARBON MONOXIDE

The other common oxide of carbon, CO, is not present in the air in any quantity but is formed in many different reactions.

a. Incomplete combustion of carbon or compounds of carbon.

$$2C + O_2 = 2CO + 53,680 \text{ cal}$$

b. Reduction of carbon dioxide by hot carbon.

$$C + CO_2 + 40,770 \text{ cal} = 2CO$$

c. Reduction of steam by hot carbon.

$$C_{(s)} + H_2O_{(g)} + 30,961 \text{ cal} = H_{2(g)} + CO_{(g)}$$

This reaction is carried out industrially by passing steam over hot coke. The mixture of hydrogen and carbon monoxide formed is called *water gas,* and the *water-gas process* is of considerable industrial importance, since it provides hydrogen and carbon monoxide at very low cost. Because the reaction is endothermic, the system cools down rapidly, and it is necessary periodically to replace the steam by air or oxygen, so that the exothermic reactions of oxygen with carbon to form oxides can again raise the temperature. The actual gas mixture produced by this alternate treatment of coke with steam and air contains not only carbon monoxide and hydrogen but also some carbon dioxide and nitrogen. (Sometimes a mixture of steam and air is used continuously and the product is called *producer gas*.)

d. Dehydration of formic or oxalic acids.

$$\text{HCOOH}_{(l)} \overset{\text{hot H}_2\text{SO}_4}{=} \text{H}_2\text{O}_{(g)} + \text{CO}_{(g)}$$
$$\text{formic acid}$$

The reaction proceeds smoothly when the liquid formic acid is allowed to drip into concentrated sulfuric acid warmed to about 150°. The strong dehydrating action of sulfuric acid ensures the rapid decomposition of formic acid, with the evolution of pure carbon monoxide gas. This method is very convenient for preparing small amounts of pure monoxide. Solid oxalic acid may be substituted for the formic acid, but in this case the monoxide is mixed with carbon dioxide.

$$\text{H}_2\text{C}_2\text{O}_{4(s)} \overset{\text{hot H}_2\text{SO}_4}{=} \text{H}_2\text{O} + \text{CO}_{(g)} + \text{CO}_{2(g)}$$
$$\text{oxalic acid}$$

The physical properties of carbon monoxide, as summarized in Table 58, are consistent with the fact that this light diatomic molecule, having essentially triple bonding between the two atoms, is only very slightly polar.

$$: \text{C} \equiv \text{O} :$$

Carbon monoxide burns readily in air with a blue flame.

$$2\text{CO}_{(g)} + \text{O}_{2(g)} = 2\text{CO}_{2(g)} + 135{,}220 \text{ cal}$$

Mixtures of carbon monoxide with oxygen or air over a considerable range of concentration are highly explosive. Because of the high heat of combustion of carbon monoxide, it is an important fuel. Table 59 compares the typical compositions and heating values of the common fuel-gas mixtures which are in use.

Carbon monoxide is a powerful reducing agent, especially at high temperatures, and can be used effectively to reduce oxides of the metals to give the metals.

$$\text{Fe}_2\text{O}_3 + 3\text{CO} = 2\text{Fe} + 3\text{CO}_2$$

Table 59.   Fuel-Gas Mixtures

Fuel	Manufacture	Per Cent Composition						Heating Value, Cal/Liter at 1 atm, 15.5°
		CO	H_2	CH_4	Other Hydro-carbons	CO_2	N_2	
Water gas	Heating steam and coke	40	50	1.2	——	4.4	3.8	2,700
Producer gas	Heating steam, air, and coke	20	21	4	——	6.8	48.3	1,600
Coal gas	Destructive distillation of coal	4.3	44.8	41	6.0	1.1	2.3	6,300
Natural gas	Gas wells	—	—	84	15	—	1.0	10,500

Carbon monoxide combines readily with many elements and compounds, furnishing the *carbonyl radical.*

$$Cl_2 + CO = \quad COCl_2$$
carbonyl chloride
(phosgene)

$$Ni + 4CO = \quad Ni(CO)_4$$
nickel carbonyl

Carbon monoxide is *highly toxic* and is dangerous to breathe even in low concentrations.   It combines with the hemoglobin of the blood.

$$\text{Hemoglobin} + CO = \text{carbon monoxide–hemoglobin}$$

The normal function of hemoglobin is to form oxyhemoglobin in the lungs, and oxygen in this form is carried by the blood stream to the cells of the body where it is needed for oxidation.   However, carbon monoxide–hemoglobin is formed preferentially if carbon monoxide is present in the lungs, and thus the cells are deprived of their supply of oxygen.   Prompt first aid should be provided for cases of carbon monoxide poisoning.   The patient should be given *artificial respiration* so that as much oxygen as possible is provided.   Since carbon monoxide frequently results from faulty furnace operation and is present in high concentrations in exhaust gases from automobile engines, the public is often exposed to this highly toxic material.   It is often a serious hazard in industry.   The danger of poisoning is particularly great because carbon monoxide has no odor, color, or taste to warn of its presence.

306. CARBON DISULFIDE

Carbon disulfide is the sulfur analogue of carbon dioxide. It is manufactured by heating coke and sulfur in an electric furnace, the carbon disulfide distilling off as a colorless liquid

$$C + 2S = CS_2$$

The carbon atom forms a double bond to each atom of sulfur, the three atoms being arranged symmetrically in a linear molecule.

$$\ddot{S}=C=\ddot{S}$$

It melts at $-110.8°$ and boils at $46.25°$, and it has a high density and refractivity. When it is very pure it has a sweet odor, but small amounts of impurities, which are usually present, give it a decidedly unpleasant smell. Carbon disulfide is an excellent solvent for iodine, sulfur, rubber, fats, and many other molecular substances. Its vapors are toxic, and it is useful as an insecticide. It is highly combustible, and mixtures of carbon disulfide and air are *very explosive*.

$$CS_2 + 3O_2 = CO_2 + 2SO_2$$

Carbon disulfide combines with sulfides to produce thiocarbonates, in which the thiocarbonate ion is the analogue of the carbonate ion.

$$BaS_{(s)} + CS_{2(l)} = BaCS_{3(s)}$$

307. CARBON TETRAHALIDES

A carbon atom combines with four halogen atoms to form a tetrahalide molecule, CX_4. In these tetrahalides the usual arrangement of four atoms at tetrahedral positions about the central carbon atom is maintained, and the molecules as a whole are nonpolar. With increasing

Fig. 98. Tetrahedral configurations of the carbon tetrahalides.

atomic weight of the halogen atoms, the molecular weights of the tetrahalides increase and their boiling points increase.

Carbon tetrachloride, CCl_4, is the most common and is typical. It is usually manufactured by the action of chlorine on carbon disulfide.

$$CS_2 + 3Cl_2 = CCl_4 + S_2Cl_2$$

The carbon tetrachloride is separated from S_2Cl_2 by distillation, the boiling points being 76.8° and 138°, respectively. It is a heavy liquid with a rather pleasant odor. Since its heavy vapor is not combustible, it is used in fire extinguishers so devised that the liquid may be sprayed on the combustible material. It smothers the fire by excluding air. It should be used cautiously on indoor fires because, at high temperatures, highly toxic CO and $COCl_2$ may be formed by hydrolysis.

$$CCl_4 + H_2O = COCl_2 + 2HCl$$

Carbon tetrachloride is an excellent solvent for fats and greases, and it is a safe and effective solvent for use in dry cleaning. It is best, however, to avoid breathing its vapor, and it is not advisable to have it in contact with the skin for protracted periods, for it is somewhat toxic itself.

The other tetrahalides, CF_4, CBr_4, and CI_4, are known, and mixed tetrahalides, such as CF_2Cl_2, can be made. The latter, a volatile inert liquid, is used under the name Freon as a refrigerant in household refrigerators and as a solvent in DDT sprays.

EXERCISES

1. Compare carbon, silicon, tin, and lead with respect to: a) electronic structure; b) size of covalent radius; c) metallic or nonmetallic character.

2. Summarize the ways in which a carbon atom can be bonded to other carbon atoms.

3. What oxidation states can carbon achieve? What is the oxidation state of carbon in: a) CaC_2? b) $COCl_2$? c) graphite? d) CS_2? e) $H_2C\!\!=\!\!C\!\!=\!\!CH_2$

4. Compare the per cent of carbon in anthracite coal, peat, and bituminous coal.

5. a) Contrast the structures of diamond and graphite.
b) What reason can you suggest to account for the fact that in graphite the C—C distance in a sheet is shorter than the C—C distance in diamond?

6. a) Describe the structures of coke and carbon black.
b) How are these substances manufactured?
c) For what are they used?

7. a) Write the equations for the complete combustion of coke, CO, CH_4, C_2H_2, and CS_2.
b) Compare the volumes of oxygen at STP necessary for the complete combustion of one mole of each of these substances.

8. a) What equilibria are established in a container in which a gas phase consisting of CO_2 is in contact with water?
b) What will be the effect on the size of the fraction of the total amount of CO_2 which is present in the gase phase of: 1) lowering the temperature? 2) adding solid Na_2CO_3? 3) adding solid NaCl? 4) adding solid KOH?

9. Account for the fact that Na_2CO_3 and $NaHCO_3$ are often used to neutralize acid systems. Write equations for the net reactions.

10. Describe the important aspects of the water-gas reaction as carried out industrially.

11. What is the spatial configuration and the electronic distribution of: a) CBr_4? b) CO_2? c) CO_3^{2-}? d) CS_2? e) CN^-? f) HCO_3^-?

12. Write a balanced equation for the preparation of: a) CO_2; b) CS_2; c) $CaCO_3$; d) CCl_4; e) water gas.

Chapter 25

▶ Organic Chemistry I
▶ The Hydrocarbons

308. THE FIELD OF ORGANIC CHEMISTRY

As pointed out in Section 298, organic chemistry comprises the study of the hydrocarbons and their derivatives, usually with some carbon-to-carbon bonding being involved in the structure. Because of the versatility shown by carbon in the way it can enter into such compounds, the total number of hydrocarbons that have been recognized is very great, and an enormous list of derivative compounds is available. In order to facilitate the study of organic compounds, it is necessary to classify them on the basis of composition and structure. This is perhaps best accomplished by first classifying and characterizing the hydrocarbons and then considering their derivatives.

309. THE HYDROCARBON SYSTEMS

Hydrocarbons are compounds built up by the combination of carbon and hydrogen atoms. In building up these substances, carbon atoms always form four bonds, and hydrogen atoms always form one bond. In the simplest case, one carbon atom combines with four hydrogen atoms to give methane, CH_4, with carbon showing its usual tendency for tetrahedral bonding. In the other hydrocarbons, some carbon-carbon bonding builds up more or less extended carbon frameworks to which hydrogen atoms are united. The ability of carbon atoms to form multiple bonds to each other gives rise to still other types of hydrocarbon systems. Since hydrogen is only slightly less electronegative than carbon, the bonds in hydrocarbons, whether they be carbon-carbon or carbon-hydrogen bonds, are covalent in character. The carbon-carbon bond is nonpolar and the carbon-hydrogen bond is only very slightly polar. Hydrocarbons are molecular in character, and those with low molecular weights are highly volatile substances. With increasing molecular weight, in general, the melting and boiling points increase. They are excellent solvents for molecular substances of low polarity. All hydrocarbons are highly combustible, burning in air to water and oxides of carbon.

390

310. ALIPHATIC HYDROCARBONS

The *aliphatic hydrocarbons* contain chains of carbon atoms. These hydrocarbons are further classified into *homologous series* on the basis of similarity in structure, all members of an homologous series being derived by a common building process from a simple parent molecule.

The *methane or paraffin series* of hydrocarbons may be thought of as derived from the methane molecule by the progressive addition of CH_2 increments.   This is shown for the first five members of the series by the following electronic and spatial formulas. By further increments of

CH_4
methane

C_2H_6
ethane

C_3H_8
n-propane

C_4H_{10}
n-butane

C_5H_{12}
n-pentane

Boiling Point
−161.5°

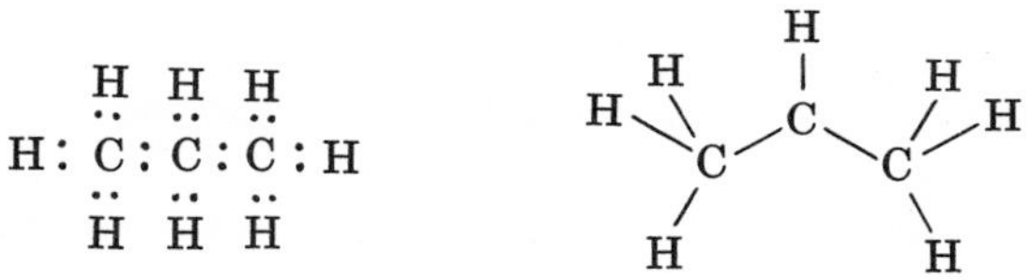

−88.6°

−42.1°

−0.5°

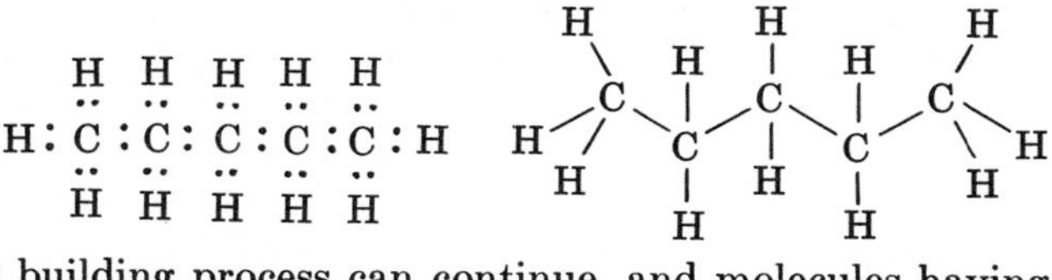

36.1°

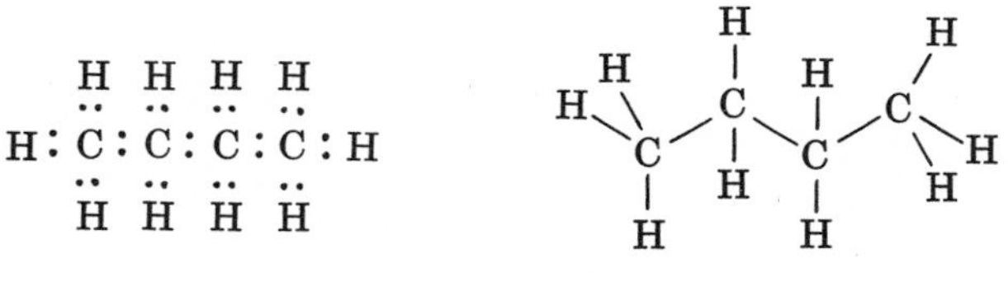

CH_2, the building process can continue, and molecules having chains of as many as 60 carbon atoms are known.   The general formula C_nH_{2n+2} is characteristic for the series.   In this homologous series there are only single bonds between carbon atoms, and the compounds are said to be *saturated hydrocarbons*.   Each carbon atom is tetrahedrally bonded to four neighboring atoms.   In the molecules shown above, the backbones of carbon atoms are puckered but are not branched.   Instead of extension of the single unbranched chain, *branching* may take place.

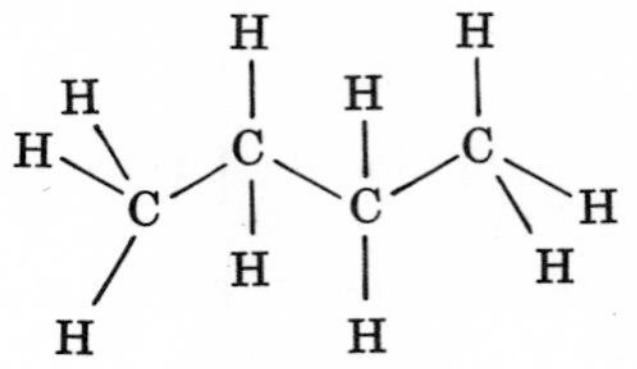

n-butane
unbranched chain
b.p., −0.5°

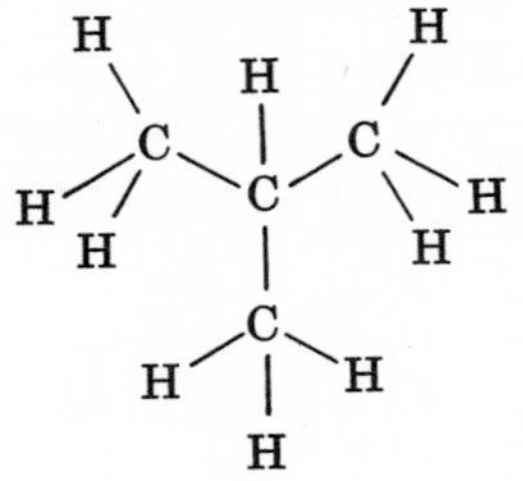

isobutane
branched chain
b.p., −11.7°

The branched-chain hydrocarbon, *isobutane, and* the unbranched-chain hydrocarbon, *n-butane, both have the same number of carbon and hydrogen atoms per molecule, but the molecular structures are different.* This is an example of *isomerism,* two different *isomers* of butane being known. With increase in the numbers of carbon and hydrogen atoms in the hydrocarbons of the series, the number of possible isomeric forms that have the same chemical composition increases. Because of the difference in the spatial configurations of isomers, the properties differ, as shown by the variation in boiling points of the butanes.

In Table 60 the decrease in volatility with increase in the molecular weight of the unbranched-chain hydrocarbons of the methane series is apparent. This is typical of the gradual change in properties of the members of an homologous series of hydrocarbons with stepwise addition of the common increment, CH_2.

Since some rotation about single bonds is possible, the puckered-chain hydrocarbon molecules may be stretched out but also may coil up in random fashion to give rather compact globular forms, as shown in Figure 99. The unbranched-chain hydrocarbons are often inaccurately referred

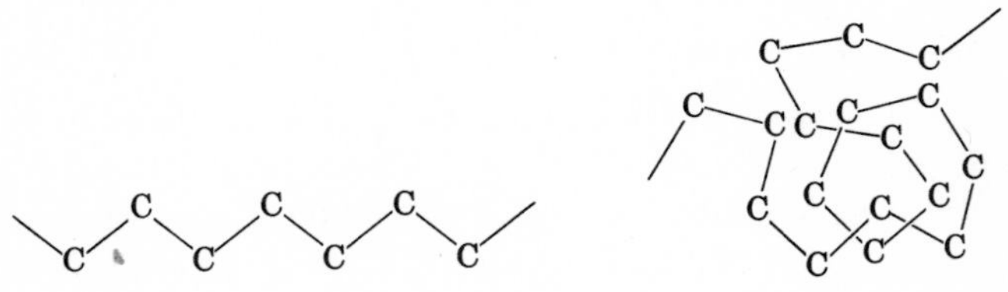

Stretched puckered chain   Coiled puckered chain

Fig. 99. Hydrocarbon chains.

to as "straight-chain hydrocarbons," giving an erroneous impression of their configurations.

Table 60.   Methane Series of Hydrocarbons

	Formula C_nH_{2n+2}	Boiling Point 1 Atm, ° C	Melting Point, ° C
Methane	CH_4	−161.5	−182.5
Ethane	C_2H_6	−88.6	−172
Propane	C_3H_8	−42.1	−187.1
n-Butane	C_4H_{10}	−0.5	−138.3 ·
n-Pentane	C_5H_{12}	36.1	−129.7
n-Hexane	C_6H_{14}	68.7	−95.3
n-Heptane	C_7H_{16}	98.4	−90.6
		.	
		.	
n-Pentadecane	$C_{15}H_{32}$	270.5	10
n-Hexadecane	$C_{16}H_{34}$	280	18.1
n-Heptadecane	$C_{17}H_{36}$	303	22
	.		
	.		
	.		
n-Hexacontane	$C_{60}H_{122}$		99

For convenience, in writing structural formulas for organic compounds usually no effort is made to show the actual three-dimensional configuration; we are content simply to use one dash to indicate each covalent bond. However, we should always remember the directional nature of these bonds as already described.

Methane, CH_4, is formed by the decomposition of plant material under water and bubbles to the surface as *marsh gas*. Natural gas is mostly methane, with small amounts of other low-boiling hydrocarbons and nitrogen. It can be made in the laboratory by heating sodium acetate with soda lime, a mixture of NaOH and $Ca(OH)_2$.

$$CH_3COONa + NaOH = Na_2CO_3 + CH_4$$
$$2CH_3COONa + Ca(OH)_2 = CaCO_3 + Na_2CO_3 + 2CH_4$$

Like the rest of the hydrocarbons of its series, methane is relatively inert at room temperature, but it will burn in the air when ignited, and therefore it is a good fuel gas.

$$CH_4 + 2O_2 = CO_2 + 2H_2O$$

The enormous amount of methane obtained from natural-gas wells is being utilized more and more for the synthesis of other organic compounds.

The *ethylene*, or *olefin*, homologous series of hydrocarbons are chain molecules in which there is a double bond between one pair of carbon atoms. The members of the series conform to the general formula C_nH_{2n}

and are derived from ethylene by the addition of the increment CH_2.

C_2H_4
ethylene

H : C :: C : H

b.p., $-102.4°$

C_3H_6
propylene

H : C :: C : C : H

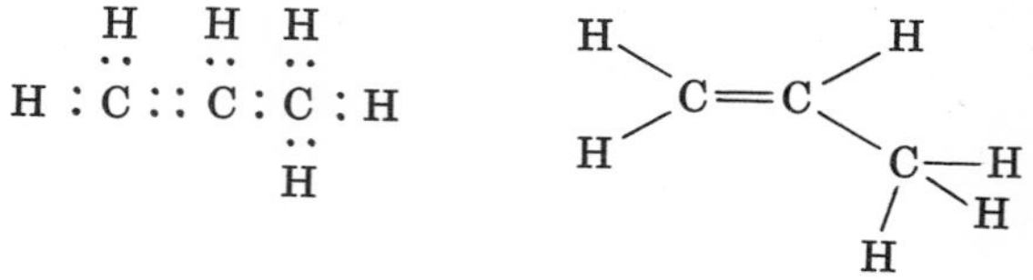

b.p., $-47.7°$

When an olefin is treated with chlorine, atoms of chlorine combine with the carbon atoms that are doubly bonded, and the double bond changes to a single bond.

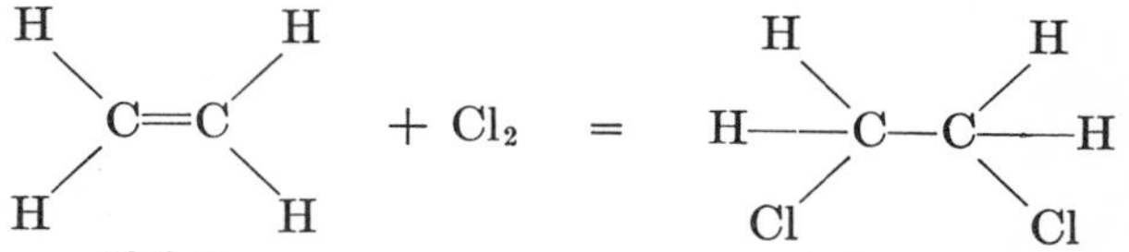

ethylene $+ Cl_2 =$ dichloroethane

Hydrocarbons in which there are multiple bonds are said to be *unsaturated* because of their ability to combine directly with other atoms.

The *acetylene series* of hydrocarbons has one triple bond between a pair of carbon atoms in the chain, the general formula being C_nH_{2n-2}.

C_2H_2
acetylene

H—C≡C—H

Sublimation
Point, $-84°$

C_3H_4
methylacetylene

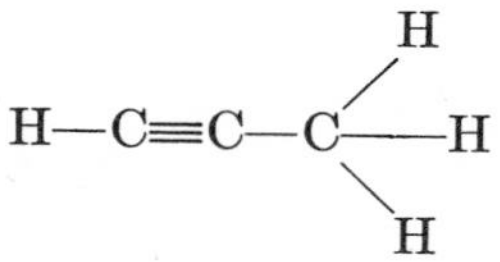

H—C≡C—C—H

b.p., $-23,2°$

Acetylene is made by dropping water on calcium carbide.

$$CaC_2 + 2H_2O = Ca(OH)_2 + C_2H_2$$

It is very combustible and has been widely used in the oxyacetylene burner to provide high temperatures for the welding and cutting of metals.

$$2C_2H_2 + 5O_2 = 4CO_2 + 2H_2O$$

A highly unsaturated hydrocarbon, acetylene is quite reactive and is used in large amounts for the synthesis of many organic substances.   For a typical synthesis involving acetylene, see Section 323.

311.   NAPHTHENIC OR ALICYCLIC HYDROCARBONS

These are saturated hydrocarbons that contain rings of carbon atoms.

C_5H_{10}
cyclopentane

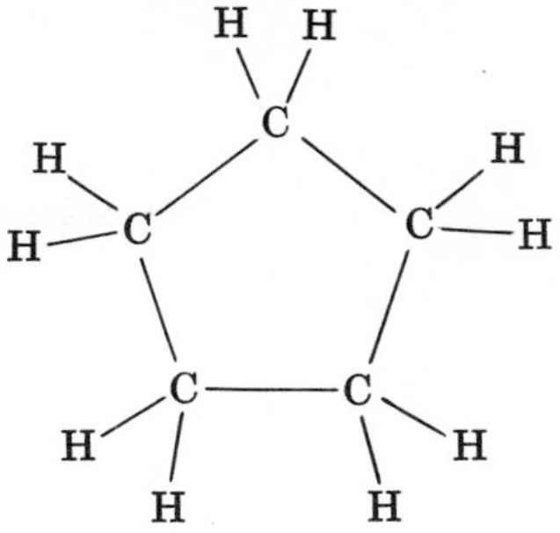

b.p., 49.3°

C_6H_{12}
cyclohexane

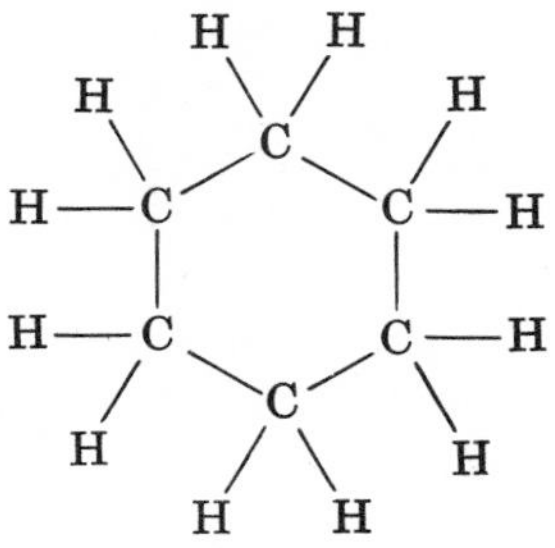

b.p., 80.7°

312. AROMATIC RING HYDROCARBONS

Unsaturated hydrocarbons that contain one or more benzene rings of carbon atoms are called *aromatic hydrocarbons*. The *benzene series* has the general formula C_nH_{2n-6}.

C_6H_6
benzene

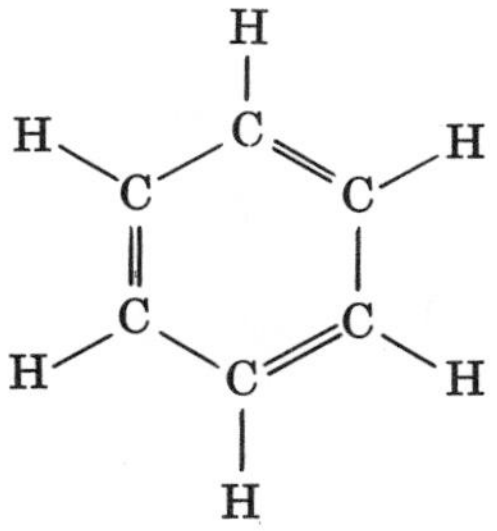

b.p., 80.1°

C_7H_8
toluene

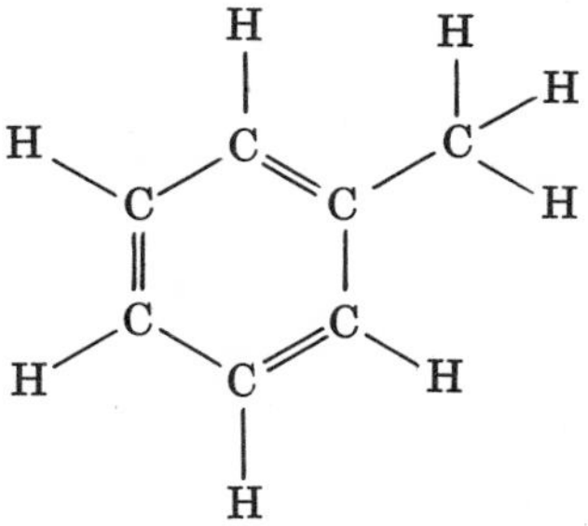

b.p., 110.6°

Benzene has been shown to have all of its carbon and hydrogen atoms lying in the same plane, as shown in Figure 100. Actually, the bonds

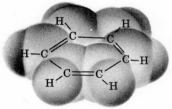

Fig. 100.   The coplanar cyclic structure of benzene.

between the carbon atoms in the benzene ring are not alternate single and double bonds, but all are equivalent and are midway between single and double bonds.   It has a resonance hybrid structure.   The benzene series of the hydrocarbons are more stable and not as reactive as the unsaturated-chain compounds.   Benzene and its homologues are obtained in large amounts as by-products of the production of coke and coal gas by the destructive distillation of soft coal.

Paraffinic or olefinic side chains may be joined to the cyclic hydrocarbons to produce still more complicated hydrocarbon systems.   Also two or more ring systems may unite to form multiple-ring hydrocarbons.

naphthalene   m.p., 80.3°   anthracene   m.p., 217°

For convenience, the benzene ring is commonly indicated by a hexagon.

benzene   toluene   naphthalene   anthracene

313. PETROLEUM

Petroleum commonly occurs trapped in porous rock between layers of impervious minerals, as shown in Figure 101.   Oil wells are drilled to tap these deposits.

Crude oil, as pumped from the ground, is principally a mixture of hydrocarbons of varying volatility.   By fractional distillation, petroleum can be separated into various fractions, each boiling over a certain range of temperature and consisting of a mixture of hydrocarbons that

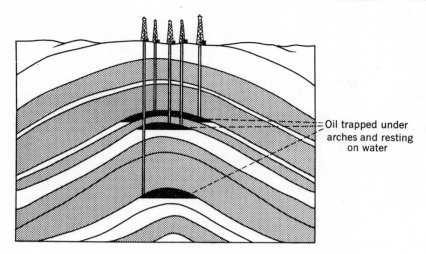

= Oil trapped under arches and resting on water

Fig. 101.   Petroleum trapped in folds of impervious shale.

are volatile in that range.   The common fractions produced industrially are given in Table 61.

In the refining of petroleum, simple distillation methods are supplemented by other processes in which the various fractions are treated to convert the less valuable hydrocarbons to those in greater demand.   By heating the fractions containing the larger hydrocarbon molecules, these may be *cracked*, or broken up, into smaller and more volatile molecules. Oil fractions may be cracked to yield gasoline.   Cracking may be facilitated and controlled by the use of *cracking catalysts*, usually solid aluminosilicates, such as certain clays.   By use of other catalysts, the smaller hydrocarbon molecules may be *re-formed*, or rearranged, to other mole-

Table 61.   Fractions Obtained by Distillation of Petroleum

Fractions	Boiling Range, ° C	Number of Carbon Atoms in Hydrocarbon Molecules Present	Uses
Gas	Below 32	1–4	Fuel gas; manufacture carbon black, gasoline, rubber
Gasoline	40–200	4–12	Engine fuel
Naphthas	50–200	7–12	Solvents
Kerosene	175–275	12–15	Lamps and heating appliances; tractor and diesel fuel; printing ink
Fuel oil	200–300	15–18	Furnace fuel
Lubricating oil	Above 300	16–20	Lubrication
Petrolatum	Above 300	18–22	Lubrication, salves
Wax	Above 300	20–34	Waterproofing, candles
Asphalt	Nonvolatile		Road making, roofing

cules which give better performance in motor fuels.   The very small hydrocarbon molecules in the gas fractions can be caused to unite to build up hydrocarbons in the gasoline range by use of proper catalysts.   This is particularly important in the manufacture of aviation gasoline.   By modern refining methods it is possible not only to separate the hydrocarbons constituting the crude petroleum into useful fractions, but also to obtain large yields of the more important hydrocarbons by remodeling the original molecules.

Vast quantities of petroleum are held in the oil-shale deposits of Colorado and other regions.   By heating these oil shales, the petroleum can be recovered.   This source of hydrocarbons has not yet been greatly exploited because of costs.   As our other reserves of crude oil dwindle, the oil shales will become more important.

314. HYDROGENATION OF COAL AND COKE

Coal has a high percentage of carbon, probably present in hydrocarbons very low in hydrogen.   By bringing powdered coal together with hydrogen in the presence of proper catalysts under suitable conditions, it is possible to convert the coal to low-molecular-weight hydrocarbons. By this process, developed by Bergius, gasoline and fuel oils may be produced.   In the Fischer-Tropsch process, hydrocarbons are synthesized by passing the water-gas mixture of carbon monoxide and hydrogen over a hot catalyst.

315. RUBBER

The natural rubber obtained from the juice or latex of the rubber tree is a hydrocarbon material having the simplest formula C_5H_8.   Actually, the molecules of rubber are high polymers built up by the polymerization of these C_5H_8 units to give giant-chain molecules of tremendous size.

monomer
C_5H_8

chain polymer of tremendous length
$(C_5H_8)n$

These giant-chain molecules are coiled up in random fashion in natural rubber. When put under tension, the molecules uncoil and stretch. When the tension is released, the molecules recoil, and the chunk of rubber resumes its original shape. Natural rubber becomes sticky when it is warmed, and brittle when it is chilled. When sulfur is mixed with the rubber and the mixture is heated, the sulfur atoms become bonded to carbon atoms in adjacent chains and set up cross links between the molecules.

This process, called *vulcanization*, improves the properties of the rubber and makes it much more useful. In the processing of rubber, *accelerators* are added to catalyze the vulcanization. Other substances, such as zinc oxide and carbon black, are also introduced into the mixture to improve the resistance of the rubber to oxidation and to make it tougher.

Ways have been discovered of synthesizing giant polymeric-chain molecules that have properties like natural rubber, and a number of *synthetic rubbers* are now available. Because they differ somewhat in composition and structure from natural rubber, they are superior to the natural product for certain uses, although they may be inferior in other respects. It seems probable that we will continue to use both natural and synthetic rubbers.

EXERCISES

1. Why are so many different hydrocarbons formed?

2. Correlate the difference in electronegativity of carbon and hydrogen with the: a) degree of polarity of the carbon hydrogen bond; b) degree of volatility of hydrocarbon systems.

3. Distinguish between aliphatic, naphthenic, and aromatic ring hydrocarbons, giving structural formulas for two examples of each class.

4. a) What is an homologous series of compounds?

b) Show how the methane series of hydrocarbons can be considered to be derived from methane.

c) How do the melting and boiling points of this series of hydrocarbons vary?

5. a) What is the meaning of the term *isomerism*?

b) Write structural formulas for all the isomers that you can imagine which have the formula C_5H_{12}.

c) Is benzene, C_6H_6, isomeric with acetylene, C_2H_2?

6. Why is the term *straight-chain hydrocarbon* somewhat misleading when applied to some of the saturated hydrocarbons?

7. What is the spatial arrangement of the atoms in: a) $H_3C—CH_3$? b) $H_2C＝CH_2$? c) $HC≡CH$? d) $H_3C—CH_2—CH_3$? e) $H—C≡C—CH_3$?

8. a) Describe the bonding and spatial configuration of benzene.

b) What is the general formula for the benzene series of hydrocarbons?

c) Give the structural formula for two other members of the series.

9. a) Outline the general methods used for exploiting petroleum as a source of hydrocarbons.

b) Name five different products of the refining of petroleum, giving their uses.

10. Describe the chemical composition and structure of natural rubber. Correlate this with the properties that make rubber bands so useful.

11. What is the essential chemistry of the vulcanization of rubber, and what desirable results does it accomplish?

Chapter 26

▶ **Organic Chemistry II**

▶ **Derivatives of the Hydrocarbons**

Organic compounds other than the hydrocarbons may be considered to be derived from the hydrocarbons by the replacement of one or more hydrogen atoms by atoms or groups of atoms of other elements. The simplest of these derivatives are those in which only one hydrogen atom of the hydrocarbon is replaced. The residual hydrocarbon group left when a hydrogen atom is replaced is called an organic *radical* and has a valence of 1. For each hydrocarbon there is a corresponding univalent radical or group which is referred to by a name derived from that of the parent hydrocarbon. The general symbol R commonly is used to refer to an organic hydrocarbon radical, such as the methyl group. In the structures for the radicals that follow, the single unshared valence electron on a carbon atom indicates that each radical is capable of forming one more covalent bond.

CH_4 — methane CH_3 — methyl radical

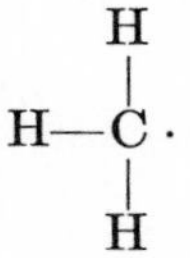

C_2H_6 — ethane C_2H_5 — ethyl radical

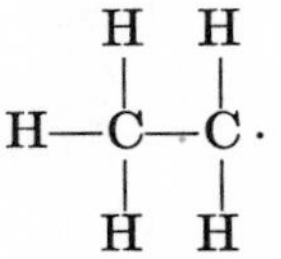

C_3H_8 — propane C_3H_7 — propyl radical

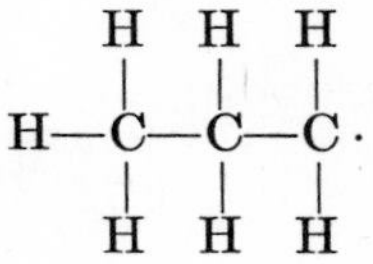

C_6H_6 — benzene C_6H_5 — phenyl radical

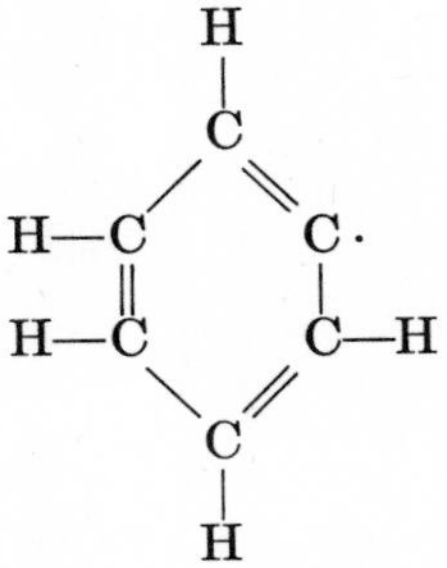

317. CLASSES OF DERIVATIVES OF HYDROCARBONS

In a derivative of a hydrocarbon, an organic radical is combined with the atoms or groups of atoms that replace the hydrogen atom. For

401

Table 62.   Common Classes of Derivatives of the Hydrocarbons

Functional Group	Class Name	Class Formula	Example
· X	Halides	R—X	CH_3Cl, 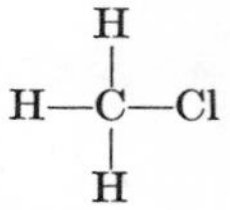 H—C—Cl (with H above and below C) methyl chloride
· OH	Alcohols	R—OH	C_2H_5OH, 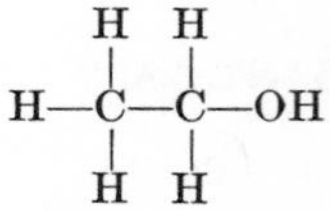 H—C—C—OH ethyl alcohol
· OR	Ethers	R—O—R	$(C_2H_5)_2O$, 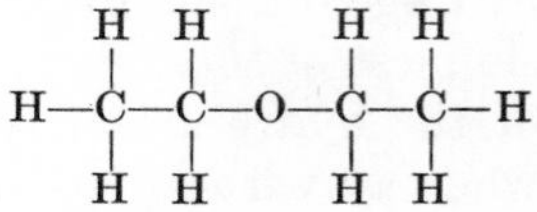 H—C—C—O—C—C—H diethyl ether
H | · C=O	Aldehydes	H | R—C=O	CH_3CHO, H—C—C=O acetaldehyde
R | · C=O	Ketones	R | R—C=O	$C_2H_5COCH_3$, 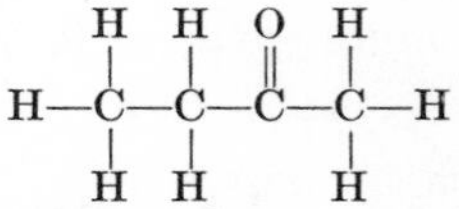 H—C—C—C—C—H ethyl methyl ketone
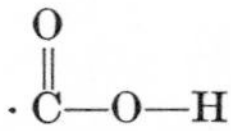 O ‖ · C—O—H	Acids	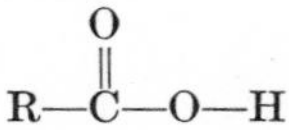 O ‖ R—C—O—H	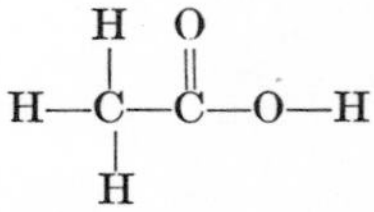 CH_3COOH, H—C—C—O—H acetic acid
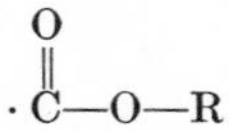 O ‖ · C—O—R	Esters	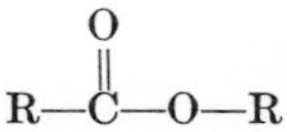 O ‖ R—C—O—R	$CH_3COOC_2H_5$, 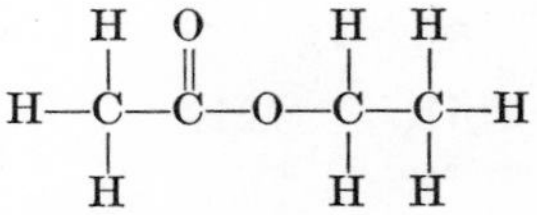 H—C—C—O—C—C—H ethyl acetate
H | · N—H	Amines	H | R—N—H	CH_3NH_2, H—C—N—H methylamine

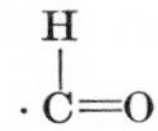

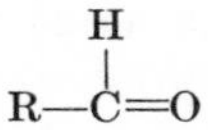

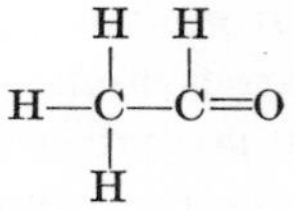

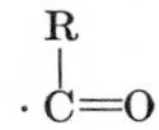

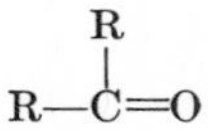

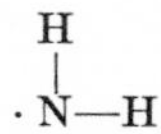

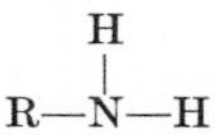

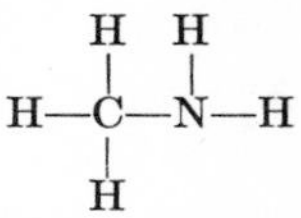

Table 62.   Common Classes of Derivatives of the Hydrocarbons (Cont.)

Functional Group	Class Name	Class Formula	Example
O $\mid$ · N=O	Nitro compounds	O $\mid$ R—N=O	$C_6H_5NO_2$, 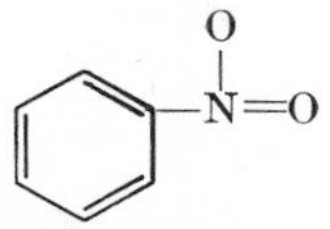 nitrobenzene
· C≡N	Nitriles	R—C≡N	CH_3CN, 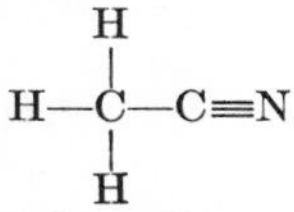 acetonitrile (methyl cyanide)

each organic radical there is possible an extended series of compounds in which the radical is combined with various other groups and which are usually referred to as *functional groups*.   Table 62 lists the more common functional groups and shows these united with organic radicals in corresponding classes of organic compounds.

By replacement of successive hydrogen atoms with functional groups, organic molecules with two or more similar or dissimilar functional groups attached to the carbon framework of the hydrocarbon may be built up.

In the types of organic compounds listed in Table 62, the bonds between the atoms are covalent in character and the compounds are molecular.   If the molecules are small, the compounds in general are low-melting and low-boiling, with decrease in volatility for the compounds of a given class with increase in molecular weight.   Reaction rates for organic compounds are usually much slower than for ionic substances, such as the inorganic salts, because changes that involve the breaking and formation of covalent bonds usually are slower than changes in which ions dissociate and associate.

318.   ORGANIC HALIDES.   R—Cl

The halogens can be caused to react directly with hydrocarbons in what is called a *substitution reaction*.

$$CH_4 + Cl_2 = CH_3Cl + HCl$$
$$\text{methyl chloride}$$

It is possible for further stepwise replacement of hydrogen by halogen to occur to give organic polyhalides.

$$CH_3Cl + Cl_2 = HCl + CH_2Cl_2$$
dichloro-
methane

$$CH_2Cl_2 + Cl_2 = HCl + CHCl_3$$
chloroform

$$CHCl_3 + Cl_2 = HCl + CCl_4$$
carbon
tetrachloride

Organic halides may also be produced by the reaction of the alcohol with the hydrohalogen acid.

$$C_2H_5OH + HCl = C_2H_5Cl + H_2O$$
ethyl alcohol   ethyl chloride

Many organic halides are powerful insecticides.   Paradichlorobenzene is used to control moths, and DDT is highly useful for killing mosquitoes, flies, and other insects.

paradichlorobenzene   dichlorodiphenyl trichloroethane, DDT

319. ALCOHOLS.   R—OH

Alcohols may be considered to represent the first stage in the oxidation of a hydrocarbon.   When an organic halide is treated with a strong base, the alcohol is formed.

$$RCl + OH^- = ROH + Cl^-$$

Methyl alcohol may be synthesized from water gas by the use of a proper catalyst.

$$CO + 2H_2 = CH_3OH$$

It also is obtained as a by-product of wood distillation.   It is an excellent solvent.

Ethyl alcohol, C_2H_5OH, is produced industrially by the fermentation of molasses and other carbohydrates in the presence of yeast (see Section 303).

Polyhydroxy alcohols have two or more OH groups per molecule. Glycerin is an important trihydroxy alcohol and may be regarded as a derivative of propane.

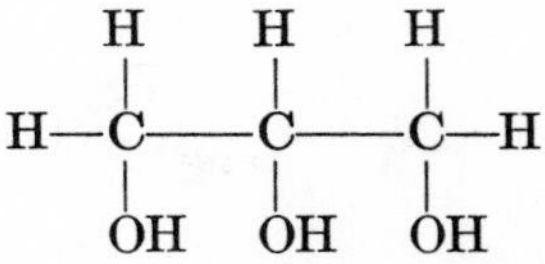

$$H-\underset{\underset{\text{OH}}{|}}{\overset{\overset{\text{H}}{|}}{C}}-\underset{\underset{\text{OH}}{|}}{\overset{\overset{\text{H}}{|}}{C}}-\underset{\underset{\text{OH}}{|}}{\overset{\overset{\text{H}}{|}}{C}}-H \qquad \text{b.p., 290°}$$

glycerin

The alcohols are frequently named by adding the ending -ol to the name of the parent hydrocarbon. Thus, methyl alcohol is called *methanol;* ethyl alcohol, *ethanol;* and glycerin, *glycerol.*

320. ETHERS. R—O—R

When alcohols undergo dehydration, ethers are formed.

$$2ROH \overset{H_2SO_4}{=} R-O-R + H_2O$$

The R groups may be identical, as in *diethyl ether,* $(C_2H_5)_2O$, or different, as in methyl ethyl ether, $CH_3OC_2H_5$. Diethyl ether is an excellent solvent and is widely used as an anesthetic.

321. ALDEHYDES. $R-\overset{\overset{\text{H}}{|}}{C}=O$

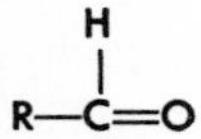

Aldehydes can be made by the oxidation of alcohols in which the hydroxyl group is on a terminal carbon.

$$CH_3CH_2OH + CuO \overset{heat}{=} Cu + CH_3CHO + H_2O$$

ethyl alcohol   acetaldehyde

Aldehydes frequently have strong fragrant odors and tastes and are responsible in considerable part for the flavors of alcoholic beverages, in which they are formed slowly by oxidation. Their common names are usually derived from the acids that are formed when they are oxidized. *Formaldehyde,* HCHO, is a colorless gas of very irritating odor. It is highly poisonous and is important as a preservative, fumigant, and disinfectant. It is commonly used as a 40 per cent aqueous solution, which is marketed under the name Formalin.

322. KETONES. $R-\overset{\overset{\text{R}}{|}}{C}=O$

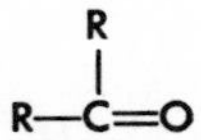

Ketones are obtained by the oxidation of alcohols that have the hydroxyl group and a hydrogen atom on a nonterminal carbon atom. Water is formed in the process. The alcohols can also be dehydrogenated by heating with a catalyst to produce ketones.

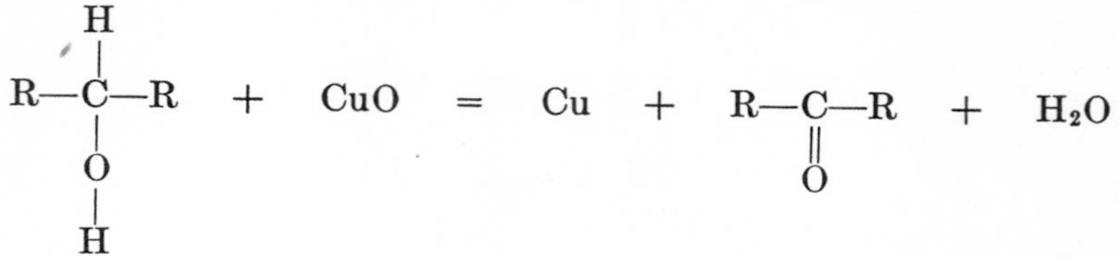

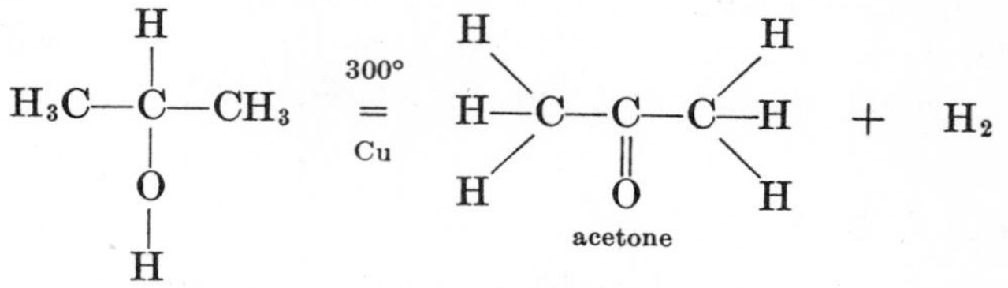

$$\begin{array}{c} H \\ | \\ R-C-R \\ | \\ O \\ | \\ H \end{array} \;+\; CuO \;=\; Cu \;+\; \begin{array}{c} R-C-R \\ \| \\ O \end{array} \;+\; H_2O$$

$$\begin{array}{c} H \\ | \\ H_3C-C-CH_3 \\ | \\ O \\ | \\ H \end{array} \;\underset{Cu}{\overset{300°}{=}}\; \begin{array}{c} H \\ \diagdown \\ H-C-C-C-H \\ / \quad \| \quad \diagdown \\ H \quad O \quad H \end{array} \;+\; H_2$$

acetone

Acetone is also a by-product of wood distillation.   Ketones are much used as solvents.

323. ACIDS. $\begin{array}{c} O \\ \| \\ R-C-O-H \end{array}$

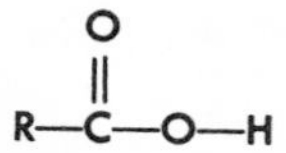

Organic acids are frequently formed by fermentation and by wood distillation.   They can be made by oxidation of aldehydes.

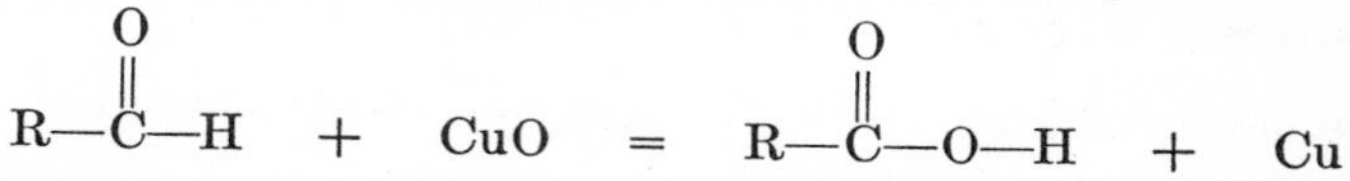

$$\begin{array}{c} O \\ \| \\ R-C-H \end{array} \;+\; CuO \;=\; \begin{array}{c} O \\ \| \\ R-C-O-H \end{array} \;+\; Cu$$

Vinegar, a dilute solution of acetic acid, is prepared by first fermenting the sugars in fruit juice to ethyl alcohol by the action of yeast and then oxidizing the alcohol to the acid.   The second reaction is accomplished by means of the "mother of vinegar" microorganism, utilizing atmospheric oxygen.

$$C_6H_{12}O_6 \;\overset{yeast}{=}\; 2C_2H_5OH + 2CO_2$$

ethyl alcohol

$$C_2H_5OH \;+\; O_2 \;\overset{mother\ of\ vinegar}{=}\; \begin{array}{c} O \\ \| \\ H_3C-C-O-H \end{array} \;+\; H_2O$$

acetic acid

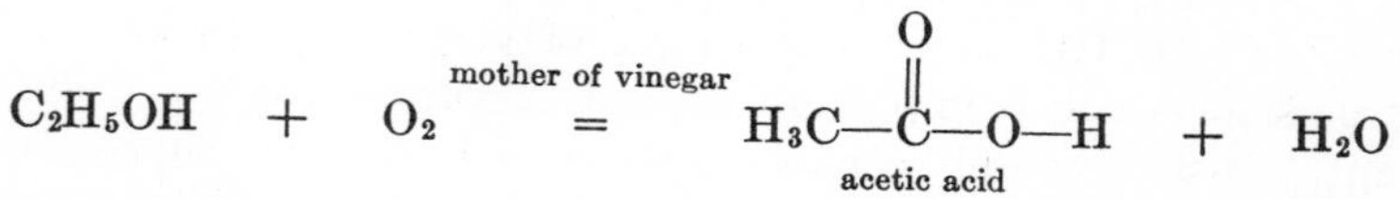

Acetic acid is also manufactured by the catalytic hydration and oxidation of acetylene.

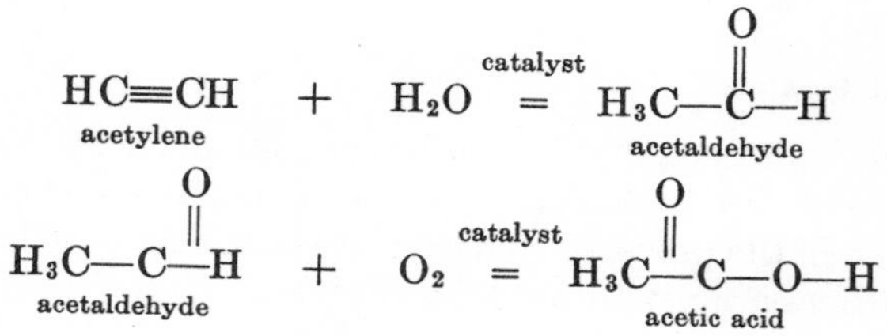

$$HC{\equiv}CH \;+\; H_2O \;\overset{catalyst}{=}\; \begin{array}{c} O \\ \| \\ H_3C-C-H \end{array}$$

acetylene   acetaldehyde

$$\begin{array}{c} O \\ \| \\ H_3C-C-H \end{array} \;+\; O_2 \;\overset{catalyst}{=}\; \begin{array}{c} O \\ \| \\ H_3C-C-O-H \end{array}$$

acetaldehyde   acetic acid

The organic acids usually are weak electrolytes, there being a small tendency for the H of the hydroxyl group to dissociate in water to give hydrogen ions and organic anions.

$$\underset{}{H_3C-\overset{\overset{\textstyle O}{\|}}{C}-O-H} \;\rightleftharpoons\; H^+ \;+\; \underset{\text{acetate ion}}{H_3C-\overset{\overset{\textstyle O}{\|}}{C}-O^-}$$

324. ESTERS. $\;R-\overset{\overset{\textstyle O}{\|}}{C}-O-R'$

Organic acids react with alcohols in the presence of sulfuric acid to form esters.

$$R-OH \;+\; R'-\overset{\overset{\textstyle O}{\|}}{C}-O-H \;\overset{H_2SO_4}{=}\; R'-\overset{\overset{\textstyle O}{\|}}{C}-O-R \;+\; H_2O$$

$$\underset{\text{ethyl alcohol}}{C_2H_5-OH} \;+\; \underset{\text{acetic acid}}{CH_3-\overset{\overset{\textstyle O}{\|}}{C}-O-H} \;\overset{H_2SO_4}{=}\; \underset{\text{ethyl acetate}}{CH_3-\overset{\overset{\textstyle O}{\|}}{C}-O-C_2H_5} \;+\; H_2O$$

Certain esters are quite volatile and are characterized by strong odors and tastes that make them of interest in perfumes and flavoring materials. The ester, methyl salicylate, is reponsible for the characteristic flavor and odor of oil of wintergreen. Notice that this substance also has the functional group of an alcohol, OH, present.

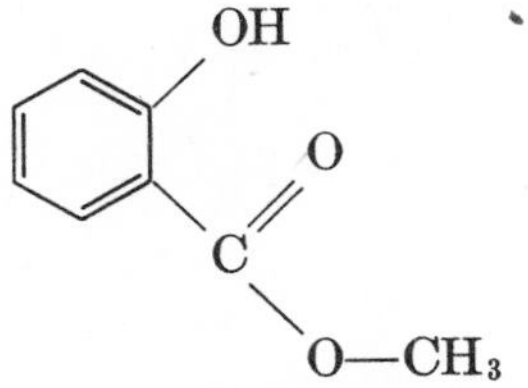

methyl salicylate

325. AMINES. $\;R-\overset{\overset{\textstyle H}{|}}{N}-H$

Amines are obtained by reacting halides with ammonia.

$$CH_3-Cl \;+\; 2NH_3 \;=\; \underset{\text{methyl amine}}{CH_3-NH_2} \;+\; NH_4Cl$$

These amines may be regarded as being analogous to ammonia. Like ammonia, they tend to associate with protons to form complex cations.

$$H_3C : \overset{\overset{H}{\cdot\cdot}}{\underset{\cdot\cdot}{N}} : H \quad + \quad H^+ \quad = \quad H_3C : \overset{\overset{H}{\cdot\cdot}}{\underset{H \cdot}{N}} : H \quad ^+$$

methylamine   methylammonium ion

326. FATS AND SOAPS

The animal and vegetable fats are esters of the organic acids with glycerin.   When they hydrolyze, glycerin and the *fatty acids* are formed.

$$
\begin{array}{c}
H_2C-O-\overset{O}{\overset{||}{C}}-C_{17}H_{35} \\
H-\overset{}{\underset{}{C}}-O-\overset{O}{\overset{||}{C}}-C_{17}H_{35} \\
H_2C-O-\overset{O}{\overset{||}{C}}-C_{17}H_{35}
\end{array}
+ 3H_2O =
3C_{17}H_{35}\overset{O}{\overset{||}{C}}-O-H +
\begin{array}{c}
H_2C-OH \\
H-\overset{}{\underset{}{C}}-OH \\
H_2C-OH
\end{array}
$$

glyceryl tristearate,
stearin,
m.p., 71°   stearic acid,
m.p., 72°   glycerin

$$
\begin{array}{c}
H_2C-O-\overset{O}{\overset{||}{C}}-C_{17}H_{33} \\
H-\overset{}{\underset{}{C}}-O-\overset{O}{\overset{||}{C}}-C_{17}H_{33} \\
H_2C-O-\overset{O}{\overset{||}{C}}-C_{17}H_{33}
\end{array}
+ 3H_2O =
3C_{17}H_{33}\overset{O}{\overset{||}{C}}-O-H +
\begin{array}{c}
H_2C-OH \\
H-\overset{}{\underset{}{C}}-OH \\
H_2C-OH
\end{array}
$$

glyceryl trioleate,
olein,
m.p., −6°   oleic acid
m.p., 16°   glycerin

$$
\begin{array}{c}
H_2C-O-\overset{O}{\overset{||}{C}}-C_{15}H_{31} \\
H-\overset{}{\underset{}{C}}-O-\overset{O}{\overset{||}{C}}-C_{15}H_{31} \\
H_2C-O-\overset{O}{\overset{||}{C}}-C_{15}H_{31}
\end{array}
+ 3H_2O =
3C_{15}H_{31}\overset{O}{\overset{||}{C}}-O-H +
\begin{array}{c}
H_2C-OH \\
H-\overset{}{\underset{}{C}}-OH \\
H_2C-OH
\end{array}
$$

glyceryl tripalmitate,
palmitin,
m.p., 65°   palmitic acid
m.p., 63°   glycerin

Stearic acid and palmitic acid are examples of *saturated fatty acids* that have no double bonds between the carbon atoms. Oleic acid is an example of the *unsaturated fatty acids* that have some double bonds between carbon atoms. *Solid fats*, such as beef tallow, are composed mostly of the glyceryl esters of the saturated acids, palmitic and stearic. *Liquid fats* or *oils*, such as olive oil and cottonseed oil, have a large proportion of the low-melting glyceryl esters of unsaturated fatty acids, such as oleic acid.

Unsaturated vegetable oils, such as cottonseed oil, are converted to solid fats (margarine, Crisco, Spry) by hydrogenating them. This conversion is accomplished easily by bubbling hydrogen into the oil in the presence of a nickel catalyst.

$$
\begin{array}{ll}
\text{H}_2\text{C}-\text{O}-\overset{\overset{\textstyle O}{\|}}{\text{C}}-\text{C}_{17}\text{H}_{33} & \qquad \text{H}_2\text{C}-\text{O}-\overset{\overset{\textstyle O}{\|}}{\text{C}}-\text{C}_{17}\text{H}_{35} \\[2mm]
\text{H}-\overset{|}{\text{C}}-\text{O}-\overset{\overset{\textstyle O}{\|}}{\text{C}}-\text{C}_{17}\text{H}_{33} \quad + \quad 3\text{H}_2 \quad \overset{\text{Ni}}{=} \quad \text{H}-\overset{|}{\text{C}}-\text{O}-\overset{\overset{\textstyle O}{\|}}{\text{C}}-\text{C}_{17}\text{H}_{35} \\[2mm]
\text{H}_2\text{C}-\text{O}-\overset{\overset{\textstyle O}{\|}}{\text{C}}-\text{C}_{17}\text{H}_{33} & \qquad \text{H}_2\text{C}-\text{O}-\overset{\overset{\textstyle O}{\|}}{\text{C}}-\text{C}_{17}\text{H}_{35}
\end{array}
$$

olein,
m.p., −6°   hydrogenation   stearin,
m.p., 71°

Coconut oil, butter, tung oil, and linseed oil are mixtures of the esters of fatty acids.

The common *household soaps* are sodium salts of the fatty acids. They are manufactured by heating fats with a solution of sodium hydroxide. The process is known as *saponification*.

$$
\begin{array}{l}
\text{H}_2\text{C}-\text{O}-\overset{\overset{\textstyle O}{\|}}{\text{C}}-\text{C}_{17}\text{H}_{35} \\[2mm]
\text{H}-\overset{|}{\text{C}}-\text{O}-\overset{\overset{\textstyle O}{\|}}{\text{C}}-\text{C}_{17}\text{H}_{35} + 3\text{NaOH} = \quad
\begin{array}{l}
\text{H}_2\text{C}-\text{OH} \\
\text{H}-\overset{|}{\underset{|}{\text{C}}}-\text{OH} \\
\text{H}_2\text{C}-\text{OH}
\end{array}
\quad + \quad 3\text{C}_{17}\text{H}_{35}-\overset{\overset{\textstyle O}{\|}}{\text{C}}-\text{ONa} \\[2mm]
\text{H}_2\text{C}-\text{O}-\overset{\overset{\textstyle O}{\|}}{\text{C}}-\text{C}_{17}\text{H}_{35}
\end{array}
$$

stearin   glycerin   sodium stearate

When the reaction is complete, salt is added to reduce the solubility of the soap by the common-ion effect, and the soap separates from the solution and can be collected. The glycerin is separated from the solution by distillation and is a very important by-product of soapmaking.

327.   CARBOHYDRATES

Plant material is composed largely of carbohydrates.   This name was originally derived from the fact that in most of the common carbohydrates a carbon framework is combined with hydrogen and oxygen, the latter two elements being present in the same atomic ratio as in water.   This is not true, however, for many substances now placed in this class.   Sugars, starch, and cellulose are all carbohydrates.

Glucose, $C_6H_{12}O_6$, also called *corn sugar*, or *dextrose*, is the most common simple sugar.

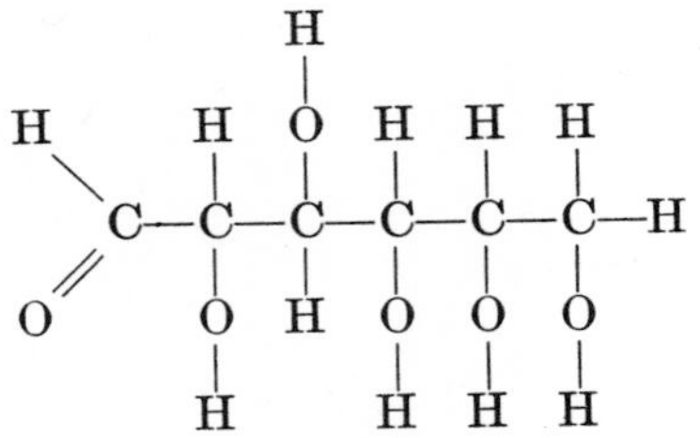

glucose

Note that this molecule has one aldehyde and five hydroxyl functional groups.   A number of other sugars isomeric with glucose are also known, the atoms having different spatial arrangements for the different isomers. *Fructose*, or fruit sugar, is common in nature.

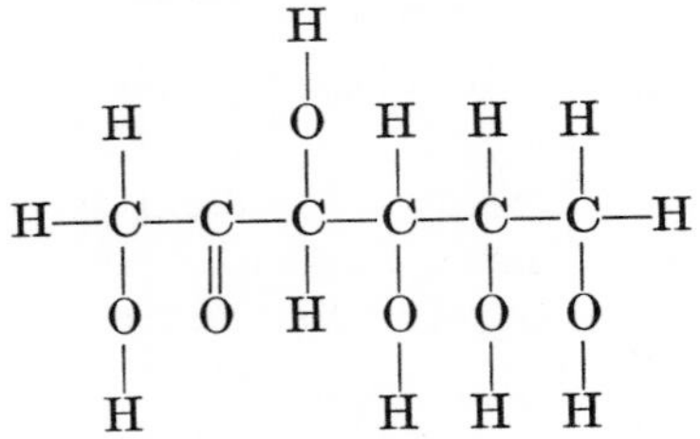

fructose

Fructose has a ketone group present as well as five hydroxyl groups.

Simple carbohydrates, such as glucose and fructose, which are not hydrolyzed to substances of smaller molecular structures are called *monosaccharides*.

Disaccharides are more complex carbohydrates which are hydrolyzed by water in the presence of acids or digestive enzymes, two molecules of monosaccharides being formed.   *Sucrose*, cane sugar, is the most familiar

$$C_{12}H_{22}O_{11} + H_2O \rightleftharpoons C_6H_{12}O_6 + C_6H_{12}O_6$$
sucrose   glucose   fructose

disaccharide.   The hydrolysis of sucrose to give equal amounts of glucose and fructose is known as the *inversion* of sugar, and the mixture produced is called *invert sugar*.   Honey is essentially invert sugar.

Starch occurs in high percentages in cereal grains and in certain plant roots, such as potatoes. It has the composition $(C_6H_{10}O_5)_n$, large molecules involving the polymerization of the primary unit constituting starch granules. Starch hydrolyzes when heated with water to give dextrins. Such dextrins are formed when starched cloth is ironed or when starch pastes are prepared. In the presence of enzymes, such as those in saliva, starch hydrolyzes to glucose, which can easily be absorbed from the alimentary tract by the blood.

$$(C_6H_{10}O_5)_n + nH_2O \overset{\text{enzymes}}{=} nC_6H_{12}O_6$$
$$\text{glucose}$$

Cellulose, present in large amounts in plant tissue, has a percentage composition represented by the formula $(C_6H_{10}O_5)_n$, the same as that of starch. Cellulose and starch, however, differ in the way the atoms are arranged, and cellulose molecules are higher polymers than starch. Cellulose has giant molecules built up of the primary unit indicated by the formula. Cotton fibers are almost pure cellulose, and wood consists predominantly of cellulose and another class of organic compounds called *lignins*. Cellulose hydrolyzes when heated with acids, and glucose is formed. Such hydrolysis does not take place in the human body because no suitable enzymes are present to act as catalysts. In the manufacture of paper from wood, the lignin is removed and the purified cellulose is formed into sheets.

328. PROTEINS AND AMINO ACIDS

Proteins are nitrogenous organic compounds that are present in all plants and animals. Seeds contain proteins, beans and peas being especially rich in such nitrogen compounds. Muscles, skin, hair, nails, feathers, the whites of eggs and the casein of milk are largely protein in composition.

Proteins are highly polymeric compounds with tremendous molecular weights estimated to range as high as 50,000,000. Proteins hydrolyze to amino acids, of which glycine is the simplest example.

glycine

In digestion, proteins are hydrolyzed to amino acids by the action of enzymes, and the amino acids pass into the blood stream. The blood delivers them to the various parts of the body where they react to build up the body proteins.

329.   ORGANIC HIGH POLYMERS

A high polymer is a substance of high molecular weight, its molecules being built up of a given recurring structural unit, referred to as the monomer.   Many natural substances, such as rubber, starch, cellulose, and the proteins, are polymeric.

A great many organic substances undergo polymerization.   This action is particularly characteristic of unsaturated compounds.   When ethylene is heated under pressure, a transparent solid polymer, polyethylene, is obtained.

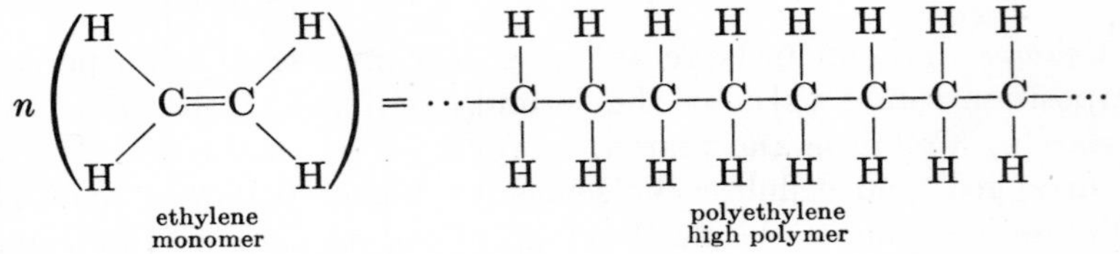

ethylene
monomer

polyethylene
high polymer

An endless-chain molecule is built up by successive addition of the C_2H_4 units, the polymerization process being known as *addition polymerization.*

In *condensation polymerization* giant molecules are built up when simple reacting molecules join, with the formation of some other simple substance, such as water or ammonia.   Thus, nylon chain molecules are obtained by the reaction of adipic acid with hexamethylenediamine, water being also formed.

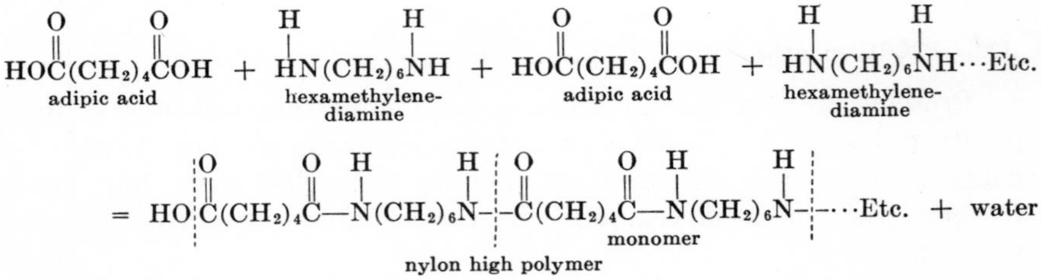

adipic acid   hexamethylene-   adipic acid   hexamethylene-
                              diamine   diamine

nylon high polymer

By forming cross links between such polymeric chains, it is possible to get two-dimensional and three-dimensional high polymeric systems. *Resins and plastics* can be produced in this fashion.

EXERCISES

1. Give five examples of organic radicals.   Account for the valences of these radicals.

2. a) What common functional groups are found in the derivatives of the hydrocarbons?

b) Write the structural formula for a derivative of benzene formed with each of these functional groups, and name each compound.

3. a) How many different chloro derivatives would you expect for ethane?

b) Write the structural formulas for as many as you can imagine.

c) Which are isomeric?

4. a) How do the structures of organic acid molecules resemble those of the oxyacids of chlorine?

b) Why would you expect organic acids to be much weaker acids than per-chloric acid?

5. What chemical reactions are involved in the preparation of vinegar from apple juice?

6. a) What structural features are characteristic of the common animal and vegetable fats?

b) Discuss the hydrolysis of these fats.

c) How can a vegetable oil be converted to a solid fat?

7. a) How is household soap prepared from a fat?

b) What other valuable product is formed?

8. Describe the reaction involved in the inversion of cane sugar. What catalysts are effective for this reaction?

9. a) How is starch related to cellulose in structure?

b) What is formed when each hydrolyzes?

c) Which of these reactions takes place in the human body?

10. What chemical treatment can you suggest that might be effective for converting sawdust into a material of nutritional value to human beings?

11. a) Why are amino acids of particular interest to us?

b) What functional groups are present in an amino acid?

12. Distinguish between addition high polymers and condensation high polymers.

13. Compare the rate of reaction when a solution of $BaCl_2$ is mixed with a solution of sulfuric acid to the rate of inversion of cane sugar. How do you account for the difference?

Chapter 27

▶ Silicon and Boron

Silicon has four valence electrons like carbon, but, because silicon has one more shell of electrons, its atoms are considerably larger than carbon atoms. Silicon is less electronegative than carbon but still is intermediate with respect to the other elements, so that it usually forms covalent bonds. Because it is larger than carbon, four large atoms can easily approach close to the silicon atom, and it therefore always forms tetrahedral single bonds to four other atoms and does not form double or triple bonds. Silicon-silicon bonds are weaker than carbon-carbon bonds, and long silicon chains are less likely than extended carbon chains. Silicon-hydrogen bonds are relatively weaker than carbon-hydrogen bonds, and the hydrides of silicon are not as stable as the hydrocarbons. Silicon-oxygen bonding is very strong, and the common compounds of silicon found in nature are usually oxycompounds. Most of the other types of silicon compounds hydrolyze rapidly to the oxycompounds and cannot persist in nature.

The silicon atom always uses all four of its valence electrons for bonding. As in the case of carbon, the oxidation states for silicon vary from $+4$, as in $SiCl_4$, to -4, as in Mg_2Si, the intermediate oxidation states depending upon how much silicon-silicon bonding occurs.

331. OCCURRENCE OF SILICON

Silicon is very abundant, about 25 per cent of the mass of the crust of the earth consisting of this element. It is invariably tied up with oxygen in nature, some 70 per cent by weight of earthy matter being silicon dioxide or silicates. Most minerals other than sulfides, sulfates, phosphates, and carbonates contain a high proportion of silicon. It plays as important a role in the chemistry of minerals as does carbon in plant and animal chemistry. Silicon never is found in nature as the free element.

Silicon dioxide, SiO_2, occurs in vast quantities as quartz, sand, sandstone, amethyst, agate, and flint. Several polymorphic forms of silicon dioxide are known. Small organisms, the diatoms, which are present in enormous numbers in sea water, build skeletons or shells of this oxide. Large deposits of these tiny skeletons accumulate on the ocean bed and

414

constitute the material known as *diatomaceous* or *fuller's earth*. This very finely divided and porous powder is in demand industrially as a good adsorbent and insulator.

Silicates occur in bewildering profusion. These are ionic substances built up of a great variety of complex silicate anions and the cations of the more common metals. The number of possible combinations is beyond reckoning. In general, such silicates are hard, insoluble, inert, high-melting materials which persist in nature in massive rock formations and in soil. Table 63 lists some of the more important classes of oxysilicate minerals and indicates a typical empirical composition of each class.

Table 63.   Some Important Silicate Minerals

Zircon	$ZrSiO_4$
Garnet	$Ca_3Al_2(SiO_4)_3$
Beryl	$Be_3Al_2Si_6O_{18}$
Asbestos	$Mg_6(OH)_6Si_4O_{11} \cdot H_2O$
Kaolin (a clay)	$Al_2(OH)_4Si_2O_5$
Talc	$Mg_3(OH)_2Si_4O_{10}$
Mica	$KAl_2(OH)_2Si_3AlO_{10}$
Feldspar	$KAlSi_3O_8$
Zeolite	$NaAlSi_2O_6 \cdot H_2O$
Ultramarine	$Na_{10}Al_6Si_6O_{24}S_2$

332.   PREPARATION, PROPERTIES, AND USES OF SILICON

Elementary silicon can be secured by heating strong reducing agents with silicon dioxide or the silicon halides.

$$SiO_{2(s)} + 2C_{(s)} = Si_{(s)} + 2CO_{(g)}$$
$$SiO_{2(s)} + 2Mg_{(s)} = Si_{(s)} + 2MgO_{(s)}$$
$$SiCl_{4(g)} + 2H_{2(g)} = Si_{(s)} + 4HCl_{(g)}$$

The reduction of purified quartz sand by coke is used industrially to produce massive but rather impure silicon.

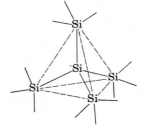

Fig. 102.   Tetrahedral bonding of silicon in its crystals.

Silicon, like carbon, forms a three-dimensional, endless, giant molecule having the diamond structure. Each silicon atom in the interior of the crystal is covalently bonded to four neighboring silicon atoms at tetrahedral positions. The substance is a hard, refractory (melting point 1420°), inert, brittle solid with a shiny dark-gray color. It is somewhat less refractory, less hard, and more active chemically than the diamond because the longer Si—Si bonds are weaker than the shorter C—C bonds. Since silicon atoms do not form double bonds, no crystalline allotropic form of this element having a graphitic type of structure has been observed.

Silicon resists attack by water and acids but is reactive toward powerful oxidizing agents and strong bases. It reacts with aqueous sodium hydroxide to produce hydrogen.

$$Si + 2OH^- + H_2O = 2H_2 + \underset{silicate}{SiO_3^{2-}}$$

Pure silicon is difficult to produce, but it is of practical interest because of its electrical properties. These make it useful in the construction of *transistors*, which are small rugged devices that can be used instead of vacuum tubes for amplifying an electric current.

333. SILICIDES OF THE METALS

Silicon reacts with metals at high temperatures to form inert, hard compounds and alloys which have not been studied extensively. These are, however, important in metallurgy because some siliceous material is likely to be present in the ores used, and the formation of silicides may take place during the production of the metals. Small amounts of such silicides in the metals may seriously alter the properties.

Silicon-iron or *ferrosilicon alloys* are produced by the reduction of a mixture of silicon dioxide and iron oxide by coke. Such silicon-iron systems are hard and show good resistance to attack by water and acids, behaving somewhat like cast iron. They are used for casting corrosion-resistant pipe and other chemical apparatus. Ferrosilicon containing a high percentage of silicon has a powerful reducing action and can be used for the reduction of magnesium oxide in the production of magnesium.

334. SILICON CARBIDE

Mixtures of sand and coke are heated in electric furnaces to produce silicon carbide.

$$SiO_{2(s)} + 3C_{(s)} = SiC_{(s)} + 2CO_{(g)}$$

By making sure that there is present a large excess of coke, the formation of silicon carbide is favored, but usually some elementary silicon and some massive graphite also form in various regions in the furnace. The hot carbon monoxide burns at the surface of the furnace when mixed with air.

Silicon carbide is obtained as beautiful irridescent crystals in which alternate silicon and carbon atoms are packed together in the diamond lattice. Each silicon atom in the interior of the crystal is tetrahedrally bonded to four carbon atoms, and each carbon atom, in turn, is bonded tetrahedrally to four silicon atoms to give a giant, three-dimensional molecule.   The compact material is very hard, refractory (m.p., 2700°), and inert, but it is an electrical conductor.   It is used in large amounts for crucibles, electrodes, and as an abrasive.

335. SILICON HYDRIDES

Like its neighbors, carbon, nitrogen, phosphorus, and the other elements in the four places preceding the inert gases, silicon forms *volatile hydrides*.   These silicon hydrides are not obtained by direct union of the two elements.   They are most readily prepared by the reaction of water or aqueous acid on a silicide of an active metal.

$$4Mg + SiO_2 \overset{\text{heat}}{=} 2MgO + \underset{\text{magnesium silicide}}{Mg_2Si}$$

$$Mg_2Si + 4H^+ = 2Mg^{2+} + SiH_{4(g)}$$

Actually, a mixture of silicon hydrides and hydrogen is obtained, the mixture igniting spontaneously in air.

$$SiH_4 + 2O_2 = 2H_2O + SiO_2$$

A series of volatile hydrides may be isolated from the mixture, the series resembling the methane series of the hydrocarbons and having similar molecular structure.

Table 64.   The Hydrides of Silicon

Silanes		Melting Point, ° C	Boiling Point, ° C
SiH_4	monosilane	-185	-112
Si_2H_6	disilane	-132	-15
Si_3H_8	trisilane	-117	53
Si_4H_{10}	tetrasilane	-93.5	109
.			
.			
.			
etc.			

The polysilanes have been shown to have chain molecules with puckered Si—Si backbones.   They are much less stable toward heat than the methane series of hydrocarbons, and they hydrolyze in water and aqueous alkalies to give hydrogen gas and silicate ions.   The silanes are particularly good examples of the strong analogy of the chemistry of silicon to that of carbon when no multiple bonding is involved.

336. SILICON DIOXIDE

Silicon dioxide, SiO_2, frequently called *silica*, is probably the commonest and most important compound of silicon.   The great variety of minerals that are composed essentially of silica has already been mentioned.

Quartz, the common crystalline form of silicon dioxide, is a hard, brittle, refractory, colorless solid which differs very markedly from carbon dioxide. Why should there be this great difference in the dioxides of silicon and carbon when both of these elements have four valence electrons and form four covalent bonds? The answer lies in the fact that silicon atoms are much larger than carbon atoms and therefore tend to surround themselves with more oxygen neighbors; silicon forms only single bonds to oxygen atoms, whereas carbon may form double bonds. Carbon atoms form double bonds to each of two oxygen atoms to produce a small, symmetrical, linear molecule that is volatile and reasonably reactive.

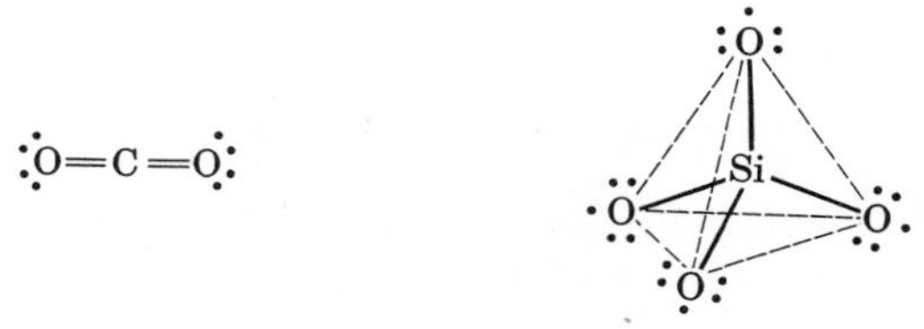

Linear   Tetrahedral

Fig. 103. Difference in coordination number of carbon and silicon in their dioxides.

The silicon atom can be approached closely by four oxygen atoms and forms a single bond to each at tetrahedral angles, as shown in Figure 103. This gives silicon a stable group of eight electrons in its outermost shell, and its valence requirements are satisfied. Each oxygen, having formed one covalent bond, has become associated with seven electrons in its valence shell. Each oxygen is therefore able to form another bond to another silicon atom, which, in turn, can be bonded to three other oxygen neighbors. This structure can be continued in three dimensions to produce a continuous, giant silicon-oxygen network extending out to give the massive silicon dioxide crystal.

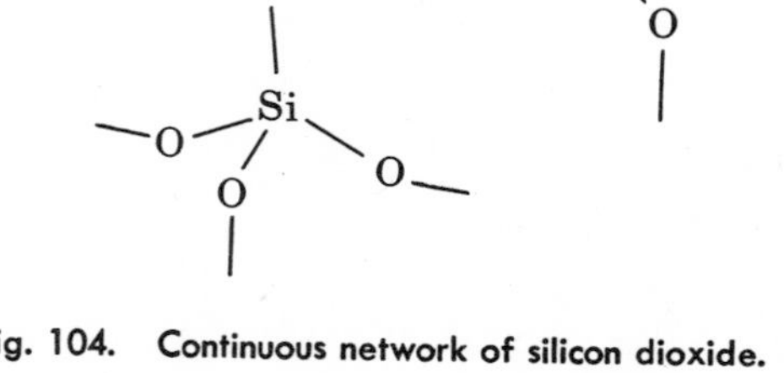

Fig. 104. Continuous network of silicon dioxide.

In the interior of the silica network, every silicon atom is bonded tetrahedrally to four oxygen atoms, and every oxygen atom is bonded to two silicon atoms. The over-all ratio of silicon to oxygen atoms is 1:2, and the simplest formula for silica therefore is SiO_2. Note, however, that this is not the molecular formula for silica, but that the whole chunk of silica must be considered to be essentially one molecule; silica is capable of endless *polymerization* and is actually a *high polymer*. The atoms of silicon and oxygen at the surface of the chunks do not have all their valence forces satisfied, as is shown by the high surface activity of silica.

In each of the various crystalline forms of silica there is a special pattern which is repeated throughout the crystal in a regular definite crystal lattice. The regular tetrahedral arrangement of four oxygen atoms about each silicon persists in each crystalline form, and each oxygen is shared by two silicon atoms, but the Si—O—Si bond angles and the rotation about each Si—O bond are different in the different polymorphic species. The properties of crystalline silica may be correlated nicely with the structure described. The silicon-oxygen bonds are strong and anchor the atoms firmly in place.

When crystalline silica is heated sufficiently, it melts to give a viscous liquid having a random structure, presumably with the silicon atoms still on the average close to four oxygen atoms and the oxygen atoms close to two silicon atoms. When this liquid silica is cooled, it does not crystallize readily, but usually it undercools tremendously and eventually becomes rigid without having undergone orientation into a regular crystal pattern. This rigid, highly undercooled liquid is called *vitreous silica* or *silica glass* (frequently incorrectly referred to as fused quartz). In the interior of this glass every silicon atom is attached tetrahedrally to four oxygen atoms, and each oxygen atom has two close silicon neighbors. Beyond this the structure is random.

Vitreous silica possesses some very interesting and useful properties, which, in combination, make it a unique material:

a) High transparency to light, especially ultraviolet light.
b) Very refractory; does not soften below 1500 to 1600° C.
c) Very low thermal expansion; withstands severe thermal shock.
d) Low thermal and electrical conduction; excellent insulator.
e) Hard, brittle, and elastic; resists wear but fractures when struck sharply.
f) Insoluble in water and inert toward many reagents.

Silica is resistant toward all acids except hydrofluoric acid. It is attacked by fused and aqueous basic substances, especially at elevated temperatures.

$$SiO_2 + 2NaOH \overset{heat}{=} \underset{silicate}{Na_2SiO_3} + H_2O$$

$$SiO_2 + 2OH^- = \underset{silicate\ ions}{SiO_3{}^{2-}} + H_2O$$

Both crystalline and vitreous silica are important in the construction of a great variety of optical and scientific apparatus because of the unique combination of properties.

Hydrous silica is obtained by the action of dilute acids on aqueous soluble silicates. Silicic acid, H_4SiO_4, is believed to form initially in solution, but this changes rapidly to hydrous silica, and the net equation can be written as

$$SiO_3{}^{2-} + 2H^+ = SiO_2 + H_2O$$

A clear colorless *silica sol* may be obtained in which the silica is suspended colloidally in water. This sol may "set" to a stiff jelly, which contains a very high percentage of water associated with the highly dispersed silica. Under other conditions a more granular white hydrous product settles out. Such gelatinous material may be considered to be a rather continuous random network of silica with much water entrapped and loosely held.

Silica gel is obtained when hydrous silica is dehydrated. This gel has a honeycomb, porous structure with tremendous surface area per gram. Apparently, valence forces are not satisfied at this surface, and one can understand the great ability that silica gel has to *adsorb gases* and to exert a *catalytic effect* on many chemical changes. It is widely used to recover the vapors of solvents, as a drying agent, as a catalyst, and as a support for other catalysts.

337. SILICATES

The silicates found in great profusion in nature are salts, ionic compounds consisting of cations of the metals associated with silicate anions. Water molecules, hydroxyl groups, and fluorine atoms are also frequently present in the crystal lattices.

Orthosilicate ion, $SiO_4{}^{4-}$ Disilicate ion, $Si_2O_7{}^{6-}$

Fig. 105. Configurations of orthosilicate and disilicate ions.

The structures of the silicate ions are now well understood. In these ions each silicon atom is always bonded to four oxygen atoms, which surround the silicon in tetrahedral positions. Each of the four coordinated oxygen atoms may gain an eighth electron by complete transfer and become charged. This will give the discrete orthosilicate ion, $SiO_4{}^{4-}$, which is known to form orthosilicates, such as Zn_2SiO_4. Or an oxygen atom attached to silicon may form another bond to a second silicon and to build up *polysilicate ions*, of which the disilicate ion is the simplest. Polysilicate ions contain two or more silicon atoms bonded together by *bridge oxygens*, the rest of the oxygen atoms gaining an electron apiece to contribute to the net negative charge of the complex ion. In this fashion a great variety of polysilicate ions are built up.

In the *metasilicates* two of the four oxygen atoms coordinated to each silicon are shared with other silicon atoms to give endless-chain or cyclic ions. These can be considered to be polymers built up by repetition of the SiO_3^{2-} unit, as seen in Figure 106.

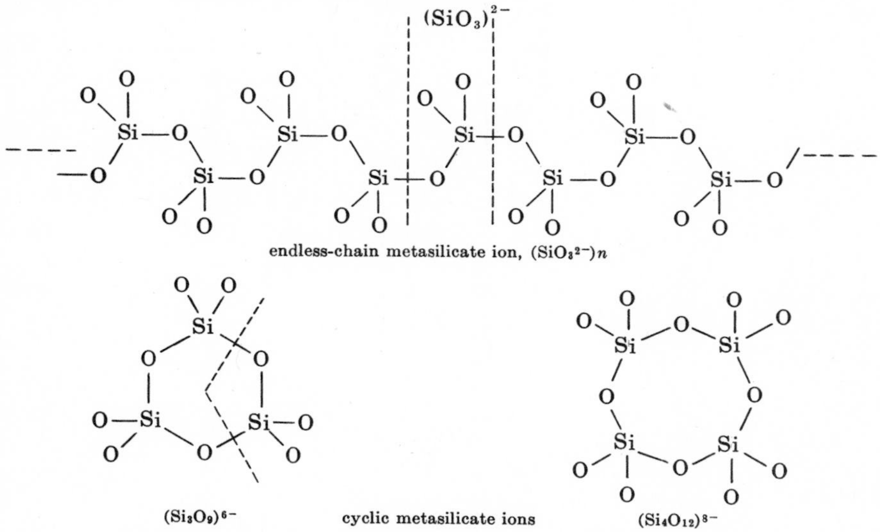

endless-chain metasilicate ion, $(SiO_3^{2-})n$

$(Si_3O_9)^{6-}$ cyclic metasilicate ions $(Si_4O_{12})^{8-}$

Fig. 106. Chain and cyclic configurations built up by SiO_3^{2-} unit.

By still more sharing of oxygen atoms, endless bands, sheets, and three-dimensional networks can be established. Thus, a great variety of silicate ions is possible.

Depending on how many oxygens are not shared but gain electrons by complete transfer and on how many of the oxygen atoms bonded to each silicon are bridge oxygens, the ratio of silicon to oxygen atoms may range from 1:4 to 1:2, and the charge on the structure per silicon atom present may vary from $4-$ to zero. In the crystalline silicates, the silicate anions are packed together in a regular pattern with the proper number of cations to give a crystal that is electrically neutral as a whole. Boron, aluminum, or other atoms may replace some of the silicon atoms in the silicate structures to produce still more complicated systems, such as the *borosilicates* or the *aluminosilicates*.

Because of the extended structures of most silicate ions and the ionic character of the crystals, the silicates in general have high melting points and are stable at high temperatures. They are hard, strong but brittle, poor conductors, and usually insoluble and inert.

Asbestos is built up of magnesium cations packed together with endless-band silicate anions which give a fibrous quality to the crystal and make it possible to separate it into long flexible filaments. Asbestos is used as a fireproof electrical and thermal insulating material.

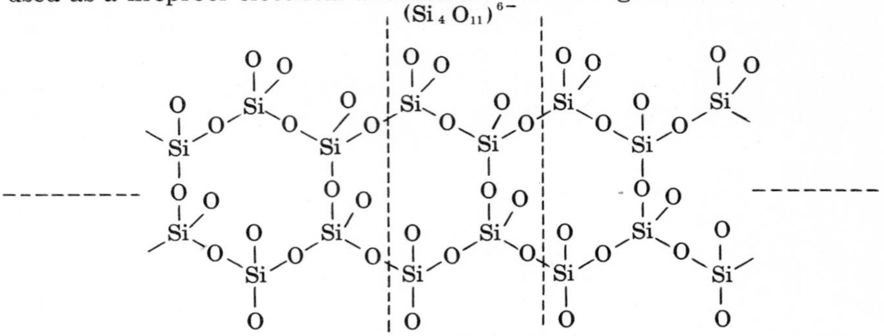

$(Si_4O_{11}^{6-})_n$, endless-band ion

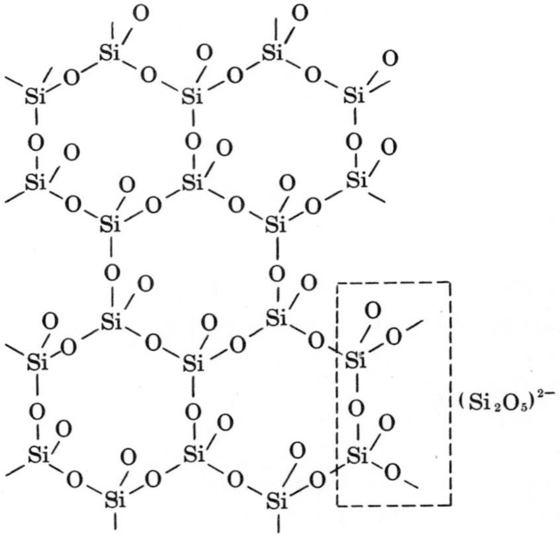

$(Si_2O_5^{2-})_n$, endless-sheet ion

Fig. 107.   Endless-band and endless-sheet silicate ions.

The *micas* are complex substances having endless aluminosilicate sheet anions combined with many different kinds of cations and other groups. They have a layer structure, with easy cleavage between the sheets so that thin transparent leaves may be peeled off.

Clays are hydrated complex aluminosilicates composed of very fine particles produced by the weathering and disintegration of massive silicate minerals. Some of the clays absorb large quantities of water and become plastic so that the material is easily molded into complicated shapes. By firing such clay bodies in ovens (kilns), bricks, pottery, china, and porcelain are produced. The firing operation drives off water, and other complicated and obscure chemical and physical changes occur. If the temperature is carried high enough, the silicates may be partially converted to glasses. The term *ceramics* refers to the art of making articles from clay. Clays are very important constituents in soils.

The *zeolites* have an open, three-dimensional, aluminosilicate framework that is negatively charged and is associated with cations. The porous structure has channels into which water molecules can penetrate and be loosely held. Other substances may also be absorbed. The positive cations in the lattice are exposed to solutions and may be interchanged with other cations. Sodium zeolites are able to remove calcium ions from hard water and are used for water softening.

338. WATER GLASS

The sodium silicates are exceptional because they are quite soluble in water. Sodium silicates are produced in large quantities by the reaction of sodium hydroxide or sodium carbonate on silica, usually by fusion.

$$2NaOH + SiO_2 = Na_2SiO_3 + H_2O$$
$$Na_2CO_3 + SiO_2 = Na_2SiO_3 + CO_2$$

The product undercools to give a glass which is called *water glass*, because it goes into solution in water. Water glass is commonly formulated as Na_2SiO_3, a metasilicate. This is an oversimplification, the glass commonly being richer in silica than this formula indicates. The concentrated solutions of water glass that are marketed are colorless and quite viscous. The silicate ions hydrolyze strongly to give basic solutions, and considerable hydrous silica may form in colloidal suspension or settle out.

$$SiO_3{}^{2-} + H_2O = \underset{\text{hydrous}}{SiO_2} + 2OH^-$$

Water glass has many important uses in soaps, cleansers, fireproofing, adhesives, and egg preservation.

339. OTHER SILICATE GLASSES

Ordinary window and bottle glasses are complex mixtures of silicates and silica that have been held in the molten state at high temperatures until they become homogeneous and then cooled to give *undercooled liquid solutions* that are quite rigid. The fundamental operations used in the manufacture of glass involve fusing sand with oxycompounds of the cations that are to be introduced into the glass. For example, calcium may be incorporated in a glass by any of the following fusion reactions:

$$SiO_2 + Ca(OH)_2 = H_2O + CaSiO_3$$
$$SiO_2 + CaCO_3 = CO_2 + CaSiO_3$$
$$SiO_2 + CaSO_4 = SO_3 + CaSiO_3$$
$$SiO_2 + CaO = CaSiO_3$$

The silicate glasses have become of very great importance in civilized life because of their remarkable properties, which may be summarized as follows:

a) Noncrystalline, amorphous structure; undercooled rigid liquids.
b) Conchoidal or rounded fracture surfaces.
c) High transparency; they are isotropic, light passing through in any direction being affected in the same manner.
d) Hard and brittle.
e) High tensile and compressional strength, comparing favorably with steel.
f) Good thermal and electrical insulation.
g) Long "working range," which makes possible the formation into shapes by blowing or pressing operations when hot.
h) Insoluble and inert toward water and acids.

The composition of silicate glasses may be varied through wide limits to give a great range of properties. An almost infinite variety of glasses may be created, and a given specified combination of properties may be achieved to produce a material best suited for certain needs. In this manner a large number of synthetic materials have been made available which have contributed much to our present civilization. Table 65 gives the composition of a number of important kinds of silicate glasses in terms of the per cents by weight of constituent oxides.

Table 65.　Silicate Glasses

Kind of Glass	SiO_2	B_2O_3	Na_2O	K_2O	MgO	CaO	ZnO	PbO	Al_2O_3	Fe_2O_3
Window	70.6		17		0.1	10.6			0.8	0.1
Bottle	74		17		3.5	5			1.5	0.4
Crown optical	74.6		9	11		5				
Borosilicate crown optical	68.1	3.5	5	16			7			
Light flint optical	54.3	1.5	3	8				33		
Heavy flint optical	38			5				57		
Pyrex chemical resistance	80.5	12	3.8	0.4					2.2	
Vycor low expansion	96	4								

Window and bottle glass are essentially a sodium silicate–calcium silicate mixture and are frequently called *soda-lime glass*. Impurities, such as iron, may impart considerable color to these glasses.

In *optical glasses* lead, barium, potassium, boron, and other elements may be introduced to give a wide range of transmission, refractivity, and dispersion.

Chemically resistant glasses contain high percentages of silicon and boron and are exceptionally inert toward water and other chemicals, particularly acids. Such high silicon and boron glasses have very low thermal expansion and may be heated or chilled rapidly with little danger of breakage.

Colored glasses are secured by adding some colorant to the mixture. The colorant may be a colored ion, such as Fe^{2+}, Co^{2+}, or Mn^{2+}, or it may be a colloidal material such as CdS or Se.

340. PORTLAND CEMENT

Portland or hydraulic cement is manufactured by heating powdered aluminosilicates, such as shale or clay, with limestone in a long rotating kiln. Complicated chemical and physical changes take place, and "clinker" is formed. The clinker is ground up to give commercial cement. When water is added to this powder and the mixture is allowed to stand, a complex "setting" process occurs, and a rigid strong body is slowly set up. The term *hydraulic cement* indicates the important role that water plays in the setting. The changes that are involved in the setting are not well understood but are believed to involve slow *hydrolysis, hydration, carbonation,* and *crystallization* to produce an interlocking mass of crystals. These changes are accompanied by a considerable evolution of heat, the "heat of setting." When large cement and concrete structures are built, elaborate methods must be used to dissipate this heat.

341. SILICON HALIDES

The silicon tetrahalides can be prepared by direct union of the elements at high temperatures or by heating silica with the halogen and a reducing agent.

$$Si + 2Cl_2 \overset{heated}{=} SiCl_4$$

$$SiO_2 + 2C + 2Cl_2 \overset{heated}{=} SiCl_4 + 2CO$$

Silicon tetrafluoride is obtained readily by the action of hydrofluoric acid on silica or silicates.

$$SiO_2 + 4HF = SiF_{4(g)} + 2H_2O$$

These tetrahalides have four halogen atoms tetrahedrally bonded to a central silicon atom to give symmetrical molecules with low molecular weights. They accordingly are quite volatile, SiF_4, $SiCl_4$, $SiBr_4$, SiI_4 boiling at $-65°$ (1,801 mm Hg), $57.6°$, $153°$, and $290°$, respectively. They hydrolyze vigorously and fume strongly in the air.

$$SiCl_4 + 2H_2O = SiO_{2(s)} + 4HCl_{(g)}$$

By combining ammonia with a stream of silicon tetrachloride vapor, very dense fumes suitable for smoke screens can be set up. The effect of change in the relative sizes of the halogen atoms on the properties of the silicon halides is interesting. When four fluorine atoms, which are quite small, have combined with silicon to form SiF_4 there is still room enough around the central silicon atom for two fluoride ions to approach close enough to combine with the silicon.

$$SiF_4 + 2F^- = \underset{\text{fluosilicate ion}}{SiF_6{}^{2-}}$$

This fluosilicate ion has the six fluorine atoms arranged at the corners of a regular octahedron, and the silicon atom is at the center, equidistant from all six fluorine atoms.

Fig. 108. Octahedral fluosilicate ion.

Chlorine, bromine, and iodine atoms are so large that it is impossible for six of them to get close enough to a silicon atom to bond strongly, and no chloro-, bromo-, or iodosilicate ions are formed. The fluosilicate ion is a stable complex anion that associates with many cations to form solid fluosilicates which are useful. $NaSiF_6$ is soluble and toxic and is important as an insecticide.

342. THE SILICONE POLYMERS

A recent development in the chemistry of silicon has been the production of compounds having —Si—O—Si—O—Si— frameworks, with some hydrocarbon radicals bonded to the silicon atoms to give polymeric neutral systems.

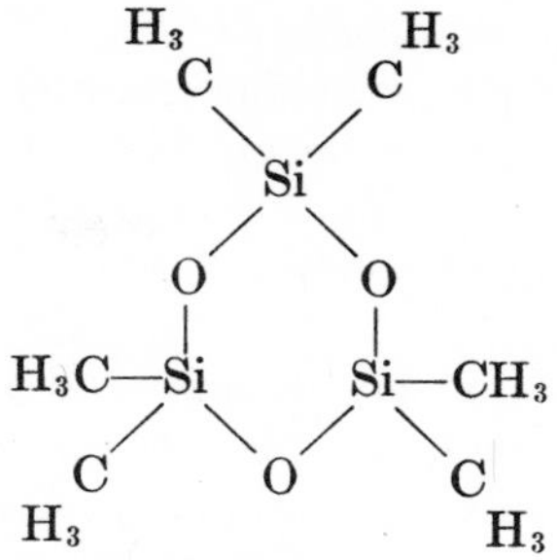

cyclic methyl silicone

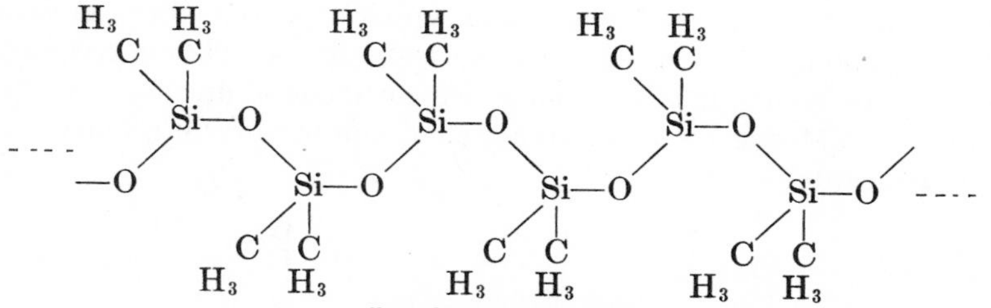

endless-chain methyl silicone

Fig. 109.   Methyl silicone polymers.

Cyclic, chain, and other highly polymerized molecular silicon compounds are thus obtained. They combine to some degree the properties of hydrocarbon systems with those of the oxysilicon systems. For instance, they are not wetted by water but are more stable to heat than organic compounds. Some of the silicones are oils and are good lubricants; others are rubberlike, while still others are hard transparent resins which withstand high temperatures. They are a new class of materials which promise to have many interesting applications because of their unique properties.

343. ATOMIC STRUCTURE, BONDING, AND OXIDATION STATES OF BORON

Boron is the only element in Group III which is nonmetallic in behavior. Its atomic number is five, and it has three valence electrons. It is the only nonmetallic element with less than four electrons in the outermost shell. This is because of the very small size of its atom. Boron resembles carbon and especially silicon in many respects.

This strong resemblance between boron and silicon is a good example of the diagonal relationships frequently found in the periodic table. An element early in a period often is remarkably like the element in the next group to the right in the next lower period. Thus, Li resembles Mg, Be resembles Al, and B resembles Si. In each of these pairs, the decrease in size and the increase in electronegativity, which usually accompany increase in atomic number in a period, are counterbalanced by the increase in size and the decrease in electronegativity which accompany increase in atomic number in a group. The two elements of each pair should be similar in size and electronegativity and should resemble each other in many ways.

Boron usually forms covalent bonds, and its common compounds either are molecular or contain complex ions in which the boron is covalently bonded to other atoms. Boron always uses all three of its valence electrons for bonding purposes, and its common oxidation states will be **+3** and **−3**. One of the outstanding features of the chemistry of boron is the ability of simple molecules containing boron to form molecular addition compounds. This comes about because, when boron has formed three covalent bonds, it still is short two electrons of an inert-gas structure and has a strong tendency to act as acceptor to form a fourth bond by donor-acceptor action.

molecular addition compound

When boron forms only three covalent bonds, these are directed toward the corners of an equilateral triangle coplanar with the boron atom. When a fourth covalent bond is formed by donor-acceptor action, the four bonds are tetrahedral.

coplanar triangular
bonding

tetrahedral
bonding

Like silicon and carbon, boron does not form ionic compounds (salts) with sulfate, nitrate, or other anionic units because boron does not form stable simple cations.

344. OCCURRENCE OF BORON

Boron is not abundant, but there are certain localized deposits of its minerals, especially in the desert regions in the southwestern United States, which offer an adequate supply of the element. It occurs in traces in most soils and has been found to be necessary in minute amounts for the proper growth of many plants. Like silicon, boron is always found in nature combined with oxygen, usually being present in *borate ions* that are associated with cations of the more active and common metals.

Borax, $Na_2B_4O_7 \cdot 10H_2O$, is found in the desert salt-lake beds, such as that at Searles Lake, California. This sodium tetraborate is separated from the other salts with which it is mixed, and is marketed as the most common compound of boron.

Other borate minerals, such as colemanite, $Ca_2B_6O_{11} \cdot 5H_2O$, and ulexite, $CaNaB_5O_9 \cdot 8H_2O$, are important sources of the element.

Orthoboric acid, H_3BO_3, is present in the steam jets or "fumaroles" found in the volcanic regions in Italy, and the acid also is found in hot spring waters. This boric acid probably is formed by the hydrolysis of borates.

$$B_4O_7{}^{2-} + 7H_2O = 4H_3BO_3 + 2OH^-$$

345. PREPARATION AND PROPERTIES OF BORON

Boron can be prepared by the reduction of the oxide, borates, or the boron halides.

$$B_2O_3 + 3Mg \overset{heat}{=} 2B + 3MgO$$

$$2BBr_3 + 3H_2 \overset{heat}{=} 2B + 6HBr$$

However, it is very difficult to produce massive boron of high purity, so that the element as yet has come into little use.

The crystal structure of boron has recently been studied. It is found to have a complicated, compact, giant three-dimensional network of boron atoms strongly bonded together. It is a shiny, black, brittle solid which is extraordinarily hard. It melts at about 2300° and is very inert chemically at ordinary temperatures. At elevated temperatures it combines with many of the other elements to form compounds which in general are highly stable.

346. BORIC OXIDE

Boron oxidizes at high temperatures to give boric oxide, B_2O_3, but this compound is usually obtained by the complete dehydration of boric acid by heating. The boric oxide is secured as a colorless glass that is soluble in water, hydrating to give boric acids. Boric oxide is an important constituent of commercial glasses, such as chemically resistant glass and certain optical glasses.

347. BORIC ACIDS AND BORATES

Orthoboric acid, H_3BO_3, is the most common acid of boron. It is prepared from borax by heating an aqueous solution with a strong acid, such as hydrochloric acid.

$$B_4O_7{}^{2-} + 2H^+ + 5H_2O = 4H_3BO_3$$

The orthoboric acid crystallizes in colorless slippery flakes which are of only limited solubility in cold water.   Boric acid is a very weak acid.

$$H_3BO_3 \rightleftharpoons H^+ + H_2BO_3^- \qquad K_{(i)} = 6 \times 10^{-10}$$

Boric acid has a mild antiseptic action, and it is used in solution as an eyewash and for other medicinal purposes.

When orthoboric acid is heated mildly, it loses water, and solid metaboric acid is formed.

$$H_3BO_3 \overset{100°}{=} H_2O + HBO_2$$

orthoboric acid   metaboric acid

With increase in temperature, more water is driven off, anhydrous boric oxide being formed.

$$2HBO_2 = H_2O + B_2O_3$$

The reverse changes are believed to occur when boric oxide hydrates at room temperature.

There is reason to believe that, in the various acids of boron and in the borate ions in borates, each boron atom is usually bonded to three oxygen atoms that are at the corners of an equilateral triangle copolanar with the central boron atom.

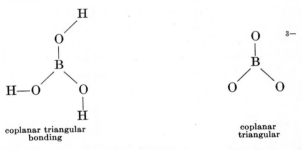

coplanar triangular bonding

coplanar triangular

In metaboric and tetraboric acid and in metaborate and tetraborate ions, some of the oxygen atoms are shared between two boron atoms to give extended polymeric structures.

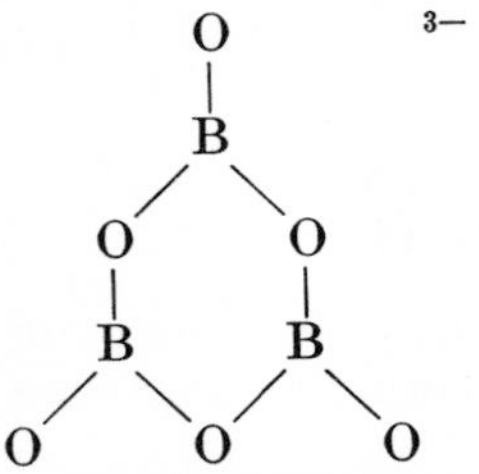

cyclic metaborate ion
$(B_3O_6)^{3-}$

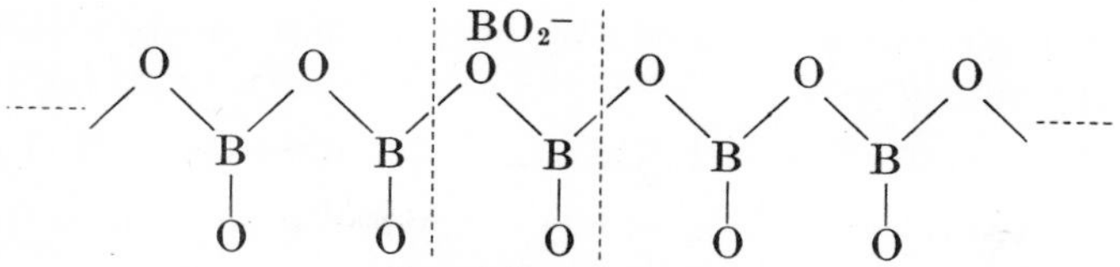

endless-chain metaborate ion
$(BO_2^-)_n$

The formulas HBO_2, $H_2B_4O_7$, BO_2^-, and $B_4O_7^{2-}$ therefore are simplest formulas, the actual systems being polymers having the boron-oxygen ratios indicated.

Since the boric acids are very weak electrolytes, borates, such as borax, show considerable hydrolysis and give mildly basic solutions.

$$B_4O_7^{2-} + 7H_2O \rightleftharpoons 4H_3BO_3 + 2OH^-$$

There will be a small amount of $H_2BO_3^-$ also produced in the hydrolysis. The basic aqueous solution of borax has antiseptic properties and is excellent for washing acid from the eyes or for treating other acid burns. Borax is widely used as a water softener, as a flux, and in the manufacture of glass. Since traces of boron are necessary for the nutrition of certain plants, soils deficient in boron are fertilized by adding borax.

348. HYDRIDES OF BORON

Boron and hydrogen form a series of volatile compounds which resemble the hydrides of carbon and silicon to some extent. The structures and the nature of the bonding in these hydrides are unusual and not well understood. They decompose when heated, hydrolyze considerably, and burn in air.

Table 66.   Hydrides of Boron

Boranes		Melting Point, ° C	Boiling Point, ° C
B_2H_6	Diborane	-165.5	-92.5
B_4H_{10}	Tetraborane	-120.0	18
B_5H_9	Pentaborane	-46.6	0° (66 mm)
B_5H_{10}	Dihydropentaborane	-129.0	65
$B_{10}H_{14}$	Decaborane	99.6	213

349. BORON HALIDES

The trihalides of boron are colorless, volatile, molecular substances that can be made by heating the halogens with elementary boron or borides.

$$2B + 3Cl_2 = 2BCl_3$$

Boron trifluoride can be obtained by heating boric oxide with calcium fluoride and sulfuric acid.

$$B_2O_3 + 3CaF_2 + 3H_2SO_4 = 2BF_3 + 3CaSO_4 + 3H_2O$$

These halides of boron hydrolyze vigorously and fume in the air.

$$BCl_3 + 3H_2O = 3H^+ + 3Cl^- + H_3BO_3$$

Boron trifluoride, BF_3, is a gas that is a valuable catalyst. It combines with fluoride ions to form fluoborate ions, which are tetrahedral.

$$BF_3 + F^- = BF_4^-$$
$$\text{fluoborate ions}$$

Several of the fluoborates, such as $NaBF_4$, are used in electrolyses. BCl_4^- is not formed, presumably because the boron atom is so small compared with the large atoms of chlorine.

350. BORIDES

Boron forms borides of the metals at high temperatures. Many of these compounds are very hard and refractory. Small amounts of boron in steel are reported to increase its hardness. Boron carbide, B_4C, is an extremely hard, refractory, and inert black solid which is now manufactured for use as an abrasive, in glass cutters, and for making sandblast nozzles, and mortars and pestles. Boron nitride, BN, has a structure like graphite. It is inert and has a high melting point, and it is a good electrical insulator at high temperatures.

EXERCISES

1. Compare the silicon and carbon atoms with respect to: a) structure; b) size; c) electronegativity; d) tendency for multiple bonding; e) tendency to form long chains of identical atoms.

2. a) Contrast the occurrence in nature of carbon and silicon.
b) How do you account for the difference in the kinds of substances found in nature containing the two elements?
c) What silicon compound is usually employed as a starting material for the preparation of other compounds of silicon?

3. What is the oxidation state of silicon in: a) SiO_2? b) SiF_4? c) SiF_6^{2-}? d) $(SiO_3^{2-})_n$? e) SiH_4? f) $H_3Si-SiH_3$? g) Mg_2Si?

4. Contrast the spatial arrangement of atoms in silicon with that in silicon carbide. Account for the fact that both are hard substances having high melting points.

5. Compare the structures of SiO_2 and CO_2, and correlate these with the differences in properties of the two substances.

6. a) What is a glass?
b) How can silica glass be prepared?
c) What properties are exploited in the uses of this material?

7. a) Write structural formulas for four members of the homologous series of silicon hydrides that start with SiH_4.

b) What is the common increment for this series?

c) How do the boiling points of these compounds vary?

8. Write balanced equations for the preparation of: a) silicon; b) silicon carbide; c) magnesium silicide; d) monosilane; e) water glass; f) hydrous silica; g) silicon tetrafluoride.

9. a) How many oxygen atoms are bonded to each silicon atom in all oxy-silicon systems?

b) Account for the fact that, although the coordination number of silicon toward oxygen is always the same, many different silicate ions are possible.

10. a) Write an equation that explains why an aqueous solution of water glass is strongly basic.

b) Why does this reaction proceed so far?

11. a) How is hydraulic cement manufactured?

b) What is the nature of the "setting" process?

c) Why did the engineers have to install a refrigerating system when Hoover Dam was poured?

12. a) Indicate the spatial configurations of SiF_4 and $SiF_6{}^{2-}$.

b) Account for the fact that although $SiF_6{}^{2-}$ is quite stable, $SiCl_6{}^{2-}$ is not formed.

13. a) What is the monomeric structural unit which by polymerization may be considered to generate both the cyclic and the endless-chain methyl silicones, whose structures are given in Section 342?

b) What unique combination of properties do such silicones provide?

14. Account for the similarity of the chemistry of boron and that of silicon on the basis of their positions in the periodic table. Mention three examples of this similarity.

15. What kind of chemical bonding, ionic or covalent, is characteristic of the boron atom? Why?

16. Why do compounds of boron have such a pronounced tendency to form molecular addition compounds?

17. Keeping in mind the coordination numbers involved, predict the spatial configuration of $H_3N:B(CH_3)_3$.

18. a) What is the characteristic coordination number of boron toward oxygen? Illustrate by describing the configurations of the orthoborate and the metaborate ions.

b) Why is this configuration number different from that of silicon toward oxygen?

19. Account for the use of borax in the treatment of acid burns.

20. Write balanced equations for: a) the formation of orthoboric acid from borax; b) the dehydration of orthoboric acid; c) the electrolytic dissociation of H_3BO_3; d) the hydrolysis of BCl_3; e) the reaction of BF_3 with fluoride ion.

Chapter 28

▶ **The Metals**

The classification of the elements as nonmetals and metals was introduced in Section 9, and these terms have been used frequently, especially in Chapter 4. The nonmetallic elements have been discussed in detail. Before proceeding with a discussion of the chemistry of specific metals, it will be worth while to compare metals with nonmetals and to consider metals in general. Table 11 (page 163 and inside of back cover) indicates the location of the metals in the periodic table. Remember that the

Table 67. Comparison of Nonmetals with Metals

Nonmetals	Metals
1. Occur toward ends of periods (usually in the four places preceding the inert gases)	1. Occur early in the periods
2. Usually have four or more electrons in outermost shell	2. Have one or only a few electrons in outermost shell (rarely more than three)
3. Many gain electrons easily to form anions	3. Usually lose electrons easily to form cations
4. Relatively good oxidizing agents	4. Relatively good reducing agents
5. Hydroxides are acidic	5. Hydroxides are basic or amphoteric
6. Molecular substances, with each atom of the active nonmetals covalently bonded to only a few, one to four, other identical atoms; the inert gases have monatomic molecules	6. All except mercury are solids STP, and in the crystals each atom has many near neighbors, 8 or 12, to which it is bonded
7. Brittle, nonductile in the solid state	7. Malleable and ductile in the solid state
8. Poor conductors of heat and electricity	8. Good conductors
9. No metallic luster; poor reflectors	9. Shiny metallic luster; good reflectors

properties of the elements change gradually across the periods and down the groups. Therefore, the dividing line between metals and nonmetals is vague. There are many exceptions to the generalizations given in Table 67, where the two classes of elements are compared.

434

352. METALLOIDS

In general, metallic properties gradually fade out and nonmetallic properties gradually develop with increase in atomic number across a period.   There are a few exceptions to this rule; in going from the IB metals to the IIB metals, there is an increase in tendency to form cations and an increase in strength as reducing agents.   In their respective groups, the metals of Period III are always more active than those of Period II.   With increase in atomic number in the IA, IIA, IIIA, VB, and VIB subgroups there is increase in metallic behavior, but in the other subgroups of the metals the reactivity decreases.   The intermediate elements have some metallic and some nonmetallic behavior.   The allotropic forms of the same element may differ with respect to metallic behavior.   One allotropic form of tin is decidedly metallic, another is nonmetallic in certain respects.   Elements that are on the border line and show hybrid behavior are sometimes called *metalloids*.   Germanium, antimony, and tellurium are good examples of such hybrids.   In Table 11 a rough attempt is made to draw a dividing line between those elements which are predominantly metallic and those which are predominantly nonmetallic in behavior.

353. TRANSITION AND NONTRANSITION METALS

The *transition metals* are those elements whose atoms have one or two electrons in their outermost shells and, in addition, are able to use one or more electrons in their second outermost shell when they form compounds.   *They have valence electrons in both their outermost shells and their second outermost shells.*   These transition metals include the elements of the IIIA subgroup and succeeding elements in each long period up to and including the IB subgroup.   This is indicated early in Table 11.

Transition metals usually have two or more positive oxidation states, usually differing by jumps of one unit.   This is a consequence of the fact that either only the electrons in the outermost shell may be used for bonding purposes, or, in addition, one or more electrons in the second outermost shell may also be involved.   Thus, in compounds, vanadium has oxidation states of $+2, +3, +4,$ and $+5$; iron, $+2, +3$; copper, $+1,$ $+2$.   Many of the cations of the transition metals are colored and have a characteristic paramagnetic behavior.   Transition metals and their compounds frequently are exceedingly good catalysts.

The rest of the metals are called *nontransition metals*.   Only the electrons in their outermost shells are valence electrons.   Those with only one or two valence electrons always use these for bonding, and generally these elements have only one oxidation state in their compounds: sodium, $+1$; magnesium, $+2$; zinc, $+2$.   Some of the nontransition metals that have three or more electrons in their outermost shells have two positive oxidation states in their compounds: thallium, **+1** and **+3**; lead, **+2** and **+4**; bismuth, **+3** and **+5**. The cations of nontransition elements are not colored.

354. CHEMICAL ACTIVITY

As we have already seen (Chapter 18), when metals react they usually undergo oxidation and form cations.

$$M = ne^- + M^{n+}$$

The chemical reactivity of metals in aqueous solutions may therefore be compared by tabulating their oxidation-reduction half reactions (Section 218) in the order of decreasing tendency to proceed in solutions of equal molarity with respect to the cations. The standard oxidation-reduction potential in volts is a quantitative measure of the tendency of a metal to undergo oxidation in solution. Table 68 lists the oxidation-reduction

Table 68.   Electromotive Series of the Metals in Aqueous 1 Molar Solutions of Their Ions, 25°

Metal	Oxidation-Reduction Half Reaction	Oxidation-Reduction Potential, Volts
Potassium	$K \rightleftharpoons e^- + K^+$	+2.92
Barium	$Ba \rightleftharpoons 2e^- + Ba^{2+}$	+2.90
Strontium	$Sr \rightleftharpoons 2e^- + Sr^{2+}$	+2.89
Calcium	$Ca \rightleftharpoons 2e^- + Ca^{2+}$	+2.87
Sodium	$Na \rightleftharpoons e^- + Na^+$	+2.71
Magnesium	$Mg \rightleftharpoons 2e^- + Mg^{2+}$	+2.34
Aluminum	$Al \rightleftharpoons 3e^- + Al^{3+}$	+1.67
Manganese	$Mn \rightleftharpoons 2e^- + Mn^{2+}$	+1.05
Zinc	$Zn \rightleftharpoons 2e^- + Zn^{2+}$	+0.762
Iron	$Fe \rightleftharpoons 2e^- + Fe^{2+}$	+0.440
Cadmium	$Cd \rightleftharpoons 2e^- + Cd^{2+}$	+0.402
Cobalt	$Co \rightleftharpoons 2e^- + Co^{2+}$	+0.277
Nickel	$Ni \rightleftharpoons 2e^- + Ni^{2+}$	+0.250
Tin	$Sn \rightleftharpoons 2e^- + Sn^{2+}$	+0.136
Lead	$Pb \rightleftharpoons 2e^- + Pb^{2+}$	+0.126
Hydrogen	$H_2 \rightleftharpoons 2e^- + 2H^+$	0.0000
Bismuth	$Bi + H_2O \rightleftharpoons 3e^- + BiO^+ + 2H^+$	−0.32
Copper	$Cu \rightleftharpoons 2e^- + Cu^{2+}$	−0.345
Silver	$Ag \rightleftharpoons e^- + Ag^+$	−0.799
Mercury	$Hg \rightleftharpoons 2e^- + Hg^{2+}$	−0.854
Platinum	$Pt \rightleftharpoons 2e^- + Pt^{2+}$	(about) −1.2
Gold	$Au \rightleftharpoons 3e^- + Au^{3+}$	−1.42

half reactions and oxidation-reduction potentials of hydrogen and the more common metals, in aqueous acid solution.

As the oxidation potentials become less positive, the metals show less tendency to react to form their cations in solution, and the activity of the metals decreases, because the driving force in such a reaction is the tendency for electron transfer to take place. This series of the metals, arranged in order of decreasing oxidation potential, is frequently called the *electromotive* or *electrochemical series*, since it tells us about the relative tendencies of the metals to react under comparable conditions. The table is very useful because it indicates the possibility of reaction of a given metal. For example, any metal above hydrogen in the table is able to react with aqueous acids, forming the cations of the metal and reducing hydrogen ions to produce hydrogen.

$$Fe + 2H^+ = Fe^{2+} + H_2$$

No metal below hydrogen in the table can reduce water or hydrogen ions, and such metals are inert toward water and the hydracids. The ability of a metal to combine with oxygen, sulfur, and the halogens, and the vigor of the reaction and the stability of the compound formed will, in general, be found to diminish as we go down the table. There may be some shift in the order when the reactions do not take place in aqueous solution $1M$ with respect to the ions. In listing the oxidation potentials of the metals when we compare them for a group, we will use the expression M/M^+, M/M^{2+}, and so forth, to designate the particular half reaction.

355. OCCURRENCE OF METALS

The relative abundance of the more common metals is summarized in Table 2. Although the bulk of our metals is tied up in minerals, significant amounts are present in sea water and in plant and animal matter. Small amounts of certain of the metals are known to be very important in plant and animal nutrition. An atom of magnesium is at the center of each molecule of chlorophyl, the green material in plants which is so important in photosynthesis. The hemoglobin in our blood contains iron atoms.

The state of combination in which a metal is found in nature depends upon the chemical activity of the metal and upon the stability and solubility of its compounds.

a) *The less active metals tend to occur as the free elements.* Gold, platinum, silver, and copper are good examples.

b) *The more active metals occur combined in*

1) *Oxides:* SnO_2, Fe_2O_3, MnO_2, TiO_2, Al_2O_3
2) *Halides:* $NaCl$, KBr, CaF_2
3) *Carbonates:* $CaCO_3$, $BaCO_3$, $MgCO_3$, Na_2CO_3
4) *Sulfides:* ZnS, PbS, Ag_2S, HgS, Cu_2S, FeS_2
5) *Sulfates:* $CaSO_4$, $BaSO_4$, Na_2SO_4
6) *Phosphates:* $Ca_3(PO_4)_2$
7) *Silicates:* $KAlSi_3O_6$
8) *Other compounds:* Na_3AlF_8, $AuTe_2$

Note that the distinction is not sharp, some metals, such as silver and copper, appearing in both categories.

In compounds the more active metals usually are present as cations and are associated with anions to give stable ionic crystals. Some metals appear in higher oxidation states in complex anions, as in $PbCrO_4$ or $FeTiO_3$.

356. METALLURGY

This branch of chemistry deals with the *extraction* and *purification* of the metals. The term *ore* is used to refer to any mineral that contains enough of a given metal to enable it to be used as a commerical source of that metal. The mineral matter that is mixed with the metal or its compounds in the ore is called *gangue*. Gangue usually is comprised of silica and silicates.

357. CONCENTRATION OF ORES

Many ores have such a high per cent of gangue that they must first be concentrated. This is frequently accomplished by *flotation*, especially when the metal is present as the sulfide. The ore is pulverized and mixed with a *wetting agent*, a liquid that will wet the sulfide particles but not the gangue. Then the mixture is churned in an agitator with air, water, and a *foaming agent*. Bubbles form and rise to the top to produce a tough foam, carrying the sulfide particles along. The foam floats off, and the sulfide is recovered from it. The gangue particles are not picked up by the foam but sink to the bottom and are drained off as worthless *tailings*. In this manner, copper sulfide can be separated practically quantitatively from low-grade ore containing less than 1 per cent of copper. In addition, by suitable selection of different flotation agents, the small amount of molybdenum sulfide that commonly accompanies the copper sulfide can be separated from the concentrate. Developments in flotation methods have made it economically feasible to exploit many low-grade ores.

358. METALLURGICAL METHODS

The method used to obtain a metal from the ore or its concentrate depends upon the type of ore that is being handled.

a. Ores containing the free metal. The metal may be separated from the gangue by *melting* the metal and running it off. Frequently, a flux such as calcium carbonate, is added; the flux combines with the gangue to form a low-melting *slag*, which may be separated easily from the molten metal.

$$\underset{\text{gangue}}{SiO_2} + \underset{\text{flux}}{CaCO_3} = \underset{\text{slag}}{CaSiO_3} + CO_{2(g)}$$

Simple gravity flotation is successful in gold-panning operations, where the gold particles are more than seven times as dense as the sand and gravel that are present.

The native metal may be extracted from its ore by taking it into solution by the action of chemical reagents. Gold is removed from its powdered ore by treatment with a solution of sodium cyanide through which air is bubbled.

$$4Au + 8CN^- + 2H_2O + O_2 = 4Au(CN)_2{}^- + 4OH^-$$

aurous
cyanide ion

The gold is then recovered from the solution by various techniques (Chapter 33).

b. Oxide ores. The oxide is reduced by heating it with such strong reducing agents as coke, charcoal, carbon monoxide, hydrogen, aluminum, magnesium, or sodium.

$$\overset{\text{heat}}{SnO_2 + 2C} = Sn + 2CO$$
$$WO_3 + 3H_2 = W + 3H_2O$$
$$Fe_2O_3 + 2Al = 2Fe + Al_2O_3$$

c. Carbonate or sulfide ores. The ore may be *roasted* by heating it in the air. This produces the oxides of the metals.

$$ZnCO_3 = ZnO + CO_2$$
$$2ZnS + 3O_2 = 2ZnO + 2SO_2$$

The oxides of the metals are then reduced as in (**b**).

d. Solution methods. The ions of the metals that are present in the ores may be taken into solution by treating the ore with acids, bases, or other reagents. The metal can then be obtained from the solution by reduction of its cations. This reduction frequently is accomplished by *electrodeposition* from aqueous or fused salt baths.

The *refining* or *purification* of the rather impure metals, usually obtained by using the common metallurgical operations just described, can be carried out in various ways. Distillation of the more volatile metals such as magnesium and zinc, especially under vacuum, gives very pure metals. The metals can be converted to compounds and then reduced to the metallic condition. Electrolytic refining methods are often used to produce deposits of the very pure metals on the cathode.

359. ALLOYS

Alloys are materials composed of two or more metals and possessing the characteristic physical properties of metals. Alloys are commonly prepared by fusing the constituent metals together and cooling the melt. Some alloys can be made by co-electrodeposition, that is, by the simul-

taneous deposition of the constituent metals at a cathode.   Most alloys
are solids at ordinary conditions.   *Amalgams* are alloys of mercury, some
amalgams being liquids and others being solids.

Metallography is the study of the structure of alloys.   By polishing
the surface of a sample of an alloy and studying it under the microscope,
much can be learned about its structure and the phases that are present.
Superficial corrosion or etching of the polished surface can be used to
produce a relief pattern that helps reveal the structural features (see
Figure 111b).   The structure of alloys may also be studied by X-ray
methods.   Investigation of the change of melting point with change in
composition for a given alloy system is very effective in establishing the
nature of the alloys.

An alloy may be:

a. A solid solution phase, each crystal having atoms of one metal
replacing some of the atoms of a second metal in its characteristic crystal
pattern, as shown in Figure 110.

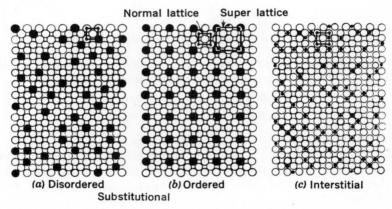

Fig. 110.   The structures of solid solutions.

b. An intermetallic "compound" phase characterized by a specific
crystal lattice which is different from those of the component metals.
The formulas for many intermetallic compounds are unusual in that the
ordinary valence rules do not seem to apply in determining the atomic
ratios; Cu_5Zn_8, $CuZn_3$, Cu_3Sn are typical.   The crystal phase characteristic of a given intermetallic compound may persist over a considerable
range of composition, apparently owing to the possibility of an excess of
one of the constituent metals going into solid solution in the crystals of
the intermetallic compounds.

c. A heterogeneous or polyphase mixture of crystals of the separate
metals, solid solutions, and intermetallic compounds (see Figure 111b).

The *properties of alloys* are determined by the properties of the constituent metals, but are different from those of the metals.   In a given

alloy system composed of certain metals, the properties vary with change in percentage composition. This is apparent when we inspect the composition freezing-point diagram for the system tin-lead, as given in Figure 111a.

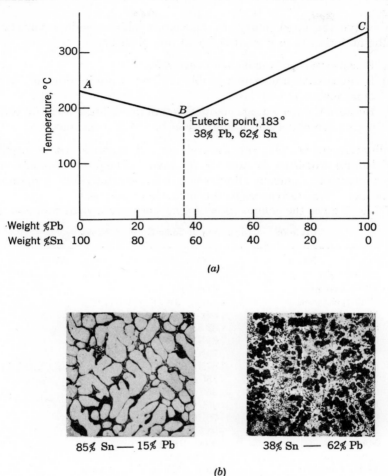

(a)

85% Sn —— 15% Pb   38% Sn —— 62% Pb

(b)

Fig. 111.   The tin-lead alloy system.

Line *ABC* is obtained by plotting the freezing points of the different alloys produced by combining tin and lead in different weight percentages. *A* is the melting point of pure tin, 232°. The addition of lead to tin lowers the freezing point of the system until the composition 62 per cent Sn, 38 per cent Pb is reached. Further increase in the percentage of lead raises the temperature until 327°, the melting point of pure lead, is reached. By varying the composition of a tin-lead alloy we can vary the melting point, the alloy with the composition of 62 per cent Sn,

38 per cent Pb, having the lowest melting point of any tin-lead alloy we can make.

Other properties, such as hardness, tensile strength, electrical conductivity, and resistance to corrosion, also change as the composition changes.

We have the opportunity of creating an almost endless variety of metallic materials with a great range of properties:

a) Because most of the elements are metals.
b) Because the number of possible different combinations of two or more metals is very large.
c) Because the percentage composition in any alloy system involving a given combination of metals can be varied continuously.

Metallurgists can set out to synthesize a metallic material with a specified set of definite properties to meet a given need.   The production of a very large number of important alloys has had an enormous effect upon our way of life.   Great advances in this field are in prospect.

Table 69 gives the composition of a number of alloys in common use.

Table 69.   Composition of Some Common Alloys

Name	Composition, Per Cent by Weight
White cast iron	97Fe, 3C
High-speed steel	75Fe, 18W, 6Cr, 0.3V, 0.7C
Manganese steel	86Fe, 13Mn, 1.0C
Stainless steel	82.5Fe, 16.5Cr, 0.65C, 0.35Mn
Chromel C	61Ni, 23Fe, 16Cr
Nichrome wire	75Ni, 11Cr, 12Fe, 2Mn
Monel B	67Ni, 30Cu, 1.4Fe, 1.0Mn, 0.15C, 0.1Si
Nickel coin, U.S.A.	75Cu, 25Ni
German silver	55Cu, 25Zn, 20Ni
Bronze	90Cu, 10Sn
Cartridge brass	70Cu, 30Zn
Dowmetal E	93.7Mg, 6Al, 0.3Mn
Magnalium	90Al, 10Mg
Type metal	70Pb, 18Sb, 10Sn, 2Cu
Wood's metal	50Bi, 12.5Cd, 25Pb, 12.5Sn
Plumber's solder	67Pb, 33Sn
Silver solder	40Ag, 40Sn, 14Cu, 6Zn
Beryllium brass	57Cu, 43Zn, 0.7Be
Lead shot	99.8Pb, 0.2As
Battery plate	94Pb, 6Sb
Dentist amalgam	70Hg, 30Cu
Inlay casting gold	90Au, 1.5Ag, 7Cu, 0.5Zn, 1.0Pt
Sterling silver	92.5Ag, 7.5Cu
Silver coin, U.S.A.	90Ag, 10Cu
Gold coin, U.S.A.	90Au, 10Cu
18 carat, yellow gold	75Au, 12.5Ag, 12.5Cu
18 carat, white gold	75Au, 3.5Cu, 16.5Ni, 5Zn

360. BONDING IN METALLIC SYSTEMS

The nature of the bonding in metals and alloys is not well understood. The electrical and optical properties of metals indicate that some of the electrons in metals are very mobile. In their crystals each atom of a metal always has a large number of near neighboring atoms, either 8 or 12, to which it is more or less strongly bonded. Moreover, the high malleability and ductility of metals indicate that the atoms can change neighbors readily without the massive solid fracturing. The usual covalent or ionic types of bonding, which we have discussed for nonmetallic systems, are not consistent with the behavior or the electronic structures of metals. Present theories of the bonding in metals and alloys suggest that all the atoms in the system contribute the valence electrons in their outermost shells to form a "cloud" of electrons held in common or shared by all the atoms present. The atoms thus are considered to be present essentially as cations, which are held in place in the lattice by the mutually shared cloud of electrons.

Those crystalline phases representing the lowest energy for the system will be most stable and will be favored. The stability of the structures seems to be a function of the ratio of the number of valence electrons to the number of atoms, and of the way in which the atoms are packed together in the crystal lattice. In general, the effective *metallic radii* of the atoms in crystals of the metals are of about the same size as the single-bond covalent radii of these atoms.

361. COMPOUNDS OF METALS WITH THE NONMETALS

The *more active metals* readily form simple cations, and these cations associate with anions of the nonmetals to produce *ionic compounds*, such as their oxides, hydroxides, and salts. The *less active metals*, while forming ionic compounds with highly electronegative groups such as the fluoride ion, frequently are bonded covalently, especially in their higher oxidation states, to give *molecular substances* or *complex ions*, such as $SnCl_4$, MnO_4^-, and $Cu(NH_3)_4^{2-}$.

In general, one finds that a metal which forms a relatively large cation has a strong tendency to form ionic compounds, while a metal which forms a relatively small cation is likely to form compounds which are molecular or to associate with other groups to set up complex ions. The barium ion is large, and barium compounds, such as BaO and $BaCl_2$, are strongly ionic. Barium does not form stable complex ions. The zinc ion is relatively small and, while $ZnSO_4$ is ionic, $Zn(CH_3)_2$ is decidedly molecular, and the complex ions $Zn(CN)_4^{2-}$ and $Zn(NH_3)_4^{2+}$ are well known. A metal that forms a cation having only one positive charge is more likely to form ionic bonds than a metal whose cation would have a higher charge. Potassium compounds, such as KCl, are almost always ionic, whereas many of the compounds of titanium are either molecular, as $TiCl_4$, or have complex ions of titanium present, such as $TiCl_6{}^{2-}$. Because the cation of a metal in a higher oxidation state is smaller and has a greater charge than its cation in a lower oxidation state, a metal is likely to form ionic compounds when in the lower oxidation state, and molecular compounds or complex ions in the higher oxidation state. Thus, $SnCl_2$ is ionic, whereas $SnCl_4$ is molecular and the complex ion $(SnCl_6)^{2-}$ is known.

The *ionic salts* of the metals can be obtained by bringing the proper ions together in solution and effecting the crystallization of the salt. If the salt has a low solubility, it may be obtained as a precipitate by mixing solutions of more soluble compounds of the necessary ions. If the hydroxide or carbonate of a metal is somewhat soluble, its salts may be obtained by treating solutions of the hydroxide or carbonate with a solution of the acids that will furnish the proper anions, since the formation of the weak electrolyte, water, and the volatile gas, carbon dioxide, will favor the reaction going to completion. Evaporation of the resulting solution will give the solid salts.

Covalent molecular compounds of the metals are often made by carrying out their synthesis in the absence of water, in order to eliminate the possibility of hydrolysis. This may involve direct union of the elements.

$$Sn + 2Cl_2 \overset{\text{heat}}{=} SnCl_4$$

The ionic compounds of the metals act as strong electrolytes when they are in solution in a proper solvent. The properties of such ionic compounds are determined by the properties of the ions that are present.

Table 70.   Solubility in Water of Compounds of the Common Metals, 20°

Oxides   Only those of Li, Na, K, Ba, Sr, and Ca are quite soluble and these react with water to give the hydroxides

Hydroxides   Only those of Li, Na, K, Ba, Ca, and Sr are quite soluble

Chlorides   All are quite soluble except those of Ag, Pb, and mercurous Hg

Sulfides   Only those of Li, Na, K, Ba, Sr, Ca, and Al are quite soluble and these hydrolyze strongly

Nitrates   The nitrates of all the metals are highly soluble.

Carbonates   Only the carbonates of Na and K are quite soluble

Sulfates   All are quite soluble except those of Ba, Sr, Ca, and Pb

Phosphates   Only the phosphates of Na and K are quite soluble

Acetates   The acetates of all the metals are quite soluble

Because of their highly polar nature, many of these compounds are quite soluble in polar solvents, such as water and liquid ammonia, but are not appreciably soluble in nonpolar solvents like the hydrocarbons or carbon tetrachloride. In a rough way, we find that the solubility of ionic compounds in water decreases with increased charge on the cations and anions that are present. This is apparent in Table 70 in which the solubilities in water of various classes of compounds of the metals are summarized. The solubility of the compounds of the metals of each group will be discussed in later chapters when each group is considered.

Compounds containing the less active metals in the form of oxyanions can best be made by fusing together oxides, hydroxides, or carbonates under suitable conditions. Thus, barium titanate can be obtained by heating barium hydroxide with titanium dioxide, and sodium aluminate can be made by heating sodium carbonate with aluminum oxide.

$$Ba(OH)_2 + TiO_2 = BaTiO_3 + H_2O$$
$$Na_2CO_3 + Al_2O_3 = 2NaAlO_2 + CO_2$$

EXERCISES

1. Compare metals with nonmetals with respect to: a) position in the periodic table; b) electronic structure; c) electronegativity; d) standard states.

2. a) Which is more malleable, sulfur or silver?
b) Which is the better electrical conductor, iron or iodine?
c) Which has the higher coordination number in the elementary form at room temperature, copper, or chlorine?
d) Which will make the better mirror, aluminum or carbon?
e) Which will be more likely to form cations, potassium or phosphorus?

3. Is there a well-defined boundary between metals and nonmetals? Explain.

4. How can the chemical activity of metals under aqueous conditions be compared quantitatively?

5. Summarize the characteristic ways in which the metals are found in their ores.

6. How can the concentration of low-grade sulfide ores be accomplished?

7. Write equations for four different reactions that are used for the recovery of metals from their ores, indicating the changes in oxidation state which occur.

8. What are alloys? Characterize the structures which alloys can have.

9. a) How are electrons believed to be involved in the bonding in metallic systems.
b) How does this account for some of the properties of such systems?

10. a) Which is more likely to form molecular compounds, sodium or aluminum? Why?

b) Will the tendency to form molecules be greatest when the metal is combined with fluorine or chlorine?   Why?

11. a) If you wished to prepare a concentrated solution of OH^-, what compound would you select?

    b) If you wished to precipitate the carbonate ion practically completely from solution, what solid compound would you add?

    c) If you wished to incorporate the phosphate ion in a fertilizer mixture that would be very soluble in water, what phosphate would you use?

    d) Is it possible to remove the nitrate ion quantitatively from solution by precipitation methods?

Chapter 29

▶ The Alkali and
Alkaline-Earth Metals

362. POSITION IN PERIODIC TABLE

The *alkali metals* are those metals occurring in the first place in each period, excluding Period I. They include the typical Group I elements, lithium and sodium, and the IA metals, potassium, rubidium, cesium, and francium. These are very active metals which produce strong alkaline solutions when they react with water. They are quite different from the IB metals, copper, silver, and gold, which will be considered later. The *alkaline-earth metals*, beryllium, magnesium, calcium, strontium, barium, and radium, directly follow the alkali metals in each period. The term *alkaline earth* was originally applied to the oxides of calcium, strontium, and barium because they react with water to give somewhat alkaline solutions. When calcium, strontium, and barium were isolated from their oxides, these elements were called the *alkaline-earth metals*. Although beryllium and magnesium oxides are less basic than those of the IIA metals, it is only a matter of degree, and it is appropriate to discuss all of these metals together. The alkali and alkaline-earth metals include the most active electropositive elements, and a study of their atomic structures, sizes, and properties will give us an excellent chance to correlate these.

363. ATOMIC STRUCTURES, SIZES, BONDING, AND OXIDATION STATES

The atomic structures of these metals are listed in Table 71. The alkali metals have only one electron in their outermost shells, with stable second outermost shells of two or eight electrons. Only the electron in the outermost shell is a valence electron, and the alkali metals have a valence of only one in their compounds. The alkaline-earth metals have two electrons in their outermost shells and are always divalent toward other elements.

In each group, as the atomic number and the number of shells of electrons increase, there is a steady increase in the sizes of the atoms and their cations. In each period there is a decrease in size as we go from the alkali metal to the alkaline-earth metal. With increase in size of the atom, the valence electrons are held less and less firmly and are more easily removed to give the cations. The decrease in ionization potential down each group is a measure of this increased ease of ionization. In any given period, it is easier to remove one electron from the alkali metal to form its singly charged cation than it is to remove two electrons from the alkaline-earth metal to form its doubly charged and smaller cation. The tendency of each metal to form its hydrated ion in aqueous solution is measured by its oxidation potential. As might be expected, usually

Table 71. Alkali and Alkaline-Earth Metals

	Atomic No.	Electronic Structure	Ionic Radius, Å	Ionization Potential, Volts	Oxidation Potential, Volts	Oxidation States
Alkali metals:						
Li	3	2, 1	0.60	5.37	+3.02	0, +1
Na	11	2, 8, 1	0.95	5.12	+2.71	0, +1
K	19	2, 8, 8, 1	1.33	4.32	+2.92	0, +1
Rb	37	2, 8, 18, 8, 1	1.48	4.16	+2.99	0, +1
Cs	55	2, 8, 18, 18, 8, 1	1.69	3.87	+3.02	0, +1
Fr	87	2, 8, 18, 32, 18, 8, 1				
Alkaline-earth metals:						
Be	4	2, 2	0.31	9.281	+1.70	0, +2
Mg	12	2, 8, 2	0.65	7.61	+2.34	0, +2
Ca	20	2, 8, 8, 2	0.99	6.09	+2.87	0, +2
Sr	38	2, 8, 18, 8, 2	1.13	5.67	+2.89	0, +2
Ba	56	2, 8, 18, 18, 8, 2	1.35	5.19	+2.90	0, +2
Ra	88	2, 8, 18, 32, 18, 8, 2	....	....	......	0, +2

these oxidation potentials increase with decrease in the ionization potentials, but the very high oxidation potential of lithium seems to be out of line. This probably is due to the very strong hydration of the small lithium ion, and such hydration effects may alter the relative positions of other metals.

The alkali metals are oxidized to the oxidation state of **+1** when they form compounds with the nonmetals, whereas the alkaline-earth metals always are in the oxidation state of **+2** in their compounds. The compounds of both groups of metals with nonmetals are highly ionic in nature and are solids at room temperature, having relatively high melting points.

364. OCCURRENCE OF ALKALI AND ALKALINE-EARTH METALS

Sodium, potassium, magnesium, and calcium are very abundant in nature, whereas lithium, rubidium, cesium, beryllium, strontium, and barium are less common. Francium has not been found in nature; its atoms have been produced artificially in the laboratory and are very unstable, so that we know very little about this metal. Radium is a rare element, of great interest because of its strong radioactivity.

The alkali and alkaline-earth metals are always found in nature as the cations M^+ and M^{2+}, respectively. These cations are present in

Table 72. Important Sources of the More Common Alkali and Alkaline-Earth Metals

Sodium	Sea water—1.14% Na^+
	NaCl—from evaporation of sea water and from beds of rock salt
	$NaNO_3$—desert deposits, Chile saltpeter
	Na_2SO_4—desert lakes and salt beds
	Na_2CO_3—desert lakes and salt beds, ashes of marine plants
	$Na_2B_4O_7 \cdot$hydrated—salt beds in desert regions
	Complex insoluble silicates
Potassium	Sea water—only 0.04% K^+
	KCl—vast amounts in salt beds
	K_2CO_3—ashes of land plants (potash)
	Complex insoluble silicates such as feldspars
Magnesium	**Sea water—0.14% Mg^{2+}**
	MgCl$_2$—salt beds
	$MgSO_4$—salt beds and certain spring waters
	$MgCO_3$—magnesite
	$CaMg(CO_3)_2$—dolomite
	Many complex silicates—asbestos, micas, clays, talc, soapstone
Calcium	Sea water—0.05% Ca^{2+}
	CaCO$_3$—calcite, marble, limestone, chalk, sea shells
	$CaMg(CO_3)_2$—dolomite
	CaF_2—fluorspar
	$CaSO_4$—anhydrite
	$CaSO_4 \cdot 2H_2O$—gypsum
	$Ca_3(PO_4)_2$—phosphate rock, bones
	Complex insoluble silicates

solution in ground and spring waters and are found in higher concentrations in sea water and in salt lakes, accompanied by equivalent amounts of certain common anions. The cations are also found in mineral deposits of their crystalline salts, in which they are associated with halide, carbonate, sulfate, nitrate, borate, silicate, and other anions. These metals are never found as oxides, hydroxides, or sulfides, because these compounds are too reactive to persist in nature.

Lithium, rubidium, cesium, and beryllium are found concentrated in complex inert silicate minerals which are rare in occurrence. Strontium and barium occur in limited deposits of their carbonates and sulfates.

Table 72 summarizes the important sources of the more common alkali and alkaline-earth metals, the sources commonly used for industrial supplies of the elements being given in heavy type.

The concentration of sodium ion in sea water is relatively high, whereas that of potassium, magnesium, and calcium ions is much lower (see Table 2, page 15). However, in the aggregate the oceans and salt lakes are tremendous reservoirs of these ions. Evaporation of large bodies of salt water has led to the deposition of enormous salt beds, in which the various salts have been laid down in an order determined by their relative solubilities and concentrations. Such salt beds offer abundant supplies of the salts, which are available very cheaply to chemical industry.

365. METALLURGY

In order to obtain the metals from their compounds, the cations must be reduced.

$$M^+ + e^- = \text{alkali metal}$$
$$M^{2+} + 2e^- = \text{alkaline-earth metal}$$

This is difficult to accomplish and only very powerful reducing action is effective. Reduction becomes easier as the oxidation potential decreases.

Two general metallurgical methods can be used as follows:

a. Simple compounds may be reduced by heating with reducing agents, such as the very active metals, carbon, or ferrosilicon. This method is successful because the metals that are formed are volatile and distill at the temperatures used.

$$2CsCl + Ca \overset{\text{heated}}{=} 2Cs + CaCl_2$$

$$K_2CO_3 + Mg \overset{\text{heated}}{=} 2K + CO_2 + MgO$$

$$2MgO + \underset{\substack{\text{ferro-} \\ \text{silicon}}}{Si} \overset{\text{heated}}{=} 2Mg + SiO_2$$

b. The molten hydroxides or salts may be electrolyzed. This is the method usually employed for the industrial production of these active metals. Sodium is manufactured in large amounts by electrolysis of fused sodium hydroxide or sodium chloride (see Section 224). Magnesium and calcium are produced by electrolysis of fused chloride baths, to which other halides may be added to lower the melting point and the temperature at which the bath must be operated. Magnesium ions are now being precipitated as the hydroxide from sea water, and the magnesium oxide obtained by dehydration of the hydroxide is converted to the chloride, which is electrolyzed. An alternate process of industrial interest employs ferrosilicon to reduce the MgO. There has been a tremendous recent expansion in the production of magnesium, which is being applied in many new ways.

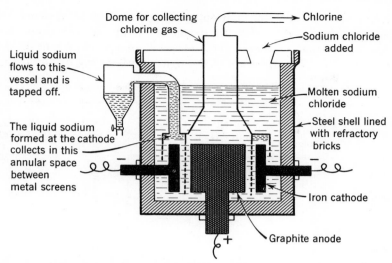

Fig. 112. Cross section of Down's cell for the electrolytic production of sodium from molten sodium chloride.

366. PROPERTIES AND USES OF THE METALS

All of these metals are silvery solids, and are excellent conductors of heat and electricity.   Sodium has been used in the hollow valve stems of airplane motors to conduct heat away from the hotter portions of the valve.   All but beryllium are rather soft and are reasonably malleable and ductile.

The correlation of the variation of melting point, boiling point, hardness, and density with change in atomic weight, atomic number, and size of the atoms, as shown in Table 73, is particularly interesting.   With increase in the distance between the centers of adjacent atoms, the bonding forces should decrease, provided that the crystal structures are similar.   Note that these metals, in general, have a long liquid range; that is, the temperature interval between the melting point and the boiling point is usually rather great, and the liquid metals do not develop appreciable vapor pressures over considerable temperature ranges.   All of these metals have low densities and are very light substances, lithium, sodium, and potassium being lighter than water.

When these metals or their compounds are heated sufficiently, their incandescent vapors emit light of characteristic colors.

Li	Na	K	Rb	Cs	Ca	Sr	Ba
red	yellow	violet	red	blue	brick red	deep crimson	green

By placing a small sample of material in a flame, the color imparted to the flame may be used to test for the presence of atoms of such elements.

The frequencies or colors of light emitted by atomic systems, when they are properly activated by the absorption of energy, are functions of the electronic structures of these atoms and will be specific for each atom (see Section 47).   The *spectrum* of the light emitted may be studied and

Table 73.   Properties of the Alkali and Alkaline-Earth Metals

	Sizes of Atoms	Melting Point, °C	Boiling Point, °C	Hardness	Density, G/Cc, 20°
Lithium		186.1	1372		0.53
Sodium		97.5	893		0.97
Potassium	Increasing	62.7	774	Decreasing	0.86
Rubidium		38.5	700		1.53
Cesium		26.0	670		1.9
Beryllium		1285	2780		1.85
Magnesium		651	1106		1.74
Calcium	Increasing	851	1487	Decreasing	1.55
Strontium		771	1383		2.6
Barium		849	1638		3.5

measured by means of a *spectroscope*, as shown in Figure 113.   *Spectroscopy* is the study of the characteristic spectra of substances.   It can be used not only to identify the elements that are present in a sample and the quantities that are present, but also to give us much information

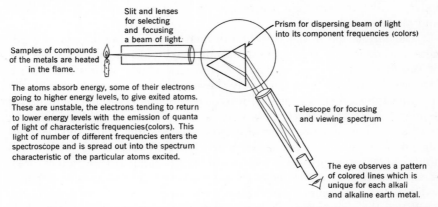

Slit and lenses for selecting and focusing a beam of light.

Prism for dispersing beam of light into its component frequencies (colors)

Samples of compounds of the metals are heated in the flame.

The atoms absorb energy, some of their electrons going to higher energy levels, to give exited atoms. These are unstable, the electrons tending to return to lower energy levels with the emission of quanta of light of characteristic frequencies(colors). This light of number of different frequencies enters the spectroscope and is spread out into the spectrum characteristic of the particular atoms excited.

Telescope for focusing and viewing spectrum

The eye observes a pattern of colored lines which is unique for each alkali and alkaline earth metal.

Fig. 113.   A prism spectroscope as used to observe the emission spectra of the alkali and alkaline-earth metals.

about electronic structures, the spatial configurations of compounds, and the strength of chemical bonds.   Because of their ability to impart color to flame, compounds of the alkali and alkaline-earth metals are used in the manufacture of fireworks and flares.

The chemical activities of the alkali and alkaline-earth metals are high, increasing with increase in atomic number down each group and decreasing from the alkali metals to the alkaline-earth metals. They all burn vigorously in oxygen or air. When finely powdered magnesium is ignited in the air, it burns to the oxide, the reaction being very highly exothermic, so that much heat and light are emitted. The use of magnesium in flashlight powders, flares, and incendiary bombs exploits this exothermic effect. Beryllium is not tarnished by atmospheric attack, but the rest of the metals soon lose their silvery appearance in the air. Magnesium rapidly becomes coated with an oxide and carbonate film, which then protects it from further corrosion, so that it can be used in air. The rest of the metals are rapidly attacked and eventually are completely converted to oxides, hydroxides, and carbonates. Cesium inflames spontaneously in moist air. All except beryllium and magnesium reduce water at room temperature to liberate hydrogen and give basic solutions. Magnesium reacts with boiling water.

$$2K + 2H_2O \overset{20°}{=} H_2 + 2K^+ + 2OH^-$$

$$Mg + 2H_2O \overset{100°}{=} H_2 + Mg(OH)_2$$

$$Ca + H_2O + CO_2 = CaCO_3 + H_2$$

All except beryllium and magnesium must be protected from atmospheric attack. This is done by immersing them in kerosene, coating them with paraffin, or sealing them in containers. Because of their great reactivity, they should always be handled with extreme caution and never touched with the hands. The heat of reaction with the moisture on the skin may melt and ignite them, and serious burns may develop. Very powerful explosions occur when large chunks of the more active metals are dropped into water. These elements are strong reducing agents and are frequently used because of this action.

$$B_2O_3 + 3Mg \overset{heat}{=} 3MgO + 2B$$

$$Al_2Cl_6 + 6Na \overset{heat}{=} 6NaCl + 2Al$$

The very active metals, such as cesium, are useful in *photoelectric cells*. This use depends upon the fact that exposure to light provides enough energy to cause cesium atoms to emit their valence electrons more readily. The surface of one of the electrodes in an evacuated cell, as shown in Figure 114, is coated with a thin film of the alkali metal. The gap between the electrodes is made just large enough to prevent the flow of electrons when a given voltage is maintained and the cell is in the dark. When light strikes the cesium, the atoms give up electrons, and they flow across to the other electrode, completing the circuit. The current produced can be used to operate relays and activate other devices. Barium

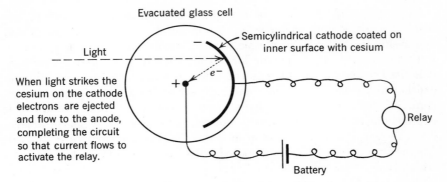

Fig. 114.   The use of cesium in a photoelectric cell.

is frequently incorporated in *vacuum tubes* because it is a good electron emitter.

367. ALLOYS

The alkali and alkaline-earth metals alloy with each other and with other metals. By alloying these very active metals with more inert metals, it is possible to moderate the vigor of their reducing action so that it may be better controlled. Sodium amalgam, made by combining sodium with mercury, and sodium-lead alloys are very useful reducing agents. The less active and very light beryllium and magnesium are incorporated in light but very strong alloys which are becoming more and more important as structural materials.

368. PROPERTIES OF THE IONS

The cations of the alkali and alkaline-earth metals are colorless, and the compounds they form with colorless anions have no color. The smaller cations associate rather strongly with water molecules to form hydrated ions, and their compounds obtained by crystallization from aqueous solution are often highly hydrated. Only the smallest of these cations, Li^+ and Be^{2+}, undergo hydrolysis to any appreciable extent. Most of the compounds of the alkali metals, with the exception of lithium, are so soluble that precipitation of the cations of these elements from solution is difficult to accomplish. The compounds of lithium and the alkaline-earth metals are lower in solubility, and precipitation of the cations may be accomplished more readily.

369. OXIDES AND PEROXIDES

The alkali metals, other than lithium, burn vigorously in air or oxygen to give peroxides, such as Na_2O_2, and superoxides, such as KO_2.

These are very powerful oxidizing agents. The normal oxides of these metals, such as Na_2O, are difficult to prepare. All of the oxides react vigorously with water to give solutions of the hydroxides.

Lithium and the alkaline-earth metals burn to give the normal oxides, the reactions being highly exothermic.

$$2Ca + O_2 = 2CaO + 303,400 \text{ cal}$$

These oxides may also be obtained by heating the hydroxides, carbonates, or nitrates.

$$Mg(OH)_2 \overset{heat}{=} MgO + H_2O$$

$$MgCO_3 \overset{heat}{=} MgO + CO_2$$

The sulfates and phosphates are too stable to be used. The ease of thermal decomposition decreases as the atomic number and activity of

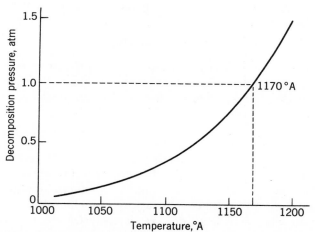

Fig. 115.   Decomposition pressure-temperature diagram for limestone.

the alkaline-earth metal increase. Barium carbonate is much more stable than calcium carbonate. The *burning of limestone* is one of our most important industrial operations.

$$CaCO_{3(s)} + 43,300 \text{ cal} = CaO_{(s)} + CO_{2(g)}$$
$$\text{limestone} \qquad\qquad\qquad \text{quicklime}$$

When limestone is heated in a closed space, equilibrium is established, there being a characteristic equilibrium pressure of carbon dioxide for each temperature (see Sections 189 and 191b). This is called the *decomposition pressure* and may be plotted against the temperature to give the decomposition vapor pressure–temperature curve for the carbonate, as shown in Figure 115.

The oxides of the alkaline-earth metals have properties that make them valuable for many uses. The high melting points (Table 74) and good insulating properties of the oxides account for their use in the construction of furnaces and crucibles.

Table 74. Melting and Boiling Points of the Oxides of the Alkaline-Earth Metals

Substance	Melting Point, °C	Boiling Point, °C
BeO	2450	3900
MgO	2800	3600
CaO	2570	2850
SrO	2430	
BaO	1923	2000

When barium oxide is heated in air, it tends to form the peroxide. At higher temperatures the reaction reverses, and oxygen and barium oxide are regenerated.

$$2BaO + O_2 = 2BaO_2$$

This reversible reaction was the basis for the Brin process, which was once used for the industrial preparation of oxygen. BaO_2 is now used for the production of hydrogen peroxide and as an oxidizing agent.

370. HYDROXIDES

The *hydroxides of the alkali metals* are soluble stable compounds that are very strong bases. They are frequently referred to as *alkalies*. NaOH and KOH are very important and are produced in large quantities by the electrolysis of aqueous solutions of the chlorides. As outlined in Section 235, when such solutions are electrolyzed, chlorine and hydrogen are formed at the electrodes, and hydroxide ions accumulate in the solution. When the solution is evaporated, the alkali metal cations associate with the hydroxide ions, and the hydroxides crystallize out. The electrolytic cells must be so designed that the chlorine formed at the anode does not have a chance to react with the hydroxide ions to form hypochlorite.

Sodium hydroxide is also made by adding lime to a solution of sodium carbonate, filtering off the precipitated $CaCO_3$, and evaporating the solution. The over-all reaction is summarized as

$$Ca(OH)_2 + Na_2CO_3 = CaCO_3 + 2NaOH$$

The hydroxides of the alkali metals are colorless, ionic solids that melt at moderate temperatures without decomposition. NaOH and KOH are marketed in the form of sticks, pellets, and flakes and are commonly called *caustic soda* and *caustic potash* because of their very corrosive basic action. When fused or in aqueous solution, they attack silicate minerals, glass, and porcelain. When they are used in fusions, vessels made of iron, nickel, or silver must be used because these are the only common materials not badly corroded by these hydroxides at high temperatures. The solid hydroxides and their solutions absorb carbon dioxide readily and can be used for removing the substance from gas mixtures.

$$2OH^- + CO_2 = H_2O + CO_3{}^{2-}$$

Standard solutions of sodium and potassium hydroxide must be protected from the carbon dioxide of the air, or the concentration of hydroxide ions will be reduced.

Caustic soda (NaOH) and *lye* (impure NaOH), as well as *caustic potash* (KOH), are used in enormous amounts in the manufacture of soaps, paper, leather, and mercerized cotton and in the refining of petroleum. They rank among our most important basic chemicals.

The *hydroxides of the alkaline-earth metals* are less soluble than the hydroxides of the alkali metals. Their solubility increases down the group, so that $Ba(OH)_2$ is fairly soluble. They are precipitated when a more soluble base, such as NaOH, is added to a strong solution of the cations.

$$Mg^{2+} + 2OH^- = Mg(OH)_{2(s)}$$

Since they are strong electrolytes, the small amount in solution at equilibrium with the solid gives mild alkaline behavior, and these hydroxides are good sources of OH^-.

Beryllium hydroxide is amphoteric and dissociates to furnish either H^+ or OH^-.

$$Be^{2+} + 2OH^- \rightleftharpoons Be(OH)_2 \rightleftharpoons H^+ + HBeO_2{}^-$$

The hydroxides of calcium, strontium, and barium are obtained when the oxides of the metals are allowed to react with water. The *slaking of lime* thus involves the highly exothermic reaction

$$\underset{\text{quicklime}}{CaO_{(s)}} + H_2O = \underset{\text{slaked lime}}{Ca(OH)_{2(s)}} + 15,900 \text{ cal}$$

The slaking should be carried out with proper precaution, since the sudden formation of steam may be dangerous.

Magnesium hydroxide suspended in its saturated solution is called *milk of magnesia*, and this mild basic material is extensively used to combat gastric acidity. *Lime water* is a solution of calcium hydroxide, and *milk of lime* is a suspension of calcium hydroxide in the saturated solution. Calcium hydroxide is more soluble than magnesium hydroxide, and it is widely used industrially as a very cheap base. These hydroxides, like those of the alkali metals, combine with carbon dioxide to give carbonate ions.

Mortar is made by mixing calcium oxide, sand, and water. The calcium oxide slakes to form calcium hydroxide, which slowly picks up carbon dioxide from the air. Crystals of calcium carbonate form slowly and interlock with the particles of sand to give a rigid and strong mass, which is very effective in cementing bricks and stones together.

Calcium hydroxide is used in large amounts for making lime-sulfur sprays, milk of lime being heated with sulfur to produce calcium polysulfides. Lime-sulfur sprays have a strong fungicidal action. Large quantities of calcium hydroxide are used to make bleaching powder and in leather tanning.

371. SALTS OF THE ALKALI AND ALKALINE-EARTH METALS

The ionic compounds of the alkali metals are particularly useful because they are so soluble and provide solutions of various anions.

The *hydrides* can be produced by treating the molten metals with hydrogen, usually under high pressures. LiH, NaH, and CaH_2 are useful as powerful reducing agents, and NaH is used for descaling iron, as described in Section 110. These are ionic compounds with the hydrogen present as the hydride ion $[:H]^-$. Hydride ions are formed only when the very active alkali and alkaline-earth metals combine with hydrogen.

Magnesium and calcium combine with nitrogen at high temperatures to form *nitrides*.

$$3Mg + N_2 = Mg_3N_{2(s)}$$
magnesium
nitride

These nitrides hydrolyze vigorously when treated with water.

$$Mg_3N_2 + 6H_2O = 2NH_3 + 3Mg(OH)_2$$

When magnesium is burned in air, a small amount of nitride is usually formed along with the oxide.

The *halides* of all these metals are their most common soluble compounds. Those of the alkali metals always crystallize in the anhydrous form from aqueous solution, whereas the halides of the alkaline-earth metals usually are hydrated. Cheap and abundant supplies of NaCl and KCl are very important in chemical industry. Anhydrous calcium chloride is a very useful desiccating agent.

The *sulfides* of these metals cannot be made by precipitation methods. because of their high solubilities and the strong tendency of the sulfide ion to hydrolyze. They are formed when the metals are heated with sulfur.

The *sulfates* of the alkali metals, beryllium, and magnesium are quite soluble, whereas those of calcium, strontium, and barium are low in solubility and can be readily precipitated from solution.

The *nitrates* are all highly soluble, and the crystalline preparations are obtained by evaporation of solutions of the proper ions. The crude sodium nitrate available in Chile has been an important source of nitric acid. KNO_3 has been employed as an oxidizing agent in black gunpowder and fireworks, and it is widely used in fertilizers. Both the potassium ions and the combined nitrogen are needed in plant nutrition.

The *carbonates* of the alkali metals are quite soluble, the bicarbonates being somewhat less soluble than the normal carbonates. *Sodium bicarbonate* is produced industrially by the Solvay process. Carbon dioxide and ammonia are passed into a concentrated solution of sodium chloride, and sodium bicarbonate precipitates out. The net reaction is

$$Na^+ + H_2O + CO_2 + NH_3 = NaHCO_{3(s)} + NH_4^+$$

When used as baking soda, $NaHCO_3$ makes available carbon dioxide. It is incorporated in baking powders with substances that will provide hydrogen ions upon hydrolysis. This leads to the liberation of carbon dioxide when the powder is moistened, and the dough is leavened.

$$H^+ + HCO_3^- = H_2O + CO_{2(g)}$$

Most of the sodium bicarbonate manufactured is converted to *sodium carbonate* by heating it mildly.

$$2NaHCO_3 = Na_2CO_3 + H_2O + CO_2$$

Anhydrous sodium carbonate is marketed as *soda ash*, which is used in very large amounts in the manufacture of glass, enamels, soap, sodium hydroxide, and paper, and for water softening and oil refining. When a solution of sodium carbonate is evaporated, $Na_2CO_3 \cdot 10H_2O$ crystallizes out at room temperature. This is commonly sold as *washing soda* because of the cleansing action of the basic solution it gives with water. The sesquicarbonate, $NaHCO_3 \cdot Na_2CO_3 \cdot 2H_2O$, is obtained by evaporation of a solution of sodium carbonate and sodium bicarbonate and is sold as *bath salts*.

The *carbonates of the alkaline-earth metals* are only slightly soluble, but the bicarbonates are somewhat more soluble. Sea shells, coral, and chalk are composed of calcium carbonate formed from ocean water. When ground water containing dissolved carbon dioxide comes in contact with limestone, the carbonate ions are converted to bicarbonate ions, and the limestone is taken into solution, caves being formed. When the solution evaporates, the reaction reverses, carbon dioxide is lost, and the calcium carbonate that crystallizes out builds up stalactites and stalagmites.

$$CaCO_{3(s)} + H_2O + CO_2 \rightleftharpoons Ca^{2+} + 2HCO_3^-$$

The *phosphates* of the alkali metals are quite soluble, whereas those of the alkaline-earth metals are very low in solubility. Sodium and calcium phosphates have been discussed in Chapter 23. We must have sufficient calcium and phosphate ions in our diet to build our skeletons.

372. AMMONIUM ION AND AMMONIUM SALTS

The ammonium ion, NH_4^+, closely resembles the cations of the alkali metals. It bears a single positive charge and has a size intermediate between that of the potassium and rubidium ions. When it forms salts with various anions, these salts are very similar to the corresponding compounds of potassium and rubidium. Ammonium salts have solubilites much like the potassium salts. Ammonium amalgam resembles sodium amalgam. The ammonium group behaves like an atom of an alkali metal, and ammonium compounds may well be classified with the compounds of these metals.

373. HARD WATER

Water that has polyvalent cations, such as Ca^{2+}, Mg^{2+}, and Fe^{3+}, in solution will not give a lather readily when soap is added. Such water is called *hard water*. The polyvalent cations associate with the anions of the soap to form insoluble salts which precipitate out as sticky curds.

$$2 \text{ stearate anion}^- + Ca^{2+} = \text{calcium stearate}_{(s)}$$

The soap is therefore not available for cleansing and is wasted. Soap in excess of that needed to precipitate the polyvalent cations must be added before a lather is formed.

When hard water is used in steam boilers where the water is heated and evaporated, any nonvolatile substances that are in solution will be precipitated on the walls of the boiler tubes. In time, thick deposits of *boiler scale* build up, this scale consisting principally of carbonates, sulfates, and silicates of calcium, magnesium, and iron. Circulation of water through the tubes is impeded, and the efficiency of the boiler is reduced because the scale is a very poor conductor of heat.

Many natural waters are quite hard, and it is important that the substances responsible for this hardness be removed before the water is used for washing or in boiler systems. The water is *softened* by removing the cations responsible for the hardness. This may be done in a variety of ways.

If there are bicarbonate ions present and the water is boiled, carbon dioxide is driven off, and the less soluble carbonates precipitate.

$$Ca^{2+} + 2HCO_3^- \overset{\text{heat}}{=} CO_2 + H_2O + CaCO_{3(s)}$$

Water that can be softened by simple boiling is called *temporarily hard water*. Such water can also be softened by treating it with substances that have a basic reaction, such as calcium hydroxide, sodium carbonate, or ammonia. The bicarbonate is converted to the carbonate, and the carbonates precipitate out.

$$Ca^{2+} + HCO_3^- + OH^- = CaCO_{3(s)} + H_2O$$

Permanently hard water is not softened by boiling because the anions present are not bicarbonate ions but are sulfate, halide, or other anions not affected by heating. Permanently hard water may be softened by adding sodium carbonate or borax, Ca^{2+} and Mg^{2+} precipitating as the carbonates or borates, and Fe^{3+} precipitating as the hydrous hydroxide. Addition of sodium phosphates can also be used to soften hard water (Section 293). The orthophosphates precipitate the polyvalent cations. Sodium metaphosphate apparently fixes the polyvalent cations in stable soluble complex ions, so that they cannot react with soap or separate out in boilers.

374. ION EXCHANGERS

Hard water may be softened very effectively by making use of an ion exchanger, such as the *zeolites*. These are complex sodium aluminosilicates, which form very porous crystals. When hard water flows over

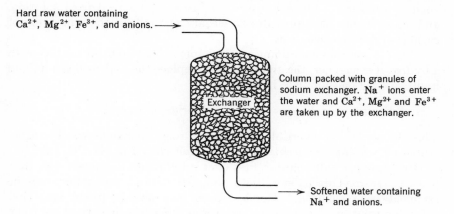

Hard raw water containing Ca^{2+}, Mg^{2+}, Fe^{3+}, and anions. ⟶

Exchanger

Column packed with granules of sodium exchanger. Na^+ ions enter the water and Ca^{2+}, Mg^{2+} and Fe^{3+} are taken up by the exchanger.

⟶ Softened water containing Na^+ and anions.

Fig. 116.   Softening hard water by use of a cation exchanger.

such a zeolite, the sodium ions in the silicate lattice are taken into solution, being displaced by the polyvalent Ca^{2+}, Mg^{2+}, and Fe^{3+}, which are then held by the zeolite. Sodium ions do not contribute to the hardness of water.

$$2Na(zeolite)_{(s)} + Ca^{2+} \rightleftharpoons Ca(zeolite)_{2(s)} + 2Na^+$$

Figure 116 illustrates how this is carried out. The reaction is reversible and can be caused to progress toward the left by greatly increasing the concentration of sodium ions. Hence, after the zeolite has been used for some time and has been pretty much converted to the calcium compound, it may be regenerated (changed back to the sodium compound) by passing a saturated solution of sodium chloride over it.

Minerals such as the zeolites, which can exchange ions with solutions, play a very important role in soil chemistry.

Recently, new synthetic types of ion exchangers have been developed. These are porous, rigid frameworks of resins or other materials that have replaceable hydrogens atoms or hydroxyl groups exposed to a solution which is passed through them.   Such systems act as *hydrogen exchangers* or *hydroxyl exchangers*, respectively.   When a solution containing various cations is brought into contact with a hydrogen exchanger, the cations replace the hydrogen in the structure and hydrogen ions enter the solution.   The solution can thus be freed of cations other than hydrogen ions, becoming acidic in the process.

$$\text{Hydrogen exchanger} + Na^+ \rightleftharpoons \text{sodium exchanger} + H^+$$

The reaction is reversible, and the hydrogen exchanger can be regenerated by passing a concentrated solution of a strong acid over the exchanger.   The tendency of different species of cations to replace hydrogen varies.   If a solution contains a mixture of cations, they can be caused to compete for exchange.   It is sometimes possible to arrange conditions so that only one species of cation is removed from solution, and ion exchange thus provides an elegant method for the separation of cations of different elements.

When a solution containing various anions is brought in contact with a hydroxyl exchanger, the anions tend to replace the hydroxyl group, and hydroxide ions accumulate in solution.

$$\text{Hydroxyl exchanger} + Cl^- \rightleftharpoons \text{chloride exchanger} + OH^-$$

This change also is reversible, and the hydroxyl exchanger can be regenerated by passing a concentrated solution of $NaOH$ or Na_2CO_3 over it.

By passing a salt solution first over a hydrogen exchanger and then over a hydroxyl exchanger, both the cations and the anions can be removed from solution.   The hydrogen ions and hydroxyl ions that enter the solution associate to form water.   Such a dual treatment can therefore be employed to *deionize* water quite completely.   Small deionizing units are available which can be used to purify water of dissolved ions as effectively as is accomplished by distillation.

EXERCISES

1. Compare the alkali and the alkaline-earth metals with respect to: a) atomic structure; b) variation in ionic radius; c) variation in ionization potential; d) variation in strength as reducing agents; e) oxidation states; f) solubility of hydroxides.

2. Describe the occurrence of the alkali and alkaline-earth metals.

3. How can the alkali and alkaline-earth metals be prepared?   Illustrate with equations for the reactions which occur.

4. Give five uses of alkali and alkaline-earth metals, and indicate what properties are the reasons for these uses.

5. Why are salts of the alkali and alkaline-earth metals used in fireworks?

6. a) What chemical reactions are involved in the corrosion of the alkali and alkaline-earth metals by the atmosphere? Illustrate with equations.
b) How are these metals protected from atmospheric attack?

7. Compare the formation of oxides by the alkali metals and the alkaline-earth metals.

8. Discuss the burning of limestone and the use of lime in plasters.

9. a) How is caustic soda produced commercially?
b) What properties does this substance have that account for its widespread use?

10. What chemical changes are important in the formation of limestone caves and in the building of stalactites?

11. a) How is sodium bicarbonate manufactured?
b) How can it be converted to sodium carbonate?
c) Account for the use of sodium bicarbonate in baking powders.
d) Why can a solution of sodium carbonate be used for neutralizing acids?

12. Explain why ammonium salts are usually classified with those of the alkali metals.

13. Distinguish between permanently hard and temporarily hard water. How can the former be treated to soften it?

14. a) What kind of structure must a system have in order to be able to serve as an ion exchanger?
b) Explain how suitable exchangers may be used to make sea water fit for drinking.

Chapter 30

▶ Aluminum

375. ALUMINUM AND THE IIIA METALS

The first element in Group III, boron, is a nonmetal and has already been discussed. The remaining elements in the group are metallic, but of these only aluminum is abundant. The IIIA elements, scandium, yttrium, and the sequence lanthanum through lutecium are transition metals. They all have very similar atoms with nine electrons in the second outermost shell and two in the outermost shell. They usually show the oxidation state of +3 in their compounds. Lanthanum and the 14 elements with atomic numbers 58 to 72, which belong in Period VI and Group IIIA, are usually called *rare-earth metals*, because they seldom are found. All of these metals have identical electronic structures, except that the number of electrons in the third outermost shell increases with increase in atomic number. Their sizes and their properties are so much alike that it is very difficult to separate them. A few uses are known. The mixed metals, obtained by electrolysis, are *pyrophoric*. When struck, they emit sparks. Alloyed with iron, these mixed rare-earth metals are used as flints in cigarette lighters. The oxides are used in glass to produce nonglare lenses and to prepare colored light filters. Cerium oxide is used in gas mantles.

Actinium and the remaining elements in Period VII form another series of closely related metals like the rare-earth elements. These actinium series metals are all radioactive. Thorium, uranium, and plutonium have isotopes that disintegrate by fission when struck by neutrons. In the disintegration, tremendous amounts of energy are liberated, so that these elements are suitable for atomic bombs and in atomic power piles (see Chapter 36). We shall discuss only aluminum in detail.

376. ATOMIC STRUCTURE, SIZE, AND OXIDATION STATES OF ALUMINUM

Aluminum has three valence electrons in its outer shell and always uses all three for bonding purposes when it forms compounds. It is less active than magnesium but still has a rather high oxidation potential. As might be expected, aluminum, having the same number of valence electrons as boron, resembles boron in many respects. But, since the

464

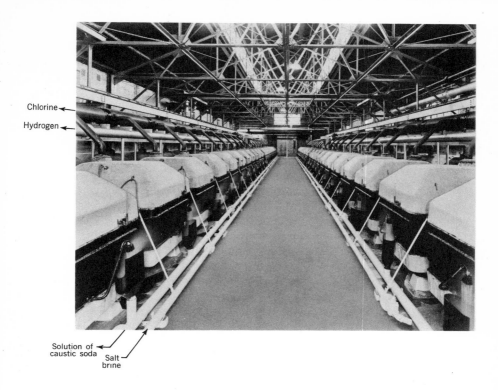

Chlorine

Hydrogen

Solution of caustic soda

Salt brine

From Salt and Water to Hydrogen, Chlorine, and Sodium Hydroxide

Photograph (*top*) and diagram (*bottom*) of Hooker *S* cells. Salt brine is pumped continuously into long rows of electrolytic cells in which the electric current produces a constant flow of hydrogen, chlorine, and a solution of sodium hydroxide. Operating twenty-four hours a day, each cell turns out more than half a ton of chlorine and three-quarters of a ton of caustic soda daily. (Courtesy of Hooker Electrochemical Company)

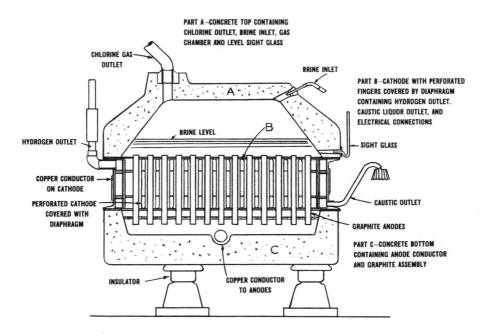

PART A—CONCRETE TOP CONTAINING CHLORINE OUTLET, BRINE INLET, GAS CHAMBER AND LEVEL SIGHT GLASS

CHLORINE GAS OUTLET

BRINE INLET

PART B—CATHODE WITH PERFORATED FINGERS COVERED BY DIAPHRAGM CONTAINING HYDROGEN OUTLET. CAUSTIC LIQUOR OUTLET, AND ELECTRICAL CONNECTIONS

A

B

BRINE LEVEL

HYDROGEN OUTLET

SIGHT GLASS

COPPER CONDUCTOR ON CATHODE

PERFORATED CATHODE COVERED WITH DIAPHRAGM

CAUSTIC OUTLET

GRAPHITE ANODES

PART C—CONCRETE BOTTOM CONTAINING ANODE CONDUCTOR AND GRAPHITE ASSEMBLY

C

INSULATOR

COPPER CONDUCTOR TO ANODES

From Air and Water or Petroleum to Ammonia

Dry air is liquefied and fractionated to provide nitrogen. This is mixed with hydrogen obtained by the electrolysis of salt brine or from hydrocarbons. The mixture is put under high pressure and passed into a reactor where a catalyst facilitates conversion to ammonia. When cooled under pressure, the ammonia liquefies and is separated from the unreacted nitrogen and hydrogen which are recycled.

Left: Compressors in an ammonia plant. (Courtesy of American Cyanamid Company)

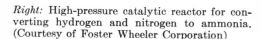

Right: High-pressure catalytic reactor for converting hydrogen and nitrogen to ammonia. (Courtesy of Foster Wheeler Corporation)

Ammonia, a source of fixed nitrogen, is an important aid to the farmer. It is used extensively as a fertilizer applied directly to the soil. This farmer is injecting the gaseous form prior to planting. In some parts of the country ammonia is released directly into the irrigation systems. (Courtesy of The Dow Chemical Company)

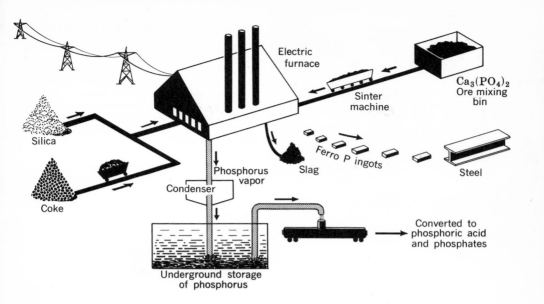

From Phosphate Rock, Sand, and Coke to Phosphorus

Concentrated $Ca_3(PO_4)_2$ ore is mixed with sand and coke and heated in an electric-arc furnace to give phosphorus, calcium-silicate slag, and carbon monoxide. Iron slugs may be added to the charge to produce some ferrophosphorus for steel making.

Electric-arc furnace for producing phosphorus. Molten slag and ferrophosphorus are tapped from the bottom of the furnace. The white hot ferrophosphorus is being formed into billets in the molds on the chain conveyer in the foreground. The phosphorus vapor is taken from the top of the furnace and condensed under water. By burning the phosphorus in moist air, phosphoric acid is produced and this may be converted into phosphates. (Both pictures, courtesy of Monsanto Chemical Company)

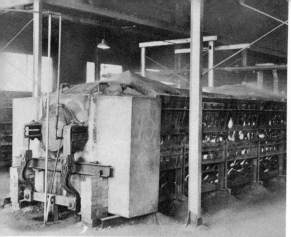

From Coke and Sand to Silicon Carbide

Left: A mixture of sand and coke, together with some sawdust to provide porosity, is heaped in this furnace around a core of granular carbon which connects the electrodes. Passage of electricity through the core heats it to over 2000°C and the SiO_2 is converted to SiC. The carbon monoxide formed in the reaction escapes to the surface where it burns. (Courtesy of Norton Company)

Right: After cooling, the silicon-carbide crystals are removed from the center of the furnace and sorted for use. Because silicon carbide is very hard, inert, and high melting, it is used for making grinding and cutting wheels and papers, and for crucibles and electrodes. The outer, unreacted part of the charge is combined with the next charge for the furnace. (Courtesy of Norton Company)

From Coke and Lime to Calcium Carbide and Acetylene

Left: In this 20,000 kilowatt furnace, electric power converts coke and lime to calcium carbide, CaC_2. The charge is fed continuously into flaming electric arcs and white-hot molten calcium carbide is tapped from the bottom of the furnace. When heated with nitrogen from the air, calcium carbide forms calcium cyanamide, $CaCN_2$, valuable as a fertilizer and for making nitrogen compounds. Large amounts of calcium carbide are treated with water to produce acetylene, a key material in the synthesis of plastics, rubber, and a great variety of organic compounds. (Courtesy of American Cyanamid Company)

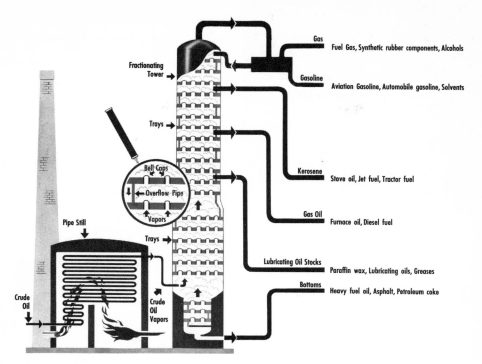

Gas — Fuel Gas, Synthetic rubber components, Alcohols

Gasoline — Aviation Gasoline, Automobile gasoline, Solvents

Kerosene — Stove oil, Jet fuel, Tractor fuel

Gas Oil — Furnace oil, Diesel fuel

Lubricating Oil Stocks — Paraffin wax, Lubricating oils, Greases

Bottoms — Heavy fuel oil, Asphalt, Petroleum coke

Fractionating Tower

Trays

Bell Caps
Overflow Pipe
Vapors

Trays

Pipe Still

Crude Oil

Crude Oil Vapors

From Petroleum to Gasoline

The various parts or fractions of crude oil vaporize at different temperatures, and because of this they can be separated in a fractionating tower. The vapors enter the tower near the bottom and rise through holes in a series of trays. They become cooler and cooler as they rise, and condense or become liquids again. The lightest fractions condense at the top and the heaviest at the bottom. The condensed fractions gather in the trays and are piped off. These fractions and some of the products which may be obtained from them by further refining are outlined in the diagram above.

This fluid "cat cracker," about twenty stories high, makes small molecules of hydrocarbons out of large ones. By means of heat and catalyst, it makes more than 600,000 gallons of gasoline and other high-grade products daily.

(Courtesy of Esso Standard Oil Company)

From Petroleum to Synthetic Rubber

Left: Butadiene, $CH_2{=}CH{-}CH{=}CH_2$, made from petroleum, and styrene, ⬡$-CH{=}CH_2$, made from benzene, are mixed with soap solution in these reactors and stirred vigorously. Polymerization produces a rubberlike latex resembling the juice from the rubber tree.

Right: The latex is pumped into a swirling acid and brine solution where the latex almost instantly coagulates into crumbs of rubber.

Left: The rubber crumbs are filtered from the acid and brine, washed with water, and dried.

Right: At the end of the line the raw synthetic rubber is compressed into bales and a sample is cut from each bale for testing. The product is called GR-S rubber and is somewhat different from natural rubber in structure and properties. (All pictures on this page, courtesy of B. F. Goodrich)

From Trees to Rayon Fibers and Cellophane Film

Right: Wood chips are "cooked" by the action of steam and chemicals to wood pulp which is pressed into sheets of cellulose. These are steeped in caustic soda to give alkali cellulose, which is treated with carbon disulfide and then dissolved in a weak solution of caustic soda to produce "viscose solution." This solution is forced through tiny holes in a platinum spinnerette into an acid bath. Upon contact with the acid the solution is changed to solid filaments of rayon, which has the same chemical composition as the original wood cellulose. Cellophane film can be produced by altering the technique.

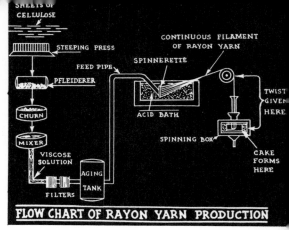

FLOW CHART OF RAYON YARN PRODUCTION

Right: Viscose solution.

Left: Spinning viscose into acid bath.

Right: Cellophane film is made by pumping viscose solution into a rectangular head which has a narrow slit along the bottom. The slit is just below the surface of an acid bath so that the viscose congeals into film as it is extruded. (All photographs this page, courtesy of American Viscose Corporation)

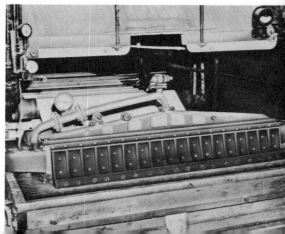

From Sand to Glass in a Tank Furnace

Sand, sodium carbonate, lime, and other raw materials are fed into the end of a tank the size of a swimming pool.

Jets of burning natural gas shoot across the tank. The raw materials melt and react at white heat.

The molten glass passes through a submerged opening in a wall which holds back impurities. As the purified glass slowly flows through the tank, gas bubbles escape. The molten glass is now ready for shaping by men and machines.

From "boot" openings just above the glass level, hand artisans make their gathers on the tip of a hollow iron pipe. Each man in the "shop" has a hard-earned specialty. Fashioned here are the innumerable items which are not adaptable to automatic machine production.

A continuous stream of glass runs from a "feeder" to a machine and is blown in spinning molds to form, automatically, glass objects by the millions. Other machines press the taffylike material into complicated shapes or draw it into tubing. (Courtesy of Corning Glass Works)

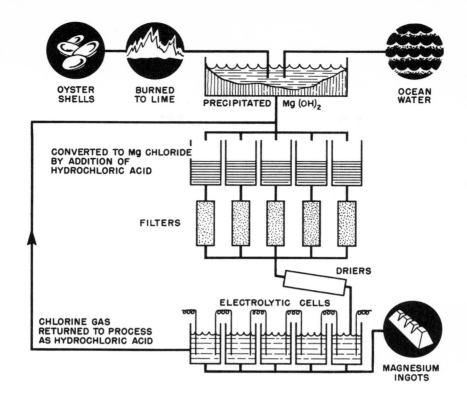

OYSTER
SHELLS

BURNED
TO LIME

PRECIPITATED Mg (OH)₂

OCEAN
WATER

CONVERTED TO Mg CHLORIDE
BY ADDITION OF
HYDROCHLORIC ACID

FILTERS

DRIERS

ELECTROLYTIC CELLS

CHLORINE GAS
RETURNED TO PROCESS
AS HYDROCHLORIC ACID

MAGNESIUM
INGOTS

From Sea Water and Oyster Shells to Magnesium

Left: Oyster shells are composed of calcium carbonate. These shells, dredged from Galveston Bay, are converted to lime by heating in long rotating kilns. Addition of the lime to sea water containing magnesium ions precipitates magnesium hydroxide.

Right: Cell for electrolyzing molten magnesium chloride. The molten magnesium metal which forms at the cathode is run off. The chlorine gas liberated at the anode is converted to hydrochloric acid which is fed back into the process. (All pictures this page, courtesy The Dow Chemical Company)

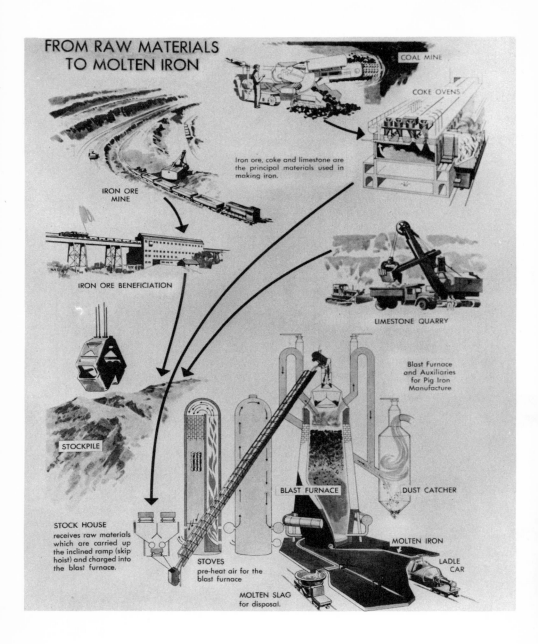

FROM RAW MATERIALS
TO MOLTEN IRON

COAL MINE

COKE OVENS

Iron ore, coke and limestone are
the principal materials used in
making iron.

IRON ORE
MINE

IRON ORE BENEFICIATION

LIMESTONE QUARRY

Blast Furnace
and Auxiliaries
for Pig Iron
Manufacture

STOCKPILE

BLAST FURNACE

DUST CATCHER

STOCK HOUSE
receives raw materials
which are carried up
the inclined ramp (skip
hoist) and charged into
the blast furnace.

STOVES
pre-heat air for the
blast furnace

MOLTEN IRON

LADLE
CAR

MOLTEN SLAG
for disposal.

From Raw Materials to Molten Iron

This simplified schematic sketch is not drawn to scale. It is intended only to show some
important steel processes and major external features of equipment. (Courtesy of
American Iron and Steel Institute)

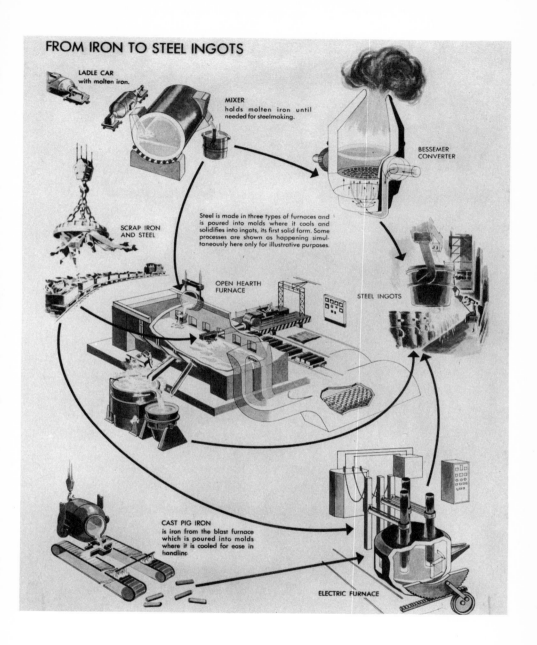

From Iron to Steel Ingots

This simplified schematic sketch is not drawn to scale. It is intended only to show some important steel processes and major external features of equipment. (Courtesy of American Iron and Steel Institute)

Blasting
The ore body is broken up by blasting.

Loading
The ore, averaging about 1 per cent copper, is loaded into ore cars by electric shovels.

Hauling
The cars of ore are hauled to the mill.

ORE

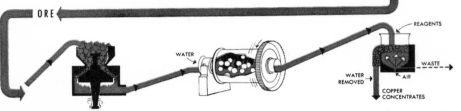

Crushing
The ore is crushed to pieces the size of walnuts.

Grinding
The crushed ore is ground to a powder.

Concentrating
The mineral-bearing particles in the powdered ore are concentrated.

COPPER CONCENTRATES

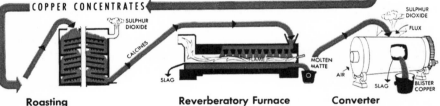

Roasting
The copper concentrates (averaging about 30 per cent copper) are roasted to remove sulphur.

Reverberatory Furnace
The roasted concentrate is smelted and a matte, containing 32-42 per cent copper, is produced.

Converter
The matte is converted into blister copper with a purity of about 99 per cent.

BLISTER COPPER

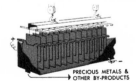

Refining Furnace
Blister copper is treated in a refining furnace.

Electrolytic Refining
Copper requiring further treatment is sent to the electrolytic refinery.

From Copper Ore to Pure Copper

(Courtesy Kennecott Copper Corporation)

aluminum atom is much larger than the very small boron atom, the former is decidedly metallic, whereas the latter is nonmetallic.

Table 75.   Properties of Aluminum

Atomic number	13
Electronic structure	2, 8, 3
Ionic radius, Al^{3+}, Å	0.50
Ionization potential, volts	5.96
Oxidation potential, M/M^{3+}, volts	+1.67
Oxidation states	**0, +3**
Melting point, ° C	656.7
Boiling point, ° C	2056
Density, g/cc, 20°	2.70

377. OCCURRENCE OF ALUMINUM

Aluminum is our most abundant metal; of all the elements, only oxygen and silicon are more abundant.   Too active to occur as the free metal, it is usually found combined with oxygen. Al_2O_3 occurs in the anhydrous condition as *corundum*, *ruby*, and *sapphire*.   The hydrous mineral *bauxite* is a mixture of AlOOH and $Al(OH)_3$.   This is the most important ore of aluminum, but unfortunately it is rather limited in supply.   *Alunite*, a complex hydrated sulfate, is also being developed as a source of this metal.   Enormous amounts of aluminum are tied up in complex aluminosilicate minerals, such as the feldspars and clays. Extraction of aluminum from these silicates is difficult and costly, but considerable progress is being made in working out methods for making use of this source.   *Cryolite*, Na_3AlF_6, found in limited amounts in Greenland, is of importance in the metallurgy of aluminum.

378. METALLURGY

The production of aluminum involves the difficult reduction of aluminum from the oxidation state of **+3**.   As in the case of the other very active metals we have studied, this must be carried out in the absence of water, since water is reduced more easily than aluminum.   In the early days the chloride was reduced by heating it with sodium, a very expensive process.

$$Al_2Cl_6 + 6Na \overset{\text{heat}}{=} 2Al + 6NaCl$$

In 1886, Hall in the United States and Héroult in France simultaneously but independently worked out the modern electrolytic process for making aluminum.   Purified aluminum oxide is dissolved in molten cryolite, and the mixture is electrolyzed at 1000°.   The aluminum that is formed at the cathode is liquid at this temperature and can be tapped off during the continuous operation of the cell.   Figure 117 shows the construction of a modern electrolytic cell for the large-scale production of aluminum.

The lower half of the cell makes up the carbon-lined shell which acts as cathode and in which the aluminum accumulates.   The anode is a huge

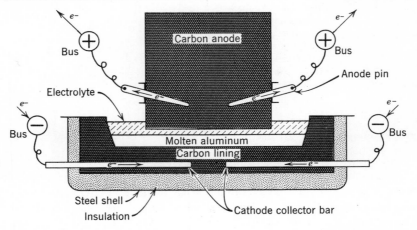

Fig. 117.   Cell of the Soederberg type for the electrolytic production of aluminum.

graphite block which is lowered into the molten electrolyte.   Such a cell produces about 2,000 lb of aluminum daily.

379. PROPERTIES AND USES

This light, soft, silvery metal is an excellent conductor of electricity and heat.   It is ductile and malleable, especially between 100 and 150°, and may be rolled, drawn, spun, or cast into shape.   It is difficult to machine when pure, but proper alloying corrects this.

Although aluminum stands rather high in the electrochemical series, close to magnesium, it is corroded only superficially by air and water, owing to the formation of a thin, adherent, colorless, and impervious film of oxide that protects the underlying metal.   When aluminum is amalgamated by coating it with mercury, the oxide does not adhere, and the whole piece of aluminum is rapidly corroded.   The high resistance to atmospheric corrosion and the lightness of the metal account for many of its uses.   However, the presence of this oxide film makes it very difficult to, weld or braze aluminum, and it has been only very recently that techniques have been perfected for accomplishing this, thus facilitating the use of aluminum and its alloys in the manufacture of airplanes and other structures.

Recently a method has been discovered for producing better, denser, and more resistant films of aluminum oxide on the metal.   Aluminum is made the anode in a dilute sulfuric or chromic acid bath, and electrolysis is carried out. This oxidizes the surface of the anodic aluminum and builds up a thick oxide film, which gives very good protection against corrosion. Because the oxide is very hard, such an anodized surface also protects the metal against abrasion, and it may be dyed any desired color. Colored panels of sheet aluminum are being used for many special purposes.

Aluminum is attacked rapidly by most acids, but it goes *passive* in concentrated nitric acid, probably because of the formation of a protective oxide coating. Bases and basic solutions corrode it rapidly, liberating hydrogen and forming soluble aluminate ions.

$$2Al + 2OH^- + 2H_2O = 3H_2 + 2AlO_2^-$$

Salt solutions corrode aluminum badly, so that aluminum and aluminum alloy fittings are not suitable for marine use.

Finely divided aluminum burns vigorously in oxygen in a highly exothermic fashion.

$$4Al + 3O_2 = 2Al_2O_3 + 760,000 \text{ cal}$$

Since much of this energy is available as light, modern photoflash bulbs make use of thin aluminum foil sealed in an atmosphere of oxygen. Aluminum is an excellent reducing agent and can be used very effectively to produce other metals by the reduction of their oxides. In the *thermit reaction* iron oxides are reduced by finely powdered aluminum.

$$Fe_2O_3 + 2Al = 2Fe + Al_2O_3 + 181,500 \text{ cal}$$

This reaction is so highly exothermic that the iron and the aluminum oxide produced are obtained at very high temperatures and are in the molten condition. The heavier iron settles to the bottom of the charge in the crucible and can be separated easily from the lighter molten aluminum oxide. This reaction is very useful, not only because it provides molten iron for various purposes, but also because it provides so much heat. It is very effective as the basis of incendiary bombs. Aluminum foil is useful as a wrapping, and is employed in heat insulation because of its high reflectivity for radiant energy. Aluminum powder, consisting of tiny leaflets, is used in aluminum paints.

380. ALLOYS

A large number of important alloys of aluminum have been developed, opening up the light-alloy field. Its alloys with magnesium, copper, manganese, and zinc are very light, strong materials that do not corrode in air. They are replacing the ferroalloys in many cases where the advantages of their special properties warrant the greater cost.

381. BONDING IN COMPOUNDS

The aluminum cation, Al^{3+}, forms ionic compounds with highly electronegative groups, like F^- or SO_4^{2-}. But this rather small and highly charged cation has a strong tendency to associate with other ions or molecules to form complex ions. In aqueous solution it is strongly hydrated. Its size in relation to that of water is such that it seems likely that six water molecules can be closely associated with it, probably at octahedral positions.

$$Al^{3+} + 6H_2O = Al(H_2O)_6^{3+}$$

Aluminum salts obtained by crystallization from solution always are highly hydrated, and X-ray studies of the crystal structures have shown

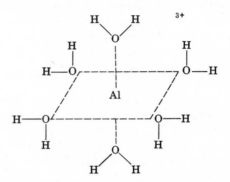

Fig. 118. Probable structure of the hydrated aluminum ion.

that the aluminum ions are associated with water molecules in the crystal lattice.

In an aqueous solution of aluminum cations there must be an equivalent amount of anionic groups. These probably have some tendency to associate with the aluminum ions to form complexes. Thus, in a solution of aluminum sulfate the ionic species, $Al(H_2O)_5SO_4^+$ and $Al(H_2O)_4(SO_4)_2^-$, may exist, as well as $Al(H_2O)_6^{3+}$. In addition, aluminum ions have a considerable tendency to hydrolyze. A solution of aluminum sulfate is acidic toward litmus. This is believed to be due to the possibility of hydrogen ions dissociating from the water molecules of the hydrated ion, leaving one or more hydroxyl groups in the complex.

$$Al(H_2O)_6^{3+} = Al(H_2O)_5OH^{2+} + H^+$$

Progressive hydrolysis would thus produce a series of complexes of varying charge: $Al(H_2O)_4(OH)_2^+$, $Al(H_2O)_3(OH)_3$, $Al(H_2O)_2(OH)_4^-$, $Al(H_2O)(OH)_5^{2-}$, and $Al(OH)_6^{3-}$. Furthermore, such hydroxy complexes probably tend to condense.

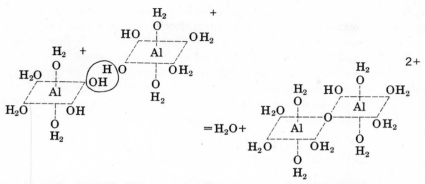

Fig. 119.   Condensation of hydroxyl groups to give oxygen bridges.

By the splitting out of water, oxygen bridges may be formed between aluminum atoms to produce extended oxystructures, either neutral or ionic.

It seems reasonable to assume that in a solution of aluminum sulfate we may be dealing with an equilibrium mixture of all or many of these complexes, and that the system is extraordinarily complicated. We have no effective method available for identifying the various complexes in this mixture and determining their exact compositions and configurations. Because we have so little specific knowledge about these systems, we usually do not attempt to indicate the amount of water of hydration but use only the simplest of empirical formulas. Hydrous basic salts of aluminum probably contain complex hydroxy- or oxycations of the type given above.

382.   ALUMINUM HYDROXIDE AND ALUMINATES

The neutral hydrated hydroxy complex of aluminum, $Al(H_2O)_3(OH)_3$, is not appreciably soluble and precipitates out as a white gelatinous material in which much excess water is trapped. Since we do not know how much water is closely bound to the aluminum, we usually write the formula $Al(OH)_3$ for this precipitate, neglecting the extent of hydration, but sometimes specifying that the material is hydrous.

The addition of a base, such as ammonium hydroxide, will furnish OH^-, and aluminum ions can be quantitatively removed from solution in this fashion. We write the equation as

$$Al^{3+} + 3OH^- = Al(OH)_{3(s)}$$

ignoring the water of hydration.

When the moist gelatinous precipitate is heated strongly in the air, water is driven off and anhydrous aluminum oxide is formed.

$$2Al(OH)_3 \overset{\text{heat}}{=} Al_2O_3 + 3H_2O$$

Crystals of $Al(OH)_3$ have been prepared by special techniques, but we have no evidence that such crystals form when aluminum ions are precipitated under ordinary conditions. Crystals of $AlOOH$, the hydroxyoxide, can be obtained by special methods and are found in nature.

Freshly precipitated hydrous aluminum hydroxide is an *amphoteric* material, capable of furnishing either OH^- or H^+. In terms of the hydrated complexes we can write the following equilibria to account for this amphoteric behavior.

$$H^+ + Al(H_2O)_2(OH)_4^- \rightleftharpoons Al(H_2O)_3(OH)_3$$
$$Al(H_2O)_3(OH)_3 + H_2O \rightleftharpoons Al(H_2O)_4(OH)_2^+ + OH^-$$

But again, because we do not know the extent of hydration, we usually simplify this, and write

$$H_2O + H^+ + \underset{\substack{\text{aluminate} \\ \text{ion}}}{AlO_2^-} \rightleftharpoons Al(OH)_3 \rightleftharpoons Al(OH)_2^+ + OH^-$$

Hydrous aluminum hydroxide dissolves in strong acids and bases because of its amphoteric character.

Dehydration condensation of the aluminate ion $Al(H_2O)_2(OH)_4^-$ would give AlO_2^-, the metaaluminate ion, which is undoubtedly highly polymeric, like metaborate, metasilicate, or metaphosphate ions. Metaaluminates, such as $NaAlO_2$, and other aluminates are obtained by heating aluminum oxide or hydroxide with the carbonates, hydroxides, or oxides of the appropriate metal. Only the alkali aluminates are appreciably soluble.

383. ALUMINUM OXIDE

Aluminum oxide, frequently called *alumina*, is obtained when aluminum is burned or when hydrous aluminum hydroxide is ignited strongly. The product is quite inert toward solutions of acids and bases. A very porous form of the oxide is obtained by special treatment. This has a tremendous surface area per gram and is an excellent adsorbent. Such *active alumina* is an excellent dehydrating agent and has strong catalytic activity. It is frequently used for supporting other catalysts.

When alumina is melted in the electric furnace and then cooled, massive crystalline alumina is obtained. This is a very hard, refractory (m.p., 2050°), and chemically inert material much used at high temperatures for crucibles and furnace linings. It is powdered and used to make abrasive papers, whetstones, and grinding and cutting wheels. When alumina powder mixed with very small amounts of a colorant, such as Cr_2O_3, is dropped through an oxyhydrogen flame, the oxide melts and can be collected on a refractory support, where it builds up a clear transparent crystalline body called a *boule*. The color can be controlled by varying the amount and composition of the colorant, and in this fashion synthetic gem stones such as rubies and sapphires can be manufactured. These synthetic stones have essentially the same composition, structure, and properties as the natural stones. Because of their great hardness, these crystals are used as bearings in watches and other fine machinery.

384. SALTS OF ALUMINUM. ALUMS

The ionic compounds of aluminum with oxyanions, such as SO_4^{2-} and NO_3^-, are crystalline hydrated salts which are usually quite soluble in water. $Al_2(SO_4)_3 \cdot 18H_2O$ is marketed in large amounts and is commonly, but mistakenly, spoken of as *alum*. This hydrated aluminum sulfate is used for treating drinking water because of its hydrolysis in dilute solutions (see Section 213). The gelatinous hydrous hydroxide, which is produced by hydrolysis, settles slowly through water and drags down bacteria and other suspended material. When this gelatinous hydrolysis product is precipitated on the surface of textile fibers, it forms brilliantly colored "lakes" with dyes and *fixes the dye*, thus acting as a *mordant*. Such mordanting of fibers makes it possible to use dyes that are not held permanently by the fiber alone.

Aluminum sulfate can be used to prepare aluminum *alums*. Alums have the general formula $M'M'''(SO_4)_2 \cdot 12H_2O$. M' is a univalent cation, such as Na^+, K^+, Rb^+, NH_4^+, or Tl^+, and M''' is a trivalent cation, such as Al^{3+}, Fe^{3+}, or Cr^{3+}. A large number of different alums have been prepared by crystallization from a solution of the proper mixture of sulfates. All the alums crystallize in the form of beautiful octahedra, which are built up of the two kinds of cations, sulfate ions, and water molecules packed in the same pattern. Since they all have the same crystalline form, the alums are said to be *isomorphous*.

385. ALUMINUM HALIDES

Aluminum fluoride is an insoluble, inert, ionic substance. Aluminum is more likely to form covalent molecular halides with the less electronegative halogens, chlorine, bromine, and iodine. Aluminum chloride is an interesting example of a compound that is ionic in one state but molecular in another. It can be prepared by direct chlorination of aluminum or by heating aluminum oxide with carbon and chlorine.

$$2Al + 3Cl_2 = 2AlCl_3$$
$$Al_2O_3 + 3C + 3Cl_2 = 2AlCl_3 + 3CO$$

The colorless crystals that form are ionic but they sublime readily, and the vapor has been shown to be built up of Al_2Cl_6 molecules. In these molecules each aluminum atom is tetrahedrally bonded to four chlorine atoms, two of these being shared by the two aluminum atoms.

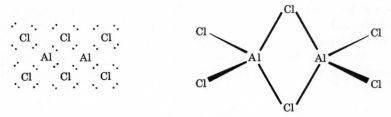

Fig. 120.   Configuration of Al_2Cl_6 molecule.

When heated sufficiently, Al_2Cl_6 vapor dissociates into the monomeric molecule $AlCl_3$.

$$Al_2Cl_6 \rightleftharpoons 2AlCl_3$$

In the association of the monomeric molecules, one chlorine atom of each molecule donates a pair of its electrons to be shared by the aluminum atom of the other molecule, and thus two chlorine bridges are set up.

When aluminum chloride is brought into contact with molecules that have strong donor atoms present, donor-acceptor bonding produces molecular addition complexes.

$$AlCl_3 + (CH_3)_3N = (CH_3)_3N : AlCl_3$$

The formation of such donor-acceptor complex compounds is believed to be responsible for the high catalytic effect obtained when aluminum chloride and the other aluminum halides are added to certain systems.

Aluminum chloride hydrolyzes very strongly when exposed to moisture.

$$AlCl_3 + 3H_2O = Al(OH)_{3(s)} + 3H^+ + 3Cl^-$$

EXERCISES

1. Compare aluminum and boron with respect to: a) atomic structure; b) size of atoms; c) electronegativity; d) tendency for covalent bonding; e) oxidation states; f) malleability.

2. a) What is unique about the atomic structures of the rare-earth metals?
   b) What other sequence of metals seems to be like the rare-earth metal sequence?

3. a) Outline the Hall process for the production of aluminum.
   b) Why cannot electrolysis of an aqueous solution be used?
   c) How many faradays of electricity would be required to produce 100 kg of aluminum?

4. Account for the high resistance of aluminum to atmospheric attack.

5. a) Write the equation for the thermit reaction.
   b) Why has thermit been important in the manufacture of incendiary bombs?

6. a) What is the probable coordination number of aluminum toward water molecules?

b) Indicate the probable spatial configuration of two different complex ions which may be present in an aqueous solution of aluminum sulfate.

7. a) Write equations summarizing the electrolytic dissociation of aluminum hydroxide.

b) How can these be used to explain why freshly precipitated aluminum hydroxide may be dissolved by the use of either HCl or NaOH?

8. a) How is crystalline aluminum oxide made?

b) What properties does it have that account for its extensive use?

c) Why is active alumina in considerable demand?

9. Account for the use of compounds of aluminum in the dyeing of fabrics.

10. a) Describe the general composition of alums.

b) Give the formulas for four different alums.

11. a) How can aluminum chloride be prepared?

b) Describe the bonding and configuration of this substance.

c) Write the equation for its hydrolysis, and explain why this hydrolysis is quite complete.

Chapter 31

► Transition Metals, I

Groups IVA, VA, VIA, VIIA

Titanium, Vanadium, Chromium,

Molybdenum, Tungsten, Manganese

386. THE TRANSITION METALS

The distinction between transition and nontransition metals has been discussed in Section 353. The term *transition metals* has been used in various ways, but we shall employ it in this book to refer to those elements in Periods IV, V, VI, and VII, which are in the subgroups IIIA through IB. Thus, in Period IV, the elements scandium, titanium, vanadium, chromium, manganese, iron, cobalt, nickel, and copper are transition elements.

Table 76. Electronic Structures and Oxidation States of Transition Metals of Period IV

Metals	Atomic No.	Electrons in Subgroups in Shells							Oxidation States Observed
		$1s$	$2s$	$2p$	$3s$	$3p$	$3d$	$4s$	
Sc	21	2	2	6	2	6	1	2	0, +2, +3
Ti	22	2	2	6	2	6	2	2	0, +2, +3, +4
V	23	2	2	6	2	6	3	2	0, +2, +3, +4, +5
Cr	24	2	2	6	2	6	5	1	0, +2, +3, +6
Mn	25	2	2	6	2	6	5	2	0, +2, +3, +4, +6, +7
Fe	26	2	2	6	2	6	6	2	0, +2, +3, +4, +6
Co	27	2	2	6	2	6	7	2	0, +2, +3, +4
Ni	28	2	2	6	2	6	8	2	0, +2, +3, +4
Cu	29	2	2	6	2	6	10	1	0, +1, +2, +3

In this sequence, as the atomic number increases, the number of electrons in the outer shell remains at two, with the exception of chromium and copper, and the d subgroup in the second outermost shell builds up to its maximum content of 10. When compounds are formed, the s electrons of the outermost shell of each of these elements are always associated with bonding, and in addition, one or more of the d electrons in the second outermost shell may be used. Transition metals are characterized by having valence electrons in their second outermost, as well as their outermost, shells. Since all or only part of these valence electrons may be used for bonding purposes, transition elements have variable valence. The oxidation states that have been recognized for each transition element of Period IV are listed in Table 76, the more common states being given in italic boldface type. As the number of electrons in the 3d subgroup increases, the maximum positive oxidation state observed increases regularly through the first half of the sequence, but then decreases again through the latter part of the sequence as the 3d subgroup approaches saturation, the higher oxidation states fading out.

The transition metals of Period V, yttrium through silver, have the electronic structures of their outer shells developing in an analogous fashion with increasing atomic number, and they show similar variations in their oxidation states. In Period VI there is a comparable development but, in addition to lanthanum, in the IIIA subgroup there follows a sequence of 14 elements, cerium through lutecium, which have exactly the same number of electrons in their outermost and second outermost shells as does lanthanum. They differ from lanthanum only in that, with increasing atomic number, electrons are added to the 4f subgroup until this becomes saturated with 14 electrons. Because they have the same electronic structures in the two outermost shells as lanthanum, these 14 elements resemble lanthanum very closely and are called *lanthanides*. Lanthanum and the lanthanides commonly go to the oxidation state of **+3** when they form compounds, but in some cases oxidation states of **+2** and **+4** also occur. Because of their scarcity and because they are usually found together in nature and behave very much alike, the oxides of the IIIA elements lanthanum through lutecium are frequently called the *rare earths*, and the metals are called the *rare-earth* metals. In period VII, actinium is the first transition metal, and the elements that follow it apparently are the first members of an incomplete *actinide* sequence, which resembles the lanthanide sequence and fits into the IIIA subgroup.

The transition metals have rather small atoms, and, in general, those in a given period decrease in size with increase in the net plus charge on the nucleus as electrons add to inner shells. With increasing atomic number down each subgroup, there usually is some increase in the size of cations from Period IV to V but only very little, if any, increase in size from the fifth to the sixth period. As a consequence, there is quite a difference in behavior from the first transition metal to the second in a subgroup, but the second resembles the third more closely. With increase in oxidation state of these metals, the size of the cations decreases as more electrons are lost.

Since their electronic structures are so similar, especially in their outermost shells, the transition metals have much in common. In particular, the successive transition metals in a given period resemble each other closely, sometimes even more than they do the other elements in their own subgroups. All the transition elements are decidedly metallic. They are shiny solids and, with the exception of copper and gold, have a silvery or gray color. The transition metals have relatively high melting points. Their densities usually increase across the periods and down the groups. Their oxidation potentials vary considerably, in general decreasing across the periods and down the groups, and their chemical activities therefore vary in the same way. Most of them are relatively unreactive toward air and water, in many cases protective films being responsible for their apparent inertness. Some of the transition metals, such as tantalum, tungsten, iridium, platinum, and gold, are remarkably resistant to corrosion by air, water, and acids.

When a transition metal is in the characteristic maximum oxidation state for the group as a whole, it usually shows considerable resemblance to the second typical element of the group. Thus, titanium, zirconium, and hafnium resemble silicon closely when they are in the oxidation state of **+4**, and chromium, molybdenum, and tungsten are somewhat like sulfur when in the oxidation state of **+6**. In lower oxidation states the transition metals do not resemble the typical elements of their group closely. When in the same oxidation state, the transition metals tend to behave very much alike, and their compounds have much in common.

Transition metals usually form cations of the type M^{2+} when they are in the *oxidation state of* **+2**, and these divalent cations form solid ionic compounds similar to those of the alkaline earth metals; $MnSO_4$, $FeSO_4$, and $CuSO_4$ resemble $MgSO_4$. Their hydroxides for this oxidation state are rather basic.

In the *oxidation state of* **+3** they are likely to be present in complex ions like those of aluminum. Hydrated $V_2(SO_4)_3$ and $Fe_2(SO_4)_3$ are typical examples, and alum formation is common for transition elements in this oxidation state; $KV(SO_4)_2 \cdot 12H_2O$ is a vanadium alum. The transition metals have some tendency to form covalent bonds in this oxidation state to produce molecules like Fe_2Cl_6 or complex ions like $Fe(CN)_6^{3-}$. Hydroxides for this state of oxidation are amphoteric, and oxyanion systems may be achieved, such as in chromite, $Fe(CrO_2)_2$.

In the *oxidation states from* **+4** *to* **+8** the transition metals are likely to form covalent bonds, simple cations being unknown, but molecules and complex ions being typical. $TiCl_4$ and VCl_4 are volatile liquids. WCl_6, UF_6, and OsO_4 are volatile molecular solids. TaF_7^{2-}, $Mo(CN)_8^{2-}$, and $PtCl_6^{2-}$ are known in their salts. The hydroxides for these higher oxidation states are usually acidic, and complex oxyanions such as TiO_3^{2-}, CrO_4^{2-}, and MnO_4^{-} are common.

Many of the ions and molecules containing transition metals are *highly colored* and frequently they are *paramagnetic;* they are attracted by a magnetic field. Ions and molecules of the nontransition metals usually are repelled slightly by a magnetic field; they are diamagnetic.

As we work through the subgroups of the metals, we shall pay particular attention to the analogous behavior of all transition metals and to the effects of the expansion of the second outermost shell of electrons on the properties of these elements.

387. THE IVA METALS

This subgroup includes titanium, zirconium, and hafnium. Of these, titanium is the most abundant and important, whereas there is very little hafnium.

Table 77.   IVA Metals

	Titanium	Zirconium	Hafnium
Symbol	Ti	Zr	Hf
Atomic number	22	40	72
Atomic structure	2, 8, 10, 2	2, 8, 18, 10, 2	2, 8, 18, 32, 10, 2
Oxidation states	0, **+2**, **+3**, **+4**	0, (**+2**), (**+3**), **+4**	0, (**+2**), (**+3**), **+4**
Abundance	0.58%	0.026%	Very little
Minerals	TiO_2, rutile; $FeTiO_3$, ilmenite; silicates	ZrO_2 $ZrSiO_4$, zircon	Found in all zirconium minerals to about 1 or 2%
Crystal radius, M^{4+}, Å	0.68	0.80	(0.80)
First ionization potential, volts	6.81	6.92	
Oxidation potential, M/MO^{2+}, volts	+0.95	+1.53	+1.68
Melting point, ° C	1800	1700	1700
Boiling point, ° C	5100	5050	5390
Density, g/cc, 20°	4.5	6.4	11.4

Since the hafnium atom is much like the zirconium atom in structure and has almost the same size, these two elements have almost identical properties, and a small amount of hafnium always accompanies zirconium in nature. It is very difficult to purify zirconium of hafnium. All three metals can use four electrons readily for bonding, and their common and most stable compounds involve the oxidation state of **+4,** the MO^{2+} ion being particularly typical. The lower oxidation states of **+2** and **+3** are well established for titanium but are doubtful for zirconium and hafnium. Titanium is typical of the group and by far the most important. In many ways titanium resembles silicon rather closely, especially when it is in the oxidation state of **+4.**

388. TITANIUM

Titanium, though one of our most abundant metals, is widely scattered in small amounts in iron ores and in complex silicates that are difficult to work as sources of the element. Only the rather restricted deposits of rutile and ilmenite are now being worked, but the uses of the element and its compounds are rapidly expanding.

Titanium metal of high quality is now being made by the reduction of titanium tetrachloride by magnesium at high temperatures.

$$TiCl_4 + 2Mg = Ti + 2MgCl_2$$

Although the cost of this process is high, titanium has such desirable properties that its production is expanding rapidly. It is a silvery-gray, high-melting, hard metal. Its tensile strength compares favorably with that of steel, and it is much lighter than steel. It has remarkable resistance to corrosion. It should be very useful for special purposes, such as airplane-engine construction. Titanium alloy steels are very tough and strong.

389. COMPOUNDS OF TITANIUM

Oxidation State	
0	Metallic titanium
+2, titanium (II)	Ti^{2+}, TiO, $TiCl_2$, $TiSO_4$
+3, titanium (III) (titanous)	Ti^{3+}, $Ti(OH)_3$, Ti_2O_3, $TiCl_3$, $Ti_2(SO_4)_3$, $KTi(SO_4)_2 \cdot 12H_2O$
+4, titanium (IV) (titanic)	$(TiO_3{}^{2-})_n$, Na_2TiO_3, TiO_2, $TiCl_4$, $TiCl_6{}^{2-}$, TiO^{2+}, $TiOSO_4$

The *oxidation state of* **+4** is the most stable one for this element under atmospheric conditions, and all the common compounds of titanium fall in this state. *Titanium dioxide*, TiO_2 (titania), is a white, insoluble, inert, refractory oxide that resembles SiO_2 in many respects. It has a continuous three-dimensional structure in which there are six oxygen atoms coordinated to each titanium atom. Titania has become very important as a white paint pigment, replacing other white pigments to a considerable extent. It is employed in procelain glazes to produce a yellow color, owing to partial reduction, and this effect is useful in tinting artificial teeth so that they will match the natural ones. As in the case of silica, no definite hydroxide or titanic acid is known, but white gelatinous *hydrous* TiO_2 is formed by the hydrolysis of titanium compounds. *Titanates*, such as Na_2TiO_3, are formed by fusing TiO_2 with the proper oxides, hydroxides, or carbonates. The *metatitanate ions*, $TiO_3{}^{2-}$, probably have extended polymeric structures like the metasilicates, except that there probably are six oxygen atoms coordinated to each atom of titanium.

Titanium tetrachloride, TiCl$_4$, is obtained as a colorless liquid by the action of a mixture of carbon and chlorine with hot TiO$_2$.

$$TiO_2 + 2C + 2Cl_2 \overset{heat}{=} \underset{\underset{136.4°}{b.p.,}}{TiCl_4} + 2CO$$

TiCl$_4$ resembles SiCl$_4$, having a symmetrical tetrahedral molecule. Like SiCl$_4$, it hydrolyzes vigorously and fumes strongly in the air.

$$TiCl_4 + 2H_2O = TiO_{2(s)} + 4HCl$$

It has been used very effectively to produce smoke screens. When it is added to concentrated hydrochloric acid, hydrolysis is prevented and the complex *hexachlorotitanate ion* is formed.

$$Ti\,Cl_4 + 2Cl^- = TiCl_6{}^{2-}$$
Hexachloro-
titanate ion

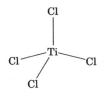

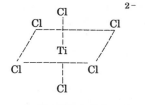

Titanium tetrachloride   Hexachlorotitanate ion
tetrahedral   octahedral

Fig. 121. Configuration of TiCl$_4$ molecules and TiCl$_6{}^{2-}$ ions.

Titanium can achieve a higher coordination number than silicon toward chlorine because the titanium atom is larger than the silicon atom. In the chlorotitanate ion the six atoms of chlorine are at the corners of a regular octahedron, equidistant from the central titanium atom. Chlorotitanate ions associate with cations to form crystalline chlorotitanates, such as Na$_2$TiCl$_6$.

Titanium carbide, TiC, is a very hard and inert material of some interest as an abrasive and for use in high-speed tools.

Compounds in which titanium is in the *oxidation state of* **+3** can be secured by reduction of titanium (IV) substances. When zinc is added to a solution of TiCl$_4$ in hydrochloric acid, the solution turns pink, owing to the formation of titanium (III) ions.

$$2TiCl_6{}^{2-} + Zn = 2Ti^{3+} + 12Cl^- + Zn^{2+}$$

TiCl$_3$ can be produced by heating TiCl$_4$ vapor with hydrogen or by electrolytic reduction. When ammonia water is added to a titanium (III) solution, a gelatinous black precipitate of *hydrous Ti(OH)$_3$* is formed. This turns white rapidly when exposed to the air, the titanium undergoing oxidation to the **+4** state.   This easy oxidation is characteristic of titanium (III) compounds, which must be protected from the atmosphere if they are to persist.   Titanium (III) solutions are used in analytical chemistry as reducing agents.

It is difficult to obtain compounds of titanium in the *oxidation state of* **+2,** and such substances oxidize very readily.   They are not important.

390.   ZIRCONIUM AND ITS COMPOUNDS

Powerful reduction methods must be used to prepare this metal. Finely powdered zirconium is pyrophoric and inflames spontaneously when dry.   *Ferrozirconium* alloys rich in zirconium give sparks when struck and can be used effectively for flints in cigarette lighters.   *Zirconium dioxide*, a hard, refractory (m.p., 2700°), and inert material, is used for furnace linings and crucibles.   The hydrated *zirconyl ion*, ZrO^{2+}, is particularly characteristic of solutions of zirconium in the oxidation state of **+4,** and the most common salts of zirconium are zirconyl compounds, such as $ZrO(SO_4)$ and $ZrOCl_2 \cdot 8H_2O$.

391.   THE VA METALS

Vanadium is reasonably abundant, and the metal and its compounds are important.   Unfortunately, it is widely scattered in nature, and most minerals containing vanadium are rather low grade.   Both *niobium* and

Table 78.   VA Metals

	Vanadium	Niobium	Tantalum
Symbol	V	Nb	Ta
Atomic number	23	41	73
Atomic structure	2, 8, 11, 2	2, 8, 18, 12, 1	2, 8, 18, 32, 11, 2
Oxidation states	**0, +2, +3, +4, +5**	**0, +3, +4, +5**	**0, +4, +5**
Abundance	0.016%	Rare	Rare
Minerals	$Pb_5(VO_4)_3Cl$, vanadinite; $KUO_2VO_4 \cdot \frac{3}{2}H_2O$, carnotite	$Fe(NbO_3)_2$, columbite	$Fe(TaO_3)_2$, tantalite
Crystal radius, M^{5+}, Å	0.59	0.70	0.70
First ionization potential, volts	6.76		
Oxidation potential, M/M^{2+}, volts	+1.5	$(M/M^{3+})ca + 1.1$	
Melting point, ° C	1710	1950	2850
Boiling point, ° C	3000	>3300	6100
Density, g/cc, 20°	5.68	8.57	16.6

tantalum are rare metals. They have atoms of practically the same size, and they behave very much alike.

These VA metals have five valence electrons distributed in the outermost and second outermost shells, and they show in their compounds oxidation states varying from $+2$ to $+5$, with the $+5$ condition being the most stable and common one. The lower oxidation states decrease in stability as we go from vanadium to niobium and tantalum. Vanadium, when it is in the oxidation state of $+5$, resembles phosphorus in many respects.

392. VANADIUM AND ITS COMPOUNDS

Vanadium oxide is extracted from the ores, and the oxide is reduced to produce the element. This is a hard, silvery metal, which is important in alloy systems. *Ferrovanadium*, made by the coreduction of iron and vanadium oxides, is used to make the special vanadium steels, which are hard and have great tensile strength.

Oxidation State	
0	Metallic vanadium
$+2$	V^{2+}, VO, VSO_4, VCl_2
$+3$	V^{3+}, V_2O_3, $V_2(SO_4)_3$, $KV(SO_4)_2 \cdot 12H_2O$, VCl_3
$+4$	VO_2, $V_4O_9{}^{2-}$, VCl_4, $VOCl_2$, VO^{2+}
$+5$	V_2O_5, $VO_4{}^{3-}$, $(VO_3{}^-)_n$, $VOCl_3$, $VO_2{}^+$

In the oxidation state of $+2$, vanadium is basic and forms ionic bonds and nonvolatile salts. Vanadium is amphoteric in its intermediate oxidation states and acidic in the $+5$ state. In the higher oxidation states, its bonding is covalent, and it forms complex ions and volatile molecules. The orange-colored *vanadium pentoxide*, V_2O_5, is the most common compound of vanadium. It is an excellent catalyst for many reactions and is sometimes used in the Haber synthesis of ammonia and in the contact process for H_2SO_4. V_2O_5 is an acidic oxide and reacts with oxides, hydroxides, and carbonates of the active metals to form vanadates, such as $NaVO_3$ and Na_3VO_4.

393. TANTALUM

Although tantalum is a rare metal, it has grown in importance because of its remarkable properties. It has a high melting point and is ductile and a good electrical conductor, and therefore it was once used for the filaments in incandescent lamps. Tantalum is remarkably resistant to corrosion by water and acids; even aqua regia does not attack it. Though it is very expensive, it is used sometimes for chemical apparatus, such as

HCl absorbers for use in the manufacture of hydrochloric acid. Surgeons find tantalum wire, pins, foil, and plates very useful in operations because the metal is not corroded in the body, and muscles become attached to it.

394. THE VIA METALS

Chromium, the first element in the subgroup, is the most abundant, and its compounds are very common. But molybdenum and tungsten are important in alloy systems because of the ability of small percentages of these elements to alter properties, especially in the case of steels. In addition, all three metals have such extraordinary properties that they are in considerable demand. The metals of this subgroup are all very important to our metallurgical industry and are strategic elements in the country's economy. The United States has a very extensive deposit of molybdenum ore but is dependent upon imports for adequate supplies of chromium and tungsten.

With six valence electrons, the oxidation states achieved in the compounds of these VIA elements can be expected to vary from $+2$ to $+6$ by jumps of one unit. This is found to be the case for molybdenum and tungsten, but the oxidation states of $+4$ and $+5$ are so unstable for chromium that we know of no compounds involving them. The molyb-

Table 79.   VIA Metals

	Chromium	Molybdenum	Tungsten
Symbol	Cr	Mo	W
Atomic number	24	42	74
Atomic structure	2, 8, 13, 1	2, 8, 18, 13, 1	2, 8, 18, 32, 12, 2
Oxidation states	0, $+2$, $+3$, $+6$	0, $+2$, $+3$, $+4$, $+5$, $+6$	0, $+2$, $+3$, $+4$, $+5$, $+6$
Abundance	0.033%	Uncommon	0.005%
Minerals	Fe(CrO$_2$)$_2$, chromite; PbCrO$_4$, crocoite; silicates	MoS$_2$, molybdenite; PbMoO$_4$, wulfenite	CaWO$_4$, scheelite; (Fe, Mn)WO$_4$, wolframite
Crystal radius Mg$^+$, Å	0.52	0.62	0.62
First ionization potential, volts	6.74	7.35	
Oxidation potential, M/M^{3+}, volts	$+0.71$	About $+0.2$	(M/MO$_2$) $+ 0.05$
Melting point, °C	1550	2620	3370
Boiling point, °C	2500	4800	5930
Density, g/cc, 20°	7.14	10.2	19.3
Tensile strength, lb/in.^{2}	. . . .	5.02×10^7	6×10^7

denum atom is larger than the chromium atom, but molybdenum and tungsten atoms have almost the same size, and these two metals and their compounds are very closely analogous in many respects. In the oxidation state of **+6,** chromium resembles sulfur rather closely.

395. CHROMIUM

Metallic chromium can be made by reducing Cr_2O_3 with aluminum or by electrodeposition from chromic solutions. The massive pure metal is very hard and difficult to machine, so that it does not come into much use. Chrome plating, however, can be used very effectively for forming thin coatings of chromium on other more corrodible metal systems, such as steel. Since chromium resists corrosion by atmospheric conditions, it

Table 80. Some Alloys of Chromium and Manganese

Alloy and Composition	Properties	Uses
Low-chrome steel: 0.4C, 0.6Mn, 1.0Cr, 98Fe	Strong and hard	Automobile parts, and the like
Medium-chrome steel: 0.4C, 12.2Cr, 87Fe	Very good resistance to atmospheric corrosion but rapidly attacked by acids and salt solutions	Marketed as "stainless" steel
High-chrome steel: 70–73Fe, 27–30Cr, 0.5Mn	Resists oxidation and corrosion and retains strength at high temperatures	Chemical apparatus and industrial equipment, reactors, pressure bombs, autoclaves, furnaces
Nichrome: 11Cr, 75Ni, 12Fe, 2Mn	Resists oxidation in air up to 1100°, and is ductile and malleable	Wire or rods used as heating elements in electrical apparatus, such as toasters, irons, heaters, furnaces, ovens
Stellite: 40–80Co, 20–35Cr, 0–24W, 0.75–2.5C	Very hard, tough, and resistant to corrosion; retains hardness and strength at high temperatures	Cutlery, surgical and dental instruments, high-speed tools
Manganin: 82Cu, 15Mn, 3Ni	High electrical resistance, which changes very little with change in temperature	Resistance units for electrical equipment
Everdur: 94.8–96Cu, 3–4Si, 1–1.2Mn	Resistant to corrosion	Laboratory apparatus

maintains its shiny bluish-silvery appearance indefinitely, and its hardness gives high resistance to abrasion. The good resistance of chromium to corrosion is believed to be a consequence of the formation of an adherent, impervious, transparent film of Cr_2O_3. The widespread practice of using chromium plating for the lavish decoration of automobiles is responsible for much shameful waste of this strategic element. *Ferrochromium* is made by the reduction of the iron chromite ore, and this alloy is then used in steelmaking to supply chromium.

There are many important alloys of chromium, characterized usually by their hardness, great strength, and good resistance to atmospheric corrosion.

396. COMPOUNDS OF CHROMIUM

Oxidation States	
0	Metallic chromium
+2, chromium (II) (chromous)	Cr^{2+}, CrO, $Cr(OH)_2$, $CrSO_4$, $CrCl_2$
+3, chromium (III) (chromic)	Cr^{3+}, Cr_2O_3, $Cr(OH)_3$, $Cr_2(SO_4)_3$, $KCr(SO_4)_2 \cdot 12H_2O$, $CrCl_3$, $Cr(NH_3)_6Cl_3$, CrO_2^-
+6, chromium (VI)	CrO_3, CrO_4^{2-}, $Cr_2O_7^{2-}$, CrO_2Cl_2

The compounds of chromium are highly colored, the color changing with change in oxidation state, so that the progress of oxidation or reduction of chromium may be easily followed. The name *chromium* was applied to this element because of the brilliant color of its compounds.

The *oxidation state of* **+2** is achieved when the chromium (II) ion is formed by reaction of the metal with acids.

$$Cr + 2H^+ = Cr^{2+} + H_2$$

Or it can be obtained by the reduction of chromium from more positive oxidation states, using active metals, such as zinc in acid solution.

$$2Cr^{3+} + Zn = Zn^{2+} + 2Cr^{2+}$$

The *hydrated* Cr^{2+} *ions* are blue and are oxidized by air or water to the chromium (III) condition. $Cr(OH)_2$ is basic and *chromium (II) salts* are ionic. *Chromium (II)* compounds are not common because of the instability of this oxidation state in the atmosphere.

The *chromium (III) compounds* are the most common ones for this element, Cr^{3+} being stable in acidic solution under atmospheric conditions. Cr^{3+} ions and their compounds are very much like aluminum and Fe^{3+} ions and their compounds.

Green crystalline Cr_2O_3, *dichromium trioxide*, is formed by the oxidation of the metal, by reduction of dichromate ions, or by the dehydration of chromium (III) hydroxide.

$$Na_2Cr_2O_7 + S \overset{heat}{=} Na_2SO_4 + Cr_2O_3$$

$$(NH_4)_2Cr_2O_7 \overset{heat}{=} N_2 + Cr_2O_3 + 4H_2O$$

$$2Cr(OH)_3 \overset{heat}{=} Cr_2O_3 + 3H_2O$$

Like Al_2O_3, Cr_2O_3 is a hard, high-melting, inert solid which is useful as an abrasive, refractory, and pigment. It is a good catalyst for certain reactions.

Gelatinous, hydrous *chromium (III) hydroxide*, $Cr(OH)_3$, is precipitated when hydroxide ions are added to *chromium (III)* solutions and when chromium (III) compounds hydrolyze. $Cr(OH)_3$ is amphoteric and dissolves in excess strong hydroxide to form *chromite ions*.

$$Cr(OH)_{3(s)} + OH^- = Cr(OH)_4^-$$

$Cr(OH)_3$ is a good mordant, forming brilliantly colored lakes with dye-stuffs. It is also important in the tanning of leather.

Chromium (III) salts are formed when Cr^{3+} ions associate with anions. The nitrate, the hydrated halides, and the sulfate are soluble in water. The sulfide and the carbonate hydrolyze completely. Chrome alum, $KCr(SO_4)_2 \cdot 12H_2O$, is used in leather tanning. Anhydrous $CrCl_3$ is a magenta-colored crystalline material that does not dissolve in water and is quite inert toward most reagents.

Complex chromium (III) compounds are formed readily and in great variety, owing to the strong tendency of the triply charged Cr^{3+} ion to associate with molecules or other ions. The situation is much like that already discussed for aluminum (Section 381), except that the rate of formation of chromium complexes is slow.

$$Cr^{3+} + \begin{matrix} \text{ions} \\ \text{or} \\ \text{molecules} \end{matrix} = \text{complex ions or molecules}$$

This is well shown by the behavior of solutions of $CrCl_3$ toward ammonia. By varying the conditions, a series of complex solids may be obtained by crystallization, having the ratios of chromium chloride to ammonia shown in the first column of Table 81.

The complex compounds vary in color and in chemical behavior. In their solutions the ammonia molecules are closely attached to the chromium atoms. The chlorine atoms may be present either as chloride ions, precipitatable by Ag^+, or tightly bonded to the chromium atoms so that they are not precipitated by Ag^+. In all these complexes there are always six groups or atoms associated with the chromium atom, this atom having a coordination number of six. X-ray studies of the solids show that the six groups coordinated to the central chromium atom are at the corners

Table 81. Complexes of Chromium (III) Chloride and Ammonia

Compound	Ions Present	Complex Formulas
$CrCl_3 \cdot 6NH_3$	$3Cl^-$ 1 complex (Cr and $6NH_3$)$^{3+}$	$[Cr(NH_3)_6]Cl_3$
$CrCl_3 \cdot 5NH_3$	$2Cl^-$ 1 complex (Cr, $5NH_3$, Cl)$^{2+}$	$[Cr(NH_3)_5Cl]Cl_2$
$CrCl_3 \cdot 4NH_3$	$1Cl^-$ 1 complex (Cr, $4NH_3$, $2Cl$)$^+$	$[Cr(NH_3)_4Cl_2]Cl$
$CrCl_3 \cdot 3NH_3$	Uncharged complex (Cr, $3NH_3$, $3Cl$)	$[Cr(NH_3)_3Cl_3]$

of an octahedron; if the groups are identical, they are at equal distances from the center of the chromium atom.

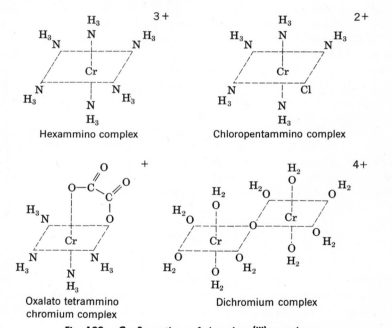

Hexammino complex

Chloropentammino complex

Oxalato tetrammino chromium complex

Dichromium complex

Fig. 122. Configurations of chromium (III) complexes.

Univalent chlorine atoms can replace the neutral molecules of ammonia at the octahedral coordination positions. The charge of the complex is determined by the charge of the Cr^{3+} ion and the charges of the groups that associate with it to build the complex.

Chromium (III) complexes can be formed by association with the Cr^{3+} ion of many different univalent groups, such as F^-, Cl^-, Br^-, I^-, NO_3^-, NO_2^-, CN^-, and so forth, and many different molecules, such as

NH_3 and H_2O. Divalent groups, such as $SO_4{}^{2-}$ and $C_2O_4{}^{2-}$, may occupy either one or two coordination positions.

A divalent group may become shared with two chromium atoms to form a polychromium complex in which two octahedra share a corner. Thus, chromium (III) is observed to form a vast number of relatively stable complex ions in which it is always associated with enough other units to produce the octahedral structure. This tendency to form complexes is so great for chromium that it is believed that in aqueous solution chromium (III) is always present in such complexes, being either in the hexahydrated ion, $Cr(H_2O)_6{}^{3+}$, or in other octahedral complexes. Notice that the Cr^{3+} ion forms complexes very much like those of aluminum but that the complex chromium octahedra are usually more stable than those for aluminum. The formation of stable complexes is particularly characteristic of the transition metals.

In the *oxidation state of* **+6,** chromium usually is bonded to oxygen to form the oxide or oxyanions. When a chromium (II) or chromium (III) compound is heated in air with an alkali or alkaline-earth hydroxide or carbonate, oxidation to *chromate ion* takes place.

$$4Fe(CrO_2)_{2(s)} + 8K_2CO_{3(s)} + 7O_{2(g)} = 2Fe_2O_{3(s)} + 8K_2CrO_{4(s)} + 8CO_{2(g)}$$
chromite ore

The soluble chromates of the alkali metals can be separated from the insoluble ferric oxide by solution and crystallization. Oxidizing agents other than atmospheric oxygen may be employed. The chromate ion has a bright-yellow color and has a tetrahedral configuration like the $SO_4{}^{2-}$ ion. Because chromium in the **+6** oxidation state is much smaller than when it is in the **+3** state, the coordination number of **+6** chromium is limited to 4 toward oxygen.

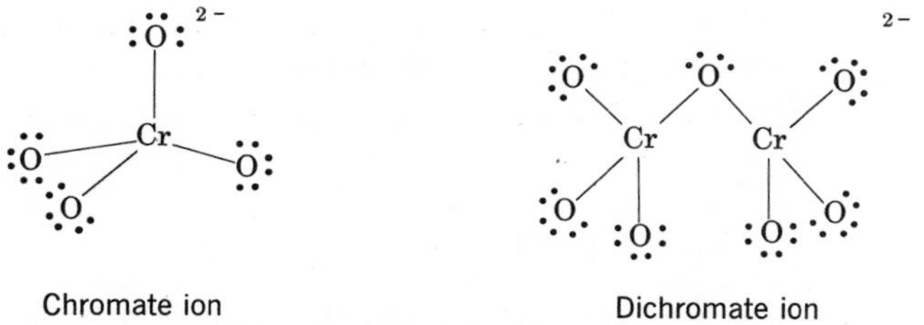

Chromate ion   Dichromate ion

Fig. 123. Configurations of $CrO_4{}^{2-}$ and $Cr_2O_7{}^{2-}$.

Since the chromate ion is the structural analogue of the sulfate ion, chromates are found to be isomorphous with sulfates and to have similar properties. The solubilities of chromates are like those of sulfates; the chromates of the alkali metals and magnesium are quite soluble in water, whereas other chromates are relatively insoluble. *Lead chromate,* $PbCrO_4$, is important as the yellow pigment, chrome yellow.

When solutions of chromates are acidified, the color changes from

yellow to orange.   This is a consequence of the formation of the orange
dichromate ions.

$$2CrO_4{}^{2-} + 2H^+ \rightleftharpoons H_2O + \underset{\substack{\text{orange dichromate}\\\text{ion}}}{Cr_2O_7{}^{2-}}$$
yellow chromate ion

One oxygen ion is removed by the hydrogen ions, and an oxygen bridge
is formed between the two chromium atoms.

Each chromium atom is tetrahedrally bonded to four oxygen atoms, one
oxygen atom being bonded to both chromium atoms.   This formation
of the dichromate ion is another example of the tendency of oxyanion
systems to condense to polyoxyanions by splitting out oxygen ions and
forming oxygen bridges.   In very highly acid solutions, further condensation of chromate ion to trichromate ion, $Cr_3O_{10}{}^{2-}$, has been observed.
The condensation is reversible, and addition of OH^- changes dichromate
ion to chromate ion.   The easy reversibility of the reaction means that
chromates and dichromates behave very much alike in aqueous solution.
In general, the dichromates are more soluble than the chromates.

Dichromate ions are powerful oxidizing agents and are very easily
reduced to Cr^{3+} by reducing agents, such as sulfurous acid, especially in
acid solution.

$$\underset{\text{orange}}{Cr_2O_7{}^{2-}} + 3H_2SO_3 + 2H^+ = \underset{\text{green}}{2Cr^{3+}} + 3SO_4{}^{2-} + 4H_2O$$

The progress of the reduction can be followed by observing the color
change from orange to green, the latter color being due to formation of
complex chromium (III) ions.

Chromic acid, H_2CrO_4, may possibly exist in solution, but it has never
been isolated.   Instead, when concentrated solutions of chromates or
dichromates are treated with concentrated sulfuric acid, one gets scarlet
crystals of CrO_3, chromium trioxide.   **Warning!**   This operation is highly
exothermic and must be carried out very cautiously to prevent spattering
of the very corrosive solution.

$$Cr_2O_7{}^{2-} + 2H^+ \overset{H_2SO_4}{=} H_2O + 2CrO_3$$

The suspension of the crystals of CrO_3 in the concentrated sulfuric acid
solution constitutes the chromic acid *cleaning mixture* used so frequently
in the laboratory for cleaning glassware.   The combination of the very
strong oxidizing action of chromium in the oxidation state of **+6** with
the powerful dehydrating and acid action of concentrated sulfuric acid
accounts for the powerful cleansing action of this cleaning mixture, especially for the removal of grease films. CrO_3 is very soluble in water and
deliquesces rapidly.

When solutions of chromates or dichromates are shaken with dilute
sulfuric acid and hydrogen peroxide, an intense blue color appears.   The

blue material formed in solution is very unstable and rapidly decomposes in the aqueous solution. However, it is very soluble in ether and may be extracted from water solution. The blue color persists in ethereal solution, probably due to complex formation. The reactions that occur to give the blue color are obscure, but it is generally believed that unstable peroxychromic acids or peroxides are formed. The appearance of the blue color may be used as a very sensitive analytical test for chromates or hydrogen peroxide.

397. MOLYBDENUM AND TUNGSTEN

The metals molybdenum and tungsten are manufactured by preparing the oxides MoO_3 and WO_3 from their ores and then reducing the oxides by heating them with hydrogen.

$$WO_3 + 3H_2 \overset{heat}{=} W + 3H_2O$$

These metals are hard but ductile and have exceptionally high melting points, that of tungsten being higher than the melting point of any other metal except the very rare rhenium. Drawn into wire or rolled into sheets, they are used in incandescent lamps and in vacuum tubes. They are very inert toward atmospheric and acid corrosion. Molybdenum and tungsten steels are hard, tough, and resilient and are much in demand for special uses, such as cutting tools.

The common compounds of molybdenum and tungsten are those for the oxidation state of **+6**. Molybdic and tungstic oxides, MoO_3 and WO_3, are refractory acidic oxides which form molybdates and tungstates when fused with basic oxides.

$$CaO + WO_3 = CaWO_4$$

398. THE VIIA METALS

Of the subgroup VIIA, only manganese is well known and important. Technetium has been worked with only as a product of radioactive change. Apparently its nuclei are very unstable, and it is doubtful that we will ever have more than very small quantities of the element to work with. Rhenium, discovered in 1925, is very rare. It is interesting because of its very high melting point. Having seven valence electrons, these VIIA elements might be expected to show oxidation states from **+2** to **+7** in their compounds. Manganese realizes all of these except **+5**, the **+2**, **+4**, and **+7** oxidation states being the most common. Rhenium is unique in that it is reported to achieve all the possible oxidation states from **−1** to **+7**. This is the only case on record of a metal achieving the oxidation state of **−1**. In the oxidation state of **+7**, manganese and rhenium show some resemblance to chlorine, forming MnO_4^- and ReO_4^-, respectively.

Table 82.   VIIA Metals

	Manganese	Technetium	Rhenium
Symbol	Mn	Tc	Re
Atomic number	25	43	75
Atomic structure	2, 8, 13, 2	2, 8, 18, 14, 1	2, 8, 18, 32, 13, 2
Oxidation states	**0, +2, +3, +4** **+6, +7**	. . . .	**−1, 0, +1, +2,** **+3, +4, +5, +6, +7**
Abundance	0.08%	Not found in nature	Rare
Minerals	MnO_2, pyrolusite Iron ores Silicates	. . . .	Accompanies Mo, Nb, Ta, W
Crystal radius, M^{7+}, Å	0.46		
First ionization potential, volts	7.41		
Oxidation potential, M/M^{2+}, volts	+1.05		
Melting point, ° C	1242	. . . .	3440
Boiling point, ° C	2151	. . . .	5870
Density, g/cc, 20°	7.44	. . . .	20

399.   MANGANESE

Manganese is abundant and widespread, but because the domestic ores are very poor, the United States imports manganese minerals.   The great importance of manganese in steelmaking and in special alloys makes this a critical metal, essential to industry.   Traces of manganese in soils are believed to play an important role in plant nutrition.   Pure massive *manganese* is not readily obtained by reduction of the oxide, but electrolytic procedures have been devised which produce the very pure metal.   Manganese is a hard, brittle metal resembling iron in appearance. It is rather active and liberates hydrogen from dilute acids and steam. Uses for the pure metal have not developed.

Ferromanganese is produced by coreduction of the oxides of manganese and iron.   Small amounts of ferromanganese are added to steel; the manganese acts as a deoxidizer and desulfurizer, thus improving the quality of the steel.   Special manganese-alloy steels are hard, tough, and wear-resisting, of particular use in crushing machinery.   Several important nonferrous alloys of manganese are also in use (see Table 80).

400. COMPOUNDS OF MANGANESE

Oxidation States

0	Metallic manganese
+2, manganese (II) (manganous)	Mn^{2+}, MnO, $Mn(OH)_2$, $MnSO_4$, $MnCl_2$
+3, manganese (III) (manganic)	Mn^{3+}, Mn_2O_3, $Mn(OH)_3$, $Mn_2(SO_4)_3$, $KMn(SO_4)_2 \cdot 12H_2O$, $MnCl_3$
+4	MnO_2, $MnO_3{}^{2-}$, $MnCl_4$
+6	MnO_3, $MnO_4{}^{2-}$, K_2MnO_4
+7	Mn_2O_7, $MnO_4{}^{-}$, $KMnO_4$

As in the case of chromium, the different oxidation states for manganese are characterized by brilliant colors.

The *Mn^{2+} ion and its salts* are typical of the *oxidation state of +2.* This pink hydrated ion is obtained in solution by the action of acids on manganese or by the reduction of manganese dioxide or permanganates in acid solution.

$$Mn + 2H^+ = Mn^{2+} + H_2$$
$$MnO_2 + 4H^+ + 2Cl^- = Mn^{2+} + 2H_2O + Cl_2$$

The Mn^{2+} ion is stable in acid solution, even in the air, and manganese (II) compounds are common, resembling those of nickel and zinc. *Manganese (II) hydroxide* is precipitated by OH^- as a gelatinous white solid.

$$Mn^{2+} + 2OH^- = Mn(OH)_{2(s)}$$

It is oxidized by air to a brown material containing manganese in the **+3** state, usually formulated as hydrous $Mn(OH)_3$.

The *oxidation state of +3* is not common for manganese, and while the ion, Mn^{3+}, and its compounds can be obtained, they are not important.

Manganese dioxide, MnO_2, is the only familiar representative of the *oxidation state of +4,* this oxide presumably owing its existence to its insolubility.   Manganese dioxide decomposes readily when heated, oxygen gas being formed.

$$3MnO_2 \overset{heat}{=} Mn_3O_4 + O_2$$

The Mn_3O_4 produced as a reduction product is a mixed oxide, some of the manganese atoms being in the oxidation state of **+2,** the others in the oxidation state of **+3.**   Manganese dioxide is a powerful oxidizing agent and is so used as a decolorizer in the manufacture of glass.   By reduction or oxidation, manganese dioxide can be converted to other compounds of manganese.   Manganites, such as Na_2MnO_3, can be prepared by fusing manganese dioxide with bases, but the manganite ion is not stable in water.

One important use of MnO_2 is in the construction of dry cells, as shown in Figure 124.   In the operation of the cell, manganese is reduced to the **+3** oxidation state, and zinc is oxidized to zinc ions.

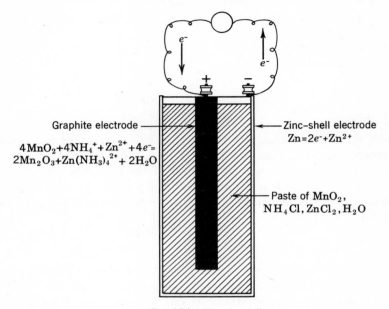

Graphite electrode

$$4MnO_2 + 4NH_4^+ + Zn^{2+} + 4e^- =$$
$$2Mn_2O_3 + Zn(NH_3)_4^{2+} + 2H_2O$$

Zinc–shell electrode
$Zn = 2e^- + Zn^{2+}$

Paste of MnO_2,
$NH_4Cl, ZnCl_2, H_2O$

Fig. 124.   The dry cell.

The *manganates*, with manganese in the *oxidation state of* **+6,** are obtained by fusion of manganese dioxide with bases under atmospheric oxidizing conditions.

$$2MnO_2 + 4KOH + O_2 = 2K_2MnO_4 + 2H_2O$$

The formation of the green MnO_4^{2-} ion may easily be followed, and the crystalline manganates can be obtained from aqueous solution of the fusion product.   Note how different the manganate ion is from the chlorate ion.   The latter has the central chlorine atom in the oxidation state of **+5.**   The manganate ion is electronically and structurally the analogue of the chromate ion, and the manganates are isomorphous with the corresponding chromates and sulfates.   The manganate ion, however, is much less stable than the chromate ion, and in solution it tends to hydrolyze and undergo auto-oxidation-reduction.

$$3MnO_4^{2-} + 2H_2O = 2MnO_4^- + MnO_2 + 4OH^-$$

It can readily be seen that addition of acid will promote this oxidation-reduction.

$$3MnO_4^{2-} + 4H^+ = 2MnO_4^- + MnO_{2(s)} + 2H_2O$$

Manganates are important chiefly as intermediates in the preparation of permanganates.

Filtration and evaporation of the acidified solution will produce deep-purple crystals of *KMnO₄*. But only two-thirds of the manganese is oxidized to MnO_4^-, the rest being reduced to MnO_2. This is not a very efficient process for preparing permanganates. In commercial practice the manganate solution is commonly oxidized by electrolysis or by the use of chlorine.

$$2MnO_4^{2-} + Cl_2 = 2Cl^- + 2MnO_4^-$$

The permanganates are very soluble in water, giving the intense pink to purple color of the permanganate ion. As a rule, permanganates are isomorphous with the corresponding perchlorates, the two anions being very similar.

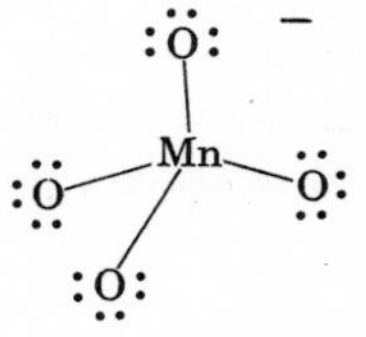

Fig. 125. Configuration of the permanganate ion.

tetrahedral

Note that there are no peroxy groups in the permanganate or perchlorate ions. The prefix per- was applied to these ions in the early days simply to indicate that they have higher percentages of oxygen than the manganate and chlorate.

Sodium permanganate is very soluble and tends to be highly hydrated, so that it is difficult to prepare pure crystals of it. The anhydrous $KMnO_4$ is easier to prepare pure, and this is the permanganate commonly in use. This salt, by virtue of the permanganate ion is a powerful oxidizing agent. If concentrated sulfuric acid is poured on solid permanganate, a violent explosion occurs.

The extent of the *oxidizing action of permanganate ions* depends upon whether the system is acidic, neutral, or basic. *In strongly acidic solution* the purple permanganate ion is reduced to give the faintly pink manganous ion, and the solution becomes practically colorless.

$$\overset{\text{Reduction}}{\overbrace{\underset{+7}{2MnO_4^-} + \underset{+4}{5H_2SO_3}}} = 4H^+ + \underset{+6}{5SO_4^{2-}} + \underset{+2}{2Mn^{2+}} + 3H_2O$$

Oxidation

As the equation shows, hydrogen from the acid combines with three of the oxygens of the permanganate ions to form water. In acidic solution the manganese undergoes a change of five units of oxidation state and has a large capacity for oxidation.

In neutral solution the permanganate ion is converted to the insoluble brown manganese dioxide.

$$
\overset{\text{Reduction}}{\overbrace{\overset{+7}{2\text{MnO}_4{}^-} + \underset{\text{Oxidation}}{\underbrace{\overset{+4}{3\text{SO}_3{}^{2-}}}} + \text{H}_2\text{O} = \overset{+6}{3\text{SO}_4{}^{2-}} + \overset{+4}{2\text{MnO}_{2(s)}} + 2\text{OH}^-}}
$$

The water entering the reaction combines with some of the oxygen atoms of the permanganate ions and OH^- is formed, the system becoming more alkaline. In neutral solution, the manganese is reduced three units in oxidation state and has only three-fifths the oxidizing capacity that it has in acidic solution.

In *basic solution* the green manganate ion is formed when a reducing agent is added, if $\text{MnO}_4{}^-$ is present in excess.

$$
\overset{\text{Reduction}}{\overbrace{\overset{+7}{2\text{MnO}_4{}^-} + \underset{\text{Oxidation}}{\underbrace{\overset{+4}{\text{SO}_3{}^{2-}}}} + 2\text{OH}^- = \overset{+6}{\text{SO}_4{}^{2-}} + \overset{+6}{2\text{MnO}_4{}^{2-}} + \text{H}_2\text{O}}}
$$

The hydroxide ions provide the oxygen necessary for the oxidation of the sulfite ion, and water is formed. The manganese suffers a reduction of only one unit in oxidation state, and the oxidizing capacity of the permanganate ion is only one-fifth as large as it is in acid solution.

EXERCISES

1. Outline the expansion in electronic structure that occurs in the sequence of transition metals from scandium through copper. Correlate with these electronic structures the oxidation states that the metals achieve.

2. Why is it reasonable to assign all the lanthanide metals to Group IIIA?

3. Summarize the relationship between the oxidation states of a transition metal and the ability of its oxides to behave as the anhydrides of acidic, basic, or amphoteric hydroxides, giving examples.

4. a) What is the most important compound of titanium and for what is it used?
b) Compare the spatial configuration of TiCl_4 and $\text{TiCl}_6{}^{2-}$.

5. a) What is the most common oxidation state for the IVA metals?
b) What ion is most common for zirconium?

6. a) What is the oxidation state of vanadium in: 1) V_2O_5? 2) $KV(SO_4)_2 \cdot 12H_2O$? 3) $VO_2{}^+$?

b) How is V_2O_5 used in chemical industry?

7. What unique properties does tantalum metal have that make it of interest to chemical engineers and to surgeons?

8. Why are alloys that have high percentages of chromium of commercial interest?

9. a) List the oxidation states known for chromium and give formulas for two ions or compounds that are examples of each state.

b) Which states are the more common?

10. Discuss the formation of complexes of chromium when it is in the oxidation state of **+3**, touching upon: a) the kinds of units entering into such complexes; b) the configuration of the complexes; c) factors determining the charges of the complexes.

11. a) How can chromates be prepared?

b) Account for the color change that occurs when chromates are acidified and the second change in color that is observed when a suitable reducing agent is added to the acidified solution.

12. How is tungsten metal obtained, and what is it used for?

13. How does manganese occur in nature? What is ferromanganese, and what is it used for?

14. Write balanced equations for the conversion of MnO_2 to: a) Mn^{2+}; b) Mn_3O_4; c) $MnO_4{}^-$.

15. Outline the action of the permanganate ion as an oxidizing agent.

16. How is manganese dioxide involved in the operation of a flashlight?

Chapter 32

▶ Transition Metals, II

Group VIII

Iron, Cobalt, Nickel,

the Platinum Metals

401. THE METALS OF GROUP VIII

The eighth group of the periodic system is unique. It includes nine elements that occur in sequences of three, sometimes called *triads*. In each long period an eighth-group triad follows the VIIA element and precedes the IB element. Mendeléeff was struck by the fact that these eighth-group elements bridged the gaps between the first and second series of his short periodic table, and he therefore referred to the triads as transition metals. In the light of our present knowledge of electronic structures, it is apparent that the metals of the eighth group are not altogether unique, but that they fit into the longer transition-metal sequences and resemble the rest of the transition metals closely.

Table 83. Electronic Structures of the Group VIII Metals

Iron triad	Iron	Cobalt	Nickel
	2, 8, 14, 2	2, 8, 15, 2	2, 8, 16, 2
Light platinum metals	Ruthenium	Rhodium	Palladium
	2, 8, 18, 15, 1	2, 8, 18, 16, 1	2, 8, 18, 18
Heavy platinum metals	Osmium	Iridium	Platinum
	2, 8, 18, 32, 14, 2	2, 8, 18, 32, 15, 2	2, 8, 18, 32, 17, 1

In each triad the number of electrons in the two outermost shells increases from 16 to 17 to 18, and this expansion is reflected in changes of the ability to form chemical bonds. The eighth-group elements might also be considered to be divided into three vertical subgroups, headed by iron, cobalt, and nickel, respectively. Each of these subgroups is characterized by the same total number of electrons in the two outermost shells, the number of shells increasing down the group. The similarity in the

496

number of electrons in the valence shells for each vertical subgroup is reflected in the oxidation states that are achieved and in the types and configurations of the compounds. The higher oxidation states fade out as the second outermost shell of electrons becomes more saturated in a given triad, and the higher oxidation states are more common for the platinum metals than for the iron triad. Iron, cobalt, and nickel are much more active metals than the platinum elements. When they are in the same oxidation state, the atoms of the light platinum triad are larger than the iron-triad atoms, but there seems to be little, if any, increase in size from the light to the heavy platinum metals. The heavy platinum metals therefore have almost twice the density of the light platinum metals and are among the densest substances known.

402. THE IRON TRIAD

Table 84. Properties of the Iron Triad

	Iron	Cobalt	Nickel
Symbol	Fe	Co	Ni
Atomic number	26	27	28
Electronic structure	2, 8, 14, 2	2, 8, 15, 2	2, 8, 16, 2
Oxidation states	0, +2, +3, +4, +6	0, +2, +3, +4	0, +2, +3, +4
Abundance	4.7%	0.001%	0.018%
Minerals	Fe_2O_3, hematite; Fe_3O_4, magnetite; $2Fe_2O_3 \cdot 3H_2O$, limonite; $FeCO_3$, siderite; FeS_2, pyrite; silicates	$CoAs_2$, smaltite; CoSAs, cobalt glance	(Ni, Cu, Fe)S, pentlandite; silicates
Crystal radius, M^{2+}, Å	0.75	0.72	0.70
First ionization potential volts	7.83	about 8.5	7.606
Oxidation potential, M/M^{2+}, volts	+0.440	+0.277	+0.250
Melting point, ° C	1535	1490	1452
Boiling point, ° C	3000	2900	2900
Density, g/cc, 20°	7.87	8.9	8.9

These three elements resemble each other very closely when they are in the metallic state. Their densities and other physical properties are much the same. They are unique among the elements in that they are the only ones that are ferromagnetic at room temperatures. The shift of stability to the lower oxidation states across this triad is particularly noteworthy.

403. OCCURRENCE OF IRON

Iron is one of our most abundant metals, and its occurrence is very widespread in nature and in many kinds of minerals. The most important iron ore is *hematite*, Fe_2O_3. Tremendous deposits of this oxide, so rich that it can be used directly for making iron, were discovered in the Lake Superior region. These have been the source of most of the iron which has been manufactured in such vast amounts in the United States. The ore is very near the surface, and it is mined simply by stripping away the overlying soil and shoveling the ore into railroad cars. Unfortunately, the end of this rich deposit is in sight, and much work is under way to develop methods for the economical utilization of other sources. Magnetite, limonite, and siderite are other ores that are exploited. The iron sulfide ores, however, are too difficult to process. Likewise, the large amount of iron tied up in complex silicates is not easily available. Iron is found only very rarely as the metal. The *iron meteorites* that reach the earth consist of iron alloyed with other metals, such as nickel, whereas *stony meteorites* are composed of silicates. A current theory suggests that the core of the earth is dense and metallic, consisting of iron and nickel. Iron occurs in only small amounts in animal and plant matter, but the element is an essential constituent of the hemoglobin of our blood.

404. PREPARATION AND PROPERTIES OF PURE IRON

The preparation of pure iron is difficult because it is not easy to separate the metal from the other elements that accompany it in its ores and are carried along with iron in the usual metallurgical operations. Pure iron powder can be made by preparing very pure ferric oxide, which then is reduced by heating with hydrogen.

$$Fe_2O_3 + 3H_2 = 2Fe + 3H_2O$$

The fine powder produced is pyrophoric, being oxidized so rapidly when it comes in contact with the air that it glows. Very pure iron can also be obtained by the electrolysis of ferrous solutions or by the thermal decomposition of iron carbonyl. By removal of the impurities in pig iron, soft iron of reasonable purity may be obtained.

Pure iron is quite soft and malleable. It becomes magnetized strongly when placed in a magnetic field. This magnetic behavior is a consequence of the electronic structure of the iron atom, being a function of the incomplete d subgroup of electrons in the second outermost shell. Each iron atom acts as a tiny magnet. The atoms become oriented in an ordered array when placed in a magnetic field, and they maintain this orientation at room temperature when the magnetic field is removed. The chunk of iron then acts as a permanent magnet. This permanent magnetism is referred to as *ferromagnetism*. Iron shows ferromagnetism more strongly than cobalt and nickel, the only other elements that behave in this fashion at room temperature. Certain alloys of iron with cobalt and nickel have very good magnetic characteristics. The magnetism of iron has been utilized in many ways which are important in modern life. It makes possible the compass, telephone, telegraph, electric motors and generators, and countless other devices.

Iron is moderately active, being well above hydrogen in the electrochemical series. Unfortunately, it rusts badly under atmospheric conditions; the combination of oxygen, water, and carbon dioxide causes rapid corrosion. Iron reduces steam and acids to give hydrogen.

$$3Fe + 4H_2O = Fe_3O_4 + 2H_2$$
$$Fe + 2H^+ = Fe^{2+} + H_2$$

When iron is dipped into concentrated nitric acid it becomes *passive* and is not corroded further. This passivity is believed to be due to the formation of unstable oxide films, and it is destroyed when the piece of iron is scratched, rubbed, or struck and the fragile protective film is destroyed. Iron is not attacked by bases, and sodium and potassium hydroxides may be fused in iron crucibles.

405. THE METALLURGY OF IRON ALLOYS

Impure iron is produced from hematite, our most common iron ore, by the *blast-furnace process*. The ore, limestone, and coke are continuously fed through a hopper to the top of the huge cylindrical blast furnace, which is lined with refractory bricks. Heated air is blown into the bottom of the furnace, and the coke burns, forming carbon monoxide and providing heat. The carbon monoxide rises through the iron ore and reduces it to the molten metal, which drops to the hearth at the bottom of the furnace where it accumulates. The siliceous gangue, such as SiO_2, which is present in the ore, reacts with the calcium oxide formed by the thermal decomposition of the limestone, and molten silicate *slag* is produced. This slag flows to the hearth where it accumulates as a second liquid layer on top of the heavier molten iron.

The chemical reactions which occur in the blast furnace are believed to be quite complicated, and the hematite probably is reduced stepwise, but the net reactions that occur can be summarized by the following equations:

$$2C + O_2 = 2CO$$
$$3CO + Fe_2O_3 = 2Fe + 3CO_2$$
$$CaCO_3 = CaO + CO_2$$
$$CaO + SiO_2 = CaSiO_3$$
$$\text{slag}$$

In addition, some of the silicon dioxide, phosphates, sulfides, and other impurities may react to give small amounts of silicon, phosphorus, sulfur, and other elements, which combine with the iron to form silicides, phosphides, and sulfides in solution.

From time to time the molten iron and the slag are tapped off separately by removing fire-clay plugs from holes in the hearth. The slag

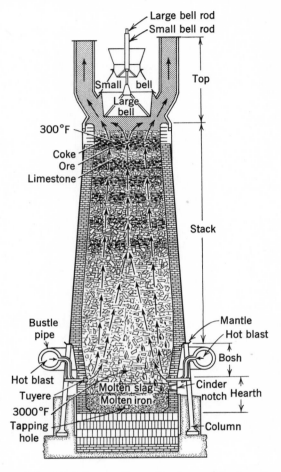

Fig. 126.   Diagram of the blast furnace for making iron.   (Courtesy American Iron and Steel Institute)

may be used for making cement, building blocks, and insulating mineral wool.

The iron that flows from the blast furnace is called *pig iron*. It is quite impure, having about the composition 92 to 94 per cent Fe, 3 to 4 per cent C, 1 to 3 per cent Si, 1 to 2 per cent Mn, and less than 1 per cent of P and S. The molten pig iron may be used directly to make iron castings or to be processed into steel, or it may be allowed to solidify into pigs to be used later. *White cast iron* is obtained by cooling the pig iron rapidly; most of the carbon remains in solution as cementite, Fe_3C, and the iron is hard and brittle. *Gray cast iron* results when the pig iron is cooled slowly so that the iron carbide has a chance to decompose to give graphite. Gray cast iron is softer and tougher than white cast iron. Formerly, much *wrought iron* was made by *puddling* (stirring) the hot pig iron on a puddling-furnace hearth made of iron oxide ore, so that oxidizing conditions prevail. In this process the carbon and other impurities are oxidized and some slag is formed. When the product is rolled or hammered, the slag gives a fibrous structure to the wrought iron, and this tough material resists corrosion well. Such wrought iron has been replaced in large part by low-carbon steels made by other methods.

Carbon steels are made by processing the pig iron from the blast furnace by the open-hearth, Bessemer, electric-furnace, or crucible methods. In the *open-hearth process*, pig iron, scrap iron, iron ore, and limestone are heated on a refractory hearth built of basic or acidic refractories. Heating is continued until the impurities have been reduced to the proper amount, and then the carbon content is adjusted. Deoxidizers and scavengers such as aluminum, magnesium, and titanium are added to remove oxygen, nitrogen, sulfur, and so on. The batch is sampled and analyzed from time to time so that the proper composition can be set up. The finished batch of molten steel is removed from the open-hearth furnace by tilting the hearth and allowing the white-hot liquid to run into huge ladles, which convey it away for processing into various forms. The open-hearth process produces vast amounts of high-grade steel of the desired composition.

In the *Bessemer process*, the molten pig iron is poured into the Bessemer converter, a pear-shaped container which is lined with acid or basic refractories. A blast of preheated air is forced through the molten metal to oxidize the impurities. After these impurities are burned out, the composition is adjusted by adding carbon alloys, scavengers, and deoxidizers. Because of the speed of the operation, the composition cannot be controlled very satisfactorily, and Bessemer steel is not of as high quality as that made by other methods. For this reason, the use of the Bessemer process is decreasing.

In the *crucible* and *electric-furnace processes*, small batches of special alloy steels are made under carefully controlled conditions, and steel of excellent quality may be obtained.

The carbon in steels varies up to 1.5 per cent. *Low-carbon steels* are soft and ductile. Increasing the carbon content produces steels that are harder and stronger. By special heating treatment, called *tempering*, the properties of steel can be altered considerably. Steel may be *case-hardened* by heating it in carbon to produce a hard surface high in carbon.

Many other metals can be added to steel to produce special *alloy steels*. Manganese, chromium, vanadium, nickel, molybdenum, tung-

Table 85. Ferroalloys Compared with Aluminum, Magnesium, and Their Alloys

Alloy and Per Cent Composition	Hardness	Tensile Strength, Lb/Sq In.	Uses
Cast-iron: 97Fe, 3C	130–210	20,000–60,000	Automobile cylinders and pistons, machine-tool castings, car wheels, dies
Low-carbon steel: 0.2C, 0.5Mn, 0.5Si, 0.05P, 0.05S, 99Fe		75,000–85,000	Locomotive frames, gear blanks, stamps, crusher jaws, pinions, car wheels, shovel teeth racks, chain, valves and fittings, and caterpillar treads
Medium-carbon steel: 0.20–0.50C		85,000–90,000	
High-carbon steel: over 0.5C, 0.5Mn, 0.5Si, 0.05P, 0.05S, 98Fe		100,000–125,000	
Chromium iron: 4–6Cr, 0.5Si, 0.5Mn, 90–91Fe, 1% each of Mo, W, Al, Cu if desired	170	60,000	In the oil-refining industry pipes, still bottoms, bolts, tie rods, furnace parts, dampers
Stainless steel: 12–15Cr, 0.35Mn, 0.2Si, 0.3–4C, 84–87Fe	500	240,000	Table knives, scissors, spatulas, cleavers, hatchets, pump shafts, pistons, and valve trim
Manganese steel: 1–1.4C, 11Mn, 0.3–1.0Si, 0.1P, 86Fe	180–220	80,000–110,000	Railway frogs, crossings, and switches; rock-crusher parts, steam-shovel dippers and teeth, chain, sprockets, gears and pinions
Aluminum	16	8,500	Cooking utensils, lightweight construction
Magnesium	30–40	13,000–25,000	Castings, rods, sheets
Duraluminum: 4Cu, 0.5Mg, 0.5Mn, 95Al	42	10,000	Sheets, nuts, bolts, rivets
Dow Metal: 10Al, 0.13Mn, 0.5Si, 89Mg	62	30,000	Typewriters, cameras, optical instruments, vacuum cleaners, goggles, conveyors

sten, cobalt, titanium, and zirconium are used to produce such alloy steels. In Table 85 a list of some of the more important ferroalloys is given, and their compositions, properties, and uses are summarized. For comparison, aluminum, magnesium, and some of their alloys are also listed.

406. COMPOUNDS OF IRON

Oxidation States

0	Metallic iron
+2, ferrous iron (II)	Fe^{2+}, FeO, $Fe(OH)_2$, $FeSO_4$, $FeCl_2$, $Fe(CN)_6^{4-}$, $K_4Fe(CN)_6$
+3, ferric iron (III)	Fe^{3+}, Fe_2O_3, $Fe(OH)_3$, $Fe_2(SO_4)_3$, $KFe(SO_4)_2 \cdot 12H_2O$, Fe_2Cl_6, $Fe(CN)_6^{3-}$, $K_3Fe(CN)_6$, FeO_2^-
+4	FeO_3^{2-}
+6, ferrate	FeO_4^{2-}, $BaFeO_4$

The oxidation state of **+2** is not stable against atmospheric oxidation, whereas the oxidation state of **+3** is stable in the air. Therefore, ferric compounds are more common than ferrous. (The terms *ferrous* and *ferric* are still very widely used and are quite unambiguous, so we will use them here.) The oxidation state of **+4** has been reported but seems to be very unstable. The **+6** state is obtained only under very basic conditions when a powerful oxidizing effect is used.

407. FERROUS COMPOUNDS

The *ferrous ion* results when iron reacts with acids or when ferric compounds are reduced.

$$Fe + 2H^+ = Fe^{2+} + H_2$$
$$Fe^{3+} + e^- = Fe^{2+}$$

The ferrous ion is colorless when anhydrous and light green when hydrated. It resembles the zinc ion rather closely, and ferrous salts show some close resemblances to zinc salts. The ferrous ion is oxidized to the ferric ion when exposed to air, but it is reasonably stable against hydrolysis.

Ferrous oxide, FeO, is a black solid and is oxidized by the air. *Ferrous hydroxide*, $Fe(OH)_2$, is formed as a greenish gelatinous hydrous precipitate when a ferrous solution is made basic. It acts as a base. When it is moist, it is rapidly oxidized by the air, with change in color to the orange-brown characteristic of ferric hydroxide.

Ferrous salts can be obtained by reacting iron with the appropriate acids and evaporating the solutions. *Ferrous sulfate*, $FeSO_4 \cdot 7H_2O$, is easily oxidized, but if it is mixed in solution with ammonium sulfate and crystallization is carried out, the complex *Mohr's salt*, $(NH_4)_2Fe(SO_4)_2 \cdot 6H_2O$, is obtained. This resists atmospheric oxidation quite well and is commonly used as a source of ferrous ions. Ferrous ion forms many other quite stable complexes, such as the ferrocyanide ion, $Fe(CN)_6^{4-}$.

This is typical of the ferro complex ions in which six groups are octahedrally coordinated to the central iron atom.

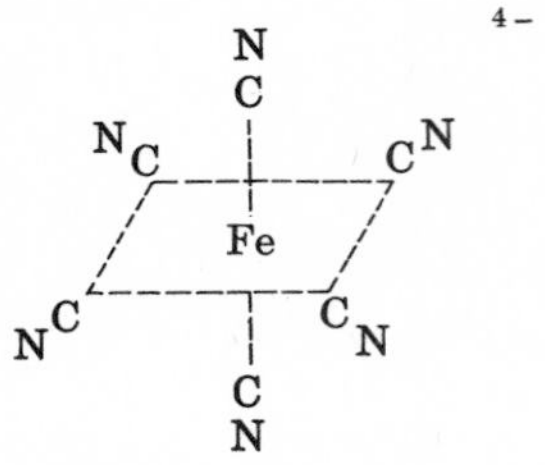

Fig. 127.   Configuration Fe (CN)$_6$$^{4-}$.

Ferrocyanide ion

Such complex ions are much more stable against atmospheric oxidation than is the ferrous ion.

408.   FERRIC COMPOUNDS

Ferric compounds can be prepared by oxidation of iron or ferrous compounds and by the action of acids on ferric oxide or hydroxide.   The *ferric ion*, although stable toward oxygen, has a strong tendency for hydration and hydrolysis.   The *hydrated ferric ion* is almost colorless, but aqueous ferric systems usually have an orange to red color, presumably due to $Fe(OH)_3$ or basic ferric complex ions formed by hydrolysis. *Ferric hydroxide*, $Fe(OH)_3$, is precipitated as a hydrous, reddish-brown, gelatinous material when the ferric ion hydrolyzes, and ferric ion can be precipitated quantitatively by the use of aqueous ammonia.

$$Fe^{3+} + 3NH_3 + 3H_2O = \underset{\text{ferric hydroxide}}{Fe(OH)_3} + 3NH_4^+$$

Hydrous ferric hydroxide is a good mordant.

When ferric hydroxide is ignited, dehydration occurs and ferric oxide is formed.

$$2Fe(OH)_3 = Fe_2O_3 + 3H_2O$$

Depending upon how the reaction is carried out and upon the state of subdivision of the oxide, its color varies from yellow through orange, to red, to dark brown.   It is used widely as a cheap pigment for paints, and as *rouge* it has been important in cosmetics.   The crystalline oxide is hard, refractory, and inert, and it resembles Al_2O_3 and Cr_2O_3 closely. It is often used as an abrasive, especially for polishing glass.   Ferric hydroxide dissolves to a very small extent in concentrated sodium hydroxide, and ferric oxide behaves like an acid anhydride at high temperatures.   When fused with basic oxides it forms *ferrites*.

$$CaO + Fe_2O_3 = \underset{\text{ferrite}}{Ca(FeO_2)_2}$$

The ferrite ion hydrolyzes strongly, and ferrites are not common.

When iron rusts, porous and partially hydrated ferric oxide is formed as a scale, which flakes away from the metal, exposing it to continued corrosion.

Fe_3O_4 has been shown to have iron present in both the ferric and the ferrous condition. Some of the iron atoms are in the oxidation state of **+3**, whereas others are in the **+2** state. This oxide may be formed as a dense, adherent, black coating on iron by exposing it to steam at high temperatures. The coating protects the underlying metal from corrosion. The name *magnetite*, used for the mineral consisting of this oxide, refers to its magnetic behavior.

Ferric sulfate and *ferric nitrate* are quite soluble in water but hydrolyze to give less soluble basic salts. Ferric sulfate forms *ferric alums*, which are more stable against hydrolysis than the sulfate.

When chlorine is passed over hot iron, dark-green crystals of Fe_2Cl_6 are formed. This product is molecular, resembling Al_2Cl_6 in structure. When ferric chloride is obtained by crystallization from aqueous solution, it forms the hexahydrate, $FeCl_3 \cdot 6H_2O$, in which the ferric iron is present in the hexahydrated complex.

Ferric complex ions are common, ferric iron having the coordination number of 6. Thus, ferric ions and cyanide ions associate to form the stable *ferricyanide ion*.

$$Fe^{3+} + 6CN^- = Fe(CN)_6{}^{3-}$$

This has exactly the same octahedral configuration as the ferrocyanide ion, but the iron is in the oxidation state of **+3**, and the complex has one less negative charge. Complex ferric ions are usually highly colored. The formation of intense red complexes when thiocyanate ions, SCN^-, combine with ferric ions provides a very sensitive test for ferric iron.

$$Fe^{3+} + SCN^- \rightleftharpoons Fe(SCN)^{2+}$$

Undoubtedly, the ferric complex ion is hydrated, probably to give the octahedral $[FeSCN(H_2O)_5]^{2+}$.

When hydrous ferric hydroxide jelly is made strongly basic and chlorine is added, brilliant purple *ferrate ions* are formed.

$$2Fe(OH)_3 + 10\,OH^- + 3Cl_2 = 2FeO_4{}^{2-} + 8H_2O + 6Cl^-$$
ferrate

These ions, analogues of manganate, chromate, and sulfate ions, are not stable in water, but if barium ions are added, $BaFeO_4$ is precipitated as a dark-red solid.

409. OXIDATION-REDUCTION OF IRON SYSTEMS

The equilibrium between the ferrous and ferric states is important in the use of iron systems.

$$Fe^{2+} \rightleftharpoons Fe^{3+} + e^-$$

Oxidizing agents, such as oxygen, chlorine, bromine, dichromates, and permanganates, oxidize ferrous compounds. Iron, iodide ion, hydrogen sulfide, and sulfite ion reduce ferric compounds. Such changes in oxidation states have frequently been exploited for practical purposes.

The use of *iron inks* involves changes in oxidation states of iron. Such inks are solutions of ferrous ions and tannic acid. Ferrous ions do not give any color with tannic acid, but ferric ions precipitate black ferric tannate. When iron ink is exposed to air, the ferrous ions are slowly oxidized to ferric ions, and the back ferric tannate forms on the paper fibers. The oxidation of the iron ink is *inhibited* in the bottle by the addition of a trace of sulfuric acid, and a dye is added to give the ink temporary color. When the ink is applied to paper, basic material in the paper neutralizes the acid, and the oxygen of the air then converts the ferrous ions to ferric ions, producing the insoluble black ferric tannate, which is permanent under ordinary conditions. Iron-ink stains can be removed by destroying the ferric tannate through the application of oxalic acid, which converts the iron to a soluble form. Oxalic acid can also be used to remove iron-rust stains from clothing.

The *iron blue pigments*, produced when ferric ions unite with ferrocyanide ions or when ferrous ions combine with ferricyanide ions, are very important. These have been called *Prussian blue* and *Turnbull's blue* and were formerly considered to be different substances. But recently they have been shown to be identical and to have the approximate composition $KFeFe(CN)_6$. This indicates considerable mobility of electrons in these pigments, presumably involving the equilibrium,

$$Fe^{2+} \; + \; Fe(CN)_6{}^{3-} \rightleftharpoons \; Fe^{3+} \; + \; Fe(CN)_6{}^{4-}$$

ferrous ion   ferricyanide ion   ferric ion   ferrocyanide ion

The blue pigment is quite stable under ordinary conditions and is a valuable colorant for paints and laundry blueing. Its formation is involved in the preparation of *blueprints*. In this procedure, paper is soaked in ferric ammonium citrate or oxalate and potassium ferricyanide solution and then is dried in a dark room. When exposed to the light, the ferricyanide ion is reduced to ferrocyanide ion by the citrate or oxalate where light strikes it. When the exposed paper is dipped into water, the ferric ions and the ferrocyanide ions associate to form the blue pigment on the paper. The unexposed soluble salts may be washed away, leaving the white color of the paper against the blue background. The complex iron cyanide ions are not stable toward bases. Ammonia bleaches blueprints, and a solution of sodium carbonate can be used to write on the blue background.

410. METALLURGY AND PROPERTIES OF COBALT AND NICKEL

These metals occur in sulfide and sulfarsenide ores associated with iron, copper, and silver. There are important deposits of these ores in

Canada.   Roasting and reduction methods are used to obtain the metals, which are difficult to purify.   Electrorefining methods are sometimes employed.   An unusual reaction has been used for purifying nickel by the Mond process.   Impure powdered nickel is heated to about 50°, and carbon monoxide is passed over it, the volatile *nickel tetracarbonyl* being formed.

$$Ni + 4CO \rightleftharpoons Ni(CO)_4$$
$$\text{b.p., 43°}$$

When nickel carbonyl is heated to 100° or above, the reaction reverses, and the compound is decomposed to pure nickel and carbon monoxide.

Physically, cobalt and nickel resemble iron closely.   But unlike iron, they are not corroded seriously by the atmosphere, nickel retaining its silvery luster indefinitely.   Nickel plating has been much used to protect steel, brass, and copper from corrosion.   Hydracids attack cobalt and nickel to give Co^{2+} and Ni^{2+} ions.   Nickel is inert toward aqueous and fused alkalies, and nickel crucibles and other nickel apparatus are frequently used in the laboratory.   Finely divided nickel is an excellent catalyst for the hydrogenation of hydrocarbons and oils.

Cobalt and nickel are used in many alloy systems, especially in steels and in magnetic alloys.   Cobalt is used to make *carboloy*, an extremely hard and tough material used for high-speed cutting tools.   Carboloy consists of tungsten carbide crystals cemented together with cobalt. Tools made of this material retain their strength and their cutting edges even when operated at red heat.   Nickel is important as a coinage metal. Alloyed with copper and iron, nickel forms the important *monel metal*, which has good resistance to atmospheric corrosion and is easily formed into all sorts of complicated shapes.   The alloy *alnico* containing aluminum, nickel, and cobalt, has excellent magnetic properties and is used for making very strong permanent magnets.

411. COMPOUNDS OF COBALT

Oxidation States	
0	Metallic cobalt
+2, cobalt (II) (cobaltous)	Co^{2+}, CoO, $Co(OH)_2$, $Co(NO_3)_2 \cdot 6H_2O$, $CoSO_4 \cdot 7H_2O$
+3, cobalt (III) (cobaltic)	Co^{3+}, Co_2O_3, $Co(OH)_3$, $[Co(NH_3)_6]^{3+}$, $Co(NH_3)_6Cl_3$
+4	CoO_2, CoO_3^{2-}

The *cobalt (II) ion* is stable under atmospheric conditions, and all the common simple compounds of cobalt involve the oxidation state of **+2.** Co^{2+} is blue when anhydrous and a light pink when hydrated.   It hydrolyzes only slightly and resembles manganous and zinc ions rather closely. This ion colors glass an intense blue.   *Cobalt hydroxide*, $Co(OH)_2$, is formed as a rose-colored precipitate when a cobaltous solution is made alkaline.   It is a basic hydroxide and forms CoO when heated.   *Cobalt (II) salts*, obtained by crystallization from aqueous solution, are hydrated and resemble nickel, manganese (II), and zinc salts.

The simple Co^{3+} *ion* is not stable, but the oxidation state of **+3** can be stabilized by formation of complex cobaltic compounds.   Such cobalt (III) complexes are readily obtained by the oxidation of cobaltous ions in the presence of coordinating groups.   The oxidizing effect of the air may be sufficient in such cases.   The formation of complex *ammino cobalt (III) chlorides* can thus be accomplished by blowing air through a cobalt (II) solution to which ammonia has been added.   By varying the method of preparation, a whole series of compounds can be obtained.

$[Co(NH_3)_6]Cl_3$ yellow
hexammino cobalt (III) trichloride

$[Co(NH_3)_5Cl]Cl_2$ purple
chloropentammino cobalt (III) dichloride

$[Co(NH_3)_4Cl_2]Cl$ green
dichlorotetrammino cobalt (III) chloride

$[Co(NH_3)_3Cl_3]$ blue-green
trichlorotriammino cobalt (III)

These are typical of a vast number of complex substances in which cobalt (III) is coordinated to six groups to form an octahedral complex, which may or may not be a charged ion, depending upon what groups are present.   Such complexes are always brilliantly colored and resemble the chromium (III) and iron (III) complex compounds, which we have already discussed.   Cobalt (III) complexes are much more stable than cobalt (II) complexes.

412.   COMPOUNDS OF NICKEL

Oxidation States	
0	Metallic nickel
+2, nickel (II)	Ni^{2+}, NiO, $Ni(OH)_2$, $NiSO_4 \cdot 7H_2O$, $Ni(CN)_4^{2-}$
+3, nickel (III)	Ni_2O_3
+4	NiO_2

Practically all the compounds of nickel have this element present in the oxidation state of **+2**. Ni^{2+} is green when hydrated and is formed by the action of acids on nickel.   *Nickel hydroxide*, $Ni(OH)_2$, forms as a gelatinous green precipitate when a solution of nickel ions is made basic. Nickel salts are usually highly hydrated and rather deliquescent.   Nickel forms the complex $Ni(CN)_4^{2-}$, which is unusual in that the four cyanide groups are not in tetrahedral positions but are at the corners of a square and are coplanar with the central nickel atom.

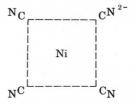

Tetracyano nickel (II) ion
square coplanar

Fig. 128. Configuration of Ni(CN)₄²⁻.

With water and ammonia molecules, the nickel ion forms octahedral complexes, such as $Ni(NH_3)_6{}^{2+}$.

Nickel dioxide, NiO_2, formed by vigorous oxidation under alkaline conditions, is an essential part of the Edison storage battery. This battery has electrodes of iron and nickel dioxide and uses a solution of sodium hydroxide.

413. THE PLATINUM METALS

These six metals are at the bottom of the electrochemical series of the metals and are very inert. Because of the low activity they, along with the neighboring element gold, are sometimes called the *noble metals*. They have high melting points, are malleable and ductile, and are good electrical conductors. They occur free in nature in alluvial sands and are usually alloyed together and associated with copper, silver, and gold. When the platinum metals do form compounds, these are easily reduced and decompose readily when heated to give the metals. The platinum-group metals are rare and expensive, and their use is limited. Platinum is most abundant of the six and is the most important. We will discuss it as typical of the group, and will be particularly concerned with the metal, rather than with its compounds.

414. PLATINUM

The principal sources of platinum are alluvial sands in Russia, South America, and South Africa. Some is produced as a by-product of the refining of copper and nickel. The separation of platinum from the other metals alloyed with it is a laborious and costly process.

Platinum is a beautiful, silvery metal that is quite soft and ductile. It is almost twice as heavy as lead, and it sinks in mercury. Unlike most soft metals, it has a relatively high melting point, and it is a good thermal and electrical conductor.

Platinum is very inert chemically. It is not attacked by oxygen or moisture, even at high temperatures. None of the simple acids corrodes it, not even hydrofluoric or nitric acids.   Aqua regia, a mixture of one part concentrated nitric acid and three parts hydrochloric acid, reacts with it rapidly, forming chloroplatinate ions, $PtCl_6^{2-}$.   Fused alkalies corrode platinum forming platinates, owing to the oxidizing effect of the

Table 86.   The Platinum Metals

Light Platinum Metals	Ruthenium	Rhodium	Palladium
Symbol	Ru	Rh	Pd
Atomic number	44	45	46
Electronic structure	2, 8, 18, 15, 1	2, 8, 18, 16, 1	2, 8, 18, 17, 1
Oxidation states	*0, 2, 3, 4, 6, 7, 8*	*0, 2, 3, 4, 6*	*0, 2, 3, 4, 6*
Abundance	Rare	Rare	Rare
First ionization potential, volts	7.5	7.7	8.3
Oxidation potential, M/M^{2+}, volts	−0.45	about −0.6	−0.98
Melting point, ° C	2450	1966	1555
Boiling point, ° C	4900	4500	3980
Density, g/cc, 20°	12.2	12.44	12.0

Heavy Platinum Metals	Osmium	Iridium	Platinum
Symbol	Os	Ir	Pt
Atomic number	76	77	78
Electronic structure	2, 8, 18, 32, 14, 2	2, 8, 18, 32, 15, 2	2, 8, 18, 32, 16, 2
Oxidation states	*0, 2, 3, 4, 6, 8*	*0, 2, 3, 4, 6*	*0, 2, 3, 4, 6*
Abundance	Rare	Rare	$1 \times 10^{-7}\%$
First ionization potential, volts	8.7	9.2	8.9
Oxidation potential, M/M^{2+}, volts	−0.7	< −1.0	about −1.2
Melting point, ° C	2700	2410	1773
Boiling point, ° C	5490	4900	4380
Density, g/cc, 20°	22.5	22.4	21.45

air.   This corrosion is especially pronounced in the presence of oxidizing agents, such as nitrates.   Sulfides, phosphorus, and carbon attack platinum at elevated temperatures.

Platinum alloys with many metals, such as lead, copper, and silver, which are readily formed by reduction.   Platinum is therefore attacked when it is heated with compounds of such metals under reducing conditions.   Because hydrogen diffuses readily through hot sheet platinum, it is not safe to heat with a gas flame any easily reducible metal oxide in a platinum crucible.

In spite of its high cost, platinum is used extensively because of its unique combination of properties.   Unfortunately for the scientist, the bulk of the platinum produced goes into the *fabrication of jewelry*, because of its beauty, ease of working, inert nontarnishing character, and expensiveness.   This large use keeps the price up and reduces the availability of the metal for scientific purposes.   Because of its inertness and workability, platinum is used in *dentistry*.   The metal is employed frequently in the construction of *electrical apparatus*, where its good conductivity, high melting point, inertness at elevated temperatures, and the fact that it can be sealed through soft glass are utilized.   *Chemical apparatus* made of platinum, such as crucibles, ignition dishes, stills, and vessels for handling hydrofluoric acid, is very useful.

Platinum adsorbs many gases strongly, especially hydrogen.   The metal accordingly has a remarkable *catalytic effect* on a large number of reactions between gases, notably in the synthesis of ammonia and in the oxidation of sulfur dioxide to sulfur trioxide.   Finely divided platinum with a maximum amount of surface per unit mass is most efficient. Catalytic preparations, such as platinum black, platinized asbestos, and platinized silica gel, are effective and can be made by electrolysis or by the thermal decomposition of compounds of platinum such as H_2PtCl_6 of $(NH_4)_2PtCl_6$.   Platinum catalysts are *poisoned* if arsenic or certain other substances come in contact with them; their catalytic activity diminishes.

415. COMPOUNDS OF PLATINUM

Only the compounds of platinum in the oxidation states of $+2$ and $+4$ are important.

Oxidation States	
0	Metallic platinum
$+2$, platinum (II) (platinous)	Pt^{2+}, PtO, $PtCl_2$, $PtCl_4{}^{2-}$, K_2PtCl_4
$+4$, platinum (IV) (platinic)	$PtCl_4$, $PtCl_6{}^{2-}$, H_2PtCl_6, K_2PtCl_6

All the compounds of platinum decompose when heated strongly.   Complex compounds are more characteristic than simple compounds.

The compounds having platinum in the oxidation state of $+4$ are most common.   *Chloroplatinic acid*, H_2PtCl_6, is obtained as orange crystals when the solution formed by the action of aqua regia on platinum is evaporated.   Platinum (IV) has a coordination number of 6 in its complex ions, which have octahedral configurations. K_2PtCl_6 and $(NH_4)_2PtCl_6$ are only very slightly soluble in water, and chloroplatinic acid may therefore be used in testing for $NH_4{}^+$ and K^+ and for the separation of Na^+ from K^+.

When chloroplatinic acid is heated mildly, it decomposes to give crystals of platinum tetrachloride.

$$H_2PtCl_6 \overset{\text{heated}}{=} 2HCl + PtCl_4$$

chloroplatinic
acid

platinum
tetrachloride

If the temperature is raised, further decomposition occurs with the liberation of chlorine and the reduction of platinum to the **+2** state.

$$PtCl_4 \overset{\text{heated}}{=} Cl_2 + PtCl_2$$

platinum
dichloride

And at still higher temperatures the platinum dichloride decomposes to yield the metal.

$$PtCl_2 \overset{\text{heated}}{=} Cl_2 + Pt$$

$PtCl_2$ dissolves in hydrochloric acid forming the *chloroplatinite ion*.

$$PtCl_2 + 2Cl^- = PtCl_4{}^{2-}$$

This ion, which is typical of the complex ions formed by divalent platinum, has a square planar configuration like the $Ni(CN)_4{}^{2-}$ ion. Such square planar complex ions seem to be restricted to auric gold and to nickel, palladium, platinum, and copper when they are in the oxidation state of **+2**.

EXERCISES

1. a) Describe the relation of the Group VIII triads to the other transition metals.

  b) What subdivisions of Group VIII can reasonably be made on the basis of atomic structures?

  c) Compare the chemical and physical properties of the elements in these subdivisions.

2. Correlate the variation in oxidation states known for the elements of Group VIII with the variations in atomic structure.

3. Discuss the occurrence and metallurgy of iron. What is meant by the term *alloy steels?*

4. What unique property is possessed by the metals of the iron triad that makes them indispensable in modern civilization? Explain.

5. a) List the oxidation states of the elements of the iron triad, and give one example of an ion or molecule for each element in each state.

  b) Which are the common oxidation states?

6. Describe the spatial configuration of one complex ion representative of:
a) ferrous iron; b) ferric iron; c) cobalt (III); d) divalent nickel.

7. Write balanced equations for: a) the blast-furnace process; b) the precipitation of ferric hydroxide; c) the formation of nickel carbonyl; d) the reaction of ferric ion with thiocyanate ion; e) the oxidation of ferrous ion by bromine; f) the reduction of ferric ion by sulfite ion.

8. How are compounds of iron involved in the preparation of blueprints?

9. Describe the properties of platinum that account for its desirability for the manufacture of jewelry and laboratory apparatus.

10. a) Why is platinum of interest in the Haber process and in the manufacture of nitric acid?

b) Write equations for the thermal decomposition of chloroplatinic acid.

c) Describe the spatial configuration of $PtCl_6^{2-}$ and of $PtCl_4^{2-}$.

Chapter 33

▶ Transition Metals, III

Group IB

Copper, Silver, Gold

416. THE IB METALS

Each of the three elements of this subgroup is at the end of a transition sequence. Although each has its second outermost electronic shell

Table 87. The IB Metals

	Copper	Silver	Gold
Symbol	Cu	Ag	Au
Atomic number	29	47	79
Electronic structure	2, 8, 18, 1	2, 8, 18, 18, 1	2, 8, 18, 32, 18, 1
Oxidation states	*0, +1, +2, +3*	*0, +1, +2, +3*	*0, +1, +2, +3*
Abundance	0.01%	$1 \times 10^{-6}\%$	$1 \times 10^{-7}\%$
Minerals	Native copper; Cu_2S, chalcocite; $CuFeS_2$, chalcopyrite; Cu_2O, cuprite; $Cu_2(OH)_2CO_3$ malachite; $Cu_3(OH)_2(CO_3)_2$, azurite	Native silver; Ag_2S, argentite; AgCl, horn silver	Native gold; $AuTe_2$
Crystal Radius, M^+, Å	0.96	1.26	1.37
First ionization potential, volts	7.68	7.54	9.2
Oxidation potential, M/M^+, volts	−0.522	−0.7995	About −1.68
Melting point, ° C	1083	960.5	1063
Boiling point, ° C	2595	2001	2966
Density, g/cc, 20°	8.94	10.5	19.3

built up to eighteen electrons, each is still able to use some of these electrons for bonding purposes, as well as the one electron in the outermost shell. They therefore definitely fall within our definition of transition

514

metals. However, although they show variable valence in the manner of transition metals, only a few low oxidation states are stable.

The IB elements, when they are in the oxidation state of **+1,** show some superficial resemblance to the alkali metals. However, the univalent cations of copper, silver, and gold are much smaller, their ionization potentials much higher, and their oxidation potentials very much lower than those of potassium, rubidium, and cesium. While the alkali metals are among the most active metals, the IB elements are among the least active; this low activity accounts for their occurrence as the free metals in nature and for the ease of reduction of their compounds. The change of relative stability of the different oxidation states for the IB elements is interesting. The common oxidation states found in the compounds of copper, silver, and gold are **+2, +1,** and **+3,** respectively. Notice that, whereas the cations of Period V and VI in the preceding transition subgroups are almost of the same size, Au^+ is considerably larger than Ag^+. As a consequence, the difference in behavior of silver and gold is much greater than that found in zirconium and hafnium, niobium and tantalum, molybdenum and tungsten, or palladium and platinum. Copper, silver, and gold are very malleable and ductile and are excellent conductors.

417. METALLURGY OF COPPER

The low-grade sulfide ores, which are generally used as industrial sources of copper, are usually concentrated by flotation, as described in Section 357. The concentrate is treated to a rather complicated roasting process, using a modified Bessemer-converter operation. The over-all reaction may be considered to be

$$Cu_2S + O_2 = 2Cu + SO_2$$

The large amount of sulfur dioxide produced may be converted to sulfuric acid. The impure copper obtained must be refined to a high state of purity if it is to be suitable for use as an electrical conductor. The presence of only 0.03 per cent of arsenic reduces the electrical conductivity of copper 14 per cent.

Electrolytic refining methods are used very effectively for purifying copper. The crude copper plates are made anodes in a bath containing copper sulfate, and sheets of pure copper are made the cathodes. At the anode, copper and the metals more active than copper, such as zinc or lead, are oxidized and their cations enter the solution.

$$Cu = 2e^- + Cu^{2+}$$

The metals lower in activity, such as silver, platinum, and gold, are not oxidized but settle to the bottom of the cell as a sludge, which is collected in bags. Silver, the platinum-group metals, and the gold are recovered from this sludge as valuable by-products. The cations migrate to the cathode where the cupric ions are reduced to metallic copper, which plates out on the cathode. The cations of the more active metals remain in solution. In electroplating with copper, cyanide solutions are often used,

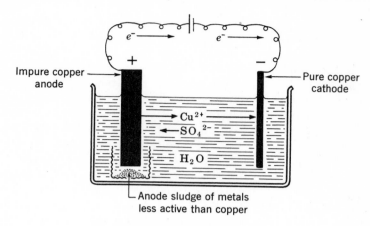

Impure copper anode — Pure copper cathode

Cu^{2+}
$SO_4{}^{2-}$
H_2O

Anode sludge of metals less active than copper

Fig. 129. Electrorefining of copper.

the copper being present in the complex $Cu(CN)_4{}^{2-}$ ions. The deposits of copper from such a solution are bright, smooth, and adherent.

418. PROPERTIES AND USES OF COPPER

Copper is unique among the metals in that its color is reddish brown. It is soft, malleable, and ductile, so that it is easily fashioned into wire, tubing, and sheets, and it is frequently cast into complicated shapes. Copper becomes harder when it is worked, but it may be softened by *annealing* (heating). The excellent electrical conduction of copper puts this metal in first place for use in electric cables, wiring, and other parts of electrical circuits. Copper is below hydrogen in the electrochemical series and is not corroded appreciably by the hydracids. Hot nitric acid and hot concentrated sulfuric acid attack it vigorously. Copper is a poor reducing agent, and cupric ions are rather good oxidizing agents. The metal is slowly attacked by moisture containing carbon dioxide, and a beautuiful green coating of $Cu_2(OH)_2CO_3$ is formed which protects the underlying metal from further corrosion.

$$2Cu + O_2 + CO_2 + H_2O = Cu_2(OH)_2CO_3$$

Because of this protection, copper is widely used for roofing and gutters and as pipes in water systems. Its inertness, coupled with its high thermal conductivity, has long made it a favorite metal for the construction of cooking utensils. Copper alloys readily with many other metals, and a large number of these alloys are important for special uses.

Table 88. Alloys of Copper, Silver, and Gold

Name and Per Cent Composition	Properties	Uses
Cartridge brass: 70Cu, 30Zn	Unusual ductility and malleability, excellent corrosion resistance, good strength	Cartridges, musical instruments, eyelets, tubes, drawing instruments
Red brass: 85Cu, 15Zn	Excellent resistance to corrosion	Hardware, radiator cores, plumbing pipe, condenser tubes, flexible hose
Aluminum bronze: 84–93Cu, 7–10Al, 4Fe(max)	Excellent resistance to corrosion, and strength and ductility of medium-carbon steel	Rods, bars, forgings, valve stems, air pumps, condenser and propeller-blade bolts, diaphragms and gears
Constantan: 55Cu, 45Ni	High electrical resistivity, low temperature coefficient of resistance, and high thermal emf against Pt	Electrical resistors and thermocouples
80–10–10: 80Cu, 10Zn, 10Pb	Low frictional quality	Bearing metal
Nickel silver: 64Cu, 18Ni, 18Zn	Resistance to corrosion	Plating silverware; hardware, ornaments, springs, resistance wire, chemical equipment
Sterling silver: 92.5Ag, 7.5Cu	Resistance to corrosion, easily worked	Sterling silver tableware, bowls, jewelery
U.S. coinage silver: 90Ag, 10Cu	Resistance to corrosion and abrasion	U.S. silver coins
Cooper's metal: 50Pt, 38Ag, 12Cu	Hard, good resistance to corrosion	Pen points
Gold solder: 55Ag, 28Cu, 12Au, 5.5Zn	Low melting point	Jewelry
White gold: 75Au, 3.5Cu, 16.5Ni, 5Zn	Resistance to corrosion, easy shaping	Optical frames, watch cases, pens and pencils, jewelry
14-carat dental gold: 50Au, 33Ag, 17Cu	Resistance to corrosion, easy working to shape	Dental braces and fillings

419. COMPOUNDS OF COPPER

Oxidation States	
0	Metallic copper
+1, copper (I) cuprous	Cu^+, Cu_2O, $CuCl$, $CuCl_2^-$, $Cu(CN)_2^-$, Cu_2SO_4
+2, copper (II) cupric	Cu^{2+}, CuO, $Cu(OH)_2$, $CuCl_2$, $CuSO_4$, CuS, $Cu(NH_3)_4^{2+}$, $Cu(CN)_4^{2-}$
+3	CuO_2^-

In most of its common compounds, copper is in the *oxidation state of* **+2.** *Cupric oxide*, CuO, is formed as a black solid when copper is heated in oxygen or air. This reaction can be used to remove traces of oxygen from other gases, such as nitrogen.

$$2Cu + O_2 \overset{300°}{=} 2CuO$$

Cupric oxide is a good oxidizing agent when it is heated, oxidizing hydrogen to water.

$$CuO + H_2 = Cu + H_2O$$

It is used in quantitative analysis to oxidize organic compounds to water and carbon dioxide. Cupric oxide does not combine with water to form the hydroxide.

The *cupric ion*, Cu^{2+}, is obtained when CuO is dissolved in an acid or when copper is treated with an oxidizing acid.

$$CuO + 2H^+ = Cu^{2+} + H_2O$$
$$Cu + 2H_2SO_4 = Cu^{2+} + SO_2 + 2H_2O + SO_4^{2-}$$

The tetrahydrated cupric ion is blue, whereas the anhydrous ion is colorless. The hydrated cupric ion is believed to have a square coplanar configuration, (Section 182). This hydrated ion hydrolyzes considerably to give an acidic solution. We may write the equation to show probable hydration, or we may neglect the water of hydration.

$$Cu(H_2O)_4^{2+} + H_2O = Cu(H_2O)_3(OH)^+ + H_3O^+$$
$$Cu^{2+} + H_2O = Cu(OH)^+ + H^+$$

Such basic cupric cations form insoluble basic salts, for example, $Cu_2(OH)_2CO_3$.

When hydroxide ion is added to a cupric solution, a hydrous, light-blue, gelatinous precipitate of *cupric hydroxide*, $Cu(OH)_2$, is formed. This hydroxide acts as a weak base and dissolves in acids. It also dissolves slightly in very concentrated sodium hydroxide, presumably forming the cuprite ion, CuO_2^{2-}. Cupric hydroxide is not very stable, and when it is heated mildly, it dehydrates to give black cupric oxide.

$$Cu(OH)_2 = CuO + H_2O$$

Cupric hydroxide dissolves in ammonium hydroxide, forming the complex *tetrammine cupric ion*, which has a deep-blue color.

$$Cu(OH)_{2(s)} + 4NH_3 = Cu(NH_3)_4{}^{2+} + 2OH^-$$

The cupric halides, nitrate, and sulfate are quite soluble. Cupric sulfate is probably the most important compound of copper. When the blue pentahydrate, $CuSO_4 \cdot 5H_2O$, is heated, the water of hydration is driven off. The anhydrous salt that forms is a good dehydrating agent, and it shows when it takes up water by turning blue. Cupric ions are toxic to fungi, and copper sulfate is frequently used as a fungicide in water reservoirs. Other copper preparations are often used to spray or dust plants to protect them from lower organisms and insects. *Cupric sulfide* is very low in solubility, even in highly acid solution.

The *oxidation state of +1* is not very stable, and *cuprous ions* undergo auto-oxidation-reduction in aqueous solution.

$$2Cu^+ = Cu + Cu^{2+}$$

The cuprous condition is stable only when the compound is insoluble or when the copper is tied up in a complex ion. *Cuprous oxide*, Cu_2O, is precipitated when a cupric solution is made alkaline and a reducing agent is added. This reaction is used to detect reducing sugars.

Cuprous chloride, CuCl, can be made by reduction of cupric chloride by heating it with copper in concentrated hydrochloric acid. The blue color disappears as the reduction proceeds, and the complex dichloro-cuprous ion is formed.

$$Cu^{2+} + Cu + 4Cl^- = 2CuCl_2{}^-$$

When the solution is diluted, the complex ion dissociates and a colorless precipitate of the insoluble CuCl is formed.

$$CuCl_2{}^- \rightleftharpoons CuCl_{(s)} + Cl^-$$

Cuprous chloride dissolves in concentrated hydrochloric acid, since the reaction is reversible. This solution is used in analytical chemistry for absorbing carbon monoxide by the formation of Cu(CO)Cl. Cuprous chloride is also soluble in ammonium hydroxide and in cyanide solutions, owing to the formation of stable complex ions.

$$CuCl_{(s)} + 2CN^- = Cu(CN)_2{}^- + Cl^-$$

420. METALLURGY OF SILVER

Amalgamation can be used to produce silver from ores in which metallic silver or silver chloride is present. The powdered ore is treated with mercury, which extracts the silver, forming *silver amalgam*. When this is heated, the mercury evaporates, and the nonvolatile silver is obtained as a residue.

In the *cyanide process*, the ore containing native silver is treated with a solution of sodium cyanide while air is bubbled through the solution. The complex silver cyanide ion is formed, taking the silver into solution.

$$4Ag + 8CN^- + O_2 + 2H_2O = 4Ag(CN)_2^- + 4OH^-$$

The silver is then precipitated by the addition of zinc, or it may be electrodeposited.

$$2Ag(CN)_2^- + Zn = Zn(CN)_4^{2-} + 2Ag$$

Considerable quantities of silver are also obtained as a by-product of the refining of copper and lead. In the winning of lead from its ores, the silver which accompanies lead in the ore is reduced to the metal along with the lead, and is in solution in the molten lead. Zinc is added and melts to form a second liquid layer, which floats on the molten lead but does not dissolve in it. The silver is more soluble in the molten zinc than it is in molten lead and accumulates in the zinc layer. This layer is then skimmed off, and the silver can easily be separated from the zinc by distillation. This separation is known as the *Parke's process* and is a special case of liquid-liquid extraction.

421. PROPERTIES AND USES OF SILVER

The beautiful color and luster of silver have made it a favorite metal for jewelry and tableware. It is soft and malleable, so that it is easily worked into intricate shapes. It also is frequently plated on stronger but less attractive base metals by electrolysis, often from cyanide solutions. Silver is less active than copper and is not corroded by atmospheric attack, but it is, however, rapidly tarnished by sulfur compounds. Nitric and sulfuric acids corrode silver, but it is more resistant to other acids than is copper. Silver is very inert toward bases, even when they are in the molten condition, so that silver crucibles are sometimes used in the laboratory.

Silver has been much used for making *mirrors* because the metal reflects light very satisfactorily. To produce a mirror, the glass surface is first carefully cleaned to remove all grease films. The glass then is brought in contact with a solution made by treating a silver nitrate solution with enough excess ammonia just to dissolve the precipitate that first forms. To this an organic reducing agent, such as glucose, is added. Metallic silver is produced and deposits on the glass as a thin shiny film. The ammoniacal silvering solution should not be allowed to stand around because an explosive solid may form. Table 88 lists some typical alloys of silver.

422. COMPOUNDS OF SILVER

Oxidation States

0	Metallic silver
+1, silver (I)	Ag^+, Ag_2O, $AgNO_3$, Ag_2SO_4, AgF, $AgCl$, $Ag(NH_3)_2^+$, $Ag(CN)_2^-$
+2, silver (II)	AgO, Ag^{2+}
+3, silver (III)	Ag_2O_3

The oxidation state of **+1** is the only one of importance for the compounds of silver. The Ag^+ ion is obtained by the action of nitric or hot concentrated sulfuric acid on the metal.

$$Ag + 2H^+ + NO_3^- = Ag^+ + H_2O + NO_2$$

The silver ion is colorless and has little tendency for hydration or hydrolysis. The salts of silver usually crystallize from solution as anhydrous materials. Ag^+ is a good oxidizing agent, and even weak reducing agents reduce the ion to metallic silver. The silver ion and the colloidal metal are highly toxic and are excellent antiseptics. Many stable complex ions, in which silver shows a coordination number of 2, are known.

When a solution of silver ions is made basic, a brownish black precipitate of *Ag₂O* is formed, the hydroxide being very unstable.

$$2Ag^+ + 2OH^- = Ag_2O_{(s)} + H_2O$$

This oxide is easily decomposed by heating to give metallic silver. It dissolves in ammonium hydroxide because of the formation of the rather stable complex ammoniated ion.

$$Ag_2O_{(s)} + 4NH_3 + H_2O = 2Ag(NH_3)_2^+ + 2OH^-$$

Silver nitrate, $AgNO_3$, is the most soluble and common silver salt. It crystallizes from solution as a colorless substance, but it is a very powerful oxidizing agent and is reduced by dust and organic material, rapidly turning black. A solution of silver nitrate stains the skin black and can be used for marking laundry indelibly. It is useful in medicine as a very powerful antiseptic. *Silver sulfate*, Ag_2SO_4, is the only other common compound of silver on the market.

The *silver halides* are important compounds. Silver fluoride, *AgF*, is colorless and is so soluble in water that it is very difficult to prepare the pure anhydrous salt. *AgCl*, *AgBr*, and *AgI* are only very slightly soluble, silver ions being used frequently to precipitate chloride ions from solution in analytical work. AgCl dissolves in aqueous ammonia, and AgBr is sparingly soluble, but AgI is not appreciably soluble in this reagent.

$$AgCl_{(s)} + 2NH_3 = Ag(NH_3)_2^+ + Cl^-$$

The silver halides are light-sensitive and turn dark when exposed to light, owing to the formation of silver.

Silver chloride and bromide are very important in *photography*. Photographic plates or films are made by coating glass or plastic films with a gelatin emulsion containing crystals of silver chloride or bromide. When the plate or film is exposed to light, a *latent image* is formed, the

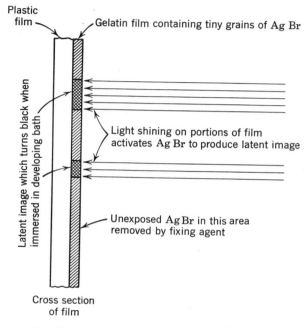

Plastic film

Gelatin film containing tiny grains of Ag Br

Latent image which turns black when immersed in developing bath

Light shining on portions of film activates Ag Br to produce latent image

Unexposed Ag Br in this area removed by fixing agent

Cross section of film

Fig. 130.   Formation of a photographic negative.

silver halide crystals absorbing energy, which is believed to activate the system and to produce an incipient reduction of the silver. The exposed plate or film is *developed* by immersing it in a solution of a mild reducing agent. This reduces to metallic silver the silver halide, which has been exposed to light, but does not rapidly affect the unexposed material. A solution of a *fixing agent* is then used to wash out the unchanged silver halide, so that it will not darken when exposed to the light for extended periods. The common fixing agent is sodium thiosulfate, $Na_2S_2O_3$. This provides thiosulfate ions, which form a soluble complex ion with the silver.

$$AgCl_{(s)} + 2S_2O_3{}^{2-} = Ag(S_2O_3)_2{}^{3-} + Cl^-$$

The finely divided silver is black, and a *negative* is produced. A *positive print* is formed by placing the negative over paper coated with more of the silver halide gelatin mixture, shining light through it, and then devel-

oping and fixing the print.   By adding sensitizers and other substances
to the photographic emulsion, various grades of films may be obtained.

Silver sulfide, Ag_2S, is very low in solubility and precipitates as a black
solid, even from high acidic solutions.

423.   METALLURGY OF GOLD

Gold occurs in the elementary state embedded in siliceous minerals.
Weathering breaks up the mineral and the gold nuggets and flakes
accumulate along with the sand and gravel in alluvial deposits.   Gold-
bearing minerals are mined and crushed, and the gold is taken into
solution as the $Au(CN)_2^-$ ion by using the cyanide procedure already
described for silver.   The aurocyanide solution is either electrolyzed or
treated with zinc to obtain metallic gold.

$$4Au + 8CN^- + 2H_2O + O_2 = 4Au(CN)_2^- + 4OH^-$$
$$2Au(CN)_2^- + Zn = Zn(CN)_4^{2-} + 2Au$$

Gold may also be removed from the crushed ore by *amalgamation*, in
which mercury dissolves the gold on contact to form gold amalgam.   The
mercury can be distilled from this amalgam, leaving a residue of gold.

The gold-bearing sands and gravels are worked by simple flotation
methods.   In *gold panning*, where the mixture is agitated with water,
the gold (density, 19.3) settles rapidly, whereas the siliceous gangue
(density, 2.6) stays suspended in the water and is washed away.   In
placer mining and *gold dredging*, the mixture of sand, gravel, and gold is
carried by water down inclined riffle boards that are provided with
transverse slats.   The heavy gold particles collect above the slats, and
the gangue is washed along.   By placing mercury above the slats, the
operation can be made more effective, and the cyanide process may also
be combined to increase the yield.

The native gold usually is alloyed with silver and the platinum metals
and must be refined by electrolytic or solution methods.

424.   PROPERTIES AND USES OF GOLD

The unique and attractive yellow color and luster of gold and its
indestructibility have always led man to treasure it.   The pure metal is
soft, malleable, and ductile.   It can be drawn into extremely fine wire,
and goldbeaters hammer the metal into very thin *gold leaf* by pounding
gold foil between sheets of parchment.   The purity of gold is rated in
carats, 24-carat gold being the pure metal and 18-carat gold being an
alloy containing 18 parts of gold per 24 parts by weight of the alloy.
By alloying gold with other metals, such as copper, it may be hardened
so that it holds its shape and resists abrasion better when used in jewelry,

coins, or false teeth. Some of the important gold alloys are listed in Table 88.

Gold is a very inert metal, being comparable to its near neighbor platinum in this respect. It is indifferent to atmospheric attack and toward all simple acids. Elementary chlorine and bromine corrode it, and aqua regia dissolves it readily.

$$Au + 4H^- + 4Cl^- + NO_3^- = AuCl_4^- + NO + 2H_2O$$

Gold, like the other inactive metals, such as platinum, silver, and copper, may be easily obtained in colloidal suspension by reduction of its compounds under suitable conditions. A dilute solution of $AuCl_4^-$ may be reduced by such agents as sulfites or hydrazine to build up gold particles so small that they tend to stay in suspension indefinitely as a *gold sol.*

$$4AuCl_4^- + 3N_2H_4 = 4Au + 3N_2 + 16Cl^- + 12H^+$$

Such gold sols vary in color from blue to red, depending upon the range of particle size. Glass may be colored red very effectively by the introduction of very small amounts of gold.

425. COMPOUNDS OF GOLD

Oxidation States	
0	Metallic gold
+1, gold (I) aurous	Au^+, Au_2O, $AuCl$, $Au(CN)_2^-$, $AuCl_2^-$
+2	AuS
+3, gold (III) auric	Au_2O_3, $Au(OH)_3$, $AuCl_4^-$, $HAuCl_4 \cdot 4H_2O$ $Au(CN)_4^-$

The analogy between platinum and gold holds for their compounds as well as for the elements. None of the compounds of gold are very stable thermally, all of them decomposing when heated vigorously to give the metal. The **+3** oxidation state is more stable toward water than the **+1** state, the situation being comparable to that for the **+2** and **+1** conditions for copper. Au^+ ions have a strong tendency to undergo auto-oxidation-reduction in water to give metallic and **+3** gold, the latter being stabilized by being tied up in a complex.

$$3Au^+ = \underset{\text{in complex}}{Au^{3+}} + 2Au$$

The *aurocyanide ion,* $Au(CN)_2^-$, is stable in aqueous solution.

In the oxidation state of **+3**, gold is usually found in complex ions in which gold has a coordination number of 4, and the most common compounds of gold contain such complexes. When a solution of gold in aqua regia is evaporated, orange crystals of *chlorauric acid* are formed, $HAuCl_4 \cdot 4H_2O$. Colored crystalline *chloraurates*, such as $NaAuCl_4 \cdot 2H_2O$, can easily be obtained. $AuCl_4^-$ has a square coplanar configuration. When $HAuCl_4$ is heated mildly, *auric chloride* is formed.

$$HAuCl_4 = HCl + AuCl_{3(s)}$$

chlorauric   auric
acid   chloride

At higher temperatures auric chloride decomposes to give *aurous chloride*.

$$AuCl_3 = Cl_2 + AuCl$$

aurous
chloride

Finally with vigorous heating, the aurous chloride dissociates into the elements.

$$2AuCl = Cl_2 + 2Au$$

Notice how similar these changes are to the progressive thermal decomposition of chloroplatinic acid.

EXERCISES

1. a) How do the electronic structures of the IB metals justify their classification as transition metals?

   b) In what respects do they show the characteristic behavior of transition metals?

2. Outline the operations used in manufacturing very pure copper from a low-grade sulfide ore.

3. a) Describe the cyanide process for the recovery of silver from its ores, indicating the changes in oxidation states that take place.

   b) How is silver obtained by the Parke's process?

4. What properties do some of the alloys of the IB metals have that make them very useful?

5. Give a balanced equation that describes the: a) formation of cupric ions from copper; b) reaction of a solution of cupric ions with a solution of sodium hydroxide; c) reaction of the product with an aqueous solution of ammonia; d) reaction of solid cuprous chloride in a solution of cyanide ions.

6. Discuss the chemistry involved in the photographic process.

7. a) How can gold be converted to the chloraurate ion?

   b) What is the spatial configuration of this ion?

   c) Write equations for the stepwise thermal decomposition that occurs when the temperature of chlorauric acid is gradually raised.

8. Compare the tendency for complex ion formation of the IB metals to that of the alkali metals. How does this correlate with the variation in size of the simple cations and the tendency to achieve higher oxidation states?

9. How does the chemistry of gold resemble rather closely that of platinum?

10. In what oxidation state does copper resemble nickel closely? Give examples of this similarity.

11. The preparation of gold sols, as described in Section 424, is facilitated by the addition of Na_2CO_3 to the solution. Why?

Chapter 34

▶ The IIB Metals

Zinc, Cadmium, Mercury

These metals occupy the places just beyond the transition metals in their respective periods.

Table 89. The IIB Metals

	Zinc	Cadmium	Mercury
Symbol	Zn	Cd	Hg
Atomic number	30	48	80
Electronic structure	2, 8, 18, 2	2, 8, 18, 18, 2	2, 8, 18, 32, 18, 2
Oxidation states	0, +2	0, +2	0, +1, +2
Abundance	0.008%	Little	$1 \times 10^{-5}\%$
Minerals	ZnS, sphalerite; ZnO, zincite; ZnCO₃, smithsonite; Zn₂SiO₄, willemite	Small amounts in all zinc ores	HgS, cinnabar
Crystal radius, M^{2+}, Å	0.74	0.97	1.10
First ionization potential, volts	9.36	8.96	10.38
Oxidation potential, M/M^{2+}, volts	+0.7620	+0.4020	−0.854
Melting point, ° C	419.4	321	−38.89
Boiling point, ° C	907	767	356.8
Density, g/cc, 20°	7.14	8.65	13.55

Only the two electrons in the outermost shells of their atoms are available for bonding purposes, and both of these electrons are used when these elements form compounds. The atoms of these three elements increase in size down the group, but they are considerably smaller than the atoms of the alkaline-earth metals and correspondingly less active. Note the big decrease in oxidation potential as we go from zinc to mercury, especially the low value for mercury. The variation in chemical activity is much like that found for the IB metals, but there is a sharp increase in chemical activity from the IB to the IIB subgroup. This is reflected in their occurrence in nature. Zinc and cadmium are not found as the uncombined metals; their compounds always occur together in the same ores. Mercury only rarely is found as the free metal. The sulfide ores of these metals are the chief sources in nature for all three metals. Zinc and cadmium are very much alike in most respects and differ markedly from mercury, so that it will be useful for us to consider zinc and cadmium together and then go on to the study of mercury.

427. METALLURGY OF ZINC AND CADMIUM

Cadmium always accompanies zinc in its ores. Although zinc is not an abundant metal, it usually is found concentrated in ores that are easy to work, so that it has been in common use for a very long time. The atomic ratio of cadmium to zinc in the ores is relatively low, so that much less cadmium is available. The sulfide and carbonate ores of zinc are concentrated, roasted, and reduced, the cadmium going along with the zinc.

$$2ZnS + 3O_2 \overset{\text{roasting}}{=} 2ZnO + 2SO_2$$
$$ZnO + C = Zn + CO$$

Sometimes the ore is treated to give soluble salts of zinc, and the metal may be obtained by electrodeposition from aqueous solution.

The crude zinc-cadmium mixture is readily refined by distillation to give *zinc dust* or the massive metal. By distillation under vacuum conditions, extremely pure zinc can be obtained. *Mossy*, or *granulated, zinc* is produced by dropping the molten metal into water. Cadmium is more volatile than zinc and boils off first, accumulating in the first distillation fractions.

428. PROPERTIES AND USES OF ZINC AND CADMIUM

Zinc and cadmium are silvery metals. Zinc is rather hard and brittle at room temperature, but it is more ductile at 100°. These two metals have rather low melting and boiling points. There is a marked decrease in melting point from the VIII group metals through the IB, IIB, and IIIB subgroups, and the melting point usually decreases down these B subgroups. Zinc and cadmium are above hydrogen in the electromotive series, zinc being more active than cadmium. Both metals are attacked superficially by the atmosphere, but surface films of basic carbonates that are formed protect the underlying metal from further corrosion. Acids attack them vigorously, the metals being oxidized to the cations and hydrogen being formed.

$$Cd + 2H^+ = Cd^{2+} + H_2$$

Very pure zinc reacts only slowly with acids, so that it is advisable either to use impure zinc in hydrogen generators or to add a little copper sulfate. Strong bases corrode zinc, owing to the formation of hydrated zincate ions.

$$Zn + OH^- + H_2O = HZnO_2^- + H_2$$

Cadmium does not give this reaction with hydroxide ion, because this metal, unlike zinc, is not amphoteric and does not form stable oxyanions.

Table 90.   Alloys of Zinc, Cadmium, and Mercury

Name and Per Cent Composition	Uses
Zinc die casting: 0.1Cu, 0.1Fe, 3.5Al, 0.03–0.08 Mg, 0.02(Pb, Cd, Sn), 96.2Zn	Washing-machine and electric-hoist gears, small motor frames, radio chassis and parts in the electrical industry, carburetors, fuel pumps, speedometer frames
Muntz metal: 59Cu, 41Zn	Architectural work, welding rods, condenser tubes, valve stems
Red brass: 90Cu, 10Zn	Screen wire, hardware, forging, screws, rivets, costume jewelry
Wood's alloy: 50Bi, 12.5Cd, 25Pb, 12.5Sn	Safety devices for fire extinguishers castings, statuettes, dental work
Fusible teaspoons: 44.5Bi, 30Pb, 16.5Sn, 5–10Hg	Trick spoons that melt in warm water
3Ni, 97Cd	Linings in heavy-duty sliding-type bearings
Aluminum solder: 75Zn, 20Cd, 5Al	For aluminum soldering
Sodium amalgam: Na, Hg	Reducing agent

Zinc and cadmium are used to protect other active metals, principally iron, from atmospheric corrosion. *Galvanized iron* is made by *pickling* mild steel, that is, immersing it in an acid bath to remove the oxide film, and then dipping it in molten zinc. *Sherardized iron* is coated by packing the iron in zinc dust and heating the system. Zinc and cadmium coatings can also be applied by electroplating. The zinc and cadmium soon form basic carbonate films, which prevent atmospheric attack, and the iron is protected from corrosion. When the system does corrode, the iron will not suffer until all the zinc has been oxidized, even after holes have been eaten through the zinc coating, because iron has a lower oxidation potential than the zinc. Zinc is used for electrodes in wet and dry batteries where advantage is taken of its action as a reducing agent.

Since these two metals have low melting points and are not very sensitive to atmospheric attack, their alloys can readily be prepared, and many are in common use.

429. COMPOUNDS OF ZINC AND CADMIUM

Oxidation States	Zinc	Cadmium
0	Metallic zinc	Metallic cadmium
+2	Zn^{2+}, ZnO, $Zn(OH)_2$, $ZnCl_2$, $ZnSO_4 \cdot 7H_2O$ ZnS, $Zn(NH_3)_4{}^{2+}$ $Zn(CN)_4{}^{2-}$, $ZnOHCl$, $HZnO_2{}^-$, $NaHZnO_2$	Cd^{2+}, CdO, $Cd(OH)_2$, $CdCl_2$, $CdSO_4 \cdot 4H_2O$, CdS, $Cd(NH_3)_4{}^{2+}$, $Cd(CN)_4{}^{2-}$

Zinc and cadmium are always in the oxidation state of **+2** in their compounds, and the common compounds are usually ionic. Zn^{2+} and Cd^{2+} are readily obtained in solution by the action of acids on the metals or oxides. These ions are colorless and are hydrated in solution, and many of their salts obtained by crystallization from water are hydrated. The ions hydrolyze to some extent, and basic salt formation is observed. Zinc ions are *astringent* (cause tissue to shrink or pucker) and are toxic to microorganisms. Compounds of zinc are used as antiseptics. Both zinc and cadmium form complex ions readily, showing the coordination number of 4.

Zinc oxide, zinc white, is a valuable white paint pigment that is not discolored by sulfurous fumes because zinc sulfide is white. It is also used for compounding rubber and in glazes and enamels. As an antiseptic it is employed in salves and adhesive tape. *Cadmium oxide* is a brown solid.

Zn(OH)₂ is precipitated by OH^-. ZnO will not hydrate under ordinary conditions to give the hydroxide, and the white hydrous hydroxide loses water readily when heated to give the oxide.

$$Zn(OH)_2 \overset{\text{heated}}{=} ZnO + H_2O$$

Zinc hydroxide dissolves readily in acids or in excess alkali owing to its amphoterism, which may be summarized by the two equilibria,

$$Zn^{2+} + 2OH^- \rightleftharpoons Zn(OH)_2 \rightleftharpoons H^+ + HZnO_2{}^-$$

When zinc oxide is fused with basic oxides, *zincates*, such as K_2ZnO_2, are formed. *Cd(OH)₂* differs from zinc hydroxide in that it is more soluble and basic and is not amphoteric. Both zinc and cadmium hydroxides dissolve when treated with ammonium hydroxide, owing to the formation of complex ions.

$$Zn(OH)_{2(s)} + 4NH_3 = Zn(NH_3)_4{}^{2+} + 2OH^-$$
$$Cd(OH)_{2(s)} + 4NH_3 = Cd(NH_3)_4{}^{2+} + 2OH^-$$

The normal halides, sulfates, and nitrates of zinc and cadmium are quite soluble. *Zinc chloride* is used as a wood preservative and in mouthwashes. It is also an excellent flux for removing oxide films from metals in brazing or welding operations. When ZnO is mixed with concentrated HCl to form a paste, this rapidly sets to a rigid strong solid which is useful as a cement. The setting is due to the formation of $ZnOHCl$ and Zn_2OCl_2. Such basic zinc compounds are important in dentistry.

ZnCO₃ can be precipitated by adding primary carbonate ions to zinc solutions, but basic carbonates form readily as a result of hydrolysis.

ZnS is the only sulfide of a common metal that is insoluble and white. It is a very active *phosphor* (light emitter without sensible heat) when traces of impurities are present, and it fluoresces strongly when it is illuminated. It and other zinc compounds are useful in fluorescent lighting tubes and in fluorescent paints. *CdS* is a bright-yellow pigment used in paints and as a colloidal colorant in glass to produce the yellow traffic-signal lenses.

430. METALLURGY OF MERCURY

Mercury can be prepared from its sulfide ore so simply that quite primitive methods are successful, and the metal has long been available. Cinnabar is roasted in air and the metal is distilled off.

$$HgS + O_2 = Hg + SO_2$$

Mercury can be purified by squeezing it through leather, by treatment with dilute nitric or sulfuric acid to get rid of the more active metals, and by vacuum distillation. Electrorefining methods also are effective.

431. PROPERTIES AND USES OF MERCURY

Mercury is the only metal that is liquid at room temperature, being the heaviest liquid available. Its freezing point is low, and its boiling point is high enough so that it remains a liquid throughout the lower temperature range in which we usually work. At room temperature its equilibrium vapor pressure is so low that usually we can ignore it. It is a good thermal and electrical conductor like other metals. Ionized mercury vapor conducts electricity well, and mercury-vapor arc lamps with silica walls are excellent sources of ultraviolet light. Mercury has such a low oxidation potential that it is low in activity, resists atmospheric attack, and does not react with hydracids. Strong oxidizing agents, such as the oxyacids and the halogens, oxidize it readily. Mercury is inert toward bases.

Mercury does not wet glass, and it expands uniformly when heated, so it is a good liquid to use in thermometers. Because of its high density, low vapor pressure, and inert character, it is useful in manometers and barometers for measuring gas pressures and as a confining liquid for handling gases.   As a good electrical conductor in the liquid state, mercury is employed for making electrical contacts in switches.   The unique combination of properties that this metal offers makes it indispensable in scientific and engineering work.

Long exposure to metallic mercury, especially to its vapor, produces serious *poisoning*, so it should always be handled and stored with proper caution.

The alloys of mercury, called *amalgams*, are useful, and some are unique in that they are liquid at room temperature.   The mercury can readily be removed from such alloys by distillation.   Gold, silver, and platinum alloy very readily with mercury, and it is wise not to bring jewelry in contact with this metal.   Iron is one of the few metals that does not alloy with mercury, and the latter is often stored in steel containers.

432. BONDING AND OXIDATION STATES OF MERCURY

Oxidation States	
0	Metallic mercury
+1, mercurous mercury (I)	Hg_2^{2+}, Hg_2O, Hg_2Cl_2, Hg_2S, $Hg_2(NO_3)_2$, $Hg_2(OH)NO_3$
+2, mercuric mercury (II)	Hg^{2+}, HgO, $HgCl_2$, $HgNH_2Cl$, $ClHgOHgNH_2$, HgS, $Hg(NO_3)_2$

Mercury is very unusual in the way it forms compounds with other elements, and the compounds of mercury are quite different in many respects from those of other metals.   The mercury atom always uses both of its valence electrons for bonding when it forms compounds. When both of these electrons are involved in bonding to atoms of other elements, mercury is in the oxidation state of **+2.**   For instance, in mercuric chloride, $HgCl_2$, the mercury atom is covalently bonded to two chlorine atoms in a linear molecule.

In mercuric sulfate, $HgSO_4$, mercury is associated with the very electronegative sulfate group, which has a strong tendency for ionic bonding, and mercuric ions are present.   Both valence electrons are stripped from the atom.

Under other conditions one valence electron of each mercury atom is used to maintain a covalent bond to a second mercury atom, the $Hg:Hg$ bond being characteristic of the mercurous compounds.   The second valence electron of each atom of mercury may be used to establish a covalent bond to an atom of another element, and a molecule such as Hg_2Cl_2 results.   Or the second valence electron of each mercury atom may be lost completely, and the complex mercurous ion, Hg_2^{2+}, is formed.

The equilibrium between the three oxidation states is important.

$$Hg_2^{2+} \rightleftharpoons Hg^{2+} + Hg$$
$$\text{mercurous} \qquad \text{mercuric} \qquad \text{mercury}$$

Although the mercurous ion is stable with respect to mercuric ion and the metal, the oxidation potentials for the various states are not very different, and the mercuric state may be favored by the formation of complex ions or of substances of low solubility. Suitable oxidizing agents convert the metal to the mercurous state; if the oxidizing agent is sufficiently strong and in excess, the oxidation will continue to the mercuric state. Reducing agents that are able to reduce mercuric mercury to the mercurous state also are able to reduce mercurous mercury to the metal.

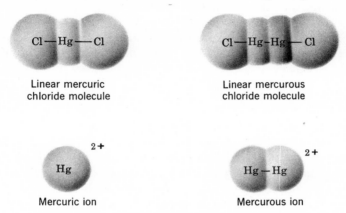

Linear mercuric chloride molecule	Linear mercurous chloride molecule
Mercuric ion	Mercurous ion

Fig. 131.   Configurations of the chlorides and ions of mercury.

Many compounds of mercury, particularly in the mercuric state, are remarkable in that they are weak electrolytes. This undoubtedly reflects the fact that the compounds are likely to be molecular in structure, with predominantly covalent bonding. This also correlates with their considerable solubilities in organic solvents, such as alcohol and ether, and with their volatility.

Compounds of mercury show little tendency for hydration, but they hydrolyze seriously to form basic salts that are only very slightly soluble. The soluble compounds are *violent poisons*. Like the compounds of gold, many compounds of mercury are readily decomposed by heating.

433. MERCUROUS COMPOUNDS

The mercurous compounds show some resemblance to those of silver, cuprous copper, and aurous gold, in spite of the fact that structurally they are quite different.

The *mercurous halides* are relatively stable compounds. Hg_2Cl_2, *calomel*, is prepared by heating a mixture of mercurous sulfate and sodium chloride.

$$Hg_2SO_{4(s)} + 2NaCl_{(s)} \overset{\text{heat}}{=} Na_2SO_{4(s)} + Hg_2Cl_{2(s)}$$

The mercurous chloride is volatile and sublimes to form colorless crystals. When it is exposed to light, it turns dark owing to the formation of mercury.

$$Hg_2Cl_2 = Hg + HgCl_2$$

The soluble mercuric chloride that is formed is very poisonous, and calomel that is to be used internally should be protected from the light. Mercurous chloride undergoes auto-oxidation-reduction when treated with ammonia, metallic mercury and insoluble basic mercuric compounds being formed.

Hg_2SO_4 and $Hg_2(NO_3)_2$ are readily formed by the action of the oxidizing acids on an excess of the metal. They hydrolyze readily to give less soluble basic salts.

434. MERCURIC COMPOUNDS

These are somewhat like the compounds of zinc. They can be prepared by the action of acids on HgO or by the oxidation of mercury or mercurous compounds. As a rule, they are more soluble than the mercurous compounds and are more likely to hydrolyze. Complex formation is common, a function of the higher state of oxidation.

Mercuric oxide, HgO, can be obtained by gently heating mercuric nitrate or by making a mercuric solution basic.

$$2Hg(NO_3)_2 = 2HgO + 4NO_2 + O_2$$
$$Hg^{2+} + 2OH^- = HgO_{(s)} + H_2O$$

HgO occurs in two different crystalline modifications, one yellow, the other red. It decomposes readily when heated to give oxygen.

Mercuric sulfide, HgS, is precipitated very completely from mercuric solutions by hydrogen sulfide. HgS is polymorphic, like the oxide, having red and black crystalline forms. The red form is the stable one found in nature as cinnabar. It is noteworthy that when precipitation is carried out in the laboratory, the metastable black form is usually obtained. Red mercuric sulfide is utilized as a paint pigment under the name *vermilion*.

The *mercuric halides* may be obtained by the action of an excess of the halogen on mercury or the mercurous halide. In fact, mercurous compounds take up halogen so readily that they are often used to remove excess chlorine or bromine from preparations. $HgCl_2$, *corrosive sublimate*, is usually made by heating mercuric sulfate and sodium chloride, the mercuric chloride volatilizing from the mixture.

$$HgSO_{4(s)} + 2NaCl_{(s)} \overset{heat}{=} Na_2SO_{4(s)} + HgCl_{2(s)}$$

It is used extensively in surgery and otherwise as an antiseptic. It is *very poisonous*, combining directly with albumin in the body. White of egg may be administered as an antidote.   Mercuric chloride reacts with liquid ammonia.

$$HgCl_2 + 2NH_3 = HgNH_2Cl_{(s)} + NH_4^+ + Cl^-$$

This is an example of *ammonolysis,* the decomposition of a salt by ammonia.   The $HgNH_2Cl$ may be called *ammonobasic mercuric chloride.*   It forms as a white precipitate.   When aqueous ammonia is added to a solution of mercuric chloride, both ammonolysis and hydrolysis can occur and, under the proper conditions, a white precipitate believed to be both an ammonobasic and an oxymercuric chloride is formed.

$$2HgCl_2 + 4NH_3 + H_2O = NH_2HgOHgCl_{(s)} + 3NH_4^+ + 3Cl^-$$

Mercuric iodide, HgI_2, can readily be formed merely by grinding or heating a mixture of mercury and iodine.   It is polymorphic; the bright scarlet form that is stable at room temperature inverts to yellow crystals when it is heated above 126°.   When cooled below 126°, the change reverses, and the yellow form changes back to red.   The yellow crystals melt at 250°.

$$HgI_{2(s)} \overset{126°}{\rightleftharpoons} HgI_{2(s)} \overset{250°}{\rightleftharpoons} HgI_{2(l)}$$
$$\text{red} \qquad\qquad \text{yellow}$$

Mercuric iodide is only very slightly soluble in water, but it dissolves readily in aqueous solutions of potassium iodide, owing to the formation of mercuric iodide complex ions.

$$HgI_2 + 2I^- = HgI_4^{2-}$$

$HgSO_4$ and $Hg(NO_3)_2$ are colorless and quite soluble salts which hydrolyze to give less soluble yellow basic salts.

Since mercury has such a considerable ability to form covalent bonds, it combines with organic radicals readily, and a large number of organomercury compounds, such as $Hg(C_2H_5)_2$, have been synthesized.

EXERCISES

1. Compare the IIB metals to the alkaline-earth metals in general with respect to: a) electronic structure; b) ionic radii; c) oxidation states; d) ionization potentials; 2) oxidation potentials.

2. Discuss the metallurgy of the IIB metals.   Which is more difficult to accomplish, the reduction of zinc compounds to the metal or the reduction of compounds of calcium?   Explain.

3. Zinc, cadmium, and mercury are treated separately with hydrochloric acid and then with aqueous sodium hydroxide.   Write equations for all the chemical changes that are observed and account for any differences in behavior of the three metals.

4. Describe the important uses of metallic mercury, correlating these uses with the properties of the metal.

5. a) How is the galvanizing of iron accomplished?

b) Account for the effectiveness of this treatment for preventing the corrosion of iron.

6. Mention four compounds of the IIB metals that are important as pigments.

7. Account for the fact that although mercury always has a total valence of 2 in its compounds, it may be in the oxidation state of $+1$ or $+2$ in these compounds.

8. Write balanced equations for the: a) action of a limited amount of chlorine with mercury; b) action of chlorine with mercurous chloride; c) auto-oxidation-reduction of mercurous chloride when exposed to light; d) ammonolysis of mercuric chloride.

9. Describe the polymorphism observed for mercuric iodide.

Chapter 35

▶ The IIIB and IVB Metals

Tin and Lead

435. THE IIIB METALS

None of these metals is common, because no ores are known that have very much of them present. However, there are at least traces of them in most sulfide ores of lead, zinc, copper, and silver, and considerable amounts of the IIIB metals could be produced as by-products of the metallurgy of the more common metals. Small amounts are coming into the market for special uses. They are all very low-melting metals and are of some practical interest in the preparation of low-melting alloys. Indium is plated on airplane engine bearings to prevent corrosion.

Table 91. The IIIB Metals

	Gallium	Indium	Thallium
Symbol	Ga	In	Tl
Atomic number	31	49	81
Electronic structure	2, 8, 18, 3	2, 8, 18, 18, 3	2, 8, 18, 32, 18, 3
Oxidation states	**0, +1, +3**	**0, +1, +3**	**0, +1, +3**
Crystal radius, M^{3+}, Å	0.62	0.81	0.95
First ionization potential, volts	5.97	5.76	6.07
Oxidation potential, M/M^+, volts	$(M/M^{3+}) + 0.52$	About $+0.25$	$+0.3363$
Melting point, ° C	29.8	161	303
Boiling point, ° C	2070	>1450	1457
Density, g/cc, 20°	5.91	7.3	11.85

These elements have three valence electrons in the outermost shell. Depending upon oxidizing conditions, they are in the oxidation states of either **+1** or **+3** in their compounds. The oxidation state of **+3** is the most common one for gallium and indium, and in this condition their compounds quite closely resemble those of aluminum. The oxidation state of **+1** is the common one for thallium, and there is some resemblance in this state to the chemistry of the alkali metals, copper, and silver. In the oxidation state of **+3,** the chemistry of thallium is somewhat like that of auric gold.

436. THE IVB METALS

This subgroup includes the familiar metals tin and lead and the unfamiliar element germanium.

Table 92.   The IVB Elements

	Germanium	Tin	Lead
Symbol	Ge	Sn	Pb
Atomic number	32	50	82
Electronic structure	2, 8, 18, 4	2, 8, 18, 18, 4	2, 8, 18, 32, 18, 4
Oxidation states	**0, +2, +4**	**0, +2, +4**	**0, +2, +4**
Abundance	$1 \times 10^{-4}\%$	$1 \times 10^{-4}\%$	0.002%
Minerals	Sulfides, silicates	SnO_2, cassiterite	PbS, galena; $PbCO_3$, cerussite; $PbSO_4$, anglesite; $PbCrO_4$, crocoite
Crystal radius, M^{4+}, Å	0.53	0.71	0.84
First ionization potential, volts	8.09	7.30	7.38
Oxidation potential, M/M^{2+}, volts	About +0.8	+0.136	+0.126
Melting point, ° C	937.2	232.0	327.3
Boiling point, ° C	2700	2270	1746
Density, g/cc, 20°	5.36	7.30	11.34

None of these IVB elements is abundant, but the ores of tin and lead occur concentrated in localized deposits, so these metals have been easily available to man for several thousand years.   Although there probably is at least as much germanium in the crust of the earth as there is tin, germanium is widely scattered, and no rich deposits of its ores are known. It is available in limited amounts as a by-product of the metallurgy of sulfide ores, but has not been exploited to any extent.

Having four electrons in the outermost shells of their atoms, these elements show valences of either 2 or 4.   In the oxidation state of **+4** they have some resemblance to silicon.   There is considerable increase in size of the atoms with increasing atomic number.   Tin and lead have definite metallic behavior, but germanium is midway between silicon and tin in its properties.   Germanium crystallizes in the same type of lattice as carbon and silicon; it is hard and brittle and has low electrical conductivity.   But it has a metallic, silvery luster and resembles tin in certain other respects.   It perhaps is best considered to be a metalloid.   Crystals of germanium with very small amounts of certain other elements present have electrical properties that are taken advantage of in making transistors (devices that may be used instead of vacuum tubes).

437. METALLURGY OF TIN AND LEAD

The oxide ore of tin, *cassiterite*, is found only in the East Indies, the Malay States, and in Bolivia. The deposits in Cornwall, which were developed by the Romans, have been pretty much exhausted. This oxide ore is concentrated and then reduced by heating it with carbon.

$$SnO_2 + 2C \overset{heat}{=} Sn + 2CO$$
cassiterite

The lead sulfide ore, *galena*, is concentrated, mixed with coke, and roasted. The reactions are complicated but may be summarized in the over-all equation

$$PbS + C + 2O_2 = Pb + SO_2 + CO_2$$

Lead and tin may be refined by *liquation,* melting the metal and running it off of the impurities.   Electrorefining may also be used.

438. PROPERTIES AND USES OF TIN AND LEAD

White tin is a soft, very malleable metal with very little strength. When it is cooled below 18°, this form of tin becomes unstable and tends to change to *gray tin,* a brittle and less metallic modification which crumbles to pieces.   This leads to the so-called *tin disease* when tin objects are held at low temperatures for protracted periods.   The objects develop spots of gray tin which spread, and eventually the metal crumbles to a powder.   White tin does not tarnish appreciably in air, in spite of the fact that it is above hydrogen in the electrochemical series.   Again, oxide film formation protects the metal.   It is acted upon slowly by acids and is rapidly corroded by alkali, owing to the formation of stannates.

Tin is in demand for the protection of other metals from corrosion. *Tin plate* is made by coating mild steel with tin by dipping the sheets into the molten tin or by electroplating.   When holes develop through the tin surface film, the underlying iron rusts very rapidly.   This is because a galvanic cell is set up when the surface is moist.   Iron has a higher oxidation potential than tin, so the iron oxidizes rapidly.   *Planished copper* has a thin surface coating of tin.

Lead has a bluish-gray appearance but soon loses its luster when exposed to air, because of the formation of basic salt films.   Lead is very soft and malleable.   It is about as active as tin.   Continued slow reaction of lead with water containing dissolved oxygen produces small amounts of lead hydroxide, which is slightly soluble in water. This leads to the danger of lead poisoning if lead pipes are used to convey drinking water. Hydrofluoric acid, sulfuric acid, and, to a lesser extent, hydrochloric acid form only very slightly soluble compounds with lead, so that they react only superficially with the metal. It is attacked seriously by alkalies.

Lead pipes can easily be made by extruding the hot metal through a die. Because of the ease with which such pipes can be bent into shape and joined together by *wiping the joint* with hot pasty plumber's solder, lead pipes are much used in plumbing installations. A lead coating is often applied to electric, telegraph, and telephone cables for protection against corrosion. When the lead is buried in the soil or placed in sea water, a very inert film of lead silicate is formed on the metal.

Both tin and lead have very low melting points and are much used to prepare low-melting alloys.

Table 93. Alloys of Tin and Lead

Alloy and Composition	Properties	Uses
Solder: 67Pb, 33Sn	Low melting	Soldering metals
Bearing metal: 75Sn, 12.5Sb, 12.5Cu	Low melting, low friction, soft	Bearings
Babbitt metal: 89Sn, 7.3Sb, 3.7Cu	Low melting, soft, low friction	Bearings
Type metal: 82Pb, 15Sb, 3Sn	Low melting, expands on cooling	Castings
Fuse metal: 50Bi, 10Cd, 26.6Pb, 13.3Sn	Low melting	Safety devices for fire extinguishers, temperature baths, castings, fuses
Rose metal: 22.9Sn, 27.1Pb, 50Bi	Low melting	Safety devices for fire extinguishers
Bronze: 88Cu, 10Sn, 2Zn	Resists corrosion, pleasing color, easy to cast	Bearings, castings, statues
Lead foil: 87Pb, 12Sn, 1Cu	Malleable, inert	Wrapping objects that are ruined by moist air
Battery plates: 94Pb, 6Sb	Easily cast	Used in batteries
Silver solder: 40Sn, 40Ag, 14Cu, 6Zn	Low melting	Soldering

439. COMPOUNDS OF TIN

Oxidation State

0	Metallic tin
+2, stannous tin (II)	Sn^{2+}, SnO, $Sn(OH)_2$, $SnCl_2 \cdot 2H_2O$, SnS, SnO_2^{2-}, K_2SnO_2
+4, stannic tin (IV)	SnO_2, SnO_3^{2-}, SnS_2, SnS_3^{2-}, $SnCl_4$, $SnCl_6^{2-}$

The oxidation states of **+2** and **+4** are about equally common for tin.

In the *stannous condition,* tin forms the colorless *stannous ion,* Sn^{2+}, and many of the tin (II) compounds are ionic. The Sn^{2+} ion has a rather strong tendency for hydrolysis, and basic stannous salts are known. Sn^{2+} may be reduced to the metal and easily oxidized to the stannic state. SnO is a black solid that oxidizes rapidly in the air to SnO_2. *Sn(OH)$_2$* precipitates as a gelatinous hydrous yellow material when a stannous solution is treated with alkalies.

$$Sn^{2+} + 2OH^- = Sn(OH)_{2(s)}$$

It is amphoteric and dissolves in excess of alkali, forming *stannite ions,* comparable to zincate ions.

$$Sn(OH)_2 + OH^- = HSnO_2^- + H_2O$$
stannite

$SnCl_2$ may be prepared by reduction of $SnCl_4$ or by dissolving tin in hydrochloric acid and evaporating the solution in the presence of HCl.

$$Sn + 2HCl = SnCl_2 + H_2$$

A solution of stannous chloride is rapidly oxidized by the air; this may be prevented by having pieces of tin present in the solution. The hydrated *tin salt,* $SnCl_2 \cdot 2H_2O$, is a useful mordant because of its rapid hydrolysis. SnS forms as a brown precipitate when hydrogen sulfide is added to a stannous solution. It dissolves in polysulfide solutions, being oxidized to the *thiostannate ion.*

$$SnS + S_2^{2-} = SnS_3^{2-}$$
thiostannate

In the **+4** *condition* simple ions are not known, but the metal forms either complex ions or molecules. *Stannic oxide,* SnO_2, is similar to TiO_2. The hydrous oxide is formed by the hydrolysis of tin (IV) compounds or by the action of nitric acid on tin. Stannic oxide is frequently used 'to produce opaque white glazes and enamels. Thin films of it on glass render the glass beautifully iridescent. When stannic oxide is fused with bases, *stannates* are formed.

$$SnO_2 + 2NaOH \overset{\text{fused}}{=} Na_2SnO_3 + H_2O$$
stannate

Stannates are also obtained by the action of concentrated aqueous alkali on the metal. In stannic oxide and in stannate ions, the tin atoms have a coordination number of 6 toward oxygen. Stannate ions must have an extended oxygen-bridge structure.

Hydrogen sulfide precipitates yellow *stannic sulfide*, SnS_2, from stannic solutions. Excess sulfide dissolves this stannic sulfide, forming thiostannate ions.

$$SnS_2 + S^{2-} = SnS_3{}^{2-}$$

Stannic chloride is formed as a colorless liquid when chlorine is passed over tin.

$$Sn + 2Cl_2 = \underset{\text{b.p., } 114°}{SnCl_4}$$

This reaction is used to recover the tin from tin cans. Tin tetrachloride resembles $TiCl_4$ and $SiCl_4$, being a tetrahedral molecule.

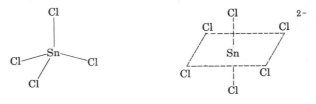

Stannic chloride   Hexachlorostannate ion

Fig. 132. Configurations of SnCl$_4$ and SnCl$_6$$^{2-}$.

Like titanium, tin is large enough so that $SnCl_4$ can combine with chloride ions to form the octahedral *hexachlorostannate ion*, $SnCl_6{}^{2-}$. Na_2SnCl_6 is used for the weighting of silk. $SnCl_4$ hydrolyzes rapidly but can be dissolved in concentrated hydrochloric acid, and when the solution is cooled, crystals of $H_2SnCl_6 \cdot 6H_2O$ appear.

440. COMPOUNDS OF LEAD

Oxidation State	
0	Metallic lead
+2, lead (II)	Pb^{2+}, PbO, $Pb(OH)_2$, $PbCl_2$, $PbSO_4$, $Pb_3(OH)_2(CO_3)_2$, $PbO_2{}^{2-}$, Na_2PbO_2
+4, lead (IV)	PbO_2, $PbO_3{}^{2-}$, $PbCl_4$, $PbCl_6{}^{2-}$, $Pb(C_2H_5)_4$

With increase in atomic number in this subgroup, the stability of the oxidation state of **+4** falls off. So the common compounds of lead are the lead (II) substances, while many of the lead (IV) compounds are unstable and are very easily reduced. Lead compounds are poisonous, the lead tending to accumulate in the body.

The *lead ion*, Pb^{2+}, is colorless and is formed when acids react with lead.

$$Pb + 2H^+ = Pb^{2+} + H_2$$

Solutions of this ion are not oxidized by the atmosphere, but they do hydrolyze readily to give basic salts which are only sparingly soluble.

Lead monoxide, PbO, is marketed under the name of *litharge*. This yellow-orange substance is formed by burning lead and is also produced when the higher oxides of lead are heated strongly. It is used extensively in the manufacture of glass, pottery, rubber, and paints. When mixed with glycerin, the paste sets to a hard inert mass that is frequently used as a plumbing cement. *Lead hydroxide*, $Pb(OH)_2$, is amphoteric, dissolving in excess alkali to form *plumbites*.

$$Pb(OH)_2 + OH^- = HPbO_2^- + H_2O$$

Solutions of *sodium plumbite*, Na_2PbO_2, are used in petroleum refining to remove sulfur.

Plumbous salts are not as soluble as stannous salts, only the nitrate and the acetate being quite soluble. $PbCl_2$, PbI_2, PbS, $PbSO_4$, and $PbCrO_4$ can be obtained readily by precipitation methods. *Lead arsenate*, $Pb_3(AsO_4)_2$, is a powerful insecticide. The black *PbS* is not soluble in excess sulfide. *Basic lead carbonate*, $Pb_3(OH)_2(CO_3)_2$, is one of our most important white paint pigments, white lead. This is manufactured by the "old Dutch process." Lead buckles are packed in earthenware jars above acetic acid, and the jars are stacked in tiers with intervening layers of tanbark in an airtight room. The moist tanbark ferments, providing heat and carbon dioxide, and the acetic acid and water vaporize. The lead buckles become deeply encrusted with white lead, which can be broken off and ground to a fine powder. The reaction is complicated, but the net change is given by the equation

$$6Pb + 3O_2 + 2H_2O + 4CO_2 = 2Pb_3(OH)_2(CO_3)_{2(s)}$$
$$\text{white lead}$$

The function of the acetic acid is obscure, but acetates probably are formed as intermediate materials.

In the **+4** *condition*, lead usually forms covalent bonds to produce complex ions or molecules, of which only the oxysystems are very stable. *Lead dioxide*, PbO_2, is a dark-brown solid obtained by the electrolytic oxidation of lead. This oxide is important in the construction and operation of the lead storage battery. PbO_2 is an excellent oxidizing agent and decomposes very readily when it is heated.

$$2PbO_2 \overset{\text{heated}}{=} 2PbO + O_2$$

Lead dioxide is not a peroxide but has the same structure as TiO_2. It dissolves in concentrated alkali to form *plumbate ions*. Lead tetrachloride, $PbCl_4$, can be obtained as an oily liquid at low temperatures by the action of concentrated hydrochloric acid on PbO_2, but this tetrachloride is unstable at room temperature and may explode when it is warmed.   *Chloroplumbate ions*, $PbCl_6^{2-}$, are more stable, and salts containing this ion are known.   *Lead tetraethyl*, $Pb(C_2H_5)_4$, is a colorless volatile liquid that is soluble in gasoline.   It is used as an antiknock agent for preventing the premature explosion of gasoline-air mixtures in engines when the mixture is compressed.   *Ethyl gasoline* has a small amount of this compound and other additives present.

Red lead, Pb_3O_4, is a mixed oxide, having lead atoms in both the $+2$ and $+2$ oxidation states.   It is made by the careful heating of PbO in air below 500°.   It is a good oxidizing agent and is used as a paint pigment and in the manufacture of glass.

Lead sesquioxide, Pb_2O_3, also has atoms of lead present in both oxidation states.

441. THE LEAD STORAGE CELL

An electric storage cell is a chemical system that can act reversibly either as a galvanic cell or an electrolytic cell.   It is constructed of electrodes and an electrolytic solution so chosen that when the electrodes are connected through an external metallic circuit, a flow of electrons will tend to take place.   Oxidation and reduction half reactions proceed at the electrodes, and chemical energy is converted to electrical energy which can be used in the external circuit.   In the course of the operation as a galvanic cell, the cell is said to *discharge;* it loses chemical energy owing to the net oxidation-reduction occurring and produces electrical energy.   The original chemical materials will be depleted by such discharge.   The storage cell may be *recharged* by reversing the chemical changes at the electrodes so that the original chemical composition is regained.   This is accomplished by imposing a sufficient potential across the cell in the reverse direction, by means of an electron pump in the external circuit, so that electrons will flow in the direction opposite to that occurring when the cell is discharging.   The oxidation-reduction reaction of the cell is thus reversed and electrical energy is converted to chemical energy, the system now operating as an electrolytic cell.   The cell accumulates energy which is thus stored until the cell is operated as a galvanic cell.   A storage battery usually is a combination of a number of such reversible cells.

Unfortunately, only a very few systems have been found that can be used economically and conveniently in this reversible fashion.   The lead storage battery has been one of the most successful reversible systems thus far devised.

Each cell in this battery has one electrode composed of metallic lead or a suitable lead alloy and the other made of lead dioxide pressed into a lead grid. Sulfuric acid is used as the electrolytic solution. When the external circuit is completed, lead is oxidized at the lead grid to Pb^{2+}, which combines with SO_4^{2-} from the solution to produce solid $PbSO_4$, which deposits on the electrodes. The PbO_2 is reduced at the other

Fig. 133. A lead storage battery, cut away to show the grid electrodes separated by insulating spacers. (Courtesy Willard Storage Battery Co.)

electrode to Pb^{2+}, which associates with SO_4^{2-} to form solid $PbSO_4$ on the electrodes. The half reactions involved are as follows:

At the lead electrode

$$Pb + SO_4^{2-} = PbSO_{4(s)} + 2e^-$$

At the lead dioxide electrode

$$PbO_2 + 4H^+ + SO_4^{2-} + 2e^- = PbSO_{4(s)} + 2H_2O$$

In the recharging process the reverse changes occur. The net reversible reaction for the cell is

$$PbO_{2(s)} + Pb_{(s)} + 4H^+ + 2SO_4^{2-} \underset{\text{charge}}{\overset{\text{discharge}}{\rightleftharpoons}} 2PbSO_{4(s)} + 2H_2O + \text{electrical energy}$$

When the battery discharges, lead and lead dioxide are converted to lead sulfate at the respective electrodes, and sulfuric acid is used up. When the battery is charged, lead sulfate is converted to lead at one electrode and to lead dioxide at the other, and sulfuric acid accumulates in the solution.   The decrease in concentration of the solution of sulfuric acid is accompanied by a decrease in its density.   By checking the density of the solution, the state of charge of the battery can be ascertained.

EXERCISES

1. Summarize the electronic structures of the IIIB and IVB metals.

2. What oxidation states are known for these metals?   Illustrate by giving the formula for one substance or ion for each oxidation state of each metal.

3. Recalling the close resemblance of compounds of gallium to those of aluminum, predict the probable molecular formula and spatial configuration of the chloride of **+3** gallium.

4. Describe the occurrences of tin and lead, and outline their metallurgy.

5. What difficulty might be encountered if food protected by tin foil was stored for long periods of time under arctic conditions?

6. Account for the protection from corrosion that is afforded steel by tin-plating.   Making use of the data given in Table 68, page 237, discuss the relative merits of galvanizing and tin-plating as methods for protecting steel from corrosion.

7. What important uses are there for tin and lead and their alloys that make these metals of critical importance?   What substitutes can you suggest for these metals in each case?

8. Write equations which summarize the amphoteric behavior of stannous and plumbous hydroxides.

9. a) Describe the spatial configuration and properties of stannic chloride.
b) What happens when this substance is treated with concentrated hydrochloric acid?
c) What is the configuration of the product of the reaction?
d) What is formed when stannic chloride is added to water?

10. List the formulas for the oxides of lead, and discuss the oxidation states of lead in each of these compounds.   What is the gram-equivalent weight of lead in each case when reduced to the element?

11. a) What lead compounds are important in the manufacture of paints?
b) How can white lead be produced?

12. Outline the part played by lead in the construction and operation of the lead storage battery.

Chapter 36

▶ Atomic Nuclei and Radioactivity

442. ATOMIC NUCLEI

In our earlier discussion of the nuclear theory of atomic structure in Chapter 4, it was pointed out that each atom has at its center a small positively charged nucleus which is responsible for practically all of the mass of the atom. We saw that it is possible to account for the charges and masses of nuclei by assuming that they are composed of protons and neutrons. The charge of a nucleus is designated by its atomic number Z, which is equal to the number of protons, and its mass number is equal to the sum of the protons and the neutrons. Isotopes of an element arise because the number of neutrons may vary, the number of protons remaining constant. In ordinary chemical change the nuclei of the atoms undergo no change, only electronic rearrangement taking place.

443. NATURAL RADIOACTIVITY

In the Middle Ages the alchemists dreamed of the possibility of *transmutation*, the conversion of one element to another. They experimented in vain to discover methods for converting common metals, such as iron and lead, to precious gold and silver. Dalton's Atomic Theory assumed that atoms of the elements persisted through all changes. But the discovery of *radioactivity* in 1896 by Becquerel and the subsequent work of the Curies, Rutherford, and other workers led to the conclusion that some of the atoms occurring in nature do undergo spontaneous disintegration to form atoms of other elements. Because such disintegration was found to be accompanied by the emission of powerful radiations, this kind of atomic change was called *radioactive change*. The process of transmutation actually does occur for some atoms in nature.

444. THE NATURE OF RADIOACTIVE CHANGE

We now know that the nucleus of a radioactive atom is unstable and tends to change spontaneously to give a more stable nucleus, liberating an enormous amount of energy in the process. This energy emitted by naturally radioactive atoms is manifested principally as alpha, beta, and gamma rays. *Alpha rays* consist of rapidly moving alpha particles shot off by the nuclei.   These alpha particles are helium ions, He^{2+}, with a mass of 4 and a positive nuclear charge of 2.   They possess very high kinetic energy owing to their mass and velocity.   When they collide with atoms or molecules, they knock off electrons to ionize these units, or they cause even more serious changes.   Eventually, alpha particles pick up two electrons and become neutral helium atoms.   *Beta rays* consist of electrons emitted at high speeds by the nuclei.   The beta particles have the characteristic negative charge and mass of the electron.   These energetic electrons also cause serious changes when they collide with atoms.   *Gamma rays* are electromagnetic waves, a form of energy comparable to X-rays.   They are able to penetrate deeply and initiate changes.

When an alpha particle is ejected by a nucleus, the nucleus loses four units of mass and two units of positive charge.   This leaves a residual new nucleus which has a mass number four less and an atomic number two less than the original nucleus.   This is the kind of nuclear change that the radium atom undergoes in its disintegration, radon atoms being formed as indicated in the following equation:

$$_{88}Ra^{226} \rightarrow {}_{2}He^4 + {}_{86}Rn^{222}$$

In writing equations for nuclear changes, the sum of the mass numbers must be the same on both sides, and the atomic numbers also must be balanced.

When a nucleus ejects a beta particle, there is a loss of one unit of negative charge by the nucleus, and this increases its net positive charge by one unit.   Its atomic number increases one unit, but only a very small change in mass occurs.   The new nucleus formed has an atomic number one greater than that of the original nucleus, but its mass is substantially the same.   The radioactive isotope of thorium, which has a mass number of 234, disintegrates by beta radiation, protactinium being formed. Thus,

$$_{90}Th^{234} \rightarrow {}_{-1}e^0 + {}_{91}Pa^{234}$$

Gamma radiation may accompany alpha or beta emission.   Since gamma rays are devoid of mass and charge, their emission does not change the atomic number or the mass number of the nucleus, but it does account for the loss of considerable energy.

445.   RADIOACTIVE DISINTEGRATION SERIES

The nucleus of the new element formed in a radioactive change may itself be radioactive and undergo disintegration to form still another new element, and the process may be repeated a considerable number of times.   Such a sequence of radioactive changes gives rise to a series of related radioactive elements.   The uranium isotope having the mass

number 238 is radioactive and is the parent substance of a long series
of other atomic species formed by successive radioactive changes.	Each
of these changes involves either alpha or beta radiation, sometimes accom-
panied by gamma radiation.	Figure 134 summarizes this sequence of
radioactive changes, indicating the nature of the radiation, the atomic

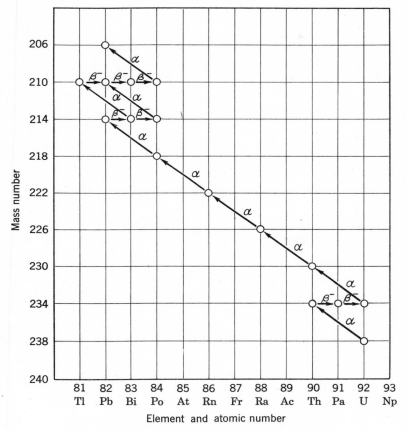

**Fig. 134.	The uranium-radium disintegration series.**

numbers and atomic masses of the nuclei formed, and the symbol of the
element of which the nucleus is isotopic.	The element that is finally
produced in this series is the isotope of lead, $_{82}Pb^{206}$.	This isotope has a
stable nucleus that has no appreciable tendency for further radioactive
change.	The radioactive atoms found in nature can all be classified in
such radioactive disintegration series.

## 446.	RATE OF RADIOACTIVE CHANGE

The kind of spontaneous radioactive change suffered by an unstable
nucleus is characteristic for that nucleus and is a function of the nuclear

structure.   The tendency of the nucleus to disintegrate is not affected by the state of chemical combination of the atom or by ordinary changes in conditions.   If we have a collection of a large number of atoms of a radioactive isotope, we find that a certain percentage of these atoms will undergo radioactive change per unit of time.   The term *half-life period* of a radioactive isotope is used to refer to the time required for half of the atoms in a sample of the isotope to change.   The half-life period of radium is 1,590 years.   If 1 g of radium is allowed to stand 1,590 years, half of the original atoms will have disintegrated, and only 0.50 g of radium will be left.   In the next 1,590 years, half of the remaining 0.50 g will disintegrate, and the sample of radium will be reduced to 0.25 g.

The half-life period of an isotope is a measure of the stability of its nuclei.   The more stable the nucleus is, the longer will be its half-life period.   Uranium 238 has a half-life period of 4.5×10^9 years.   Its nuclei are much more stable than those of radium.   Polonium 213 has a half-life period of only 3×10^{-6} sec, its nuclei being very unstable indeed.   Such very unstable nuclei have little chance to accumulate in nature.

447. ARTIFICIAL NUCLEAR CHANGES

Following the discovery of the spontaneous natural transmutation of certain unstable nuclei, the possibility of causing stable nuclei to undergo changes to other nuclei became a fascinating goal for research.   This was first realized by Rutherford in 1919.   He bombarded nitrogen atoms with alpha particles shot off by naturally radioactive material.   He was able to prove that when an alpha particle moving at a high speed smashed into a nitrogen nucleus, a proton and a stable oxygen nucleus were formed.

$$_7\text{N}^{14} + {}_2\text{He}^4 \rightarrow {}_8\text{O}^{17} + {}_1\text{H}^1$$

Rutherford thus demonstrated that stable nuclei could be caused to undergo transmutation by bombarding them with suitable projectiles. Atom-smashing techniques have been rapidly developed, and hundreds of such transmutations have been studied.

In addition to the alpha particles emitted by naturally radioactive substances, other energetic particles have proved effective as bullets. Charged particles, such as protons, deuterons, alpha particles, and electrons are accelerated to high velocities in electrical devices such as cyclotrons, betatrons, and synchrotrons.   This provides the particles with sufficient energy so that when they hit nuclei, changes result.   When beryllium is bombarded with alpha particles, carbon and neutrons are formed.

$$_4\text{Be}^9 + {}_2\text{He}^4 \rightarrow {}_0\text{n}^1 + {}_6\text{C}^{12}$$

Neutrons liberated by this and similar nuclear changes are very effective as projectiles because they are not repelled by the positive changes of nuclei, as are alpha particles, protons, and deuterons.

448. PARTICLES ASSOCIATED WITH NUCLEAR CHANGES

Further studies of nuclear changes have led to the discovery of a number of particles, other than those already mentioned, that result when atomic nuclei disintegrate. Some of these particles also add to nuclei to give more complicated structures. Table 94 summarizes the particles that are more commonly encountered in nuclear change and gives their characteristic masses in atomic mass units and also their charges. The last column indicates the symbols commonly used for each kind of particle.

Table 94.   Some Particles Associated with Nuclei

Particles	Mass Units ($O^{16} = 16$)	Charge	Symbol
Electron	0.000548	1 −	$_{-1}e$, β^-
Proton	1.00756	1 +	$_1H^1$
Deuteron	2.014160	1 +	$_1H^2$, $_1D^2$
Alpha particle	4.00280	2 +	$_2He^4$, α
Positron	0.000548	1 +	$_{+1}e$, β^+
Neutron	1.00893	0	$_0n^1$, n
Neutrino	very small	0	ν
π Meson	0.156	±1 or 0	π
μ Meson	0.118	±1 or 0	μ

449. INDUCED RADIOACTIVITY

In some cases, when an energetic projectile strikes a nucleus, this is converted directly to another stable nucleus which shows no radioactivity. In other reactions an unstable nucleus is formed, and this, in turn, undergoes radioactive change according to its particular half-life period. Thus, when silicon 28 is bombarded by protons, a radioactive isotope of phosphorus is formed. This then disintegrates to give positrons and a stable isotope of silicon.

$$_{14}Si^{28} + {}_1H^1 \rightarrow \underset{\text{radioactive}}{{}_{15}P^{29}} \rightarrow {}_{+1}e + \underset{\text{stable}}{{}_{14}Si^{29}}$$
$$\underset{\text{stable}}{}$$

When we start with a nonradioactive material and transmute it to a radioactive substance, we have an example of *induced radioactivity*. The following equations describe other examples of induced radioactivity, using bombarding particles:

$$_{14}\text{Si}^{28} + {}_1\text{D}^2 \rightarrow {}_0n^1 + {}_{15}\text{P}^{29}$$
$$\text{stable} \qquad\qquad\qquad \text{radioactive}$$
$$\hookrightarrow {}_{+1}e + {}_{14}\text{Si}^{29}$$
$$\text{stable}$$

$$_5\text{B}^{10} + {}_2\text{He}^4 \rightarrow {}_0n^1 + {}_7\text{N}^{13}$$
$$\text{stable} \qquad\qquad\qquad \text{radioactive}$$
$$\hookrightarrow {}_{+1}e + {}_6\text{C}^{13}$$
$$\text{stable}$$

$$_6\text{C}^{12} + {}_0\gamma^0 \rightarrow {}_0n^1 + {}_6\text{C}^{11}$$
$$\text{stable} \quad \text{gamma} \qquad\qquad \text{radioactive}$$
$$\text{ray}$$
$$\hookrightarrow {}_{+1}e + {}_5\text{B}^{11}$$
$$\text{stable}$$

$$_{11}\text{Na}^{23} + {}_0n^1 \rightarrow {}_{11}\text{Na}^{24} \rightarrow {}_{-1}e + {}_{12}\text{Mg}^{24}$$
$$\text{stable} \qquad\qquad \text{radioactive} \qquad\qquad \text{stable}$$

450. TRANSURANIUM ELEMENTS

By nuclear bombardment many unstable isotopes that are not found in nature have been made in the laboratory. Especially interesting has been the building up of a number of *transuranium elements*, elements having higher atomic numbers than uranium. This has been accomplished by the bombardment of uranium or other heavy nuclei by neutrons. For instance, when the nuclei of uranium 238 are struck by neutrons, uranium 239 is formed.

$$_{92}\text{U}^{238} + {}_0n^1 \rightarrow {}_{92}\text{U}^{239}$$

Uranium 239 has a half-life period of only 23 min and ejects electrons forming nuclei with atomic number 93. These are nuclei of a new element, which has been called *neptunium*.

$$_{92}\text{U}^{239} \rightarrow {}_{-1}e + {}_{93}\text{Np}^{239}$$

The neptunium nuclei are, in turn, radioactive, with the half-life period of 2.3 days. They change spontaneously to nuclei of atomic number 94, nuclei of another new element, *plutonium*.

$$_{93}\text{Np}^{239} \rightarrow {}_{-1}e + {}_{94}\text{Pu}^{239}$$

Plutonium has a half-life of 24,100 years. For every electron ejected from the nucleus, the atomic number increases one unit. Other nuclear reactions have been used to produce atoms of *americium* ($_{95}\text{Am}$), *curium* ($_{96}\text{Cm}$), *berkelium* ($_{97}\text{Bk}$), *californium* ($_{98}\text{Cf}$), *einsteinium* ($_{99}\text{E}$), *fermium* ($_{100}\text{Fm}$), and *mendelevium* ($_{101}\text{Mv}$).

Man has discovered not only how to cause the degradation of atoms to those of lower mass and atomic number but also how to build up more complex, heavier atomic systems and extend the list of known elements.

451. NUCLEAR FISSION

In the nuclear changes discussed so far, the particles ejected have been relatively small, and the residual nucleus left has always been a close neighbor of the original nucleus. The change in mass has been only four or less mass units, and the change in atomic number has been no more than one or two units. In 1939 Hahn and Strassman reported that when they bombarded uranium with neutrons, one of the elements formed was barium, not a close neighbor of uranium. The barium atom has not much more than half the mass and atomic number of uranium. Meitner and Frisch explained this by guessing that the neutron was splitting the uranium nucleus into two parts, each about half of the original

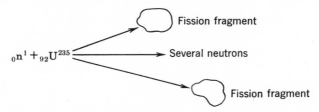

$$_0n^1 + {}_{92}U^{235}$$

Fission fragment

Several neutrons

Fission fragment

Fig. 135. Fission of uranium 235.

nucleus. This theory has turned out to be correct, and this entirely new kind of nuclear change has been termed *nuclear fission*. In the fission of uranium, a neutron causes the splitting of the isotope of uranium 235 into two fission fragments and several neutrons. The fission fragments are nuclei of elements having atomic numbers between 30 and 64. Usually two such nuclei are produced in each fission, and the sum of their atomic numbers is 92, the atomic number of the original uranium nucleus. The sum of the masses of these two fragments and of the neutrons produced is less than that of the uranium nucleus and the bombarding neutron. The mass lost, roughly one-thousandth of the mass of the uranium atom, is converted to energy. A very great quantity of energy is thus released. It is estimated that the fission of 1 lb of pure uranium 235 would furnish as much energy as the combustion of 4,000,000 lb of coal.

Plutonium 239 also undergoes nuclear fission when bombarded by neutrons. Thorium nuclei can be transmuted to uranium 233, which is a third nuclear species known to undergo fission.

452. NUCLEAR CHAIN REACTIONS

The emission of several neutrons when the fission of a nucleus occurs makes possible the setting up of a *chain reaction*. This term is used for a reaction in which one of the products is also one of the reactants. The neutrons liberated by fission may strike other uranium nuclei to cause their fission to produce more neutrons, and the reaction will thus keep going, even though only one neutron was provided originally. Figure 136 shows diagrammatically this fission chain reaction.

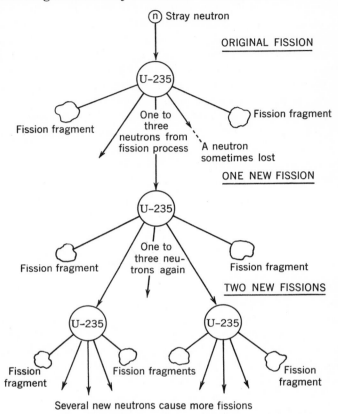

Fig. 136.   Diagram of fission chain reaction (after Smyth).

In atomic bombs, arrangements are made so that the chain reaction pyramids very rapidly to give an enormous number of fissions in a very short time. The tremendous amount of energy liberated produces terrific explosions.

453. NUCLEAR POWER

The conversion of mass to energy offered by nuclear-fission chain reactions has given us a new source of power, which has very far-reaching possibilities. By combining fissionable materials with moderating substances, Fermi and co-workers in 1942 showed that it was possible to construct an *atomic pile* in which a nuclear-fission chain reaction could be maintained under careful control, so that no explosion occurs. The

Fig. 137. Drawing of the "pile" of uranium and graphite built in 1942 by Fermi and co-workers under the West Stands of the University of Chicago's athletic field, where nuclear energy was first released in a sustained chain reaction. (Photo by U. S. Army Signal Corps)

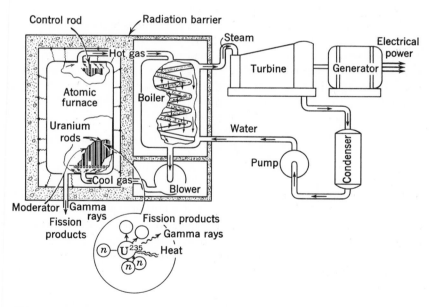

Fig. 138. Diagram of a proposed procedure for driving a turbine and generator with steam boiled by atomic energy. The energy of uranium fission would heat a gas that would turn water into steam for the turbine. An alternate plan suggests circulating molten sodium to absorb the heat of fission and then use the hot sodium to change water into steam.

tremendous amount of energy emitted continuously in such a pile can be used to convert water to steam, which can be used to generate other forms of energy to be employed for useful purposes.   It is estimated that the fission of 1 kg of uranium 235 per day in such a pile would release approximately 24,000,000 kw-hr per day, whereas 3,000 tons of coal would have to be burned per day to provide this amount of energy, enough to supply the power and lighting needs of a city of 1,000,000 people. Much research is now under way for the purpose of developing nuclear energy for peaceful uses.

The term *atomic energy* has come to be used widely to refer to the energy released by nuclear changes.   It should be pointed out that energy liberated when planetary electrons undergo rearrangement is also a kind of atomic energy.   The energy made available by exothermic chemical changes of the ordinary kind is atomic energy.   It would be more appropriate to use the term *nuclear energy* when we wish to refer specifically to that made available by nuclear changes.

454. SOLAR ENERGY.   THE HYDROGEN BOMB

Speculation as to the source of the enormous amount of energy continually being radiated by the sun has always been popular.   Knowledge of the nature of nuclear changes has made it possible to develop a theory that seems to be reasonable in the light of what is known about the solar system.   When it was recognized that nuclear changes can yield enormous amounts of energy, owing to the conversion of small amounts of mass to energy, it was suggested that such changes may be occurring in the sun.   Bethe has proposed a series of nuclear reactions that appear to be reasonable at the extremely high temperature existing on the sun.

$$_1H^1 + {}_1H^1 \rightarrow {}_1D^2 + {}_{+1}e$$
$$_1D^2 + {}_1H^1 \rightarrow {}_2He^3$$
$$_2He^3 + {}_2He^3 \rightarrow {}_2He^4 + {}_1H^1 + {}_1H^1$$

The net change for this series of reactions involves the conversion of hydrogen to helium.   This should entail a loss of mass for the system by conversion to energy in amounts sufficient to account for the total radiation by the sun.   In the hydrogen bomb the fission of uranium or plutonium produces the very high temperature necessary to start the conversion of hydrogen to helium, which then proceeds with incredible violence.

455. RADIOACTIVE TRACERS

Because of their radioactivity, very small amounts of radioactive isotopes can be detected and identified.   If a small amount of a radioactive isotope of a given element is mixed with the stable isotopes of that element, the radioactive atoms will undergo the same ordinary changes as do the stable isotopes. The course of the radioactive atoms can easily be followed because of the radiation emitted. The radioactive isotope can be used as a *tracer* to tell us what is happening to all the atoms of the element. For example, it is desirable to know how fast phosphorus, furnished as phosphates in the diet, is used to build up the bony skeleton of an animal. Phosphates containing a small amount of a radioactive isotope of phosphorus were fed to experimental animals, and the appearance of radioactivity in the bones was checked. It was possible to conclude that phosphate ions in the bones are replaced quite rapidly by phosphate ions provided in the diet. Radioactive tracers are being applied very widely in research.

When nuclear fission is maintained in a large atomic pile, large quantities of radioactive isotopes of a great many elements are produced. These radioactive isotopes are being separated and are now available for tracer studies.

EXERCISES

1. According to the modern theory of atomic structure, what units and how many of each are believed to be present in each nucleus of: a) $_9F^{20}$? b) $_9F^{17}$? c) $_{47}Ag^{107}$? d) $_{29}Cu^{63}$? e) $_{79}Au^{197}$? How many electrons will be associated with each of these nuclei in the neutral atoms?

2. Write the symbols for four nuclei that would be isotopic with $_{26}Fe^{56}$:

3. How do radioactive disintegrations differ from ordinary chemical changes?

4. a) If the radioactive nucleus $_{83}Bi^{211}$ disintegrates by the loss of an alpha particle, what will be the mass number and atomic number of the nucleus formed? In what group and period of the periodic system will it belong?

  b) If the radioactive nucleus $_{80}Hg^{205}$ ejects an electron, what nucleus will be formed?

5. Write nuclear equations to show the: a) reaction of $_{15}P^{31}$ with a neutron to give a proton and a radioactive nucleus; b) radioactive change of this nucleus to give an electron and a nucleus.

6. How are the members of a radioactive disintegration series related?

7. How many protons and neutrons are believed to be present in the nuclei of each of the first five members of the uranium-radium disintegration series shown in Figure 134?

8. What is meant by the term *induced radioactivity*? In general, how can this be carried out?

9. a) How does nuclear fission differ from the more common kinds of nuclear change?

  b) What features of the fission of uranium 235 make it possible to set up a self-maintaining chain reaction?

10. What reasonable explanation has been suggested to account for the fact that the sun can continue to radiate such huge quantities of energy?

► Appendix

I. THE METRIC SYSTEM OF WEIGHTS AND MEASURES WITH EQUIVALENTS IN THE FOOT-POUND SYSTEM

The units of length, volume, and weight in the metric system are, respectively, the meter, the liter, and the gram. A decimal system of multiples and fractions of these units is obtained by the use of suitable prefixes attached to the particular unit. Kilo- is equivalent to 1,000; deci- to 0.1; centi- to 0.01; and milli- to 0.001.

Measures of Length

1 kilometer (km)	= 1,000 meters (m)		=	0.6214 mile
1 meter (m)			=	39.37 inches
1 decimeter (dm)	=	0.1 meter	=	3.937 inches
1 centimeter (cm)	=	0.01 meter	=	0.3937 inch
1 millimeter (mm)	=	0.001 meter	=	0.03937 inch
1 angstrom (Å)	=	10^{-8} centimeter	=	3.9370×10^{-9} inch

Measures of Volume

1 liter = 1,000.027 cubic centimeters (cc) = 1.057 liquid quarts
1 milliliter (ml) = 0.001 liter = 1.000027 cc = 0.0338 liquid ounce

(Note that 1 ml is so very nearly equal to 1 cc that for most purposes it is sufficiently accurate to use them interchangeably. Use of the milliliter has the advantage that 1 ml of pure water at 4° centigrade weighs exactly 1 g.)

Measures of Weight

1 kilogram (kg)	= 1,000 grams (g)	=	2.2046 pounds, av
1 gram (g)		=	0.03215 ounce, troy
1 milligram (mg)	=	0.001 gram	= 0.0154 grain

II. EXPONENTIAL METHOD OF EXPRESSING NUMBERS

For convenience in writing and manipulation, numbers are often expressed as factors of appropriate powers of 10. The following examples will illustrate:

6,020,000,000	may be written 6.02×10^9
602	may be written 6.02×10^2
0.602	may be written 6.02×10^{-1}
0.000000602	may be written 6.02×10^{-7}

Such numbers are added or subtracted by converting all to the same power and taking the sum or difference of the factors of this power.

$$6.02 \times 10^{-9} + 3.12 \times 10^{-9} = 9.14 \times 10^{-9}$$

Exponential numbers are multiplied by multiplying the factors and adding the powers.

$$(6.0 \times 10^{-9})(5.0 \times 10^{-11}) = 30 \times 10^{-20} = 3.0 \times 10^{-19}$$
$$(6.0 \times 10^{9})(5.0 \times 10^{11}) \quad = 30 \times 10^{20} \quad = 3.0 \times 10^{21}$$
$$(6.0 \times 10^{-9})(5.0 \times 10^{11}) \quad = 30 \times 10^{2} \quad = 3.0 \times 10^{3}$$

Exponential numbers are divided by dividing the factor of the dividend by the factor of the divisor and subtracting the power of the divisor from the power of the dividend. Thus,

$$\frac{6.0 \times 10^{-9}}{2.0 \times 10^{-3}} = 3.0 \times 10^{-6}$$

$$\frac{6.0 \times 10^{9}}{2.0 \times 10^{3}} = 3.0 \times 10^{6}$$

$$\frac{6.0 \times 10^{9}}{2.0 \times 10^{-3}} = 3.0 \times 10^{12}$$

$$\frac{2.0 \times 10^{3}}{5.0 \times 10^{8}} = 4.0 \times 10^{-6}$$

III. SIGNIFICANT FIGURES

In making chemical calculations involving measured quantities, we are normally dealing with numbers that represent approximations rather than exact quantities. To indicate the reliability of these approximations, we make use of the concept of significant figures. By convention, the significant figures in a number are those that are known with certainty and the first doubtful digit. An example may make this clear. In measuring the volume of water contained in an ordinary measuring cylinder marked in milliliters, we note that the meniscus is between the 14- and the 15-ml markings and seems to be about halfway between them. We record the volume as 14.5 ml. In doing so, we are using three significant figures; the 1 and the 4 are known with certainty, but the 5 is a guess. Obviously, it would be foolish to record numbers to the right of the 5 since they would have no significance.

A zero may or may not be significant. When used solely to locate the decimal point, as in 0.0054, zeros are not significant. On the other hand, the zeros are obviously significant in a number such as 5004.3. Zeros that occur at the end of a number offer a special problem, and various conventions have been adopted by different people. In this book, we shall arbitrarily say that zeros occurring at the end of a number are significant, *provided that* they occur to the right of the decimal point. The proviso is added because of the ambiguity that arises in recording large numbers. The number 96,500 has five significant figures only if the number is known to within one unit. It has three significant figures if the number is known only to 100 units, the 9 and the 6 being known with certainty and the 5 being the first doubtful digit.

In order to avoid this ambiguity, we frequently make use of the exponential method of expressing numbers, as described in Appendix II. Using this method of expressing numbers, 96,500 with five significant numbers would be written as 9.6500×10^4, and 96,500 with three significant numbers would be written as 9.65×10^4.

Suggestions for the Use of Significant Figures

1. In addition and subtraction, the last digit retained in the result should correspond to the first doubtful decimal place in any of the added numbers.

$$0.234\underline{4}$$
$$0.002\underline{1}$$
$$0.236\underline{6}$$

(The doubtful digits are underlined)

2. In multiplication and division, the result must contain no more figures than the least number of significant figures entering into the calculation.

$$0.01214\underline{9} \times 2.\underline{4} = 0.02\underline{9}$$

3. In dropping superfluous figures, increase the last figure retained by 1 if the following figure is 5 or more.

27.55 becomes 27.6 if the answer is known only to
three significant figures

It is important to remember that the foregoing discussion of significant figures does not apply to *exact numbers*, because these are not subject to the uncertainties of measurement. For example, if we wish to specify $10 \times$ a given experimentally determined quantity, such as 2.568 g, the product 25.68 g will still have four significant figures. Exact numbers, such as 10 in this example, can be considered to have an unlimited number of significant figures which we do not write down.

IV. STANDARD OXIDATION-REDUCTION POTENTIALS, ACID SOLUTIONS

(After Latimer)

Potential, volts	Half Reaction	
	Reducing Agents	Oxidizing Agents
3.02	Li	$\rightleftharpoons$ $Li^+ + e^-$
2.92	K	$\rightleftharpoons$ $K^+ + e^-$
2.90	Ba	$\rightleftharpoons$ $Ba^{2+} + 2e^-$
2.87	Ca	$\rightleftharpoons$ $Ca^{2+} + 2e^-$
2.71	Na	$\rightleftharpoons$ $Na^+ + e^-$
2.34	Mg	$\rightleftharpoons$ $Mg^{2+} + 2e^-$
1.67	Al	$\rightleftharpoons$ $Al^{3+} + 3e^-$
1.05	Mn	$\rightleftharpoons$ $Mn^{2+} + 2e^-$
0.762	Zn	$\rightleftharpoons$ $Zn^{2+} + 2e^-$
0.71	Cr	$\rightleftharpoons$ $Cr^{3+} + 3e^-$
0.440	Fe	$\rightleftharpoons$ $Fe^{2+} + 2e^-$
0.41	Cr^{2+}	$\rightleftharpoons$ $Cr^{3+} + e^-$
0.402	Cd	$\rightleftharpoons$ $Cd^{2+} + 2e^-$
0.355	$Pb + SO_4^{2-}$	$\rightleftharpoons$ $PbSO_4 + 2e^-$
0.250	Ni	$\rightleftharpoons$ $Ni^{2+} + 2e^-$
0.136	Sn	$\rightleftharpoons$ $Sn^{2+} + 2e^-$
0.126	Pb	$\rightleftharpoons$ $Pb^{2+} + 2e^-$
0.000	H_2	$\rightleftharpoons$ $2H^+ + 2e^-$
−0.141	H_2S	$\rightleftharpoons$ $S + 2H^+ + 2e^-$
−0.15	Sn^{2+}	$\rightleftharpoons$ $Sn^{4+} + 2e^-$
−0.167	Cu^+	$\rightleftharpoons$ $Cu^{2+} + e^-$
−0.345	Cu	$\rightleftharpoons$ $Cu^{2+} + 2e^-$
−0.45	$S + 3H_2O$	$\rightleftharpoons$ $H_2SO_3 + 4H^+ + 4e^-$
−0.522	Cu	$\rightleftharpoons$ $Cu^+ + e^-$
−0.535	$2I^-$	$\rightleftharpoons$ $I_2 + 2e^-$
−0.682	H_2O_2	$\rightleftharpoons$ $O_2 + 2H^+ + 2e^-$
−0.771	Fe^{2+}	$\rightleftharpoons$ $Fe^{3+} + e^-$
−0.7986	$2Hg$	$\rightleftharpoons$ $Hg_2^{2+} + 2e^-$
−0.7995	Ag	$\rightleftharpoons$ $Ag^+ + e^-$
−0.854	Hg	$\rightleftharpoons$ $Hg^{2+} + 2e^-$
−0.91	Hg_2^{2+}	$\rightleftharpoons$ $2Hg^{2+} + 2e^-$
−0.94	$HNO_2 + H_2O$	$\rightleftharpoons$ $NO_3^- + 3H^+ + 2e^-$
−1.065	$2Br^-$	$\rightleftharpoons$ $Br_{2(l)} + 2e^-$
−1.229	$2H_2O$	$\rightleftharpoons$ $O_2 + 4H^+ + 4e^-$
−1.358	$2Cl^-$	$\rightleftharpoons$ $Cl_2 + 2e^-$
−1.36	$2Cr^{3+} + 7H_2O$	$\rightleftharpoons$ $Cr_2O_7^{2-} + 14H^+ + 6e^-$
−1.42	Au	$\rightleftharpoons$ $Au^{3+} + 3e^-$
−1.44	$Br^- + 3H_2O$	$\rightleftharpoons$ $BrO_3^- + 6H^+ + 6e^-$
−1.45	$Cl^- + 3H_2O$	$\rightleftharpoons$ $ClO_3^- + 6H^+ + 6e^-$
−1.456	$Pb^{2+} + 2H_2O$	$\rightleftharpoons$ $PbO_2 + 4H^+ + 2e^-$
−1.52	$Mn^{2+} + 4H_2O$	$\rightleftharpoons$ $MnO_4^- + 8H^+ + 5e^-$
−1.67	$MnO_2 + 2H_2O$	$\rightleftharpoons$ $MnO_4^- + 4H^+ + 3e^-$
−1.685	$PbSO_4 + 2H_2O$	$\rightleftharpoons$ $PbO_2 + SO_4^{2-} + 4H^+ + 2e^-$
−2.01	$2SO_4^{2-}$	$\rightleftharpoons$ $S_2O_8^{2-} + 2e^-$
−2.07	$O_2 + H_2O$	$\rightleftharpoons$ $O_3 + 2H^+ + 2e^-$
−2.85	$2F^-$	$\rightleftharpoons$ $F_2 + 2e^-$

V. LOGARITHMS OF NUMBERS

N	0	1	2	3	4	5	6	7	8	9
10	0000	0043	0086	0128	0170	0212	0253	0294	0334	0374
11	0414	0453	0492	0531	0569	0607	0645	0682	0719	0755
12	0792	0828	0864	0899	0934	0969	1004	1038	1072	1106
13	1139	1173	1206	1239	1271	1303	1335	1367	1399	1430
14	1461	1492	1523	1553	1584	1614	1644	1673	1703	1732
15	1761	1790	1818	1847	1875	1903	1931	1959	1987	2014
16	2041	2068	2095	2122	2148	2175	2201	2227	2253	2279
17	2304	2330	2355	2380	2405	2430	2455	2480	2504	2529
18	2553	2577	2601	2625	2648	2672	2695	2718	2742	2765
19	2788	2810	2833	2856	2878	2900	2923	2945	2967	2989
20	3010	3032	3054	3075	3096	3118	3139	3160	3181	3201
21	3222	3243	3263	3284	3304	3324	3345	3365	3385	3404
22	3424	3444	3464	3483	3502	3522	3541	3560	3579	3598
23	3617	3636	3655	3674	3692	3711	3729	3747	3766	3784
24	3802	3820	3838	3856	3874	3892	3909	3927	3945	3962
25	3979	3997	4014	4031	4048	4065	4082	4099	4116	4133
26	4150	4166	4183	4200	4216	4232	4249	4265	4281	4298
27	4314	4330	4346	4362	4378	4393	4409	4425	4440	4456
28	4472	4487	4502	4518	4533	4548	4564	4579	4594	4609
29	4624	4639	4654	4669	4683	4698	4713	4728	4742	4757
30	4771	4786	4800	4814	4829	4843	4857	4871	4886	4900
31	4914	4928	4942	4955	4969	4983	4997	5011	5024	5038
32	5051	5065	5079	5092	5105	5119	5132	5145	5159	5172
33	5185	5198	5211	5224	5237	5250	5263	5276	5289	5302
34	5315	5328	5340	5353	5366	5378	5391	5403	5416	5428
35	5441	5453	5465	5478	5490	5502	5514	5527	5539	5551
36	5563	5575	5587	5599	5611	5623	5635	5647	5658	5670
37	5682	5694	5705	5717	5729	5740	5752	5763	5775	5786
38	5798	5809	5821	5832	5843	5855	5866	5877	5888	5899
39	5911	5922	5933	5944	5955	5966	5977	5988	5999	6010
40	6021	6031	6042	6053	6064	6075	6085	6096	6107	6117
41	6128	6138	6149	6160	6170	6180	6191	6201	6212	6222
42	6232	6243	6253	6263	6274	6284	6294	6304	6314	6325
43	6335	6345	6355	6365	6375	6385	6395	6405	6415	6425
44	6435	6444	6454	6464	6474	6484	6493	6503	6513	6522
45	6532	6542	6551	6561	6571	6580	6590	6599	6609	6618
46	6628	6637	6646	6656	6665	6675	6684	6693	6702	6712
47	6721	6730	6739	6749	6758	6767	6776	6785	6794	6803
48	6812	6821	6830	6839	6848	6857	6866	6875	6884	6893
49	6902	6911	6920	6928	6937	6946	6955	6964	6972	6981
50	6990	6998	7007	7016	7024	7033	7042	7050	7059	7067
51	7076	7084	7093	7101	7110	7118	7126	7135	7143	7152
52	7160	7168	7177	7185	7193	7202	7210	7218	7226	7235
53	7243	7251	7259	7267	7275	7284	7292	7300	7308	7316
54	7324	7332	7340	7348	7356	7364	7372	7380	7388	7396
N	0	1	2	3	4	5	6	7	8	9

V.   LOGARITHMS OF NUMBERS (Continued)

N	0	1	2	3	4	5	6	7	8	9
55	7404	7412	7419	7427	7435	7443	7451	7459	7466	7474
56	7482	7490	7497	7505	7513	7520	7528	7536	7543	7551
57	7559	7566	7574	7582	7589	7597	7604	7612	7619	7627
58	7634	7642	7649	7657	7664	7672	7679	7686	7694	7701
59	7709	7716	7723	7731	7738	7745	7752	7760	7767	7774
60	7782	7789	7796	7803	7810	7818	7825	7832	7839	7846
61	7853	7860	7868	7875	7882	7889	7896	7903	7910	7917
62	7924	7931	7938	7945	7952	7959	7966	7973	7980	7987
63	7993	8000	8007	8014	8021	8028	8035	8041	8048	8055
64	8062	8069	8075	8082	8089	8096	8102	8109	8116	8122
65	8129	8136	8142	8149	8156	8162	8169	8176	8182	8189
66	8195	8202	8209	8215	8222	8228	8235	8241	8248	8254
67	8261	8267	8274	8280	8287	8293	8299	8306	8312	8319
68	8325	8331	8338	8344	8351	8357	8363	8370	8376	8382
69	8388	8395	8401	8407	8414	8420	8426	8432	8439	8445
70	8451	8457	8463	8470	8476	8482	8488	8494	8500	8506
71	8513	8519	8525	8531	8537	8543	8549	8555	8561	8567
72	8573	8579	8585	8591	8597	8603	8609	8615	8621	8627
73	8633	8639	8645	8651	8657	8663	8669	8675	8681	8686
74	8692	8698	8704	8710	8716	8722	8727	8733	8739	8745
75	8751	8756	8762	8768	8774	8779	8785	8791	8797	8802
76	8808	8814	8820	8825	8831	8837	8842	8848	8854	8859
77	8865	8871	8876	8882	8887	8893	8899	8904	8910	8915
78	8921	8927	8932	8938	8943	8949	8954	8960	8965	8971
79	8976	8982	8987	8993	8998	9004	9009	9015	9020	9025
80	9031	9036	9042	9047	9053	9058	9063	9069	9074	9079
81	9085	9090	9096	9101	9106	9112	9117	9122	9128	9133
82	9138	9143	9149	9154	9159	9165	9170	9175	9180	9186
83	9191	9196	9201	9206	9212	9217	9222	9227	9232	9238
84	9243	9248	9253	9258	9263	9269	9274	9279	9284	9289
85	9294	9299	9304	9309	9315	9320	9325	9330	9335	9340
86	9345	9350	9355	9360	9365	9370	9375	9380	9385	9390
87	9395	9400	9405	9410	9415	9420	9425	9430	9435	9440
88	9445	9450	9455	9460	9465	9469	9474	9479	9484	9489
89	9494	9499	9504	9509	9513	9518	9523	9528	9533	9538
90	9542	9547	9552	9557	9562	9566	9571	9576	9581	9586
91	9590	9595	9600	9605	9609	9614	9619	9624	9628	9633
92	9638	9643	9647	9652	9657	9661	9666	9671	9675	9680
93	9685	9689	9694	9699	9703	9708	9713	9717	9722	9727
94	9731	9736	9741	9745	9750	9754	9759	9763	9768	9773
95	9777	9782	9786	9791	9795	9800	9805	9809	9814	9818
96	9823	9827	9832	9836	9841	9845	9850	9854	9859	9863
97	9868	9872	9877	9881	9886	9890	9894	9899	9903	9908
98	9912	9917	9921	9926	9930	9934	9939	9943	9948	9952
99	9956	9961	9965	9969	9974	9978	9983	9987	9991	9996
N	0	1	2	3	4	5	6	7	8	9

VI. ANSWERS TO NUMERICAL EXERCISES

Chapter 1

4. a) 5×10^5 cm, 5×10^6 mm, 5×10^{13} Å; b) 0.125 liter, 125 cc, 0.132 qt; c) 0.400 kg, 4.00×10^5 mg, 0.882 lb

5. 200,000 atoms

12. 3.01×10^{24} atoms

14. 2 atoms

11. a) 22.997 g; b) 3.82×10^{-23} g

13. 197

15. a) 63.6; b) Cu

Chapter 2

2. a) 40% S, 60% O

4. CH_2

7. WF_6

8. a) 36.1% Ca, 63.9% Cl; b) 361 tons

10. a) SrO, SrO_2; b) 1:1 compared to 0.5:1

11. 46.00 g

12. 75.3% Ag in AgCl compared to 87.1% in Ag_2S

13. a) 20.5 g; b) 20% X, 80% Y; c) XY_2; d) 0.250 gram-formula weights; e) 0.50 gram atoms; f) 1.51×10^{23} atoms; g) 4

14. 24.74 g

16. 14.0 g, 3.50 g

3. 74.2% Na, 25.8% O

6. SO_2

15. 18.08 g

Chapter 3

3. The first

7. 9×10^{16} erg

9. a) 110; b) 114.75; c) 3

4. $_{17}Cl^{35}$

8. 2×10^9 g

Chapter 4

4. a) 1.2×10^{16} cm; b) 7.5×10^{10} miles

5. $1 \times 10^{-12}\%$

6. a) 83 protons and 127 neutrons; 83 electrons

Chapter 5

18. a) 0.6 Å; b) 1.5 Å; c) 1.0 Å; d) 1.3 Å

Chapter 6

1. a) 2; b) 4; c) 3; d) 1; e) 3   **2.** a) 1; b) 4; c) 3

5. a) 260 g; b) 6.02×10^{24}; c) 1.20×10^{25}; d) 92.3% C, 7.7% H

VI. ANSWERS TO NUMERICAL EXERCISES (Continued)

6. 0.50000 mole, 1.50000 gram ions of Mg, 6.02×10^{23} phosphate ions

7. 4 gram equivalents

8. a) 3.60×10^{24} Ca^{2+}, 7.20×10^{24} Cl^-; b) 1.20×10^{24} Ca^{2+}, 2.41×10^{24} Cl^-

9. a) 120 g; b) 1.20×10^{24} carbonate ions, 1.20×10^{24} carbon atoms, 3.61×10^{24} oxygen atoms, 2.41×10^{24} negative charges, 2.41×10^{24} units combining capacity, 4 gram-equivalent weights

10. a) 3.000 moles; b) 1.806×10^{24} molecules; c) 1.806×10^{24} nitrogen atoms; d) 5.418×10^{24} hydrogen atoms; e) 5.418×10^{24} covalent bonds; f) 5.418 $\times 10^{24}$ units of combining capacity; g) 9.000 gram-equivalent weights

12. b) 1:1; c) 2:1; d) 126.92 g

13. b) 0.75 mole of oxygen per mole aluminum; c) 1.5 moles of aluminum; d) 1.1 moles of oxygen; e) 36 g of oxygen

14. a) 1:11:12, 342:198:144, 1:11:12; b) 1440 g; c) 5.8 lb

15. a) 277 g; b) 3.0×10^{24} Cl^- **16.**   19.7 tons

17. 5 moles O_2 **18.**   f) 7.14×10^{-20} cal

19. 16.5 tons NaCl, 2.52×10^{10} cal

20. a) 3.2×10^4 cal; b) 606,800 cal; c) 1.7×10^4 cal

Chapter 7

1. 6, 4, 6, 6, 18

2. b) 0.5 mole O_2 per mole KNO_3; b) 10 moles; c) 5 moles; d) 160 g

3. 33.3%   **7.** a) 63.54 g, 31.77 g; b) 1, 2

8. 16.0 g

Chapter 8

7. b) 2.890×10^5 cal

16. 63.02 g for HNO_3, 85.69 g for $Ba(OH)_2$

17. a) 20.04 g; b) 26.62 g

Chapter 9

4. $R_A = \frac{3}{2} R_B$ **5.**   5 ml

6. 875 mm

7. a) 500 ml; b) 50 ml; c) 319° C; d) 1000 mm

8. a) 2000 liters; b) 89.3 moles   **9.**   118° C

10. 2.86 g   **11.** 32 g, N_2H_4

12. a) 28.0 g; b) CH_2; c) C_2H_4 **13.** 134.4 atm

14. 89.6 liters   **15.** 4 atm

16. a) 2.858 h; b) 0.715 g   **17.** 5 liters oxygen, 10 liters water vapor

18. 112 liters   **19.** 56 liters hydrogen, 56 liters chlorine

VI. ANSWERS TO NUMERICAL EXERCISES (Continued)

Chapter 10

5. 3105 cal   **6.** 1 liter

Chapter 11

6. a) 112 cal;   b) 864 cal;   c) 51,790 cal

Chapter 12

3. 0.025 moles   **4.** 1.2×10^{22} Na$^+$
5. 3 liters   **6.** 5.4 molar
7. a) 26°;   b) $3.7M$ KNO$_3$, $5M$ KCl, $6.3M$ NaCl
8. a) 126 g, 12.6 g;   b) 20 ml;   c) 50 ml
9. 0.2712 molal, 0.0123 mole fraction I$_2$, 0.9877 mole fraction C$_2$H$_5$OH
10. ·1675 mg   **18.** 212
19. 38.4   **20.** 77.5°
21. 99.7%   **23.** a) 30 g;   b) 160 g

Chapter 15

8. a) 1.00;   b) 1.00

Chapter 16

3. a) **1.5** moles; b) 1.5 moles; c) 1.0 mole; d) 1.0 mole; e) 1.5 moles
f) 1.0 mole
5. 66.7%   **6.** 50%
7. 0.346°   **8.** 2.5×10^{-7}
9. 8.13×10^{18} **14.** 1.2×10^{12}
15. 1×10^{-6} **16.** 1×10^{-9}

Chapter 17

1. $5 \times 10^{-13}M$ **2.** $1.85 \times 10^{-2}M$
3. 1.6×10^{-13} **4.** 2.0×10^{-9} g
5. $4.5 \times 10^{-16}M$ **6.** a) Yes; b) No
7. $7.1 \times 10^{-5}M$ **9.** a) $1 \times 10^{-8}M$; b) $1 \times 10^{-2}M$
13. a) $1 \times 10^{-9}M$ H$^+$, $1 \times 10^{-5}M$ OH$^-$

VI. ANSWERS TO NUMERICAL EXERCISES (Continued)

Chapter 18
10. The first   **11.** a) The first; b) The first

Chapter 19
6. a) 40 faradays; b) 20 moles; c) 1.93×10^6 sec
7. 6.02×10^{21}
8. c) 12,200 faradays; d) 12,200 g moles K, 6,100 g moles Cl_2
11. a) 0.122 g; b) 0.119 g

Chapter 20
16. a) 213 g, 7.21 liters; b) 42.5 g

Chapter 21
12. a) 32.7 tons; b) 49.0 tons of oxygen gas; c) 3.11×10^7 liters
13. a) 49.4 liters; b) 49.4 liters

Chapter 22
9. 5 liters

Chapter 30
3. c) 1.1×10^4 faradays

INDEX

▶ Index